CRC

Handbook of Chromatography

Volume II

EDITORS

GUNTER ZWEIG, Ph.D.

Syracuse University Research Corporation
Syracuse, New York

JOSEPH SHERMA, Ph.D.

Lafayette College
Easton, Pennsylvania

published by:

CRC PRESS

A DIVISION OF
THE CHEMICAL RUBBER CO.
18901 Cranwood Parkway • Cleveland, Ohio 44128

This book presents data obtained from authentic and highly regarded sources. Reprinted material is quoted with permission, and sources are indicated. A wide variety of references are listed. Every reasonable effort has been made to give reliable data and information but the editor and the publisher cannot assume responsibility for the validity of all materials or for the consequences of their use.

Library of Congress Card No. 76-163067
Printed in the United States of America

International Standard Book Number 0-87819-560-2 Complete set
International Standard Book Number 0-87819-562-9 Volume Two

HANDBOOK SERIES

Handbook of Chemistry and Physics, 53rd edition
Standard Mathematical Tables, 20th edition
Handbook of tables for Mathematics, 4th edition
Handbook of tables for Organic Compound Identification, 3rd edition
Handbook of Biochemistry, selected data for Molecular Biology, 2nd edition
Handbook of Clinical Laboratory Data, 2nd edition
Manual for Clinical Laboratory Procedures, 2nd edition
Manual of Nuclear Medicine Procedures, 1st edition
Handbook of Laboratory Safety, 2nd edition
Handbook of tables for Probability and Statistics, 2nd edition
Fenaroli's Handbook of Flavor Ingredients, 1st edition
Handbook of Analytical Toxicology, 1st edition
Manual of Laboratory Procedures in Toxicology, 1st edition
Handbook of tables for Applied Engineering Science, 2nd edition
Handbook of Chromatography, 1st edition
Handbook of Environmental Control, 1st edition
Handbook of Food Additives, 2nd edition
Handbook of Radioactive Nuclides, 1st edition
Handbook of Lasers, 1st edition
Handbook of Microbiology, 1st edition
Handbook of Engineering in Medicine and Biology, 1st edition
*Handbook of Marine Sciences, 1st edition
*Handbook of Material Science, 1st edition
*Handbook of Spectroscopy, 1st edition
*Atlas of Spectral Data and Physical Constants for Organic Compounds, 1st edition

*Currently in preparation.

PREFACE

Volumes One and Two of the *Handbook of Chromatography* represent over three years of intensive labor by the editors and members of the Editorial Advisory Board. When the Publishers first suggested the production of a Handbook for Chromatographic Data, it seemed to the editors to be just a simple compilation of R_F-tables and retention times or volumes. However, a quick perusal of the literature of chromatography, accumulated during approximately twenty-five years of modern chromatography, revealed that the task would be a formidable one and could not be accomplished in one year, as was first estimated.

The Handbook, as it finally appears, should serve chemists in all fields as a working manual and reference book which should aid in their search for identification of unknowns as well as suggest quantitative methods of analysis.

Volume One of the Handbook contains over 549 tables of chromatographic data expressed in uniform terms of R_F values, retention times and retention volumes as well as other terms used in chromatography. Each table has literature citations which will refer to the primary and sometimes secondary sources. Over 12,000 compounds are cross-indexed to direct the reader to appropriate tables in this volume. Thus, for example, the amino acid alanine will have entries in tables under gas, liquid-column, paper, and thin-layer chromatography.

Volume Two of the Handbook has been designed to give the researcher, even the novice in chromatography, a working knowledge of the theory and practices of the various fields of chromatography–gas, liquid-column, paper, and thin-layer chromatography.

Volume Two also contains two useful sections. One is on detection reagents for paper and thin-layer chromatography, with an alphabetical index for chemical classes and "name" reagents. This section is very helpful for the interpretation of the tables in Volume One. The other section describes selected methods for sample preparations, which will be expanded in future editions of the Handbook. Subsequent sub-sections in **PRACTICAL APPLICATIONS** supply the researcher with useful information on commercial sources of all types of chromatographic supplies.

A Book Directory at the close of Volume Two should serve as a good source for more detailed reading in chromatography.

The editors would be ungrateful if they did not acknowledge the invaluable help and advice from the members of the Advisory Editorial Board.

Special thanks are due to the industrious group of compilers, especially Mrs. Ellen Burton, Miss Susan Rodems, Miss Irene Zweig, Mrs. Frances K. Zweig, and Dr. and Mrs. Coleman Hamel. Special thanks are also due to Dr. Irving Sunshine whose initiative and perseverance are in no small manner responsible for the writing and creation of this Handbook, and to Mrs. Florence Thomas and Mrs. Ruth Pokorney of The Chemical Rubber Co. for their unstinting effort in the production and final editing of the books.

The editors would greatly appreciate suggestions for improvements and additions in future editions from any interested persons.

Gunter Zweig

Joseph Sherma

November 1972

Advisory Board

TABLE OF CONTENTS

VOLUME I

CHROMATOGRAPHIC DATA

VOLUME II

PRINCIPLES AND TECHNIQUES

PRACTICAL APPLICATIONS

VOLUME TWO
SECTION I

PRINCIPLES AND TECHNIQUES

Joseph Sherma

The author of Volume Two is grateful to those members of the Advisory Board who reviewed the material covering their fields of expertise and made numerous recommendations for changes, corrections and improvements.

Section I

PRINCIPLES AND TECHNIQUES

Joseph Sherma

I.I. Introduction

A. HISTORY

A *definition* of *chromatography* similar to one originally stated by Strain is as follows: Chromatography is a separation method in which a mixture is applied as a narrow initial zone to a stationary, porous sorbent and the components are caused to undergo differential migration by the flow of the mobile phase, a liquid or a gas.

The originator of chromatography as it is practiced today was Michael Tswett (1872–1919). In 1906, Tswett, a Russian botanist, published a paper (which has been translated into English and evaluated (*1*)) describing the separation and isolation of green and yellow chloroplast pigments by column adsorption chromatography.

In his original experiments, Tswett tamped a fine powder (such as sucrose) into a glass tube to produce a column of the desired height. After extracting the pigments from leaves and transferring them to petroleum ether, he poured a small volume of the solution onto the column. When the solution had percolated and formed a narrow initial zone beneath the top of the adsorbent, fresh solvent (e.g., petroleum ether) was added and pressure applied to the top of the column. As the solvent flowed through the column the individual pigments moved at different rates and eventually separated from each other. Figure 1 illustrates the development of a chromatogram by Tswett's chromatographic method with a solvent employed by Strain in his extensive studies of chloroplast pigments.

The key features of Tswett's technique were the application of the mixture as a narrow initial zone and the development of the chromatogram by application of fresh solvent. Other early workers had employed procedures based on the phenomena of adsorption or partition, but these lacked Tswett's critical development step and therefore did not yield extensive resolution of the mixtures.

Tswett's original column adsorption chromatographic method has been modified in many ways resulting in the different types of chromatography described in the sections below. The *history* of *chromatography* is outlined by the following chronological listing of some of the key contributions to the development of these modifications:

1848	Way and Thompson	Recognized the phenomenon of ion exchange in solids.
1850–1900	Runge, Schoenbein, and Goeppelsroeder	Studied capillary analysis on paper.
1876	Lemberg	Illustrated the reversibility and stoichiometry of ion exchange in aluminum silicate minerals.
1892	Reed	First recorded column separation: tubes of kaolin used for separation of $FeCl_3$ from $CuSO_4$.
1903–1906	Tswett	Invented chromatography with use of pure solvent to develop the chromatogram; devised nomenclature; used mild adsorbents to resolve chloroplast pigments.
1930–1932	Karrer, Kuhn, and Strain	Used activated lime, alumina and magnesia adsorbents.
1935	Holmes and Adams	Synthesized synthetic organic ion-exchange resins.
1938	Reichstein	Introduced the liquid or flowing chromatogram, thus extending application of chromatography to colorless substances.
1938	Izmailov and Schraiber	Discussed the use of a thin layer of unbound alumina spread on a glass plate.
1939	Brown	First use of circular paper chromatography.

1940–1943	Tiselius	Devised frontal analysis and method of displacement development.
1941	Martin and Synge	Introduced column partition chromatography.
1944	Consden, Gordon, and Martin	First described paper partition chromatography.
1947–1950	Boyd, Tompkins, Spedding, Rieman, and others	Ion-exchange chromatography applied to various analytical problems.
1948	M. Lederer and Linstead	Applied paper chromatography to inorganic compounds.
1951	Kirchner	Introduced thin-layer chromatography as it is practiced today.
1952	James and Martin	Developed gas chromatography.
1956	Sober and Peterson	Prepared first ion-exchange celluloses.
1956	Lathe and Ruthvan	Used natural and modified starch molecular sieves for molecular weight estimation.
1959	Porath and Flodin	Introduced cross-linked dextran for molecular sieving.
1964	J. C. Moore	Gel permeation chromatography developed as a practical method.

B. NOMENCLATURE

Tswett is responsible for much of the nomenclature that is used by most chromatographers today. A glass or metal *tube* (or column) is filled with an active solid (*adsorbent*) to form a chromatographic *column*. The mixture to be separated is applied in an *initial zone* and it is washed with the *solvent*, *wash liquid*, or *developer*. The resultant series of zones is the *chromatogram*, and the washing of the initial zone to form the chromatogram is the *formation* or *development* of the chromatogram.

If the separated zones are colorless they must be detected in some way. (See Reference (*2*) for a general discussion of detection methods.) If the chromatogram is treated with a chemical reagent to form colored derivatives, the chromatogram is sometimes referred to as having been *developed*. It is best, however, to reserve this term for the formation of the chromatogram by washing with solvent.

The combination of the solvent, the mixture and the sorbent is termed the *chromatographic system*. Each chromatographic system is composed, then, of a *mobile phase* (the solvent) and a stationary phase (e.g., the column). The generalized term *sorbent* may be used in place of adsorbent, ion-exchange resin, paper sheet, etc., when referring to the stationary phase.

If the components of the mixture are analyzed quantitatively as well as separated, the term *evaluation*, *quantification* or *quantitation* is used. If the separated solute is removed from the sorbent by washing (either in a chromatographic fashion or not) before this analysis, it is said to be *eluted* and the solution to be analyzed is the *eluate*. In ion-exchange and gel permeation chromatography, many workers use this term *elution* for the development of the chromatogram, and *eluant* for the solvent or wash liquid; the liquid emerging from the bottom of the column is then the *elutrient* or the *effluent*.

C. CLASSIFICATION OF CHROMATOGRAPHY

The subject of chromatography may be divided and subdivided as follows to include the great variety of methods which have evolved from Tswett's original chromatographic method.

The two major classifications of chromatography are solution or liquid chromatography (LC) and gas chromatography (GC). In the former a liquid carries the dissolved solutes through the sorbent, which can be a column, paper or thin layer. In the latter an inert wash gas (carrier gas) carries the gaseous mixture through the sorption column.

Within each of these major divisions, subdivisions based on the stationary phase are designated. Thus gas-solid chromatography (GSC) involves a column packed with an adsorbent, and gas-liquid chromatography (GLC) involves a solid coated with a stationary liquid as the sorbent.

Liquid chromatography in columns can be liquid-solid chromatography (LSC) or liquid-liquid (partition) chromatography (LLC). If the solid stationary phase is an adsorbent, the process is called liquid adsorption chromatography. If it is an ion-exchange material, either organic or inorganic, it is termed ion-exchange chromatography (IXC). If it is a nonionic polymeric gel (e.g., polystyrene or Sephadex) the term gel permeation chromatography (GPC), gel filtration chromatography or molecular exclusion chromatography is used.

Other subdivisions of non-column liquid chromatography are paper chromatography (PC) and thin-layer chromatography (TLC). These subdivisions include separations on all kinds of paper and thin layers whether the mechanism of separation is adsorption, partition or ion exchange.

Liquid-liquid chromatography in columns or on paper may be further subdivided into normal-phase partition chromatography (fixed polar liquids) and reversed-phase partition chromatography (fixed non-polar liquids).

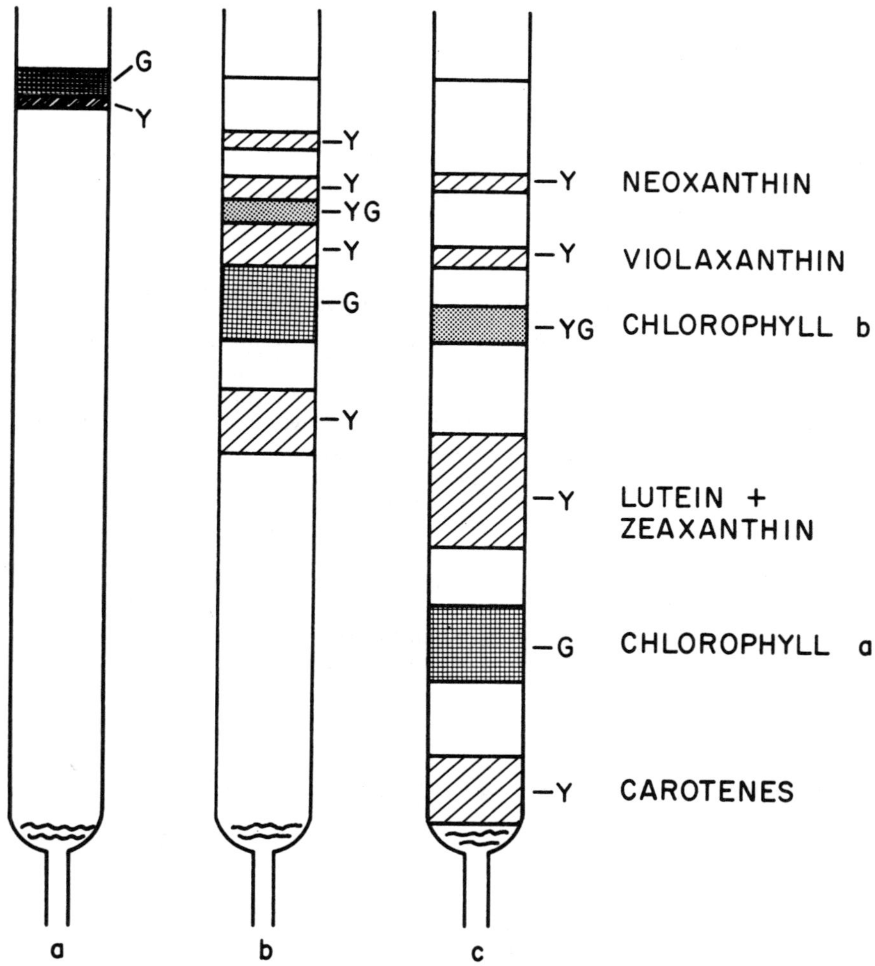

Figure 1. Successive steps in the formation of a chromatogram. Chloroplast pigments of flowering plants, ferns, mosses and lichens and many green algae dissolved in petroleum ether, adsorbed in a column of powdered sugar (a) and washed with petroleum ether plus 0.5 per cent *n*-propanol (b, c). Y = yellow; G = green.

D. MECHANISM OF CHROMATOGRAPHY

The movement of substances during chromatography is the result of two opposing forces, the driving force of the mobile phase and the resistive or retarding action of the sorbent. The driving force acts to move the substances from the origin in the direction of the mobile-phase flow. The resistive action impedes the movement of the substances by dragging them out of the flowing phase back onto the sorbent. Each molecule alternates between a sorbed and unsorbed condition, following a stop and go path through the sorbent. Although the zone moves constantly ahead, only a fraction of the molecules in the zone is moving at any one time. At the end of development, each zone has migrated a certain mean distance and has spread because of the fluctuations in the movement of individual molecules in the zone. The distance travelled by each solute zone in a given time is the resultant of the driving and resistive forces. Substances which move slowly are attracted more strongly to the stationary phase, while those that move quickly spend a smaller fraction of their time in the stationary phase because of less solubility in or affinity for that phase.

The ability to achieve differential migration (i.e., separations) among the mixture components is the result of the selectivity of the chromatographic system. The flow of the mobile phase is nonselective in that it affects all unsorbed solutes equally. As part of the chromatographic system, however, the mobile phase may be selective (e.g., in liquid chromatography) if it helps determine the relative sorbability of the solutes. The sorbent is also part of the chromatographic system and its resistive action (ion exchange, adsorption, etc.) is a selective force. To put this another way, all eluted or nonsorbed components spend equal time in the mobile phase. If there is differential migration, the components spend different amounts of time on the sorbent as determined by the interactions of the chromatographic system.

E. *R* VALUES

The *R* value or retention ratio of a substance indicates its migration relative to that of the mobile phase:

$$R = \frac{\text{solute velocity}}{\text{mobile-phase velocity}}. \qquad [1]$$

The *R* value indicates the fraction of time the solute molecules spend in the mobile phase relative to the time in the sorbent.

In paper and thin-layer chromatography it is customary to use migration distances rather than velocities, and to calculate R_F values:

$$R_F = \frac{\text{distance travelled by the center of the solute zone}}{\text{distance travelled by the solvent front}} \times 100. \qquad [2]$$

This ratio is similar in idea to *R* as defined above, but R_F values are usually lower than *R* values because the solvent front moves faster over the dry sorbent than does the bulk solvent. The R_F equation also assumes a constant velocity during the run which it does not actually obtain in these techniques.

R and R_F values are not chromatographic constants but vary with the experimental conditions employed during the run. All conditions (such as the nature and preparation of the solvent and sorbent, the arrangement and conditions for the development, the sample size, the temperature, etc.) should be stated when recording *R* values, so that they will have maximum significance. Even then, one should not expect to be able to reproduce exactly *R* values reported by others. The major practical use of *R* values is to indicate relative sorbability and to show which systems may be useful for obtaining the separation of a certain mixture.

The dependence of *R* values on experimental conditions can be lessened if solute migration is described relative to a reference standard which is naturally present in the sample or is added to it. This is especially useful for biological samples containing various impurities (e.g., lipids, inorganic salts) which might alter migration behavior. These values are called R_X values (or *R* values relative to *X*):

$$R_X = \frac{\text{velocity of (or distance travelled by) solute zone}}{\text{velocity of (or distance travelled by) compound } X}. \qquad [3]$$

F. SIGNIFICANCE, USES AND APPLICATIONS OF CHROMATOGRAPHY

Chromatography is primarily an analytical tool effective for the separation of mixtures and the qualitative and quantitative analysis of the separated substances. Ideally, each component of the mixture will be completely separated from the other components (it will, of course, be mixed with the mobile phase) and each substance will yield a single, well-defined, regularly-shaped zone. In some cases, however, results are anomalous leading to irregularly shaped zones or multiple zonation (a single substance yields more than one zone).

Chromatography is useful for the comparison of substances, for providing clues as to the structure of organic substances, and for the detection of structural changes produced by various chemical reagents or nuclear and biological processes. Chromatography, combined with conventional chemical and instrumental analytical methods, serves to identify chemical species. Chromatography alone is not adequate for positive qualitative identification even when a sample, prepared by mixing the unknown with an authentic standard it is suspected of being, is found to be inseparable under various dissimilar conditions (this procedure is called co-chromatography). In such a case, the unknown and the standard might be either identical or very similar (e.g., isotopes or isomers). If two substances separate chromatographically, this is positive proof that they are not identical.

Chromatographic methods have a nearly unlimited range of applicability. They can be used to separate the smallest molecules (H_2, D_2) as well as the biggest (proteins, nucleic acids). Isotopes can be separated by gas chromatography and less readily by solution chromatography. Because systems making use of all kinds of physico-chemical interactions can be employed, any substance which is either present in a gaseous state at ambient temperature, vaporizable, or soluble is amenable to chromatographic separation under some obtainable conditions. Quantities in the picogram range can be separated and detected by gas chromatography combined with mass spectrometry, while at the other end of the weight range, multigram quantities can be separated and isolated by preparative column chromatographic methods.

Despite significant recent advances in chromatographic theory [see Reference (*3*), for example] which have provided much information about the mechanism of separations and zone migration, the selectivity of chromatographic systems is still incompletely understood so that the conditions required to separate a given mixture cannot usually be theoretically predicted. For most workers, the experimental approach in chromatography is largely an empirical one, based upon analogy, controlled trial and error, and intuition and experience. Therefore, collations of data such as those presented in this Handbook are extremely useful, because the worker who is interested in applying chromatography to a particular problem can benefit from the experiences of others who have worked with the same or similar compounds. By adopting or adapting previously successful systems, effective separation conditions will usually be found. The more successful users of chromatography strive to understand the physico-chemical causes of successful separations and the reasons for the choice of particular operating conditions, and are thereby better able to determine parameters which may lead to, and improve, separations.

The sections below are designed to introduce the various kinds of chromatography to those who may not be entirely familiar with them and their basic methods. All these modifications are related, because they involve the application of a narrow initial zone of mixture, the presence of a mobile and stationary phase (i.e., a driving force and a resistive action), and the achievement of separations due to differential migration of the components of the mixture.

REFERENCES

1. Strain, H. H. and J. Sherma, *J. Chem. Educ.* **44**, 235–42 (1967).
2. Polesuk, J., *American Laboratory*, p. 27, May 1970, and p. 37, June 1970.
3. Rony, P. R., *American Laboratory*, p. 10, May 1970.

VOLUME TWO
SECTION I

PRINCIPLES AND TECHNIQUES

I.II Gas Chromatography

Section I.II

GAS CHROMATOGRAPHY

In GC the mobile phase is an inert gas and the stationary phase is either a solid or a fixed liquid packed into a column. The solid in gas-solid chromatography (GSC) is commonly alumina, silica gel, charcoal or a molecular sieve, and selective sorption on these solids allows the separation of certain permanent gases and low molecular weight hydrocarbons. Aliphatic and aromatic hydrocarbons have also been separated on salt-modified adsorbents.

Gas-liquid chromatography (GLC) is much more important and will be discussed for the rest of this section, although much of what is written applies to both techniques. The carrier gas drives the mixture through the column wherein the solutes partition between the gas and the stationary liquid. In addition to partition, adsorption of the solutes on the solid support and at the gas-liquid interface is also a factor in many cases. Differential migration results if the distribution coefficients of the solutes are different enough to allow the sorbent to selectively retard them. In gas chromatography, unlike liquid chromatography, the mobile phase is always nonselective. There is, however, the added temperature variable which aids in achieving resolution in GC.

A. BASIC APPARATUS FOR GC

A schematic drawing of the basic apparatus necessary for GC is shown in Figure 2. The parts include:

1. A high pressure cylinder of carrier gas. The gas chosen must be suitable for the detector employed, and beyond this should be inert, pure, inexpensive and as heavy (high molecular weight) as possible so as to minimize solute diffusion. If speed is important but highest column efficiency is not, a low-molecular-weight gas such as helium or hydrogen may be used.

2. Pressure regulators and flow-control valves are used to obtain a uniform rate of gas flow, which is measured by a flow meter of the float, capillary or soap bubble type. The latter type is placed at the outlet of the column. Typical flow rates are 25–125 ml/min depending upon the size of the column. The optimum flow rate is chosen by making a van Deemter plot and noting the minimum value of HETP (see "Theory" below).

3. Samples are injected quickly onto the column through a self-sealing septum at the injection port. Gas-tight syringes are used for gas samples and liquid syringes for liquids and dissolved solids. Typical sample sizes range from 0.1–10 μl for gases and 0.004–0.5 μl for liquids on $\frac{1}{16}$ in. capillary columns, to 0.05–5 l for gases and 0.02–2 ml for liquids on 1 in. preparative columns. Regular analytical columns ($\frac{1}{8}$ and $\frac{1}{4}$ in. O.D.) usually receive 0.1–50 ml of gases and 0.04–20 μl of liquids. The sample size (column capacity) depends upon the amount of the liquid phase as well as the column size. Small samples are often applied by injecting 1–2 μl of sample and delivering only part of this to the column via a sample splitter.

The recommended sample injection technique for liquids in gas chromatography is the solvent flush method (*1*). Pure solvent is drawn into the syringe barrel followed by an air pocket, then the sample solution, and finally another air pocket. The sample volume is read, and then the sample is injected. The flush solvent behind the sample assures that the entire sample is flushed into the column without hang-up.

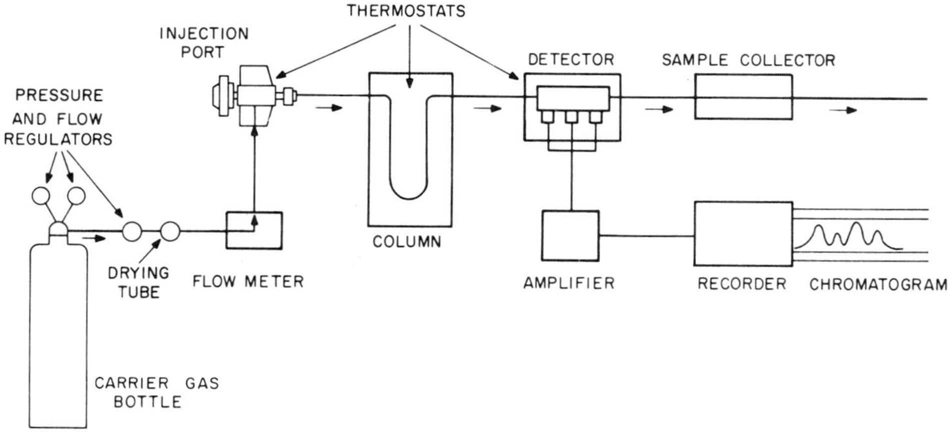

Figure 2. Schematic drawing of apparatus for gas chromatography (not to scale). Arrows show path of gas flow.

4. Columns are made from copper, stainless steel or glass tubing and are straight, bent or coiled. Except for glass, the columns are packed while straight and then bent. General analytical columns are 6–20 ft in length and $\frac{1}{8}$–$\frac{1}{4}$ in. O.D. Preparative columns can measure up to 2 in. I.D. but are most often $\frac{3}{8}$–$\frac{1}{2}$ in. and 20 ft in length. Capillary columns 0.01–0.03 in. I.D. and 100–1000 ft in length are usual. The nature of the column is discussed further below. Column efficiency generally improves with decreasing column diameter.

5. The detector indicates and measures the solutes in the carrier gas stream. A good detector is highly sensitive, has a linear response over a large concentration range and is relatively insensitive to flow and temperature variations. Either universality or selectivity of response can be advantageous. A further discussion of detectors is found below.

6. Pure samples may be collected from the column effluent in cooled capillary tubing, or in glass collection bottles for larger samples.

7. The signal from the detector must be amplified and fed to a recorder where the chromatogram is drawn on a strip chart. A 1 mv, 1 sec (full scale) recorder is generally useful for gas chromatographs.

8. The temperature must be controlled in three places (Figure 2). The injection port is kept hot enough to vaporize the sample rapidly but not so hot as to decompos[illegible]. A temperature 10–50° above that of the column is often recommended. The port need not be heated for gas samples. The temperature of the column is kept as low as possible consistent with good resolution but high enough to obtain reasonably fast separations. Isothermal operation is often adequate for mixtures with a narrow boiling range. For mixtures with a wide boiling range, temperature programming is recommended (see below). The temperature of the detector must be high enough to resist condensation of the sample or the liquid phase or any products formed in the detector if ionization is involved. Temperature control of the column within ±2 °C is usually adequate; close temperature control for some detectors (thermal conductivity) is critical but for others (flame ionization) is not.

B. THEORY

The theory of gas chromatography will be given in some detail in this section. The theory of the other chromatographic methods is essentially the same although there are some differences in terms and actual differences due to variations in the techniques.

The separation of solute peaks in chromatography depends upon the separation of the peak centers and the degree of spreading of the peaks. Obviously, complete separation of narrow peaks can be obtained with the peak centers closer together than if the peaks are spread (Figure 3).

The location of the peak centers depends upon the solute's sorptive equilibrium as determined by the respective distribution (partition) coefficients and the temperature. The interactions between the solutes and the sorbent leading to dissimilar partition coefficients are hydrogen bonds, Debye forces, Van der Waals' forces and specific chemical interactions (the partition coefficient K = the amount of solute per unit volume of liquid phase/the amount of solute per unit volume of gas phase). [4]

Peak width or spread is determined by mass transport and kinetic processes and is related to the column efficiency. Column efficiency is measured by the number of theoretical plates in the column or better by the resolution of the column. The longer a peak is in a column, the broader it becomes (under isothermal conditions).

The number of theoretical plates (N) is measured from the actual chromatogram. Tangents are drawn to the peak at the points of inflection (about two-thirds of the height). Then, referring to Figure 4, N for the first peak is given by

$$N = 16\left(\frac{X}{W_1}\right)^2, \qquad [5]$$

where X is the distance from the point of injection to the peak maximum and W is the length of base line enclosed by the two tangents. Both the numerator and denominator must be in the same units, most conveniently in cm measured along the chart paper.

HETP or height equivalent to a theoretical plate is the column length divided by N. A good column has a large number of theoretical plates and a small HETP (less than one mm for GC). The HETP may be different for each solute on a given column. It should be emphasized that HETP is a function not only of the width of the peak but of its retention time. Therefore a wide peak with a high retention time can represent the same HETP as a narrow peak which is eluted earlier.

The separation of two adjacent peaks is measured by the resolution (R) (see Figure 4):

$$R = \frac{2d}{W_1 + W_2}. \qquad [6]$$

When recording resolution, the specific compounds being considered should be stated. As defined in equation [6], an R of 1 indicates "perfect" (near base-line) separation.

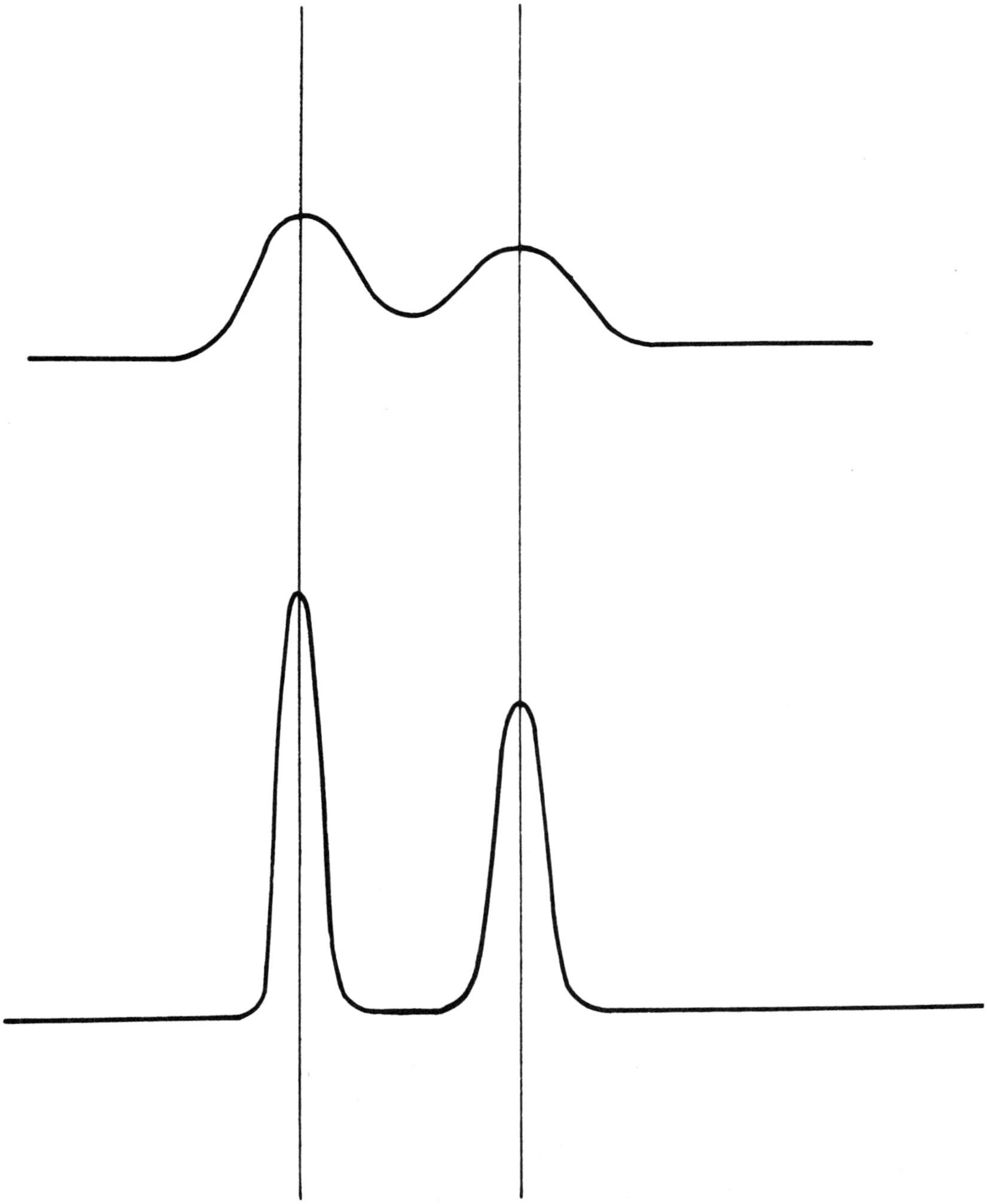

Figure 3. Two chromatograms showing the effect of increased column efficiency on the degree of separation obtained.

For describing the performance of a column, both relative retentions and plate numbers are important considerations. That is, one can obtain a good separation of two components whose relative retentions are significantly different even on a column with a low number of plates. However, if the relative retentions are very similar, even a column with many plates may not provide the desired separation.

Another parameter often used to evaluate column performance is the *Separation Factor*, which is the ratio of the adjusted retention times or volumes (Section F3) for two adjacent peaks.

HETP can be theoretically calculated by means of the van Deemter equation. This equation treats chromatography as the flowing system it is, and allows one to see what conditions should be adopted in order to optimize the system. According to this equation

$$\text{HETP} = 2\lambda dp + \frac{2\gamma D_g}{\mu} + \frac{8k'd_f^2}{\pi^2(1 + k')^2 D_l}\mu. \qquad [7]$$

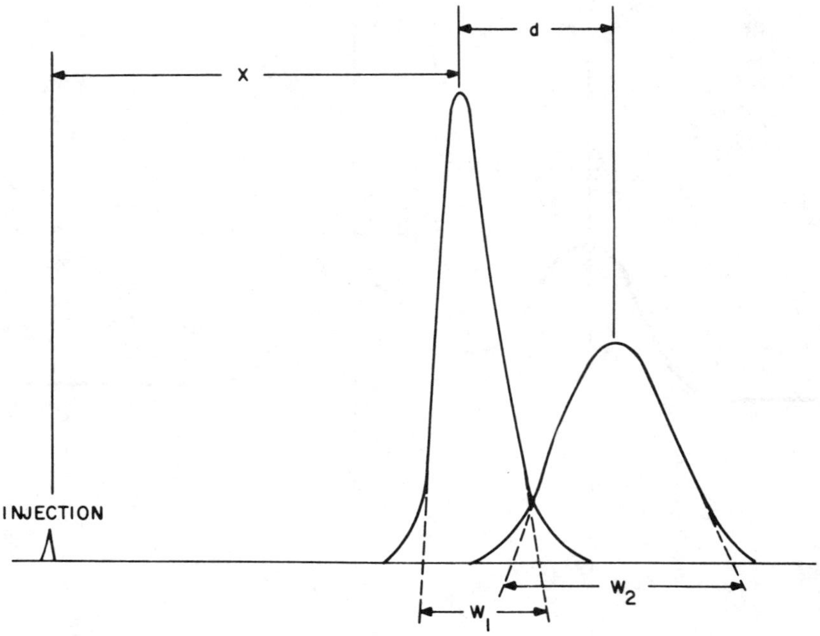

Figure 4. Calculation of *N* and *R* from a chromatogram.

where

λ = a constant measuring packing irregularities
dp = the average particle diameter of the support
γ = tortuosity factor
D_g = coefficient of solute diffusion in the gas phase
D_l = coefficient of liquid diffusion
μ = the average linear gas velocity
k' = ratio of the capacity of the liquid phase to that of the gas phase
d_f = average thickness of the liquid film coated on the support particles

Equation [7] can be reduced to

$$\text{HETP} = A + \frac{B}{\mu} + C\mu. \quad [8]$$

The *A* term is the multiple path or Eddy diffusion term which is independent of flow rate. It describes peak spread due to molecules taking different paths through the packed column. To decrease HETP (and increase column efficiency), one should use particles as small (low *dp*) and uniform (low λ) as possible, consistent with an adequate gas flow and a low pressure drop. The *B* term accounts for the normal longitudinal molecular diffusion of the solute in the carrier gas due to the concentration gradient in the zone. Diffusion is inverse to flow rate and decreases when a high-molecular-weight carrier gas is used (low D_g). The *C* term involves resistance to mass transfer and is proportional to flow rate. To decrease this term, a thin, uniform film of low-viscosity liquid should be used as the stationary phase (low d_f and high D_l). Lowering d_f changes k' and this complicates prediction of the optimum value of this term.

The optimum carrier-gas flow rate is determined by plotting HETP *vs* μ and choosing a value at or slightly above the minimum in the curve. Since the outlet pressure is usually one atmosphere, the flow rate chosen will dictate the inlet pressure to be used.

C. THE COLUMN

The choice of the column packing is the most critical in GC. In GLC, the column can be one of two types, either packed or capillary. Packed columns contain an inert solid support with a thin coating of the liquid phase. As seen above, small, uniform particle sizes (40–60 to 100–120 mesh) give the highest efficiency columns. The support is usually diatomaceous earth (kieselguhr), e.g., the Chromosorbs (see Section II.III, Table 2). In order to reduce tailing and decomposition of certain classes of compounds (steroids), the support surface must be made entirely inert by reacting surface hydroxyl and oxide groups with a compound such as dimethyldichlorosilane.

The liquid phase (see Section II.III, Table 1) should have a low viscosity and a high and differential solubility (leading to different distribution coefficients) for the mixture components. A loading of 2–10% of the liquid is generally used; less-loaded columns give faster separations at lower temperature but have lower sample capacity and may require inactive solid supports (e.g., VarAport 30 or Teflon). Retention times decrease (at a given temperature) as the loading becomes lighter, and adjacent peaks become narrower with centers which are less separated. The liquid should neither react with the support or the solutes nor "bleed" appreciably from the column during the run. There is a recommended maximum column temperature for each liquid phase.

Liquid phases can be classified according to their polarity: the most polar liquids are capable of forming strong hydrogen bonds (e.g., FFAP, Carbowaxes, Hallcomid, etc.) while the least-polar can interact only by forming weak Van der Waals' bonds (e.g., SE-30, OV-1, squalene, etc.). Solutes can be classified in the same way, ranging from polar (alcohols, acids, phenols) to nonpolar (saturated hydrocarbons). Liquid phases which are similar to the components retard these components compared to liquid phases which are not similar. Separations are best achieved by matching the solute and liquid types; for example, hydrocarbons are best separated on squalene, alcohols on Carbowax, and fatty acid methyl esters on polyesters (see Section II.III, Table 1). For mixtures containing solutes of different polarity, it is best to choose the liquid to match the most polar solutes. It should be recalled that "polarity" is a function of temperature and that dipole interactions become very weak at high temperature.

Some liquid phases react chemically with certain solutes and are very selective for these compounds. Selective liquid phases give large differences in retention times and require fewer plates (shorter columns) to achieve a desired separation.

Porapak porous polymer resins (Section II.III, Table 2) are used for GLC with no liquid phase. The mechanism of separations on Porapak is apparently a combination of partition, adsorption, and sieving based on size.

Capillary (or open tubular) columns originally contained a liquid film of ca. 0.5 μ thickness coated onto the inside wall of a glass or metal tube. Lately, solid-coated capillary columns containing a layer of coated support around the inside tube wall but still having an open center have been employed. These latter columns are superior because more sample can be applied and the optimum flow rate is higher (about 2–5 ml per min rather than 1 ml per min). Because more sample can be applied, analytical sensitivities are greater and the use of a sample splitter (or other special splitless injection techniques) might be avoided. Support-coated capillary columns must be purchased commercially, whereas wall-coated columns can be prepared in the laboratory. Workers often do not specify in the literature the exact percentage composition of the solution they used to coat a capillary column, but instead state only the phase and the solvent. Ten percent coating solutions are generally used for coating open tubular capillary columns by the dynamic coating method, and two percent solutions or less for the static coating method (*2*).

The number of plates per foot with either type of capillary column is similar to packed columns, but the maximum total number of plates is much higher (several hundred thousand) because very long capillary columns can be employed in the absence of a pressure drop. A disadvantage is that the void volume of capillary columns is so large relative to packed columns that the capacity ratios are significantly smaller. As a result, resolution in the two types of columns is not too different.

Capillary columns with a complete loose packing have also been described (*3*), as have sandwiched capillary columns consisting of one or more carbon threads inserted in a glass capillary and coated with the stationary liquid (*4*). The performance of sandwiched capillary columns is between open tubular and classical packed columns. Their advantage lies in the ease of preparation and lower pressure drop corresponding to a minimum plate height.

A new type of stationary phase developed by Halasz consists of organic molecules attached chemically to the surface of an inorganic support. [See Reference (*5*) for a review of these phases.] The stationary phase is then like a brush with organic bristles on the inorganic surface. Such a material may be produced by esterifying the surface hydroxide groups of silica gel with an alcohol. Changing the esterifying agent results in a change in the polarity of the organic bristle. These brushes (available commercially from Waters Associates under the trade name Durapak) are useful in both gas and liquid chromatography and typically provide 4–25 effective plates per second (GC) as compared with 0.1–4 for packed columns and 30–100 for open (capillary) columns. They have highly ordered interfaces leading to unusually high mass transfer, so that separations in columns packed with brushes are about as fast as those with open tubes. They have low sublimation pressure (i.e., bond decomposition, which in this case corresponds to "bleed") and can be employed at temperatures up to 145°C with normal tank N_2 or above 200°C with dried nitrogen. HETP for these columns is independent of temperature, retention time or sample type and load.

Still another new class of stationary phases contains those substances described by Annino and McCrea (*6*) which undergo reversible temperature-dependent compositional changes to produce large variations in selectivity for various classes of solutes. By combining substances differing in melting point and solute selectivity (e.g., stearic acid and 1,9-nonanedioic acid), a mixture is produced which can be used to prepare a column exhibiting varying degrees of specificity through choice of an appropriate column temperature. Positive relative retention shifts of the order of 100% can be achieved with a 20° increase in temperature, facilitating solute identification and resolution.

D. COLUMN TEMPERATURE

Lowering the temperature usually improves resolution while increasing the temperature will decrease the analysis time. The temperature chosen for an isothermal separation must therefore be a compromise. If the liquid loading is reduced a lower temperature can be used, a condition which could be beneficial for the separation of heat-labile solutes. The column temperature should, of course, never be high enough to either change the sample or to decompose or cause excessive vaporization of the stationary liquid. Because of possible decomposition, isomerization, etc. of the sample, chromatography above 250 °C is seldom practical. As a first approximation, a column temperature around the average boiling point of the major components of the mixture can be tried.

For wide boiling range mixtures, better resolution at the low end and faster elution at the higher end is obtained if temperature programming is employed. This method, which usually involves a controlled linear increase in temperature during the run, sharpens the later peaks and makes the sensitivity of analysis the same for both high- and low-boiling components.

Temperature programming is also advantageous for preparative GC. A large sample can be slowly applied (directly on column, if possible) by repeated application of small increments with boiling-off of the solvent in between. The temperature of the column is then slowly raised and the components migrate down the column in the order of their boiling points. This results in sharp, high-concentration peaks which can be easily trapped.

The program can be started at sub-ambient temperatures by placing a chunk of dry ice in the column compartment. The detector is generally hot throughout the run. It should be recalled that the viscosities of gases increase as the temperature increases, so that flow rate tends to decrease during the temperature program. A differential flow controller is employed to keep the gas flow constant.

Bleeding of the liquid phase is often a problem with programmed temperature GC. Use of a dual-column gas chromatograph, with both columns containing the same liquid but not necessarily of the same length, can be used to mask (not eliminate) the bleeding and maintain a reasonably level base line. This method works with a thermal conductivity detector but not ionization detectors. Alternatively, the bleeding material can be trapped by a column of an appropriate, highly-stable sorbent placed between the analytical column and the detector. Column bleed can be checked by measuring periodically the decrease in retention time of a standard compound.

An alternate technique that can be used to separate a wide boiling-point mixture is flow (pressure) programming GC. This method, in which the flow rate of the carrier gas is changed during the run, is described in detail in Reference (7).

E. DETECTORS

The two most widely-used detectors are the thermal conductivity (TC) detector (katharometer) and the flame ionization detector (FID).

1. *Thermal conductivity detector*—This detector consists of two identical metal cells, each containing a tungsten, rhenium-tungsten or gold-sheathed tungsten wire filament or a thermistor (Figure 5). The column effluent flows through one cell and pure carrier gas with a high thermal conductivity (H_2 or He) through the other. On the sample side the gas flows directly over the filament while on the reference side the gas may pass over the wire or pass near and diffuse to the wire (Figure 5). The wires are heated by an electric current. The temperature of the wires, and their resistance, depends upon the composition of the gas flowing over them. When pure carrier gas flows through both cells the temperatures are the same and the detector is balanced. When a gas with a lower thermal conductivity appears in the effluent cavity, the temperature of the wire will rise (heat will not be so quickly lost to the wall of the cell) and its resistance will rise. The cell is initially arranged as part of a balanced Wheatstone bridge circuit, so that the resistance increase will cause an imbalance in the bridge and gives rise to an electrical signal which is amplified and fed to a strip-chart recorder where it shows up as a peak.

For maximum sensitivity, the filament temperature is increased, the block temperature and flow rate are decreased, and a carrier gas with a high thermal conductivity is chosen (most organic gases have relatively low heat conductivities). Operation at a high temperature shortens the life of the wire filaments, of course. The TC detector is nondestructive and responds to any gas with a TC different from the carrier gas. The response is concentration dependent, but correction must be made depending upon the molecular weight of the gas being detected.

2. *Flame ionization detector*. Components in the column effluent are ionized by burning them in a hydrogen-air (or oxygen, for increased sensitivity) flame. This allows the gas in the detector to conduct an electrical current. Above the flame, a collector electrode, to which a DC potential is applied, measures this conductivity. When pure carrier gas (H_2) is combusted, few ions are formed and the conductivity is low. The combustion of organic compounds increases the conductivity and the resultant current is amplified and fed to a recorder.

This detector is highly sensitive and therefore often used with capillary columns, and its range of linear response to increasing concentration is very wide. It responds to almost all compounds except the inorganic

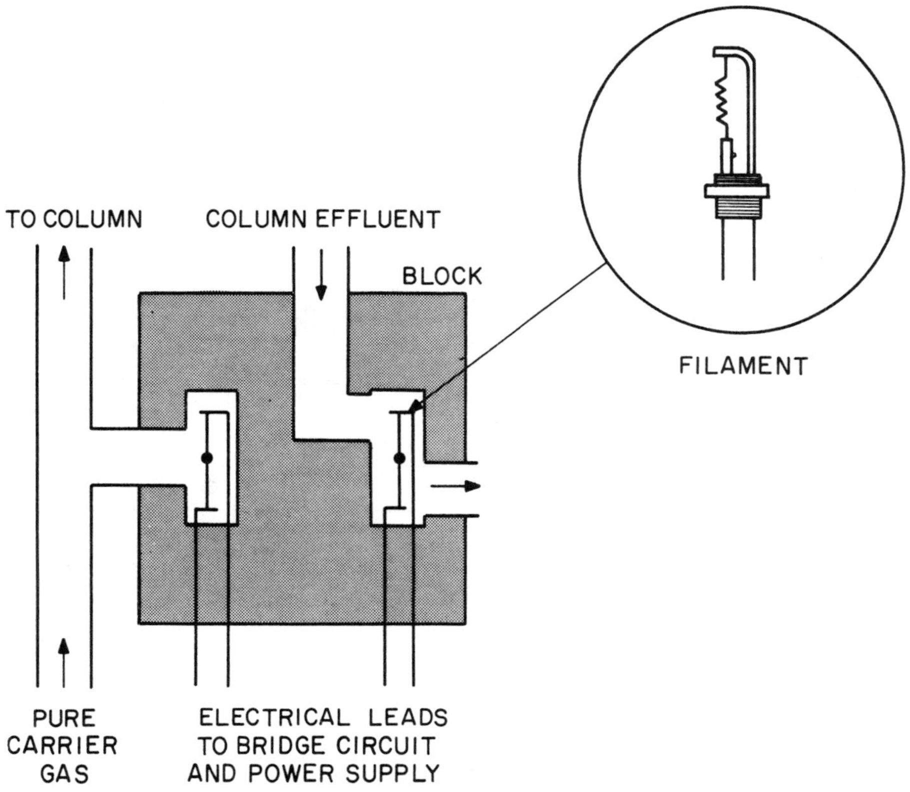

Figure 5. Schematic drawing of a thermal conductivity detector employing thermistor beads (black dots) or wire filaments (insert).

gases, CS_2 and COS. The response is based on the carbon weight percentage in the molecule; as the level of oxidation increases (e.g., from saturated hydrocarbon to alcohol to acid), the response of the detector decreases. A disadvantage is that the detector is destructive; if the concentration is sufficiently high, the effluent stream is often split and part of the solutes collected for confirmatory analysis by other methods.

The *flame ionization detector* responds to mass flow rate, i.e., the peak area is proportional to the total mass of eluted component. The *thermal conductivity detector* responds rather to concentration, and for accurate quantitative analysis with such a detector, constant flow rate is critical. Constant flow rate is therefore not so critical for a flame ionization detector as for a thermal conductivity detector.

3. *Other detectors*. The *electron capture detector* is highly sensitive to halides and is therefore valuable for pesticide analyses. It gives little response to hydrocarbons other than conjugated carbonyls.

The *alkali flame detector* is a flame ionization detector with a KCl or CsBr salt tip placed on the burner jet. It is especially sensitive for phosphorus detection.

The *helium detector* is used for fixed gases separated by GSC. It cannot be used with partition columns because it is so sensitive to organic liquids bleeding from the support.

A *flame photometric detector* (developed by Brody and Chaney) is a flame emission detector in which a photomultiplier tube monitors the chemiluminescent emission from a hydrogen-air flame. If appropriate filters are inserted between the detector and photomultiplier, the response is selective for sulfur (394 nm) or phosphorus (526 nm).

A *reaction coulometer* can be used as an absolute detector for compounds combustible over a platinum catalyst. Oxygen coming from a generator at a constant rate mixes with the carrier-gas stream and passes into a reactor where any combustible materials in the stream are burned. An *oxygen detector* senses an oxygen deficiency caused by the burning and produces a signal which is amplified and fed to the generator, so that its output increases to make up the oxygen deficiency. A recorder or integrator records the extra amount of oxygen needed, from which the amount of each solute is calculated without reference to calibration standards.

The properties of various GC detectors are given in Table I, page 14.

TABLE I
SUMMARY OF DETECTOR PARAMETERS (*8*)

Detector	Principle of operation	Selectivity	Sensitivity (gm/sec)	Response (ccul/gm)	Linear range	Minimum detectable quantity (gm)	Stability	Temp limit °C	Carrier gas	Remarks
Thermal conductivity	Measures thermal conductivity of gases	Universal—responds to all compounds	6×10^{-10}	—	10^4	2–5 μg 10^{-5} of CH_4 per ml of detector effluent	good	450	He, H_2, N_2	Non destructive—requires good temp and flow control. Simple, inexpensive and rugged
Gas density balance	Difference of molecular weight of gases	Universal—responds to all compounds whose MW differs from carrier gas	Variable in range of T.C.D.	—	10^3		good	Better sensitivity 150	N_2, CO_2, Ar	Good for analysis of corrosive compounds. Non-destructive
Flame ionization	H_2–O_2 Flame 2000°C Plasma	Responds to organic compounds Not to fixed gases or water	9×10^{-13} for Alkanes	0.01	10^7	2×10^{-11} for Alkanes	excellent	400	H3, N_2	H_2O + CS_2 good solvents because no response. Destructive
Electron capture ^3H ^{63}Ni	$N_2 + \beta \rightarrow e^-$ e^- + sample → loss of signal.	Response to electron adsorbing compounds esp. halogens, nitrates and conjugated carbonyls	2×10^{-14} for CCl_4 5×10^{-14} for CCl_4	— —	5×10^2 50	10^{-13} for lindane 4×10^{-12} for lindane	fair fair	225 350	N_2 or Ar+ 10% CH_4	Detector is easily contaminated and easy to clean. Sensitive to water; carrier gas must be dry. Can be operated in pulsed or D.C. mode. Non-destructive
Alkali Flame P compd.	Alkali modified H_2–O_2 flame 1600°C plasma	Enhanced response to phosphorus cmpds.	4×10^{-14}	—	10^3	2×10^{-12} parathion	fair	300	N_2	Destructive—requires flow controller for hydrogen and air
N compd.		Enhanced response to nitrogen compounds	7×10^{-12}	—	10^3	2×10^{-10} azobenzene	fair	300	He	Destructive—requires flow controller for hydrogen and air, high sensitivity operating in starved O_2 mode.
Helium	He + $\beta \rightarrow$ He* Sample $\xrightarrow{He^*}$ I_0	Universal—responds to all compounds	2×10^{-14} for methane	28	5×10^3	10^{-12} for fixed gases	poor	100	He	High sensitivity to bleed precludes its uses with columns other than active solids. Non-destructive
Cross section	β + sample → I_0	Universal—responds to all compounds	10^{-9}	—	10^4	10^{-5}	good	225	H_2 or He+ 3% CH_4	

Reproduced with permission from "Basic Gas Chromatography," 5th Edition, 1969 pp. 118, 119, **McNair**, H. M. and Bonelli, E. J., Varian Aerograph, Walnut Creek, Calif.

TABLE I (continued)

PERFORMANCE CHARACTERISTICS OF OTHER GAS CHROMATOGRAPHY DETECTORS (*9*)

Detector	Detectability, sample weight	Universal (U), specific (S)	Species detected	Carrier recommended	Complexity factor[a]	Linearity (some estimated)	Other comments
Thermistor	Nanogram	U		He, H_2	1	50 (est)	Best detectability at low temperature Very small detector volume
Argon	Picogram	U		Ar	3	10^5	Uses unpopular Sr^{90} source No sensitivity to methane
Microwave emission	Subnanogram	S	Halides, phosphorus	85% He, 15% Ar	9	10^3 (est)	Low detector pressures recommended Good specificity to all compounds
Photoionization	Picrogram	U		Ar, H_2, N_2	8	10^5	Application: fixed gas analysis
Nonradioactive helium ionization	Subnanogram	U		He	4	10^4 (est)	Application: fixed gas analysis
Radio frequency	Nanogram	U		He, Ar	4	10^3	Application: fixed gas analysis
Radio gc	Subnano-Curie	S	^3H, ^{14}C	N_2, He, Ar	8	10^4	Very high specificity factor to nonradioactive species
Ultrasonic	Nanogram	U		He, H_2, Ar, N_2, O_2, Air	6	10^6	Best for fixed gas analysis Use of any carrier eliminates solvent
Microcoulometric	Nanogram	S	Halides, sulfur, nitrogen	N_2, He, Ar	6	10^4 (est)	High specificity factors to all interferences
Electrolytic conductivity	Nanogram	S	Halides, sulfur, nitrogen	N_2, He, Ar	5	10^3 (est)	High specificity factors to all interferences
Reaction coulometric	High nanogram	U	Organics	N_2, He, Ar	7	10^4	Can be used to detect O or H in sample molecule Self calibrating
Infrared spectrometer	High microgram	S	Ir absorber	He, N_2	10	none	Special interfacing to gc required
Mass spectrometer	High nanogram	U		He, H_2	10	10^6	Special interfacing to gc required
Far ultraviolet spectrometer	High nanogram	S	UV absorber	He	9	None	Application: low molecular weight organics Special interfacing to gc required
Spectrophotofluorometric	Nanogram	S	Fluorescent compounds	N_2	8	10^3	Special interfacing problems

[a] Author's arbitrary rating on scale from 0–10 (higher numbers—more complexity). Complexity factor considers number of parameters to be adjusted and the amount of accessory equipment needed.

Reproduced with permission from American Chemical Society; C. H. Hartman, *Anal. Chem.* **43**, 124A, 1971.

F. QUALITATIVE ANALYSIS

To begin this section some terms will have to be defined (see Figure 6).

1. The *Uncorrected Retention Volume* (V_R) is the volume of gas required to elute the peak of the constituent in question:

$$V_R = t_r F_C \quad [9]$$

where t_r is the retention time from injection and F_C is the flow rate of the carrier gas measured at the exit of the column. Since the chart paper moves at a constant rate, t_r is measured as a linear distance along the paper, and the same distance can be termed V_R (Figure 6). In other words, the abscissa of Figure 6 can be expressed in inches (or cm), time or volume.

2. The *Dead Volume* or *Gas Holdup* (V_M) is the uncorrected retention volume of the nonsorbed air peak. This volume is in the injection port, tubing, detector and column. The dead volume in the column is called the void or interstitial volume by workers in liquid ion-exchange chromatography.

3. The *Adjusted Retention Volume* (V_R') is the uncorrected retention volume minus the dead volume:

$$V_R' = V_R - V_M. \quad [10]$$

4. The *Corrected Retention Volume* (V_R^0) is

$$V_R^0 = jV_R \quad [11]$$

where j corrects for differences in pressure at the column inlet and outlet (the pressure drop):

$$j = \frac{3\,(\text{inlet pressure/outlet pressure})^2 - 1}{2\,(\text{inlet pressure/outlet pressure})^3 - 1} \quad [12]$$

$j \cong 0.65$ for the typical case when the inlet pressure is double the outlet pressure. V_R^0 is in effect based on the average flow through the column. The inlet pressure is measured by inserting a special commercial device for this purpose into the injection-port septum.

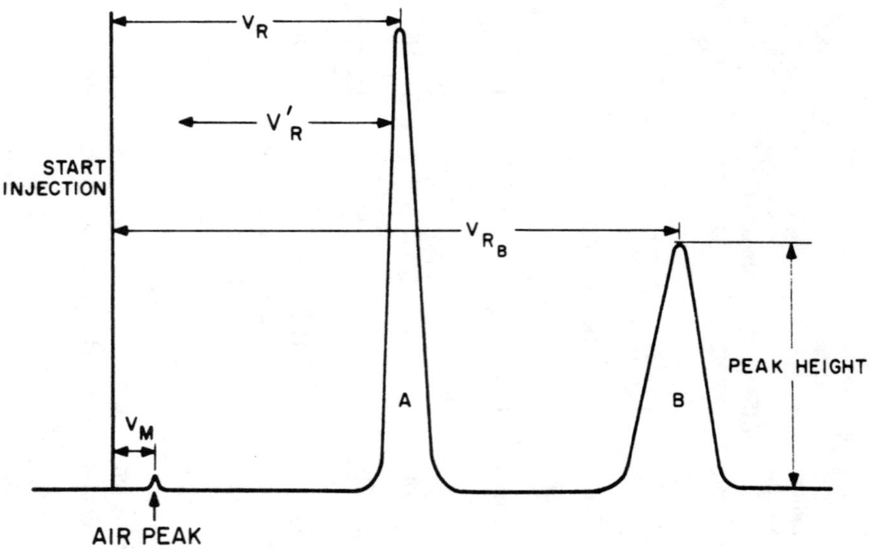

Figure 6. Retention ratio and peak-height calculations from a chromatogram.

5. The *Net Retention Volume* (V_N) is corrected for both pressure differences and dead volume:

$$V_N = jV_R' = j(V_R - V_M). \quad [13]$$

6. The *Specific Retention Volume* (V_g) is the net retention volume at 0 °C with one gram of liquid phase in the column:

$$V_g = \frac{273\,V_N}{TW_L} \quad [14]$$

where T is the column temperature in degrees Kelvin and W_L is the weight of the liquid phase.

7. The *Relative Retention Volume* (r) is the ratio of any of the above retention expressions for a solute relative to a standard component in the same column under the same conditions. If peak B is the standard in Figure 6, r for peak A would be the distance in cm to peak A/distance in cm to peak B, both measured from the air peak, or:

$$r = \frac{V_R}{V_{R_B}}. \qquad [15]$$

Values of r are dependent only on the column temperature and the liquid phase.

The basis of qualitative analysis is that retention volumes reflect the thermodynamic partition coefficients of the solutes. The partition coefficient (K) (defined above in equation [4]) is related to the retention volume as follows:

$$V_R^0 = V_G + KV_L \qquad [16]$$

where $V_G = jV_M$ and V_L is the volume occupied by the liquid phase in the column. Further,

$$V_R^0 - V_G = KV_L = V_N. \qquad [17]$$

Therefore,

$$K = \frac{V_N}{V_L}. \qquad [18]$$

In practice, identification can be made by comparing uncorrected retention volumes for the unknown and standards run at the same time under identical conditions in several systems of very different polarity. It is better to measure adjusted, corrected relative retention volumes. These values should be relatively constant from day to day and lab to lab and can be compared with lists of data compiled earlier for standards to make a tentative identification of unknown peaks.

The Kováts retention index system for reporting retention data is the most precise and repeatable and is becoming widely accepted. This system is based on retentions relative to n-alkanes and the retention index is a logarithmic interpolation between two standards. The equation for the relative retention index is

$$I = 100\left[n\frac{\log R_X - \log R_Z}{\log R_{Z+n} - \log R_Z} + Z\right] \qquad [19]$$

where R_X is the retention time of unknown substance X, R_Z is the retention time of the normal alkane having z carbon atoms, R_{Z+n} is the retention time of the normal alkane having $z + n$ carbon atoms, and n is the difference in the number of carbon atoms for the normal alkanes. The less widely used methylene unit value for characterizing peak positions is obtained by dividing I by 100.

Adjacent members of a homologous series should be about 100 units apart in this system, so knowing the index of any one member gives an idea of the values for all others. Also, the difference in the retention index for a compound on two different columns (polar and nonpolar) gives information concerning its structure. The retention index is temperature dependent. [For details, the reader is referred to Ref. (*10*).]

Another system of indexing GC retention data is the Arithmetic Index of Harbourn (*11*) which is defined by the expression

$$I_A = 100N + 100\left[\frac{R_X - R_N}{R_{N+1} - R_N}\right] \qquad [20]$$

where R_X is the retention time of the unknown peak, R_N and R_{N+1} are the retention times of n-alkane standards and N is the number of carbons in the lower molecular weight standard. This system is mathematically simpler than the Kováts Index and requires only raw retentions rather than adjusted data.

Members of a homologous series can be identified by a plot of log retention time *vs* number of carbon atoms. Once the plot is established with two or three members of the series, other members falling on the line may be identified. Different classes of compounds yield lines of differing slopes.

Information helpful in making identification can also be obtained by splitting the column effluent and passing it through two detectors (e.g., flame ionization and electron capture) sensitive to different compound types. The response ratio is characteristic of different compounds.

The method of reaction GC developed by Beroza for obtaining structural information can be also mentioned. A hot catalyst bed placed at the injection port strips off the functional groups of the solutes and allows the carbon skeleton through. Depending upon the exact conditions, hydrogenation, dehydrogenation or hydrogenolysis may occur. Ozonolysis and subtraction reactions have also been carried out in conjunction with GC (*12,13*). The catalytic hydrogenation method of Franc (*14*) allows a portion of the sample to pass unchanged while the rest is hydrogenated. The difference in retention of the hydrogenated and nonhydrogenated components is a function of the original structure of the material.

Molecular weight and retention data in combination are often adequate for positive qualitative identification of compounds. The technique of mass (molecular weight) chromatography provides this information.

In this method, a sample is split and analyzed simultaneously with two matched columns and two gas density detectors using different carrier gases. Molecular weight is calculated from

$$MW_X = \frac{[K(A_1/A_2)]\,(MW_{CG_2} - MW_{CG_1})}{K[(A_1/A_2) - 1]} \qquad [21]$$

where K is an instrumental constant, A_1 and A_2 are the area responses for the unknown compound in the two detectors, and MW_{CG_1} and MW_{CG_2} are the molecular weights of the two carrier gases. See Reference (*15*) for details of procedures and equipment.

Finally, nonvolatile substances can be pyrolyzed with a heated filament, electric furnace or laser, the pyrolyzate chromatographed, and the resulting chromatogram (pyrogram) used as a fingerprint to identify the substance by comparison to pyrograms of known standards (*16*).

For positive qualitative identification, gas chromatography must usually be combined with other analytical techniques. The column effluent is collected and then analyzed by wet or instrumental methods or it is fed directly to a colorimeter (after reaction with an appropriate reagent in a bubbler), or to an infra-red, mass, flame-emission or atomic absorption spectrometer.

G. QUANTITATIVE ANALYSIS

Quantitative analysis is based on a detector response that is linear with respect to concentration (Figure 7), hopefully over a wide range of concentrations. The accuracy of any GC analysis is limited by the overall error encountered, including errors due to the sampling technique, possible sample decomposition (which is checked by comparing IR spectra taken before the injection and on the column effluent), detector and recorder performance, integration, calculations, etc. With good technique (precision), accuracy can be obtained by employing standards properly. Results of an analysis are reported as the average ± the standard deviation of the replicates.

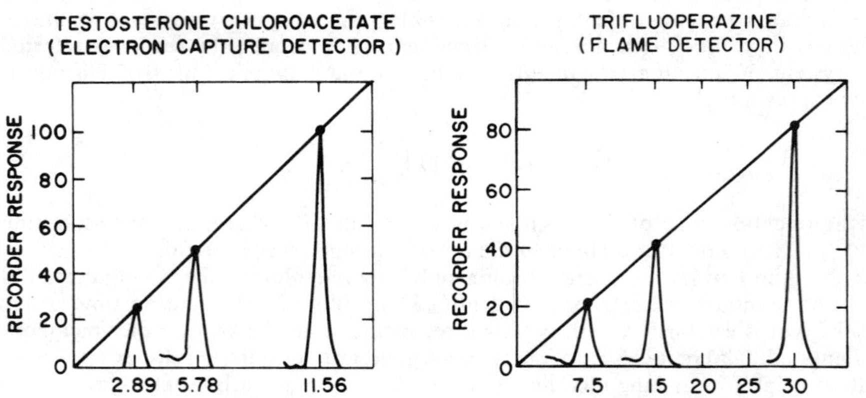

Figure 7. Linear response of the HP Model 402 High-Efficiency GC to nanogram amounts of testosterone chloroacetate and trifluoroperazine (reprinted with permission from Hewlett–Packard, Avondale, Pa.).

Peak areas (or heights) may be employed for analyses in two ways: In the absolute calibration method peak area is plotted *vs* weight for a series of standard solutions, and the weight of the unknown is read from the curve. In this method it is critical that the injections be precise and that the response of the detector remains constant for all solutions. A better method employs internal standardization wherein a calibration curve is prepared from known weight blends of the sample and standard and the ratio of areas of the sample and standard peaks are plotted *vs* the weight ratios. A known amount of the standard is also added to the unknown and from the area ratios of the peaks the weight ratio is read from the graph. The sample preparation is most critical in this method.

The percentage composition of the sample is obtained by normalizing the peak areas. For component X among n components:

$$\%X = \frac{A_X F_X}{\Sigma A_n F_n} \quad [22]$$

where A is the area of the peaks and F is the factor to correct for different detector response. The detector must especially be calibrated when working with low molecular weight, dissimilar compounds.

Peak areas are obtained in various ways. Listed in order of increasing precision these are: planimetry, triangulation, height x width at the baseline or at some fraction (usually 0.25 or 0.50) of the peak height, cutting out peaks from chart paper and weighing, disc integration and computer methods.

The recommended methods for quantitative analysis are internal standardization combined with:

(1) Peak height (see Figure 6)—This is useful with sharp peaks as obtained with temperature programmed GC. With good flow and temperature control, 2% relative standard deviation can be obtained, and the method is quite fast.

(2) Disc integration increases precision to better than 1%.

(3) Digital (computer) integration saves much time and increases precision to around 0.5%.

If a fast read-out computer is available, bracketing standards can conceivably be run before and after each unknown. This continual standardization would allow the instrument to be run under less-demanding conditions of flow and temperature control and would permit, in general, cheaper instruments to yield results with good accuracy and precision. The computer can perform all operations on a chromatogram that an analyst can, including measurement of peak locations, heights or areas, and can also correct for base-line shift, noise and other factors. The computer can also be coupled to a gas chromatograph and to a neighboring IR spectrometer or other analytical instrument for rapid, accurate qualitative and quantitative analyses.

Digital recording of data combined with digital control of sample introduction and improved control of flow rate and column temperature can lead to great improvement in the reproducibility of retention times. This allows more meaningful interpretations to be made in the determination of fundamental properties (thermodynamic constants) from GC data as well as aiding qualitative identification and quantitative reproducibility.

A comparison of integration methods for GC has appeared in the literature (*17*).

H. APPLICATIONS

There are presently some 70–80,000 gas chromatographs in use, and they are being used to solve all kinds of scientific problems. GC can separate only gases and volatile substances. However, since only very small samples are required, vapor pressure of the substances need only be a few mm of mercury. Certain columns can be operated in excess of 400 °C at which temperature most compounds, even high-molecular-weight organic compounds, have appreciable vapor pressures. Alternatively, compounds can be made into derivatives with suitable vapor pressures (see Section II.II). Carbohydrates, for example, have been successfully chromatographed as alkyl ethers, acetals and ketals, acetate esters and trimethylsilyl ethers. Hyper-pressure GC (e.g., up to 3100 lb/in.^{2}) allows the satisfactory separation of nonvolatile compounds and compounds which are thermally unstable in some cases (*18*). Figures 8–10 show typical separations achieved by GC.

Many inorganic compounds are readily separated by GC. Various metal chlorides, fluorides, alkyls, chelates, carbides, oxides, sulfides and nitrates have been separated and quantitatively determined.

I. INSTRUMENTS AND COLUMN PACKING

Gas chromatographs and accessories are available in many price ranges from many different manufacturers. Columns can be purchased already packed or can be packed by the worker himself. Once set up, it is best to leave instruments always on with a trickle of gas flowing through. Most instrument manufacturers have active research divisions and are happy to try to answer specific questions such as the choice of a column for a specific separation, the best detector to use, the best temperature and flow rate, etc.

1. *Coating the support.* The support is chosen to be finely divided (2–5 meter ^{2}/g) and should have a uniform particle size within the range of 60–100 mesh. If the limits are closer (e.g., 90–100 mesh), the column will be more efficient.

Liquid is coated on the support as follows: weigh out the required amount of liquid phase relative to the amount of support to be coated and dissolve the phase in a sufficient volume of volatile solvent to cover the support entirely. Mix together the phase, the support and the solvent and shake to form a wet slurry. Evaporate the solvent by carefully warming the slurry, with shaking, under vacuum; a rotary vacuum evaporator is convenient to use for this purpose. After the solvent has evaporated, further dry the coated support in an oven at 90 °C.

Another method for preparing the packing is *solution coating*. This procedure is simple and yields uniform distribution of the stationary phase on the support and is especially recommended if the concentration of the stationary phase is below 5% on the support. The method involves wetting the support with a

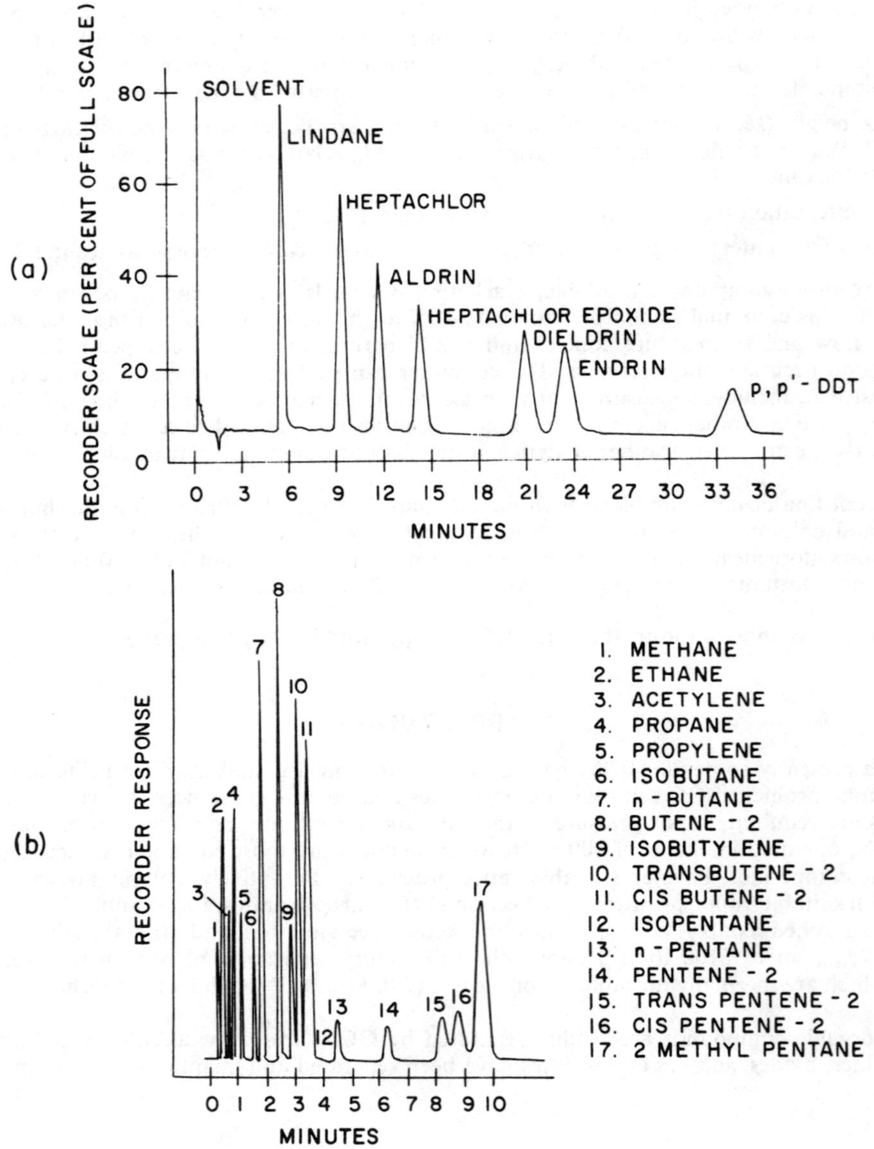

Figure 8. Isothermal GC separation of (a) pesticides on Gas-Chrom Q (silane-treated diatomaceous earth support), 100–120 mesh coated with 10 wt. % D.C. 200. Column: 6 ft × 4 mm I.D. glass U-tube. Detector: Electron Capture. Column temperature: 200 °C. Carrier gas flow rate: 70 ml/min at 25 psig inlet pressure. Sample: 1.0 ng of each component. [Reprinted with permission from Gas-Chrom Newsletter, vol. 9, May, 1968, Applied Science Laboratories, Inc., State College, Pa.]; and (b) C_1-C_5 hydrocarbons on 1.5 m × 0.23 cm column of Durapak *n*-Octane/Porasil C, 120–150 mesh; 25° C; N_2 carrier gas at 25 ml/min; flame ionization detector. [Reprinted with permission from Waters Associates, Framingham, Mass.].

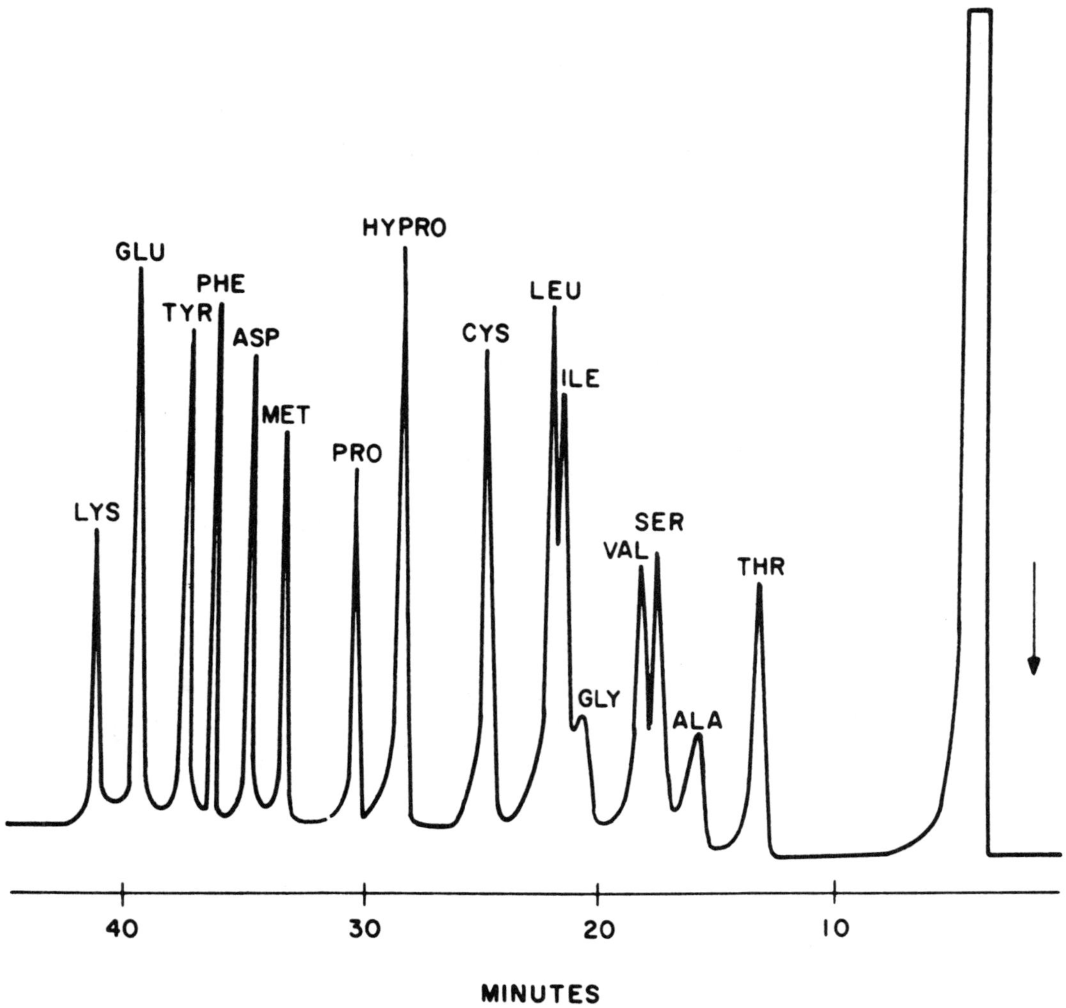

Figure 9. Gas chromatographic separation of amino acid derivatives (N-TFA-O-butyl esters) in a stainless steel capillary column (75 m long by 0.076 cm, I.D.) coated with Polysev [m-bis-m(phenoxyphenoxy)-phenoxy benzene]. LKB 9000 gas chromatograph-mass spectrometer combination. Helium carrier; 1054 kg/cm^2. Isothermal at 85 °C for 5 minutes, then programmed at 2 °C per minute to 200 °C [after (*19*)]. From Figure 1, Gelpi et al., *J. Chromatogr. Sci.* **7**, 605 (1969). Permission to reproduce from Journal of Chromatographic Science, Evanston, Ill.

solution of stationary phase in a volatile solvent. The excess solution is carefully removed with the aid of suction, after which the damp support is air-dried or dried in a commercial packing dryer. The solid is not vigorously mixed with the liquid so that fine particles are not formed.

2. *Packing the column.* To pack the column, a straight piece of metal tubing of the required length is plugged with glass wool at the bottom. A funnel is attached to the top with rubber tubing, and the coated support is added in increments through the funnel. The tubing is agitated and tapped on the floor to aid packing. Finally, the top of the column is plugged with glass wool, and the column is bent or coiled as required. Glass columns are either U-shaped or coiled. The former are packed by introducing coated support through a funnel into one leg of the vertical column and then tapping and vibrating until the solid is well packed. Additional solid is added and the process continued until the column is completely packed, after which glass wool plugs are inserted into both ends. The inlet leg of the column is not packed in the part which will be in the flash heater section of the chromatograph. Coiled columns are packed by plugging one end with glass wool and then applying slight vacuum to this end to suck the packing in increments into the tube. The tube is vibrated throughout to get a firm, uniform packing. When fully packed, the other end is plugged with glass wool.

The ultimate test of whether a column is well packed is its performance in terms of efficiency and peak symmetry. The number of grams of packing used per foot compared with efficient columns used earlier will indicate if the column is either too loosely or too tightly packed and therefore will allow prediction of column performance.

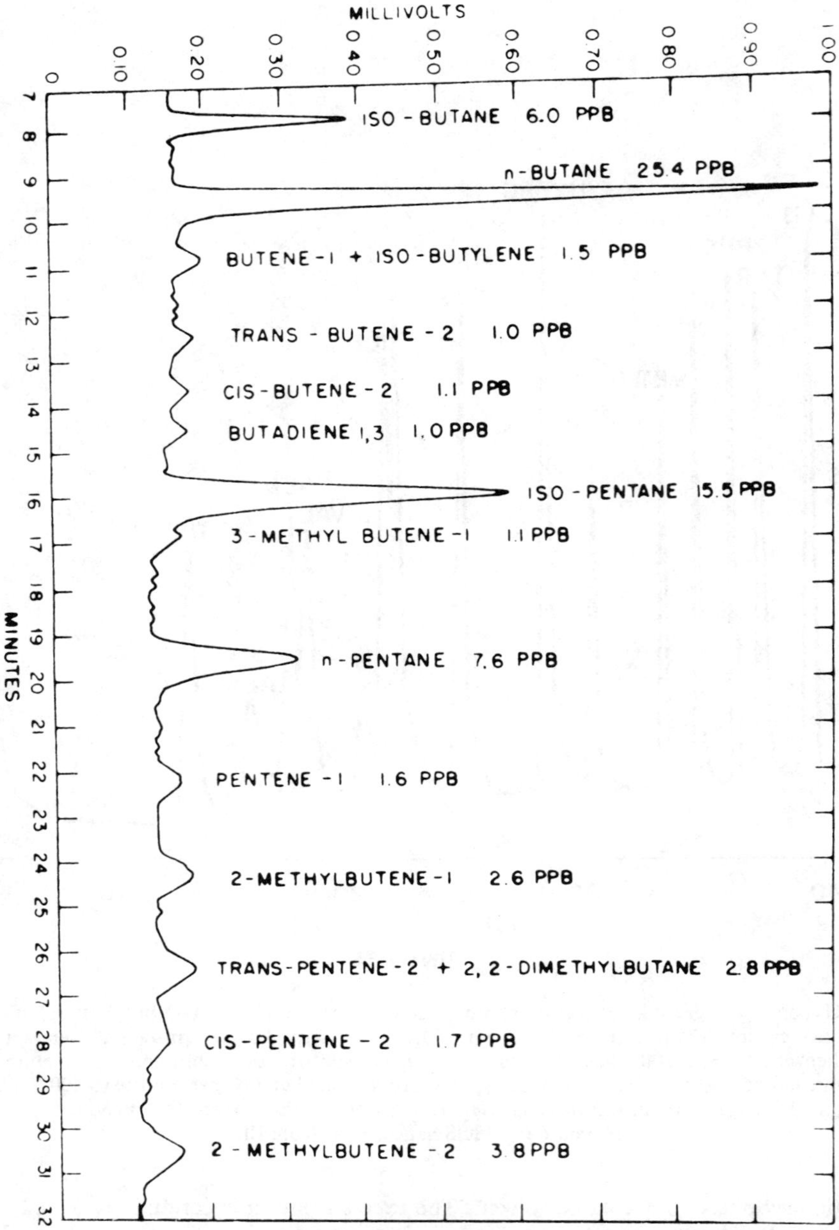

Figure 10. Gas chromatogram of aliphatic hydrocarbons in Cincinnati air. Column was stainless steel $\frac{3}{16}$ inch O.D., 0.035 wall thickness, containing 6 feet β-methyl ethyl adipate and 21 feet dibutyl maleate as the stationary phase. Temperature, 37 °C. Flow rate of helium was 26 cc/min. Sample, 200 cc air. Figure 1, page 245, Giddings/Keller, *Advances in Chromatography*, Vol. 5 "Atmospheric Analysis by Gas Chromatography" by A. P. Altshuller. Permission received to reproduce from Marcel Dekker, Inc., New York.

Both glass and metal columns should be cleaned before packing by rinsing with appropriate solutions such as acids and organic solvents. To dry before filling, attach one end to a vacuum line for 5 min and then flame lightly.

3. *Conditioning the column.* After packing, the column is conditioned to remove any excess liquid or volatile materials from the stationary phase. To do this, connect the inlet of the column to the chromatograph but do not attach the outlet to the detector. Pass carrier gas through the column and heat the column to within 10 °C of the maximum recommended operating temperature for the phase. Keep at this temperature for at least 12 hours. A separate column conditioner may also be used.

REFERENCES

1. Kruppa, R. F. and R. S. Henley, *American Laboratory*, p. 41, May 1971.
2. Ettre, L. S., "Open Tubular Columns", Plenum Press, N.Y., 1965, Chapter 3.
3. Halasz, I. and E. Heine, *Advances in Chromatography*, **4**, 207 (1967).
4. Fritz, D., Goretti, G., and A. Liberti, *J. Chromatogr.* **49**, 57 (1970).
5. Karasek, F. W., *Research/Development*, p. 34, June, 1971.
6. Annino, R. and P. F. McCrea, *Anal. Chem.* **42**, 1486 (1970).
7. Wolf, C. J. and J. Q. Walker, *American Laboratory*, p. 10, May 1971.
8. McNair, H. M. and E. J. Bonelli, "Basic Gas Chromatography", Varian Aerograph, Walnut Creek, California, pp. 118–119 (1969).
9. Hartmann, C. H., *Anal. Chem.* **43**, 124A, 1971.
10. E. sz. Kováts, *Advances in Chromatography*, **1**, 229 (1965).
11. Harbourn, C. L. A., *J. Chromatogr. Sci.* **8**, p. 42A, February, 1970.
12. Beroza, M. and F. Acree, Jr., *J. Ass. Offic. Agr. Chem.* **47**, 1 (1964).
13. Beroza, M. and R. Sarmiento, *Anal. Chem.* **36**, 1744 (1964).
14. Franc, J. and V. Kaloušková, *J. Chromatogr.* **17**, 221 (1965).
15. Bennett, C. E., DiCave, L. W., Paul, D. G., Wegener, J. A., and L. J. Levase, *American Laboratory*, p. 67, May 1971.
16. Perry, S. G., *Advances in Chromatography*, **7**, 221 (1968).
17. Feldman, G. L., Maude, M., and A. Windeler, *American Laboratory*, February 1970, p. 61.
18. Karayannis, N. M., and A. H. Corwin, *Anal. Biochem.* **26**, 34 (1968).
19. Gelpi, E., Koenig, W. A., Gilbert J., and J. Oro, *J. Chromatogr. Sci.* **7**, 605 (1969).
20. Altschuller, A. P., *Advances in Chromatography*, **5**, 245 (1968).

VOLUME TWO
SECTION I

PRINCIPLES AND TECHNIQUES

Section I.III

LIQUID COLUMN CHROMATOGRAPHY[1]

This section will be divided into four parts according to the mechanism of separation, which reflects the nature of the stationary phase: adsorption, partition, gel filtration and permeation and ion-exchange chromatography. The boundaries between these different types of chromatography are not fixed, since, for example, certain separations on ion-exchange resins can be due to partition, adsorption (on the resin matrix) and molecular sieving effects as well as to simple ion exchange. Much of what is discussed in the section on adsorption chromatography will be generally applicable to all types of liquid chromatography, e.g., many of the procedural details, the theory, the design of automatic machines including the continuous detectors, etc.

A. LIQUID–SOLID (ADSORPTION) COLUMN CHROMATOGRAPHY (LSCC)[2]

For liquid column adsorption chromatography, the stationary phase is a surface-active solid (e.g., alumina, silica gel or charcoal) packed into a column, and the mobile phase is a solvent composed of one or more organic liquids. The separation of a mixture results from the differential adsorption of the components onto the surface of the solid. Weakly adsorbed solutes travel more quickly while strongly adsorbed solutes are retarded. The molecular interactions involved in adsorption can be of several types depending upon the nature (polarity) of the surface, the adsorbed solutes, and the solvent: London dispersion forces, hydrogen bonds, electrostatic forces, and charge transfer forces.

1. *Traditional Techniques*

Many successful separations are still performed today with simple apparatus of the type used by Tswett when he developed LSCC over 60 years ago. For example, Figure 1 shows the successful resolution of the plant pigments which can be obtained on a column of powdered sugar packed into a glass tube. Development can be performed with gravity flow in a tube such as shown in Figure 11(a). Chromatography tubes are fitted with a fritted glass disc or a plug of glass wool to support the solid, and they may or may not have a stop-cock. Development can be speeded up by applying pressure at the top of the column (Figure 11b) or vacuum at the bottom (11c).

If the zones are adequately separated when the solvent front has reached the bottom of the column, as shown in Figure 1, development can be terminated and the zones dug out with a long metal spatula. Each zone is then packed into a separate tube and the solute removed from the adsorbent by elution with a very polar liquid such as ethanol. Alternatively, development can be continued and each zone collected as it emerges from the column. It is often necessary to rechromatograph the separated solutes in order to increase their purity.

If the components of the mixture are not naturally colored as are the chloroplast pigments, the location of the zones must be detected in some way. Most often small fractions of the eluant are collected, and each fraction is analyzed by physical or chemical detection methods for each component. Another method is to carefully extrude the column of adsorbent and to treat it with a reagent which forms colored derivatives with the bound solutes or examine it under UV light if the solutes fluoresce. Columns with a standard-taper joint at the bottom facilitate this extrusion.

2. *Modern Instruments*

Due to an increased understanding of the ways in which separation efficiency varies with experimental conditions and the commercial availability of automatic instruments for separations at high pressures, liquid chromatography has entered upon a new era. These instruments provide generation and control of liquid flows at high pressures, efficient column performance, continuous general purpose detectors, and rapid analyses down to the picogram range. Separations by LSCC can now be faster and more efficient than comparable thin layer separations although they are still not as efficient nor rapid as separations by GC. However, LSCC and GC should be considered as complementary techniques since the former is useful for many samples (e.g., high boiling or heat labile) not successfully handled by GC.

In its crudest form, high pressure liquid chromatography can be carried out by pressurizing a solvent reservoir above a column with gas (e.g., Figure 11a). The basic components of a modern, rapid, high efficiency liquid chromatography instrument are constant flow rate pumps (mechanical or pneumatic; 500–1000 psi minimum pressure), sample injection valves, efficient columns, and detectors. A block diagram of one possible arrangement of basic components is shown in Figure 12. Additional equipment which may be desirable includes a solvent filter and pulse damper after the pump, a column pressure monitor and high pressure alarm, a guard column to protect the analytical column against dirty samples, and perhaps a fraction

[1] See "Modern Practice of Liquid Chromatography", J. J. Kirkland, ed., Wiley, N.Y., 1971.
[2] See "Principles of Adsorption Chromatography", L. R. Snyder, Marcel Dekker, N.Y., 1968.

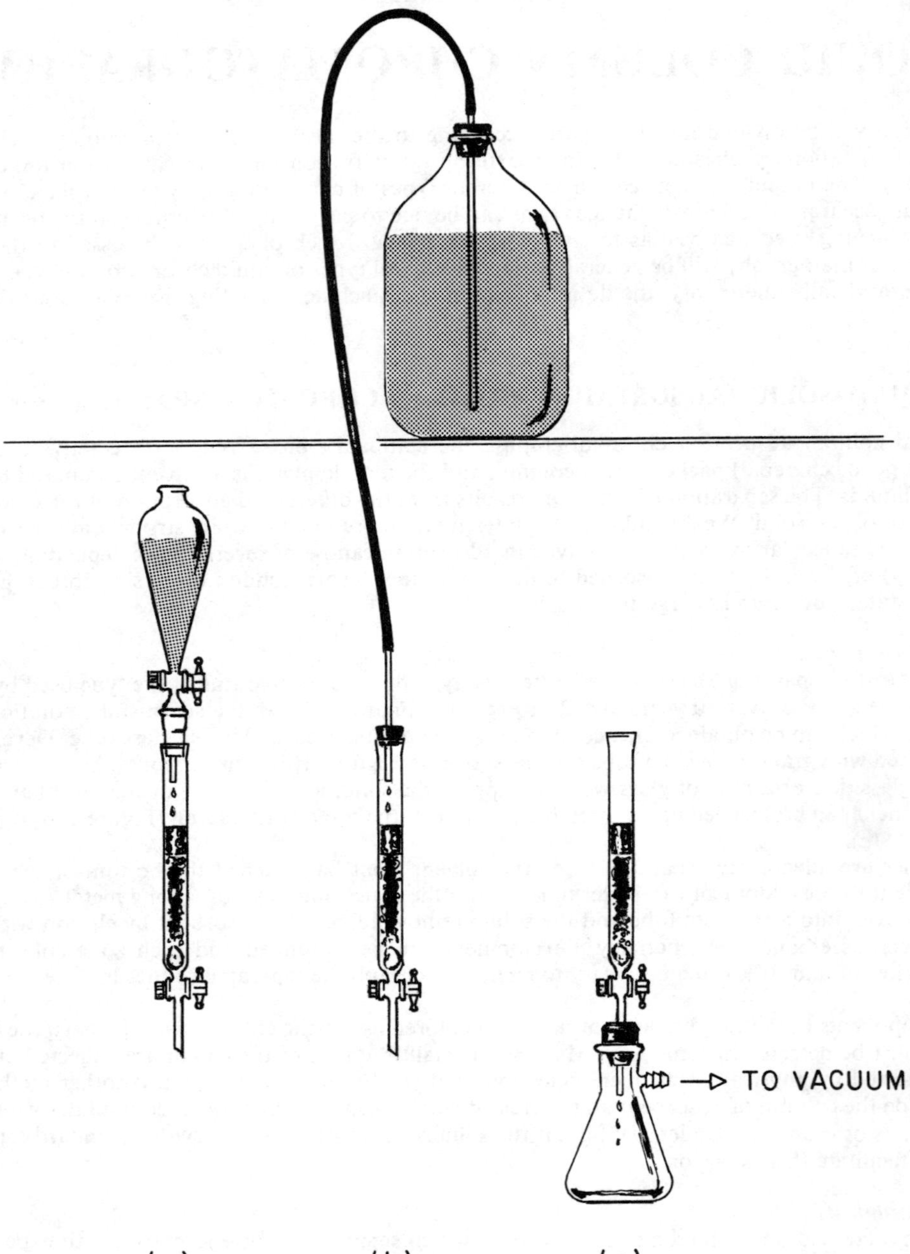

Figure 11. Chromatography tube fitted with a reservoir for holding the solvent (a); fitted with a tube attached to an elevated bottle of solvent for development under the pressure of the column of liquid (b); and inserted into a filtering flask which is attached to a source of vacuum (c).

collector. For high efficiency, the fittings and detector must have low dead volume. Means for precise control of the column and detector temperature may be desirable, especially for partition and ion-exchange chromatography. Precise control of carrier composition and flow rate is also desirable. A diagram of a commercial dual column split-flow instrument (The Waters Associates ALC 100) is shown in Figure 13. This instrument contains a variable-gradient solvent programmer and differential refractive index detector. A second pump and column provide dual-column split flow to the detector; when a UV detector is used, single column operation is satisfactory. In addition to Waters, other companies offering an assortment of LC instruments and accessories are DuPont, Nester Faust and Varian Aerograph.

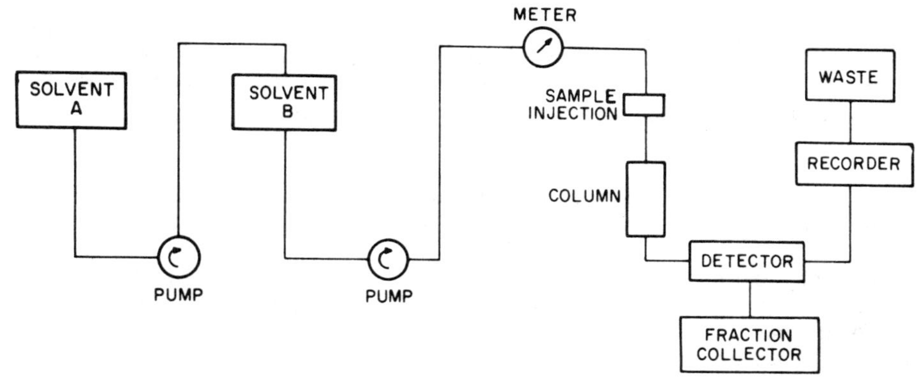

Figure 12. Block diagram showing the basic components of a modern liquid chromatographic instrument.

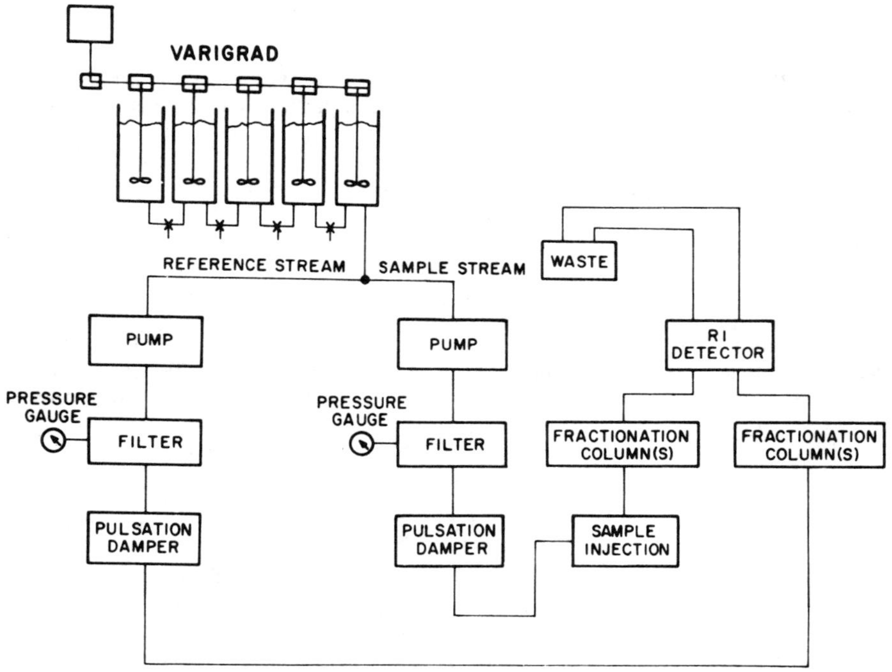

Figure 13. Block diagram of a dual column-split flow liquid chromatography system (The Waters ALC 100), after (*17*); introduced originally in reference (*18*). Permission received from International Scientific Communications, Inc, American Laboratory, and Elsevier Publishing Co.

3. *Theory*[1]

Much of what was written in the section on GC theory applies as well to LC, but additional considerations pertain to modern liquid chromatography. For example, the resolution of zones is directly proportional to zone center separation and inversely proportional to zone width. The former is dependent on the selectivity of the column, the latter on the efficiency of the column. The sources of zone spreading are again flow velocity inequalities, longitudinal molecular diffusion (generally unimportant in LC), and mass transfer considerations.

Gas chromatography is at present a faster and more powerful separation technique than even modern LC. The spreading factor is at least ten times greater in LC (i.e., speed of mass transfer is at least 10 times slower leading to broader peaks). However, LC has the added advantage of being able to utilize two phases for separation, and there are an enormous number of moving and stationary phases that can be used. LC

[1] From "Modern Liquid Chromatography", L. R. Snyder and J. J. Kirkland, American Chemical Society, 1971, Chapters 1 and 3.

therefore provides a very large range in sample selectivity and can achieve elegant separations of complex samples in many situations. Modern LC has the advantages of greater convenience, greater separation efficiency and greater separation speed compared with classical LC methods (column, PC, and TLC).

In LC, the distribution ratio is defined as shown above for GC (equation [4]) as the ratio of concentrations for a given compound in the stationary (s) and mobile (m) phases

$$K = [X]_s/[X]_m.$$

The larger the K value the more likely the molecules are to be found on the stationary phase and the more slowly the compound will migrate through the column. Differences in K values lead to differential migration through the column.

Individual chromatographic bands are again characterized by t_r, the retention time, and t_w, the baseline band width in time units, or the equivalent volume units $V_R = Ft_r$ and $W = Ft_w$, where F is the flow rate of solvent and W is the band width in volume units.

Another important parameter in LC is the capacity factor (ratio) k' (or K')

$$k' = \frac{\text{total amount of } X \text{ in the stationary phase}}{\text{total amount of } X \text{ in the moving phase}} \quad [23]$$

$$= V_s[X]_s/V_M[X]_m$$

$$= (V_s/V_M)K = \frac{V_R - V_M}{V_M} \quad [24]$$

where V_s and V_M are the volumes of stationary and moving phases within the column.

Using the expression above, several other important LC equations can be easily derived. These are

$$t_R = t^0(1 + k') \quad [24a]$$

where t^0 is the retention time of a nonretained band ($k' = 0$)

$$V_R = V_M(1 + k') \quad [24b]$$

and

$$V_R = V_M + V_sK. \quad [24c]$$

V_M, the volume of the moving phase within the column, is the retention volume of a nonretained band.

The above equations are related to peak position in LC, which is a function of the thermodynamics of the system. Equations related to peak broadening are the same as those in the section on GC:

$$N = 16(t_r/t_w)^2$$

or the equivalent

$$N = 16(V_R/W)^2 \qquad \text{(see equation [5])}$$

N, the number of plates, equals the total column length divided by HETP (see equation [7]). Resolution (R or R_s), as given by equation [6], is the distance between peak centers divided by the average peak width.

Adequate resolution between two peaks is a very important consideration in terms of sample analysis. As an example, for two bands representing a 1 : 1 ratio (equal size peaks), a resolution of 0.4 (equation [6]) does not provide observable band centers (both peaks merge into one large peak). If the resolution is raised to 0.6, two band centers are observable, but the apparent band centers do not coincide with the true band centers, leading to an error in the determination of t_r for qualitative identification purposes. Resolution would have to be further increased to 0.7 or 0.8 for the true and observed centers to coincide. An increase to R_s = 1.0 would be required if fractions of 98% purity were to be isolated for analysis by other means (cut point occurring at the valley between band centers). For quantitation based on peak areas accurate within 5% for the minor component, resolution must be adequate to reduce the valley between the two band centers to a value no higher than half the height of the minor band (e.g., R_s must be 1.0–1.25 for bands with a ratio of 4 : 1).

In view of the importance of resolution in sample analysis and preparative separations by LC, it is vital to understand how to control resolution. The basic resolution equation is

$$R_s = \tfrac{1}{4}(\alpha - 1)\sqrt{N}[k'/(1 + k')] \quad [24d]$$

where α is the separation factor (ratio of k' values for two bands). This equation can be considered in three independent parts, i.e., resolution can be altered by varying α, N or k'.

Varying k'. It has been found that k' values between 1.5 and 4 provide optimum separation (adequate resolution, minimum time). Values of k' are altered by varying solvent strength in adsorption, partition and ion exchange, or the column packing in exclusion chromatography (the solvent normally has no effect on band migration in this method). For example, assume $R_s = 0.6$ for two bands and $k' = 1.0$. To increase R_s to 0.8, k' must be increased to 2.0, an increase that would be brought about, for example, by lowering solvent strength. It is not possible, at present to predict which solvent will give exactly the required change, so the change would be made by trial and error.

Varying N. If k' is in the optimum range, increases in plate number should be considered. The typical plot of plate height (H) *vs* solvent velocity (u) for LC indicates that H increases with u but at a decreasing rate. This is a different relationship than exists in GC.

N can be increased most simply by reducing the flow rate, but this leads to increased separation time. If instead the column length is increased (fixed column pressure), a proportional decrease in flow rate will result while separation time will increase with the square of the column length. Finally, N can be increased without increasing separation time by increasing pressure and column length simultaneously. This approach is not valid in GC for several reasons, e.g. because of the compressibility of the gas at high pressures, and is one of the keys that allows rapid, high resolution work to be done with modern LC.

For a comparison of these three approaches, assume initial conditions of 100 cm column length, (L), 1000 psi pressure, a separation time of 100 sec, a flow rate of 2 cm/sec and an H of 0.156 leading to 640 plates. A decrease in pressure to 180 psi would double the plate number to 1280 but increase separation time to 560 sec. An increase in L to 164 cm at 1000 psi would also provide 1280 plates, but with an increase in separation time to only 270 sec. This option is, however, generally less convenient. An increase in L to 320 cm and a simultaneous increase to 10^4 psi would provide 1280 plates with the original separation time (100 sec). The preferred option in modern LC for increasing resolution is to use the longest columns and highest flow rates possible, up to the limit of pressure of the available instrument.

Varying α. If k' is in the optimum range and the required change in N is impractical, resolution can be increased by changing selectivity. The approach is to hold solvent strength (k') roughly constant while changing the solvent composition by a trial and error approach. Neher has provided a guide for choosing solvents of different composition but with the same strength [R. Neher, *Steroid Chromatography*, Elsevier Publishing Co., 1964, p. 249].

Snyder has published equations relating the efficiency of presently obtainable columns to the variables p (column pressure), t (separation time) and d_p (particle size)(*1*). For normal columns with the optimum average value for the partition ratios of the components:

$$NQ^2 = 0.34P^{0.3}t^{0.7}d_p{}^{-0.3} \quad [25]$$

where NQ^2 is the number of effective plates, a measure of column efficiency which is proportional to resolution. For regularly packed columns (if they could be obtained in practice) with the optimum average partition ratio value:

$$NQ^2 = 0.026P^{0.3}t^{0.7}d_p{}^{-0.8}. \quad [26]$$

Equations [25] and [26] show that maximum efficiency (high values of NQ^2) is favored by large values of P and t and a small value for d_p. Since efficiency increases as the 0.3 power of pressure, a ten-fold increase in pressure is required to double efficiency. There is a similar small increase in efficiency as the particle size decreases (equation [25]). There are, of course, experimental difficulties involved with the use of very high pressures and very small particles. If regular columns could be packed with very small particles, equation [26] shows that a substantial increase in efficiency would result. Dr. Snyder predicts that in the near future, with the use of higher pressures (10,000 psi), smaller particles (1 μ) and adsorbents and packing techniques that provide regular packing structures, 20–50 effective plates per sec will be achieved in liquid chromatography.

Direct comparisons of plate efficiencies in GLC and LLC have been made in terms of reduced plate heights, h, and reduced fluid velocities, v:

$$h = H/d_p \quad [27]$$

and

$$v = \mu d_p/D_g \quad [28]$$

where H = the experimental plate height obtained from the chromatogram as explained in section IIB, d_p is the particle diameter, μ is the linear velocity of the mobile phase at the column outlet, and D_g is the diffusion coefficient of the solute in the mobile fluid at the column outlet. In one study of sorbed and unsorbed solutes on several supports the most extreme ratio of h values from GC and from LC on identical columns was 0.6 (*2*). Both in GC and LC, performance was found to deteriorate (h increased) when K' (equation [24]) was increased or when the particle size was decreased, the latter being due to the difficulties involved in uniformly packing small particles.

4. *Operational Considerations*

a. *Adsorbents* (Section II.III, Table 3). Adsorbents are activated by heating to remove water from the surface sites. The Brockmann Index is a scale of activity for rating adsorbents from grade I (most active) to V (least active) based on actual results obtained when standard azo dyes are chromatographed on the adsorbent. Grade I alumina, for example, is prepared by heating commercial basic alumina at 400° for 3 hours with occasional stirring. Less active grades are prepared by adding various amounts of water to the grade I alumina (3, 6, 10 and 15 ml for grades II–V, respectively). The activity of raw adsorbents can also be lowered by adding salts or by silanization.

Silica gel (SiO_2; also silica, silicic acid, quartz, porous glass) is the most widely used and versatile adsorbent. Grade I silica gel is prepared by heating at 160° with occasional stirring for 4 hr. The activity of this adsorbent is due to the presence of hydroxyl groups (attached to surface Si atoms and of several different types) which hydrogen bond with polar and unsaturated molecules. For modern LC, silica with a surface area of 350–400 m^2/g and a water content of 10% is recommended. The water content is controlled by activation and water addition. The water content affects retention times and so must be held constant. It also affects column efficiency (a dry column is one-third as efficient as one with 10% water), suppresses sample reactions and irreversible adsorption, and increases column linear capacity.

Basic alumina (Al_2O_3) strongly adsorbs all kinds of polar and unsaturated organic molecules. The mechanism of the adsorption is not yet definite, although surface hydroxyl groups do not appear to be involved. Acidic and neutral alumina can be prepared in the laboratory by treating the basic form with appropriate solutions. All three kinds are commercially available. Neutral alumina (pH ~ 7) has the widest range of applications and serves to separate hydrocarbons, steroids, alkaloids, esters, aldehydes, alcohols, weak organic acids and bases, etc. It is employed usually in systems with organic solvents. Basic alumina (pH ~ 10) adsorbs hydrocarbons, aromatics and other unsaturated compounds from organic solvents. It acts as a cation exchanger in aqueous media, adsorbing basic amino acids, amines, etc. Acid alumina (pH ~ 4) exchanges inorganic and organic anions such as amino acids, aromatic acids and carboxylic acids. The ion exchange behavior of alumina is opposite to that of synthetic organic exchangers (see Section I.III, D), in that resins with acidic groups function as cation exchangers and those with basic groups as anion exchangers.

Kieselguhr (Celite, diatomaceous earth) is a weak adsorbent used for the separation of very polar solutes. It is often used as a filter aid in mixture with more active adsorbents to achieve faster flow rates of solvent, or as a support for a liquid phase in partition chromatography.

Sucrose is a mild adsorbent useful, as described above, for separations of chloroplast pigments. It is best to rub commercial sugar through a coarse sieve prior to use, and to add additional cornstarch in humid weather.

Magnesia [MgO or $Mg(OH)_2$] is commercially available (Sea Sorb 43, Fisher Scientific Co.) in the form of a very fine powder which is mixed with an equal weight of a filter aid (e.g., Celite 545) before use. Magnesia exhibits preferential adsorption for unsaturated molecules and, unlike silica gel, sugar, cellulose, etc., can separate compounds differing only in the arrangement of double bonds.

Charcoal is of two types, nonpolar and polar (oxygenated). Nonpolar charcoal preferentially adsorbs large, nonpolar molecules, primarily by London forces. Oxidized charcoals are similar to alumina and silica gel in their preference for polar and unsaturated solutes.

Other adsorbents which have been used include magnesium and calcium silicate, calcium sulfate, calcium carbonate, zinc carbonate and hydroxyapatite [$Ca_2(PO_4)_3$]. Cellulose is also considered by some to be an adsorbent, but its properties will be discussed in section B3c below.

The ability of particular adsorbents to attract certain solutes is a function of the polarity of the adsorbent. Polar adsorbents such as alumina and silica gel have great affinity for polar compounds (e.g., amino acids, carbohydrates) and require highly polar wash liquids for development (see below). Polar solutes are usually better separated by partition chromatography than by adsorption chromatography. Hydrocarbons and other less polar solutes are better separated by adsorption methods.

b. *Column size*[1]. For a constant amount of adsorbent, column efficiency increases in proportion with the length to width ratio of the column. Ratios of 5 : 1 to 100 : 1 are currently used with traditional techniques. Glass tubes 1 cm I.D. × 25 cm or 2 cm × 30 cm, and 50 ml analytical burets have been conveniently used by the author for small-scale pigment separations, and tubes 8 × 40 cm and 5 × 60 cm for preparative separations. To pack a 30 cm column in the former tube requires about 3 lb of powdered sugar. For modern high pressure instruments, ratios of 100 : 1 to 1000 : 1 are sometimes used. Preferred column dimensions for such instruments are 50–100 cm in length and 2–3 mm I.D.; Straight columns are more efficient than coiled columns. Individual straight columns are connected in series using low dead-volume fittings (also used to connect the column to the detector) to provide longer columns with high efficiency. Columns are usually operated in a vertical position with an upward or downward solvent flow direction.

The ratio of sample size to amount of adsorbent should be roughly 1 : 20–100 for crude separations or preparative work and 1 : 200–2000 for analytical separations of complex mixtures.

Columns for use in LC instruments are usually composed of metal (e.g., stainless steel) or heavy wall glass. Kirkland has reported that the efficiency of "Trubore" glass and precision-bore stainless steel columns is higher than that of columns made with ordinary stainless steel tubing. Other workers have found this to be true only for one packing procedure, and have obtained equal efficiency for other tubes when the packing procedure was optimized for each tube.

c. *Preparation of the column*. Column packings used for both adsorption and partition columns are typically 100–200 mesh (~100 μ) for classical LC and 5–15 μ for high speed ion exchange and 20–50 μ for the other methods. As stated above, smaller particles improve efficiency because of fast mass transfer but greatly decrease flow rates causing higher pressures to be required. A small particle-size range also

[1] For a discussion of columns for modern analytical LC, see J. J. Kirkland, *Anal. Chem.* **43**, 36A, 1971.

improves column efficiency. Mixing a filter aid with a small-particle adsorbent often yields both excellent resolution and reasonable flow rates in classical LC.

Columns can be packed dry or wet. For dry packing, small amounts of adsorbent are introduced into the column and each portion is tamped firmly with a plunger having a flattened end. For coarser adsorbents, vibration of the column may be used in place of tamping. Some workers place the sample directly onto the dry column and then add the solvent, while others prewash the column with the first solvent (or a less polar solvent) before introducing the sample.

For wet packing, the adsorbent is slurried with a solvent (usually the first solvent to be used for the chromatography), and the slurry is poured into the tube. The tube is tapped gently to promote uniform settling. After each portion has settled, excess liquid is drained out (but the liquid level is always kept above the level of the solid) and more slurry is added until a column of the desired height is obtained. Usually the column is then washed with additional amounts of the initial development solvent, after which the liquid level is drained to the top of the column and the sample is introduced.

So that the top of the bed is not disturbed during sample or solvent addition, it can be covered with a circle of filter paper, a loose plug of glass wool, glass beads, sand, etc.

The "best" method for packing a particular column is an area of controversy. The particular packing method employed seems to be more important for wide columns than for narrow ones. For silica gel, some kind of dry fill-vibration-tamping procedure is usually employed; studies by Stewart, *et al.* (*3*) indicate that gentle tamping combined with a dry fill-vibration procedure becomes more advantageous in terms of efficiency as the particle size of the silica decreases. For very small particles, it has been suggested by Knox and Saleem that packing columns under vacuum (so that all particles fall at the same speed and air currents leading to the fractionation of particles of different sizes are eliminated) will lead to improved performance. Polystyrene resins used in ion-exchange and gel permeation chromatography are usually packed by gravity or high-pressure wet-slurry methods (see Section I.IIId below). Soft gels are packed by low-pressure slurry methods (see Section II.III, Table 4). Because columns may be used over and over in most cases, it is worth the initial time and effort to prepare the best one possible.

Alkali-treated open glass capillary columns have recently been employed for the liquid-solid chromatographic separation of DNS-amino acids (*4*). However, the widespread use of open columns does not appear likely for LC.

d. *Sample introduction*. For conventional separations, a small volume of the sample solution is applied as a narrow zone to the top of the column with a pipette. After the sample has just percolated into the bed, one or two small portions of the solvent in which the sample is dissolved are introduced to wash down the walls of the tube. Then a layer of developing solvent is added above the bed, a reservoir of this solvent is attached, if necessary, to the column and the chromatography is begun. As an alternative, the sample solution is slurried with Celite or some of the same adsorbent as in the column, and this solid is added to the top of the bed.

The solvent in which the sample is dissolved may be different than the developing solvent. For example, plant pigments are dissolved in very weakly polar liquids (e.g., petroleum ether) for the initial adsorption and the zone of mixture is then developed with more polar liquids or mixtures of liquids. In this procedure, compounds which fail to dissolve in the least polar liquids may be dissolved by a more polar liquid later on during development. If this does not occur, precipitation effects can cause poor separations or multiple zonation.

It is the best procedure to be sure that the solutes applied are in solution and that the developing solvents used will not allow precipitation on the column. If this requires such polar liquids that the fastest moving (least polar) solutes are then poorly separated, these should be collected and later rechromatographed in less polar solvents.

Injection techniques used with liquid chromatography instruments resemble those described above for GC. Injection of samples can be accomplished with a syringe through a rubber or Teflon septum port, or accessories for automatic injection, available with some machines, can be utilized. In general, use of a syringe is recommended for scouting work and a sample valve for routine work once a system is chosen. A back pressure of up to 2000 lb can be withstood by a syringe; for pressures in excess of this, the flow of liquid is stopped and injection carried out when the pressure falls to zero. Low solute diffusion in LC allows stoppage of flow during chromatography.

e. *Selection of solvents* (*wash liquids*). For elution (as contrasted to frontal or displacement) chromatography, the adsorbed sample is washed with a solvent which provides optimum values of k'. The developing solvent must therefore be selected in relation to the mixture and the adsorbent. In general, weakly-polar solutes require weakly-polar solvents and strongly-polar solutes require strongly-polar solvents. However, solvents that permit only moderate adsorption of certain solutes on a weak adsorbent (sugar, cellulose) will allow great adsorption on a strong adsorbent (magnesia, lime). Therefore, for a given mixture, less polar solvents would be used on sugar than on magnesia. A table ranking various solvents in terms of their elution strength is given below. This table is a compilation of several series published in the literature and should be taken only as a rough guide. In fact, each individual adsorbent has its own elutropic series. For mixtures of liquids, the polarity varies primarily with the concentration of the most polar substances. (See also Table I, p. 38).

Solvents in Approximate Order of Their Polarity or Eluting Power

(least eluting)	Petroleum ether (hexane)
	n-Heptane
	Decane
	CCl_4
	Cyclohexane
	Diethyl ether
	Carbon disulfide
	Benzene
	Esters
	Acetone
	1,2-Dichloroethane
	Chloroform
	n-Propanol
	Ethanol
	Methanol
	Water
	Pyridine
	Organic acids
(most eluting)	Inorganic acids and bases

Solvents of high purity should always be used. Commercial reagent-grade products are generally adequate although prior purification (by extraction, distillation or chromatography) may be desirable in some cases. As an example, chloroform contains about 0.75% ethanol as a preservative. If necessary, this can be removed by two extractions with equal volumes of water.

The solvent must not promote decomposition of the solutes: as examples, plant pigments decompose when developed with (or dissolved in) benzene if exposed to bright light; and chloroform-containing solvents may liberate HCl, which can alter chlorophylls and isomerize epoxy carotenoid pigments. The solvent should be compatible with the detection method being used, and should be volatile so that eluted solutes can be easily recovered. Finally, solvents of low viscosity promote fast flow rates and short analyses times when long columns and fine particles are being used.

For modern LC instruments, solvents are degassed by heating the solvent in a bottle while drawing vacuum. Failure to degas can adversely effect detectors and soft gel columns.

For preparative separations, the solubility of the solute in the solvent is an important consideration.

f. *Gradient elution* (*solvent programming*). The use of solvent gradients is indispensable in liquid chromatography for increasing resolution and reducing analysis time. Solvent gradients in LC serve the same purposes as temperature gradients in GC: better resolution of poorly-separated, faster moving peaks and faster, sharper elution of well-separated, badly spread late peaks. Gradient elution also decreases tailing. Isocratic conditions are best for quantitative LC, just as are isothermal conditions for quantitative GC.

A major cause of tailed zones is the existence of a convex adsorption isotherm such as illustrated in Figure 14. (Other causes include overloading of the sample, excessive flow rates and chemisorption of part of the sample on active adsorbent sites.) Convex isotherms are quite common in adsorption and ion-exchange chromatography (especially at ordinarily-used solute concentration levels), while linear isotherms are usual in partition chromatography. Concave isotherms, which would lead to zones with fronting, are rare in chromatography.

In zones governed by convex isotherms, tailing occurs because the solute travels more rapidly when present in higher concentration than at lower concentration (i.e., relatively more solute is on the adsorbent than in solution at lower concentration). Due to effects such as diffusion, incomplete equilibrium, etc., it is normal for the concentration of a migrating zone to become uneven, the concentration being highest in the

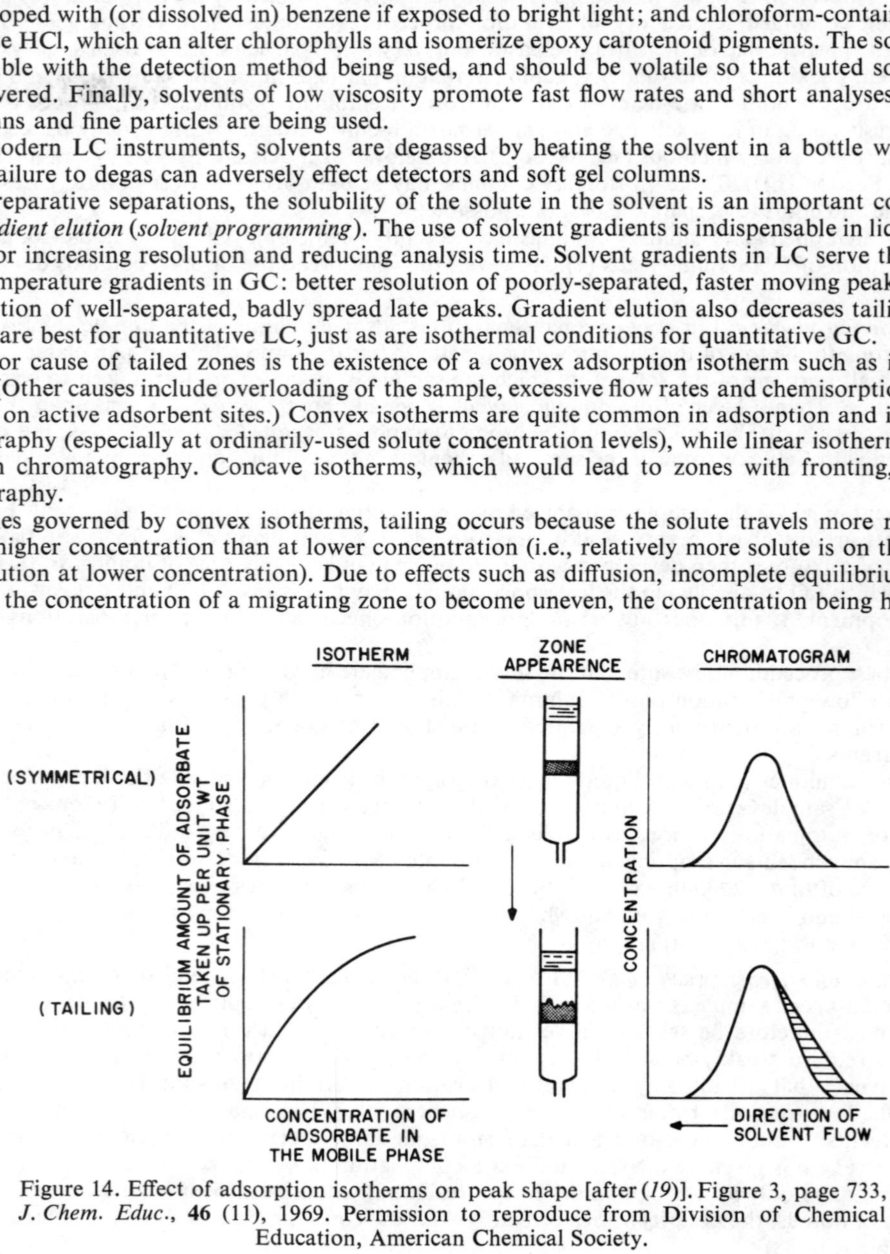

Figure 14. Effect of adsorption isotherms on peak shape [after (*19*)]. Figure 3, page 733, *J. Chem. Educ.*, **46** (11), 1969. Permission to reproduce from Division of Chemical Education, American Chemical Society.

center and lower at the leading and trailing edges. When migration is governed by a convex isotherm, the concentrated zone center will move most rapidly, overtaking the front and keeping it sharp. The low-concentrated rear of the zone will move ever more slowly and be left behind as a tail (trail).

Gradient elution techniques involve a steady increase in the effectiveness (e.g., polarity) of the solvent during the run. This leads to the formation of a concentration gradient down the column so that the rear of the zone is maintained in a stronger eluting medium than the front. This causes the rear of the zone to catch-up with the front producing a sharper zone.

In practice, gradient elution can be carried out in a stepwise or continuous fashion. The former is often used for known mixtures where tailing is not significant or for less complex unknowns. It may involve elution of the sample in turn with solvents of the elutropic series, beginning with petroleum ether and increasing in strength, on a column of an active adsorbent. Development is continued with each solvent until nothing more comes off the column, and small volume fractions are collected all along the way. Or, development can be started with a weak solvent (A), one or several changes can be made to solvents containing A plus increasing amounts of a stronger solvent (B), and finally development with (B) is employed. If the mixture to be separated contains known compounds, preliminary studies with the individual, pure solutes can determine exactly what combinations of A and B and what volumes are required for a maximized separation of the mixture.

Continuous gradients are used in modern LC machines and are produced by beginning with a developing solvent of low strength and adding with mixing a stronger component to the solvent in a chamber which drains into the column. Continuous gradients are more convenient in that they are easily reproducible and, once set up, require no attention. A continuous gradient will give superior results for complex or unknown mixtures and badly tailed zones.

The nature of the gradient can be controlled in various ways, the simplest being to vary the absolute volumes and pumping rates of two pumps. If the volumes of the pumps are equal ($V_1 = V_2$) and the pumping rates are equal ($R_1 = R_2$), an almost linear gradient will result (Figure 15a). A useful rule of thumb is to

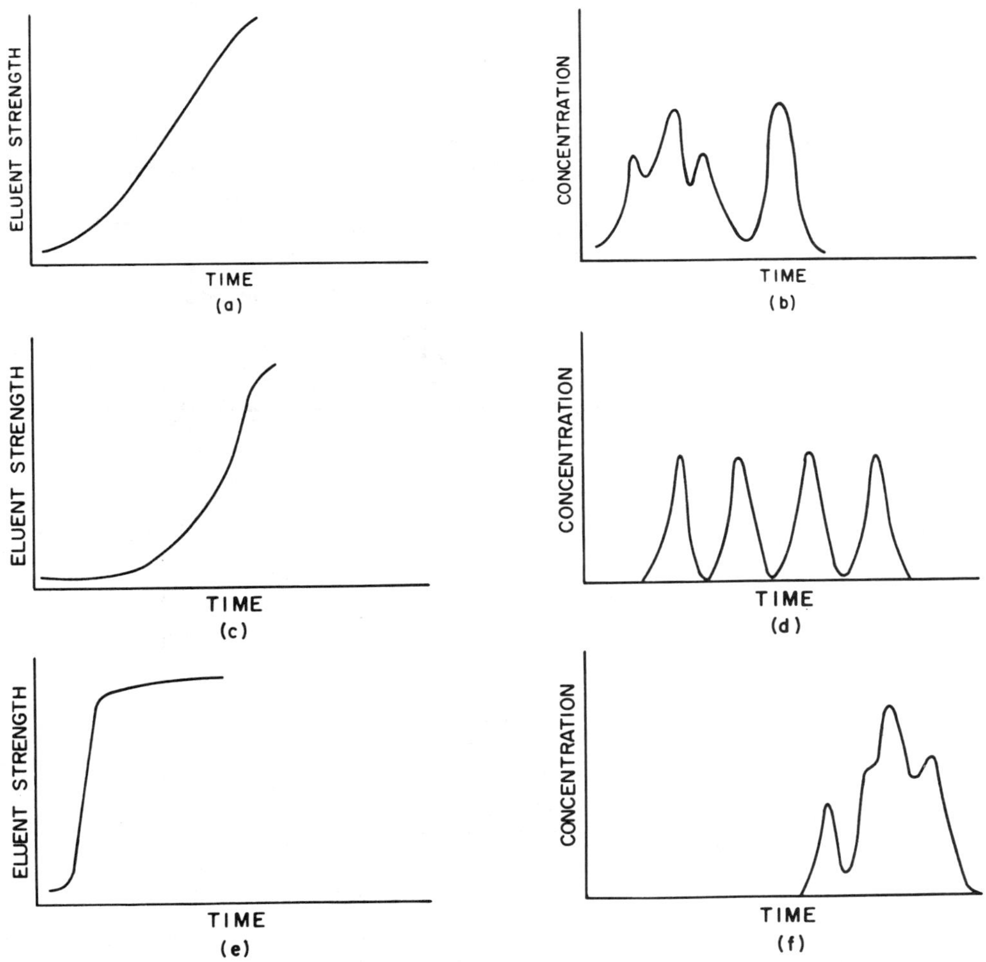

Figure 15. Elution gradients and resulting chromatograms [after (*15*)]. Permission received from American Laboratory and International Scientific Communications, Inc.

begin with a solvent only strong (polar) enough to elute the least polar sample component and to end the gradient with a solvent just able to elute the most polar sample. If the chromatogram shown in (b) results from a linear gradient, this indicates that the solvent has become too polar too quickly. By making $R_2 > R_1$ (R_2 would be the rate of addition of liquid to the column, R_1 would be rate of transfer between pumps) a concave gradient (c) would be produced and result in a good separation (d). If the linear gradient causes the chromatogram shown in (f), a convex gradient (e), formed by making $R_1 > R_2$ and $V_1 < V_2$, would cause a more rapid increase in polarity but a lower eventual limit of elution power so that a separation similar to (d) would again result. Concave gradients are more generally useful. More complicated gradients sometimes involving more than two components have been produced in various other ways.

In addition to polarity gradients with organic solvents, pH and ionic strength gradients (separate or superimposed) can be generated in a similar manner. The latter are especially useful for ion-exchange separations (Figure 16).

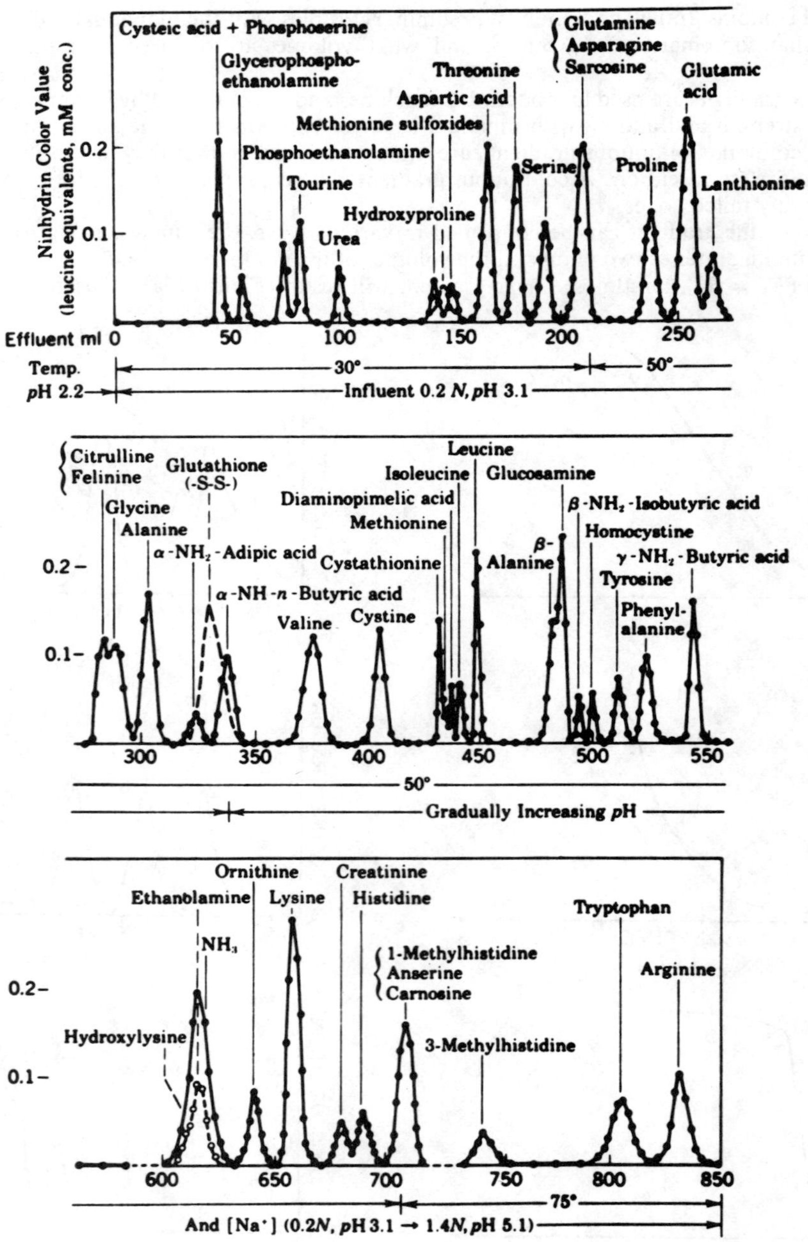

Figure 16. Separation of amino acids and related compounds on Dowex ®50-X4 sulfonic-acid cation-exchange resin [after (*20*)]. Figure 1 from S. Moore and W. H. Stein, *J. Biol. Chem.* **211**, 893 (1954). Permission to reproduce received from authors and The American Society of Biological Chemists, Inc.

At the end of the run, the column is regenerated by reverse programming. Passing several column volumes of the initial solvent through the bed will strip off the polar solvent and prepare the column for the next separation.

Solvent programming has been used most in adsorption and ion-exchange chromatography. It is generally not used in gel permeation chromatography (K' values are low so it is not needed) and can lead to difficulties in liquid-liquid partition column chromatography if the equilibrium between the stationary liquid and mobile liquid is not maintained as the mobile phase changes (see below).

g. *Mobile phase flow rate.* Although there is an optimum flow rate in terms of minimum plate height, most separations are carried out at flow rates in excess of this rate. Therefore, separations can usually be improved by lowering the flow rate if sufficient time is available. Typical operating conditions for contemporary high pressure column adsorption LC are as follows:

Flow rate	0.5–5 ml/min
Column	½–1 in. diameter, 15–30 in. length
Adsorbent	100–300 mesh
Pressure drop	30–100 psi
Separation times	20 min–12 hr or more

Column lengths can be much greater than shown here.

Solvent velocity changes can be made during the run, and indeed flow programming can be employed to obtain highest resolution and speed in some separations.

Flow rates through the column are controlled by varying the height of the solvent level above the column (gravity methods), by altering the pressure at the column inlet, or by applying vacuum at the column outlet. For qualitative and quantitative analysis by LC, it is important that the flow rate be known so that the time of the run and volume of effluent may be related. Constant flow rate pumps are used in LC machines for this purpose.

h. *Temperature.* Room temperature is most often used for column LC. Alterations in the adsorbent and/or solvent are generally easier and more effective than changes in temperature. Elevated temperature could be an advantage for a solute with a low solubility in the solvent, but the activity of the adsorbent would be decreased at the higher temperature. Temperature programming has been used in combination with solvent programming for separations of macromolecules by adsorption chromatography (the Baker–Williams Method). Temperature programming introduces many problems (e.g., many good solvents cannot be used because of low boiling points, solvent degassers are required at elevated temperature, viscosity changes can adversely effect the results of the separation, etc.), and in LC it is only a minor effect useful in special cases rather than an effective general substitute for solvent programming. Figure 16 shows an example of superimposed temperature, pH and ionic strength gradients used for the separation of amino acids by ion-exchange chromatography.

i. *Comparison of techniques for separating multicomponent samples.* Snyder (*5*) has compared several techniques on a theoretical and experimental basis for the liquid-solid adsorption chromatography of multicomponent samples which involve a wide range in retention volume values. Resolution per unit time was shown to decrease in order: solvent programming (best) > coupled columns (stationary phase programming) > temperature programming $\simeq$ flow programming > normal elution (poorest). Only solvent programming was found useful for extremely wide range samples.

j. *Detection of resolved solutes.* In traditional procedures, fractions of eluant are collected from the column in constant intervals of time or volume. These fractions are then analyzed for the components of interest by physical (fluorescence, spectral absorption, pH, optical activity, refractive index, etc.), chemical (addition of a reagent to cause the formation of a colored or fluorescent product), nuclear (radioactive tracers, neutron activation) or biological (growth stimulation or inhibition) methods. The presence of the solvent in each fraction must always be considered. Tests on the fractions can be qualitative and aimed only at locating the positions of the zones or quantitative (e.g., a color-forming reagent is added to each fraction and the degree of spectral absorption related to that produced by standard amounts of solutes). Quantitative analysis is also possible on fractions known to contain only one solute by evaporating the solvent and weighing the residue.

Column separations can be monitored by performing paper, thin-layer or gas chromatography on a small portion of each fraction. The number of zones resolved (hopefully one, if the original separation is good) will indicate the composition of each fraction and the relative sizes of the zones will give an idea of the amount of each solute present in each fraction. With TLC, the same adsorbent and solvent as with the column can be used, or various solvents if the column is being developed by gradient elution.

Many types of continuous detectors for automatic LC machines are now commercially available. Short descriptions of some of these follow:

Refractive index detector. The differential refractive index between the solute and solvent is detected. Operation is based on measuring either the change in the bending angle of the light through a wedge-shaped sample of the flowing solvent or the intensity of reflected light, which varies inversely with refractive index (the latter are termed "Fresnel-type" refractometers). With proper solvent selection and instrument design, or solvent evaporation followed by continuous dissolving of the residue in a single solvent, the differential refractometer can be used with solvent programming.

This is a so-called nonselective or "universal" detector, others of which are based on the measurement of infrared adsorption, dielectric constant and heat of adsorption. Conlon (*6*) states that the minimum sample size (mg) to be used for this detector is roughly the reciprocal of the difference in refractive index between the solvent and the sample. The sensitivity is approximately 10 μg/ml.

Ultraviolet absorption detector. These detectors can operate at several wavelengths, but the predominate 254 nm line emitted by a low pressure mercury discharge lamp is usually used. The detector is sensitive to compounds which absorb UV light (all compounds having π or nonbonding electrons, e.g., carbonyls, aromatic, olefins, nucleotides, nucleosides, and *N*-bases). If a high quality interference filter is used to isolate the 254 nm line, these detectors will have linear response within 1% over the range of 0–3.0 O.D. (optical density) units. This is a selective detector, as are continuous detectors based on fluorescence, acid titration and polarography. This specificity makes the detector relatively insensitive to flow and temperature fluctuations and solvent programming. A single column can be employed or a reference and analysis column. The sensitivity of detectors is usually increased by measuring the difference in a physical property between a reference and sample stream rather than measuring an absolute value of that property. The solvent must necessarily be transparent to UV light. According to Conlon (*6*), the minimum sample size is 10–100 mg, but Bakalyar has shown that the UV detector is capable of detecting 10^{-9} g (*7*), making them about two–three orders of magnitude more sensitive than the refractive index detector. Most UV detectors have flow cell optical path lengths between 1–10 mm.

The UV detector is not temperature sensitive, while the refractive index detector, like all bulk-property detectors, is temperature sensitive. The refractive index and ultraviolet detectors are the only two with any real importance for colorless samples at present. The refractive-index detector is used mainly in gel permeation chromatography, where the use of wider columns obviates its lower sensitivity.

Colorimetric detectors. As an example, carbohydrates and amino acids are detected by adding a color-forming reagent to the column effluent and then monitoring the stream with a visible absorption photometer. A time delay is involved in such a system to allow for mixing of the reagents and development of the color. This and the dilution effect of the added reagent may lead to broadening of the chromatographic zone. Commercial detectors of this type generally employ a visible (4000–8000 Å) source with an infrared filter, photocell detectors and interference filters available in 100 Å increments for the selection of the appropriate wavelength. Some systems have two channels for detection at either of two wavelengths (5700 and 4400 Å for amino acids).

Electrical conductivity detector. This detector is used mainly with aqueous systems. It responds to changes in conductivity between the solvent and sample, and under conditions of constant flow rate and temperature, amounts as low as 10 μg are detectable. This detector has found much use in gel filtration chromatography.

Adsorption detector. This is a differential detector containing two cells: the reference side is packed with a nonadsorbing material (e.g., glass beads), the active side with an adsorbent such as silica gel. Thermistors are imbedded in each cell and made part of a Wheatstone bridge. Temperature changes due to the adsorption and desorption of solutes in the active cell are detected, amplified and recorded as peaks which have the shape of the differential of a Gaussian curve. After early high hopes for this "universal" detector as a column monitor, it has been found to be nonquantitative and insensitive compared to a refractometer or ultraviolet detector under normal elution conditions, and little or no successful work has been reported with it.

Moving-wire flame ionization detector. This detector is at present only crudely quantitative. It is useful with gradient elution systems since the flame ionization detector responds to changes in mass. A moving chain or wire picks up drops of sample as they come out of the column and carries the sample, after removal of the solvent in an evaporating oven, to the flame of a GC flame ionization detector (see Section II, E, 2). In one variation of this detector the sample is burned directly on the wire; in another, the sample is removed from the wire in a pyrolysis chamber, and the gaseous pyrolysis products are swept into the flame. This detector is, of course, destructive.

Scott and Lawrence (*8*) have modified the detector so that the solute obtained after evaporating the mobile phase is not pyrolyzed but is burned in O_2 to CO_2 and H_2O. The CO_2 and excess O_2 are mixed with H_2 and passed over a nickel catalyst to convert the CO_2 to methane, which is detected by a flame ionization detector. An increase in ultimate sensitivity from 4 μg/ml to 1.1 μg/ml and a quantitative, linear response to solute mass are claimed for this modification. The sensitivity increase is especially marked for oxygenated compounds.

Radioactivity detectors. Continuous flow measurement of beta radiation over suspended scintillators provides advantages over the static counting of fractions (*9*). Continuous gamma ray spectrometer detectors have also been used.

With liquid detectors as with the gas detectors, the signal from the detector is amplified and fed to a recorder where peaks representing the eluted compounds are drawn. Retention times are used for qualitative analysis and peak areas for quantitative analysis as described above for GC.

Methods involving the collection of fractions are advantageous because the species present in each fraction can be characterized by several independent chemical and instrumental methods if desirable. The two modes of detection can be combined by continuously monitoring the solvent stream with a nondestructive detector and then collecting fractions at some point beyond this detector.

k. *Loading and zone detection.* The amount of sample loaded onto the sorbent is intimately related to the detection of the separated zones. There is a minimum load for the determination of each solute after its migration and concomitant dilution. A less sensitive detection method can make a poor separation look better if only the zone centers, but not the more dilute edges of the zones, which might be overlapped, are detected.

In theory, the lighter the loading, the more effective is the separation. Unfortunately, at low loading there is more difficulty in detecting the zones, especially those of minor constituents. At higher loadings these minor zones would be more easily detected, but they might be overlapped by major zones.

In practice, a chromatographic system can be considered to be overloaded when the number of separated zones is less than that observed with lower loading (i.e., some zones have run together). It is underloaded when the number of detectable zones is less than that obtained with slightly higher loadings (i.e., some zones are lost). Another indication of overloading in chromatography is when the chromatogram obtained for a mixture is not simply the graphical sum of the chromatograms for the individual solutes alone. That is, each component should behave the same whether alone or as part of a mixture.

For equal lengths of a packed sorbent, comparable amounts of the sorbent are present in equal cross-sectional regions. This means that for the same degree of separation with the same distance of migration, the loading of a 1 cm I.D. column can be about thirty-one times that of a 1 cm spot in a 0.25 mm thin layer of the same adsorbent. A column 10 cm in diameter can separate 1000–10,000 times more mixture than would be separable from a spot in a thin layer.

In preparative work it is often advantageous to overload the column and sacrifice resolution, the separations being completed by readsorption of fractions of the mixture.

l. *Sample recovery.* Fractions of effluent containing the same compound are combined. The solvents are evaporated under vacuum (a rotary evaporator is convenient), and the residue is further purified, if necessary, by rechromatography and/or recrystallization.

With high speed machines, samples are conveniently collected manually. First a dye sample is injected into the instrument to measure the lag time between the detector and the collection point (typically a few seconds). Then one watches for the proper cut point to appear on the recorder during the separation of interest, adds the time lag, and begins manual collection.

m. *Prescreening systems by TLC.* Preliminary screening by TLC (see Section I.V) on layers of various adsorbents with a range of solvents can quickly provide information concerning the polarities of the solutes present in a mixture and the nature of the chromatographic system which might provide a column separation of the mixture. Results cannot be directly transferred between the two techniques, because the properties of TLC and column adsorbents are not identical. A solvent composed of two liquids, one polar and one nonpolar, which yields a separation of a mixture by TLC will often provide a good separation on a column of the same adsorbent, if the solvent is modified by somewhat lowering the concentration of the polar constituent. In some cases, TLC adsorbents have been used directly as column adsorbents with virtually identical results (*10*).

n. *Quantitative analysis.* Use is made of the internal standardization method when possible. The height or area ratio of the sample peak to the standard peak is plotted *vs* the concentration of sample (mg/ml). The plot should go through zero if the chromatography was carried out in a proper manner. Calculation based on peak areas is more accurate, assuming adequate resolution of the peaks.

5. *Applications*

Liquid column chromatography serves to separate and analyze complex mixtures of nonvolatile and thermally unstable substances. Adsorption chromatography is most useful for mixtures containing a wide range of solutes with different functional groups. Partition chromatography is applicable to separations of homologs, especially polar, hydrophilic compounds. Compounds of similar structure which differ in size or molecular weight are separated by gel permeation chromatography, and ionic substances are separated by ion-exchange chromatography (see the end of Section B for a further comparison of adsorption and partition chromatography). Figures 17 and 18 illustrate typical separations by column adsorption chromatography employing a modern LC instrument. Table I, page 38, shows information and guidelines useful in the selection of solvent systems for liquid chromatographic separations.

B. LIQUID–LIQUID (PARTITION) COLUMN CHROMATOGRAPHY (LLCC)

In this method, a column is packed with a solid support of high surface area which is coated with the stationary liquid phase. The mixture is applied as a narrow zone and is developed by passing a mobile liquid immiscible with the stationary liquid through the column. Separations result because solutes relatively more soluble in the stationary liquid migrate more slowly than those with a greater relative solubility in the mobile liquid.

In all cases the solutes are more soluble in the stationary than in the mobile phase. For the separation of polar mixture, therefore, a polar liquid (e.g., water) is the stationary phase and a less polar liquid (an organic solvent) is the developing solvent. This is called normal partition chromatography.

TABLE I
PROPERTIES OF COMMON CHROMATOGRAPHIC SOLVENTS

Solvent	E°(Al_2O_3)[a]	Viscosity (cP, 20°)	RI	UVcutoff/nm
Fluoroalkanes	−0.25	—	1.25	—
***n*-Pentane**	0.00	0.23	1.358	210
******Hexane*	*0.00*	—	1.375	210
***Isooctane**	0.01	—	1.404	210
Petroleum ether, Skellysolve B, etc.	0.01	0.3	—	210
***n*-Decane**	0.04	0.92	1.412	—
Cyclohexane	0.04	1.00	1.427	210
Cyclopentane	0.05	0.47	1.406	210
Diisobutylene	0.06	—	1.411	210
1-Pentene	0.08	—	1.371	—
Carbon disulfide	0.15	0.37	1.626	380
Carbon tetrachloride	0.18	0.97	1.466	265
Amyl chloride	0.26	0.43	1.413	225
***Butyl chloride**	0.26	—	1.436	220
Xylene	0.26	0.62–0.81	~1.50	290
****i*-Propyl ether**	0.28	0.37	1.368	220
***i*-Propyl chloride**	0.29	0.33	1.378	225
Toluene	0.29	0.59	1.496	285
***n*-Propyl chloride**	0.30	0.35	1.389	225
Chlorobenzene	0.30	0.80	1.525	—
Benzene	*0.32*	0.65	1.501	280
Ethyl bromide	0.37	—	1.424	—
Ethyl ether	*0.38*	0.23	1.353	220
Ethyl sulfide	0.38	0.45	1.442	290
***Chloroform**	0.40	0.57	1.443	245
Methylene chloride	*0.42*	0.44	1.424	245
Methyl-i-butylketone	0.43	—	1.394	330
***Tetrahydrofurane**	0.45	—	1.408	220
Ethylene dichloride	0.49	0.79	1.445	230
Methyl ethyl ketone	0.51	—	1.381	330
1-Nitropropane	0.53	—	1.400	380
Acetone	0.56	0.32	1.359	330
***Dioxane**	0.56	1.54	1.422	220
Ethyl acetate	*0.58*	0.45	1.370	260
Methyl acetate	0.60	0.37	1.362	260
***Amyl alcohol**	0.61	4.1	1.410	210
Dimethyl sulfoxide	0.62	2.24	—	—
Aniline	0.62	4.4	1.586	—
Diethyl amine	0.63	0.38	1.387	275
Nitromethane	0.64	0.67	1.394	380
******Acetonitrile*	*0.65*	0.37	1.344	210
Pyridine	0.71	0.94	1.510	305
Butyl cellusolve	0.74	—	—	220
****i*-propanol, *n*-propanol**	0.82	2.3	1.38	210
Ethanol	0.88	1.20	1.361	210
***Methanol**	0.95	0.60	1.329	210
Ethylene glycol	1.11	19.9	1.427	210
Acetic acid	Large	1.26	1.372	—
***Water**	Larger	—	1.333	—
Salts and buffers	Very large	—	—	—

* Most commonly used with U.V. Detector.

[a] The Hildebrandt solvent scale is a list of common solvents used in liquid Chromatography in order of increasing energy of adsorption on alumina. The values are different, but the order is essentially the same on silica gel as on alumina.

The starting solvent selected for a given separation can be chosen by matching the relative polarity of the solvent to that of the sample. This is done as a first approximation by selecting the solvent to match the most polar functional group on the sample molecule. (e.g. alcohols for OH, amines for NH_2 etc.) From this first attempt the separation can be refined by the following procedure:

1. If the sample appears at the solvent front then the solvent is too polar to allow the adsorbent to retard the sample. Go to a solvent higher up (lower polarity) on the scale.
2. Conversely if the sample does not appear in a reasonable time go to a solvent or solvent blend lower down (higher polarity) on the scale.

Solvent blends are most useful when they are composed of pairs which differ in adsorption energy by no more than 100%. (Example propanol at energy 0.82 and chloroform at energy 0.40).

Solvent gradients should be generated on the same basis of no more than doubling the energy of the starting solvent. This range is more than sufficient for most if not all L C separations.

When changing solvents or when regenerating after a gradient, a minimum of 5 column volumes of the new starting solvent should flow through the system before another sample injection is made.

[b] [Information contained in data sheet supplied by Nester/Faust, 2401 Ogletown Rd., Newark, Del., 19711].

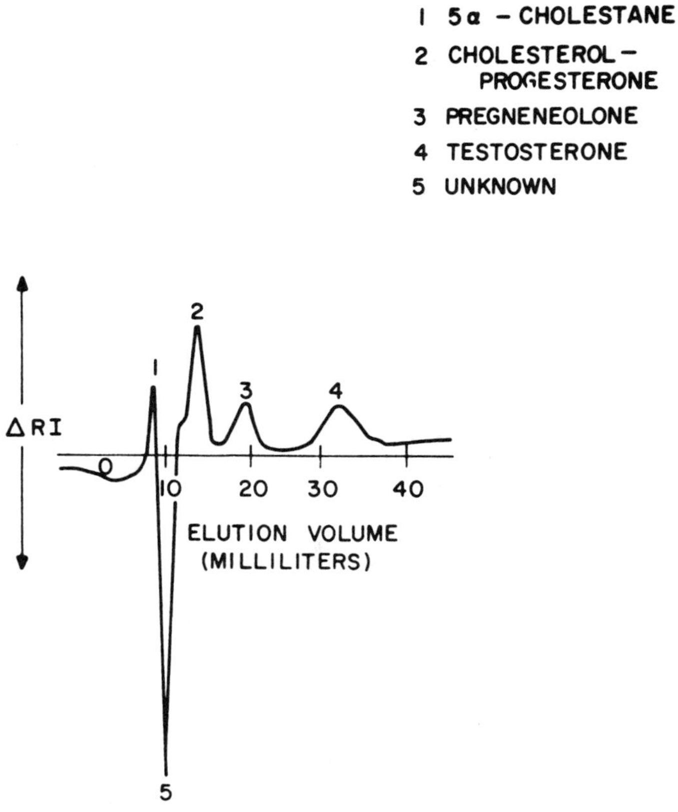

Figure 17. Separation of steroids by liquid-solid adsorption chromatography; instrument: Waters ALC-100 with differential refractometer detector; 1 ft × ¼ in. O.D. Porasil 60 column; 5 mg sample; solvent: acetone-chloroform (1 : 9 v/v) at 0.9 ml/min; ambient temperature (*21*). Permission to reproduce received from Waters Associates, Inc.

In reversed-phase partition chromatography, nonpolar solutes are separated on a less polar stationary phase (e.g., mineral oil) with a more polar mobile phase (methanol).

The intermolecular forces operative in partition are of the same types as those involved in adsorption, namely hydrogen bonds, induced dipole forces, dispersion forces and specific interaction forces.

1. *Theory*

The theoretical considerations presented in the two sections above are applicable to LLCC. For a theoretical discussion pertaining directly to partition chromatography, the reader is referred to Chapter 6 of Heftmann's *Chromatography* (*11*). The choice of phases in LLCC is largely empirical. Useful guides are previous results from batch studies and paper chromatography. Solvent systems are chosen to provide k' values of 2–5 (see equation [23]).

2. *Columns*

Length to width ratios are similar to those for adsorption, but the minimum is about 20 : 1. The ratio of solute amount to sorbent amount varies greatly but is generally lower than for adsorption separations.

3. *Column Supports*

An ideal support will hold a large amount of stationary liquid but will not interact with the solutes. Various procedures are used to block active support sites, for example, silanization of silica gel and kieselguhr. Column efficiency is increased by reducing particle size and reducing the thickness of the layer of liquid on each particle. Particles with an average size of 30–40 μ are used for modern LLCC.

a. *Silica gel.* A good grade of commercial silica gel need only be dried at ca. 105° for about one hour before impregnation with the stationary liquid. Particles around 200 mesh are typically employed for partition chromatography. Impure silica gel should be washed in turn with 6 *N* HCl, distilled water and methanol prior to drying and impregnation. Ordinary silica gels can adsorb 50–75% of their weight of a polar liquid phase. Whatman SG 34 silica gel is specially prepared with a high pore volume for partition column chromatography. It remains free-flowing even when mixed with 90% of its own weight of water.

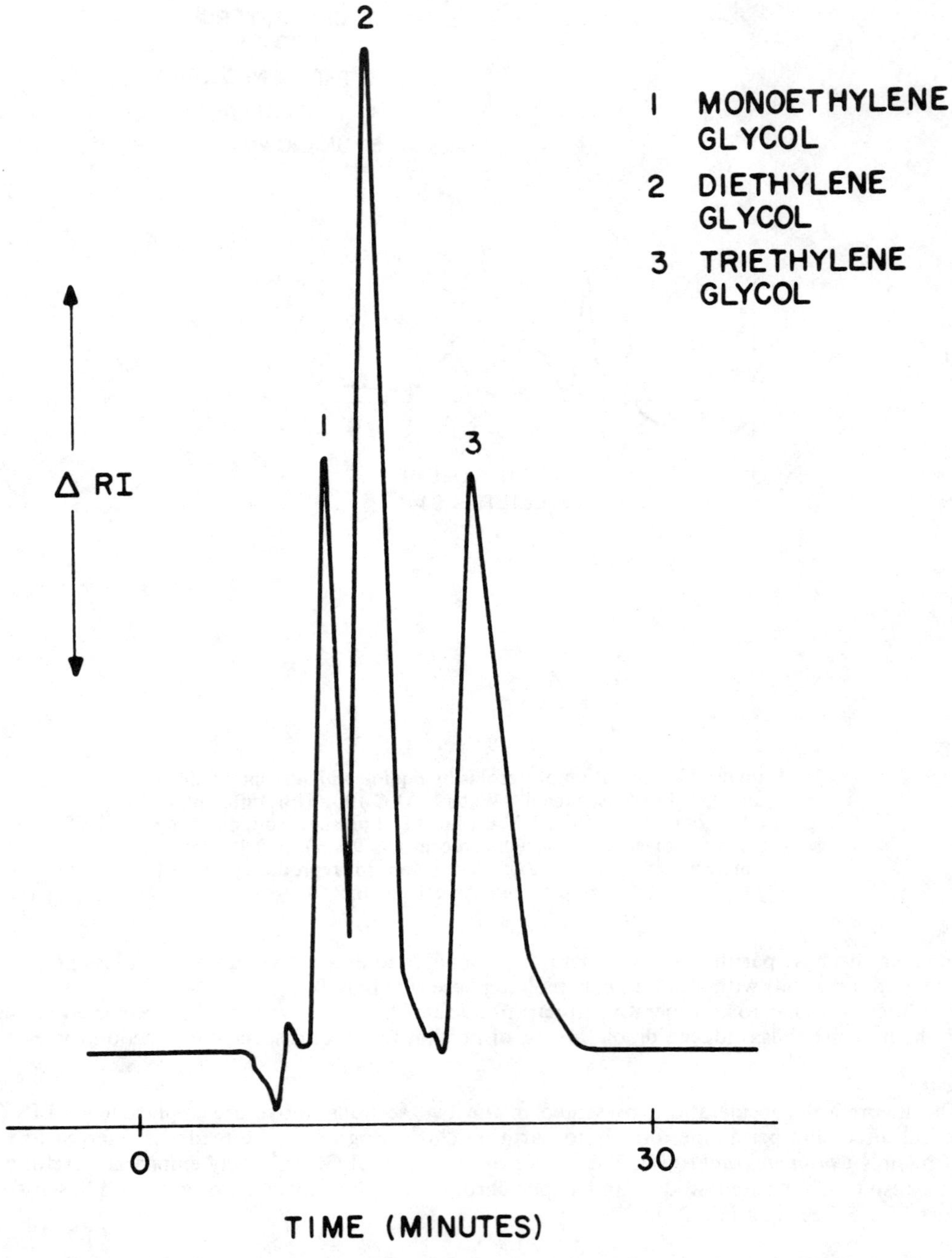

Figure 18. Separation of glycols by liquid-solid adsorption chromatography; instrument: Waters ALC-100 with differential refractometer detector; 1 ft × $\frac{1}{8}$ in. O.D. Porasil 60 column; 5 μl sample; solvent: 2.5% H_2O in methyl ethyl ketone at 0.4 ml/minute; ambient temperature (*21*). Permission to reproduce received from Waters Associates, Inc.

The pore structure of the support has an effect on mass transfer within the particle and therefore on bed efficiency in both adsorption and partition chromatography. Packings with deep pores can cause the formation of pools of stationary liquid leading to broadened peaks. Kirkland recommends the use of controlled surface porosity packings (spherical siliceous particles with a porous surface of controlled thickness and pore size and a solid, impervious core) on which a thin film of liquid is uniformly dispersed for packing more regular (efficient) columns. These coated beads have the advantage of reduced mass transfer distances within the particle leading to sharp peaks, a less steep dependence of h upon v (see eqs. [27] and [28]), and superior efficiency at high velocities. There is some loss in capacity and therefore analytical sensitivity with this type of packing.

Karger *et al.* (*12*) have employed surface-etched glass beads (30 and 40 μ, Corning GLC-100) coated with 0.2% OPN and packed in Trubore glass columns (50 cm length × 3 mm I.D.) to achieve efficient columns with flow velocities up to 4 cm/sec (ca. 15 ml/min). High efficiencies are possible because of the easily accessible shallow pores of the packing.

b. *Kieselguhr* (*Celite*). This is a more inert material than silica gel and is a very widely used support for partition chromatography, especially the reversed-phase modification. High quality commercial kieselguhr is used as received without further treatment.

c. *Cellulose*. (See also Section I.IV A.) Whether cellulose chromatography is an adsorption or partition process has been argued for years. Because the exact nature of the cellulose surface is unknown, the term "water-cellulose complex" is often used, and chromatography on cellulose (column or paper) can be considered a process in which the rate of migration of a solute depends upon its overall attraction to this complex surface. This attraction can be due to adsorption on fiber sites or at liquid-liquid interfaces as well as to liquid-liquid partition between the mobile liquid and the stationary "gel". In either case, the same types of intermolecular forces are involved.

The polymeric chains of fibrous cellulose are composed of glucose units which are capable of forming many hydrogen bonds due to the presence of hydroxyl groups. Much of this hydrogen bonding occurs between cellulose chains so that fibrous cellulose is considered as a discontinuous linear crystal.

Both fibrous and crystalline Whatman cellulose powders are available from H. Reeve Angel & Co. The fibrous powders yield large-scale column separations which are similar to those that can be made on paper. There is a coarse grind available for more rapid flow rates and a standard grind (passes 200 mesh sieve) for a more closely packed column. Either is available in ashless quality if desired. The crystalline powder is a free flowing material which disperses easily in water. It is available in 100–200 mesh size and provides columns which are generally slower but more efficient than columns of fibrous cellulose. Schleicher and Schuell Co. supplies acetylated cellulose powder in addition to regular cellulose powder (see Section II.III, Table 3).

d. *Other supports*. Other "inert" supports which have been used for reversed-phase partition chromatography include Teflon-6, Kel-F and microporous polyethylene. Recent research has shown that Teflon is not truly an inert support for certain separations despite formation of symmetrical peaks.

Partition chromatography on beds of Sephadex (see Section II.III, Table 4) have been used to separate antibiotics, amino acids, etc. The Sephadex is swollen and packed in an aqueous liquid and the column is then equilibrated for long periods by the flow of an organic solvent.

4. *Solvents*

The solvent system consists of an equilibrated pair of immiscible liquids. One of these is placed on the support and the other is used to develop the chromatogram. A serious difficulty with partition chromatography is "bleeding" of the stationary liquid from the support. The liquids and the experimental conditions must be chosen so as to minimize this effect. Liquids should be chosen which have low mutual solubility (i.e., one should have a low "solubility parameter" and one a high parameter). The phases are saturated with each other by mixing in a separatory funnel before use, or a precolumn may be used to saturate the mobile phase with the stationary phase prior to elution. Polymeric stationary phases (e.g., Carbowax) have low solubility in many solvents, but they are highly viscous so that slow solute diffusion rates and inefficient columns may result.

The "brush" packings developed by Halasz and described above (Section IIC) are produced by attaching the liquid partitioning molecules onto the support by a chemical reaction. The partitioning phase is therefore attached chemically to the support at one end, with the rest of the molecule available to interact with the solutes. The permanently bonded liquid phase will not dissolve in the mobile phase, so bleeding is eliminated. Liquid chromatographic separations generating almost one effective plate per second have been reported with these brushes. Brush packings available from Waters Associates include OPN, Carbowax 400 or *n*-octane on Porasil C. A new Dupont support for LLCC (Permasphase) has chemically bonded silicone polymers which are nonextractable and thermally and hydrolytically stable.

Relative eluant strengths can be estimated for partition solvents using the "solubility parameter" of Hildebrand and Scott (*13*). The solutes should be much (ca. 1000 times) more soluble in the stationary phase than in the mobile phase. Although all the solutes will have a much lower solubility in the mobile phase than in the stationary phase, it is the relative solubilities in the two phases which determine if differential migration occurs. Stationary phases which have been used for normal partition chromatography include water; water + acid, base, or buffers; alcohols; glycols; formamide or dimethylformamide (with or without added water). Mobile phases include higher alcohols (e.g., butanols), hydrocarbons, chloroform, esters and ketones. For reversed phase systems, paraffin, mineral or silicone oil is often the stationary phase and water, lower alcohols or formamide the mobile phase.

5. *Preparation of the Column*

The support is coated with the stationary phase as described above for GC (rotatory evaporator or filtration techniques). A simple procedure useful for fragile supports (diatomaceous earth) involves stirring the support and dissolved phase in a shallow dish while blowing nitrogen or heating with a heat lamp until dry. As a general rule, the highest liquid phase loading which does not badly degrade column efficiency is used. This impregnated powder can then be packed dry into the column, after which the sample is applied and development with equilibrated mobile phase begun. Or, the wetted powder can be slurried with equilibrated mobile phase and packed by the slurry method described above. With kieselguhr, each portion of slurry must be tamped down because good columns do not usually result from the action of gravity alone. Cellulose columns can be packed by the slurry method with acetone. The mobile phase saturated with water is then passed through until the column is equilibrated.

For reversed-phase chromatography, dry support is treated with the nonpolar phase dissolved in a volatile solvent. The coated support is air-dried or oven-dried at 60–110°, and the column is then packed by tamping, or by the slurry method after the support is mixed with the equilibrated polar mobile phase.

Many variations of these methods are used by different individual workers to obtain "satisfactory" partition columns.

6. *Column Development*

The sample (25–100 µl for 2–3 mm I.D. columns, containing 1–100 µg solute), dissolved in equilibrated mobile phase, is added to the top of the column. If the sample is not soluble in the mobile phase, it can be dissolved in the stationary phase liquid. This is sorbed on a small amount of solid support which is then put on top of the bed. In general, however, it is best to dissolve the sample in the carrier liquid.

The sample is developed with a single solvent or a stepwise gradient can be used, each new solvent being pre-equilibrated with the stationary phase. Continuous gradient elution is more difficult to employ in LLCC because the equilibrium between the stationary and mobile liquids cannot be perfectly maintained as the mobile phase changes. Portions of the stationary liquid are continually removed from the support causing reduced column efficiency and increased difficulty with detection. Even so, some success has been reported with solvent programmed LLCC, notably in the separation of acidic and basic compounds whose degree of ionization can be controlled. For example, Freeman (*14*) has separated organic acids on silica gel impregnated with 0.5 N H_2SO_4 (to retard ionization of the acids) with a gradient of chloroform-*n*-butanol mixtures. Bonded phase supports appear to hold great promise for successful use in gradient elution LLCC.

In place of solvent programming, a systematic screening of the sample in widely differing solvent systems can be employed. Bombaugh suggests the following systems: isooctane-glycol, water-isooctane, isooctane-β,β'-oxydipropionitrile, water-chloroform, or the organic and aqueous layers of ternary mixtures such as water-alcohol-chloroform.

Presaturation of the carrier solvent with the stationary phase is obtained by overnight rapid stirring (use an Erlenmeyer flask and magnetic stirrer to form a vortex) of deaerated phases to produce turbidity. Use of a precolumn (e.g., $\frac{1}{4}$ × 50 cm) containing 20% stationary phase on 120–140 mesh diatomaceous earth, just before the analytical column and at the same temperature, helps ensure true equilibrium.

7. *Temperature*

The temperature during equilibration must be the same as that used for the separation so that the solubility characteristics of the system do not change during the run.

It is possible that in special cases selectivity could be controlled by temperature programming since the solubilities of the solutes in the two phases, and therefore their distribution coefficients, would be altered. Temperature programming is not generally practical or useful in LLCC, however.

Typical contemporary experimental conditions for partition chromatography as summarized by Gilding (*15*) are as follows:

Bed size	—	20–40 inches length, 1–3 mm diameter
Packing	—	surface textured spherical particles of 20–40 I.D. containing 1–3% liquid loadings
Flow rate	—	0.5–3 ml/min
Pressure drop	—	700–800 psi
Separation time	—	several minutes to 2 hr.

Eluant pressures up to 60,000 lb/in² were used in one study to obtain improved chromatographic resolutions (*16*).

8. *Applications*

Figures 19 and 20 indicate examples of partition separations possible with an LC instrument.

9. *Adsorption* vs *Partition Chromatography*

Presented below is a summary comparison of adsorption and partition chromatography:

a. Larger samples can be separated by adsorption. Low sample capacity can cause problems with detection in partition chromatography.

b. Partition yields symmetrical peaks, adsorption often yields tailed peaks; however, with control of water content on the adsorbent and reasonable sample sizes, linear isotherms and symmetrical peaks can be achieved in adsorption chromatography.

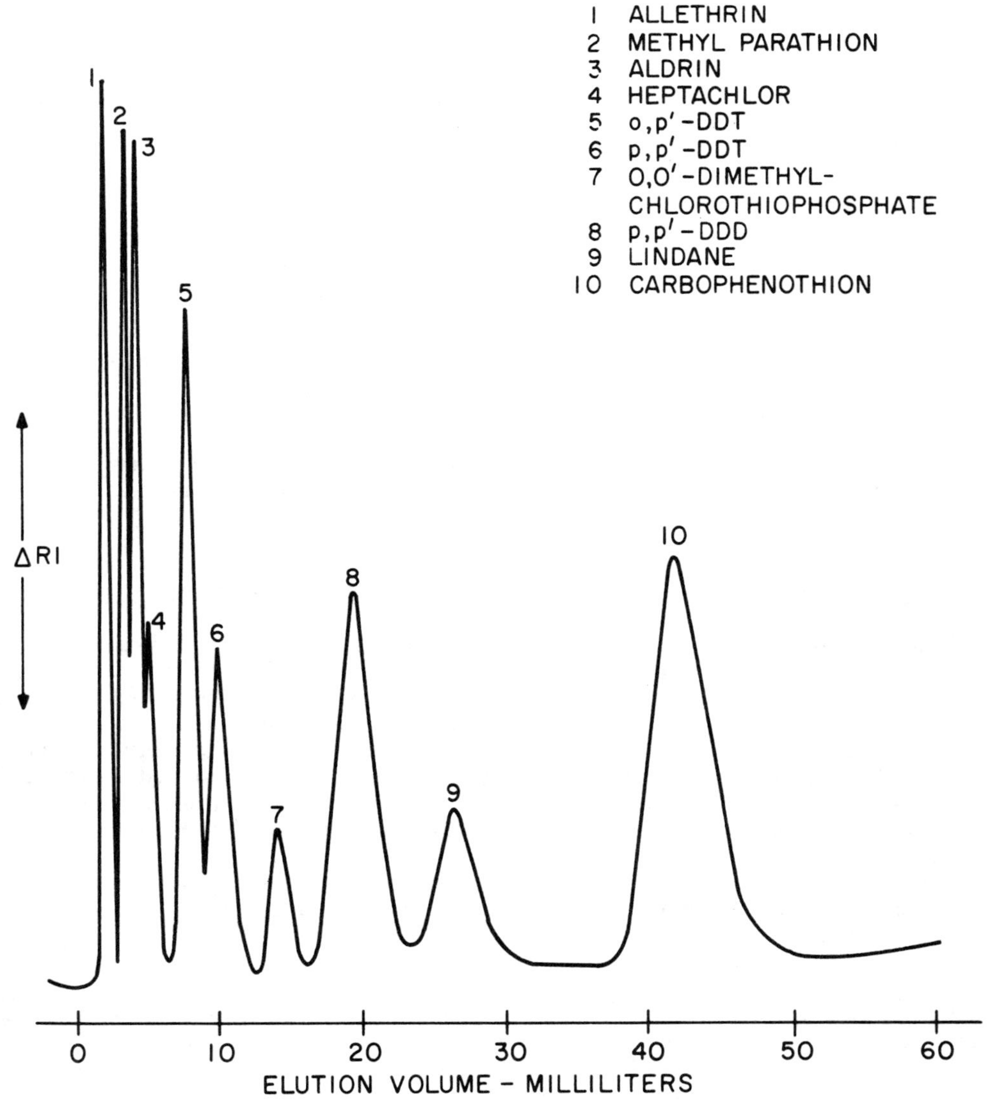

Figure 19. Liquid-liquid partition chromatographic separation of insecticides; instrument: Waters ALC 100 with differential refractometer detector; 4 ft × 0.09 in. I.D. column containing 10% β,β'-oxydipropionitrile on Porasil 60; 20 μl sample; isooctane solvent at 0.9 ml/min; ambient temperature. Permission to reproduce from Waters Associates, Inc.

c. It is easier to predict column results from batch studies in partition, although the literature of TLC is a very useful guide in designing adsorption separations.

d. Polar solutes are best separated by partition.

e. Partition is useful for separating polar, hydrophilic compounds, including homologs. Adsorption is best for relatively nonpolar solutes which differ widely in structure (isomers). Both methods are satisfactory for compounds up to molecular weight of about 10^3. By reversing phases, partition can be applied to nonpolar samples.

f. Adsorption more often causes chemical change of the solutes.

g. It is easier to prepare uniform partition systems than uniform adsorbents; however, it is often not easy to equilibrate partition systems, and in general adsorption is operationally more simple.

h. Partition chromatography is more efficient than adsorption. Partition chromatography permits the highest separation speeds of all four types of LC, is a gentle method, and allows preparation of very reproducible columns.

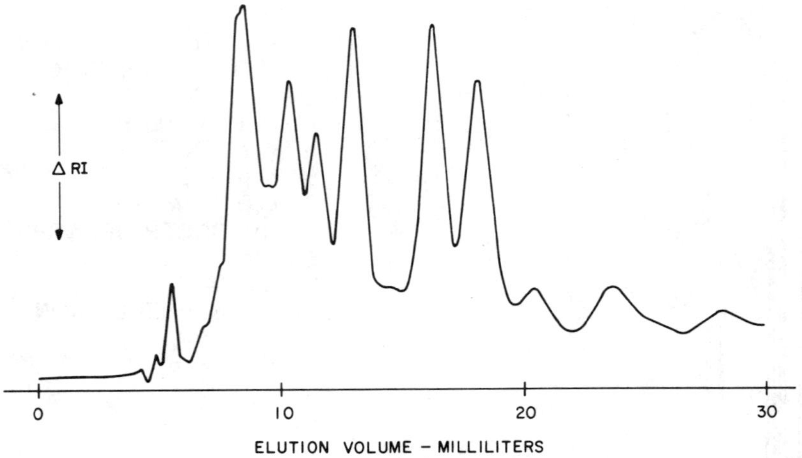

Figure 20. Liquid-liquid chromatography of chlordane on Waters ALC-100, 3 ft × 0.090 in. I.D. column as in Fig. 19; 25 μl sample; isooctane solvent at 0.25 ml/min [courtesy of Waters Associates, Inc.].

C. GEL FILTRATION AND GEL PERMEATION COLUMN CHROMATOGRAPHY

In gel filtration chromatography (GFC), the stationary phase is a solvent-swollen hydrophilic gel in the form of porous beads, and the mobile phase is an aqueous solvent. If the gel is hydrophobic and the solvent organic, the technique is called gel permeation chromatography (GPC). The generalized term "molecular exclusion (or inclusion) chromatography" can be used for both of these. The liquid outside the beads (the mobile phase) and that inside the beads is the same in each case, except that the liquid inside is immobilized.

When a sample containing small and large molecules is applied to the top of the bed and eluted through the column, the solutes will have a differential distribution between the liquid outside and inside the beads. The small molecules penetrate the gel particles and are retarded and eluted later than the large molecules, which will move only in the interstitial volume.

These techniques have had great application in industrial and polymer science (GPC) and biochemistry (GFC) for the determination of the molecular weight distribution of natural and synthetic polymers and for desalting and purification procedures (see "Applications" below).

1. *Theory and Mechanism*

Separations in GPC are based upon the molecular volume of the solute and the distribution of pore sizes available in the gel particles. The size of the molecule determines the percentage of the pore volume available to it; large molecules have no access to the beads and are therefore eluted quickly in the interstitial liquid. Smaller molecules can penetrate the gel to a greater or lesser degree and therefore travel down the column in a more tortuous (statistically longer) path and are eluted later. Polar molecules can be adsorbed by the substrate so that their movement would be slower than that predicted by size considerations alone.

The total volume (V_t) of a gel filtration or permeation bed can be represented by

$$V_t = V_M + V_s + V_g \qquad [29]$$

where V_M is the volume surrounding the gel beads (the interstitial volume), V_s is the liquid space within the beads and V_g is the space occupied by the gel matrix. V_M and V_s correspond to the volumes of mobile and stationary liquid in LLCC. Molecules larger than the average pore size of the gel are excluded and remain in the V_M volume of the column. Molecules smaller than the pores are distributed between V_M and V_s and travel at a rate depending upon the fraction of V_s available to them.

The distribution coefficient K (often termed K_d) is then

$$K_d = \frac{V_R - V_M}{V_s} \qquad [30]$$

where V_R is the elution volume of the solute. Large, completely excluded molecules have $V_R = V_M$, and $K_d = 0$. Very small molecules have about equal opportunity of being inside or outside the gel, so $V_R \simeq V_M + V_s$, in which case K_d is about 1. K_d values between 0 and 1 are to be expected then for molecules separated on the basis of size alone. K_d values >1 indicate the occurrence of adsorption between the gel matrix and the solute.

In practice, K_d values are difficult to determine because V_s and V_g cannot be easily measured. An alternate expression for solute migration, K_{av}, considers the whole gel ($V_g + V_s$) as the stationary phase rather than just the liquid inside the gel (V_s) as in [30]:

$$K_{av} = \frac{V_R - V_M}{V_t - V_M}. \qquad [31]$$

Values of K_{av} are easily obtained in the following manner: V_R for the solute is read from the chromatogram (Figure 6), V_t is calculated from the column geometry, and V_M is taken as the V_R of an excluded molecule, e.g., blue dextran 2000, molecular weight of ca. 2×10^6, for Sephadex gels. [Blue dextran is not eluted from Sephadex if an old solution is used. Further, blue dextran can accumulate on columns even when fresh solutions are eluted, so that protein samples may become bound to such columns causing anomalous results (*22*)].

The number of theoretical plates (N) in GPC, as in other methods, depends upon the conditions under which the column is operated and on the solute of interest. N is determined from the chromatogram using equation [5] as described in Section I.II. To obtain a rough estimate of N for a GPC column, the chromatogram of a single standard compound such as *o*-dichlorobenzene or tetrahydrofuran can be used.

In gel permeation chromatography, unlike sorption chromatography, peak width (W) is virtually constant as elution volume (V_R) increases. (In general, in GC and LC N is constant for different V_R values, i.e., band width increases in proportion to V_R.) For example, polystyrene ($K_d = 0.37$) eluted from 160 ft (40×4 ft columns) of Styragel at 873 ml had $W = 14.5$ ml while *o*-dichlorobenzene ($K_d = 1.0$) was eluted at 1579 ml with $W = 14.8$ ml (*23*). The number of theoretical plates increases with V_R, ranging from 100,000 for polystyrene to 180,000 for *o*-dichlorobenzene, but this represented only a range of 5000 to 36,000 effective plates (n) when correction was made for the dead (void) volume of the system. The fact that peak width values are independent of K_d indicates that all band spreading occurs in the mobile phase and not inside the gel phase in the Styragel system. The greatest difference between N and n values in GPC will occur for those compounds with the smallest K' values (see equation [24]), and the major difference between plate numbers in GC and GPC (in which N is customarily determined for the last peak with $K_d = 1$) is in the small K' values commonly available in GPC.

The peak capacity of a system is the maximum number of peaks resolvable between the volumes of elution of the first and last peaks. The peak capacity in GPC at constant efficiency (i.e., columns which yield equal plates N per unit length) is a function of column length and is equal to

$$\frac{V_R \text{ of last peak} - V_R \text{ of first peak}}{W}. \qquad [32]$$

In the absence of adsorption, the peaks in GPC are limited to a volume range between V_M ($K_d = 0$) and the total solvent volume $V_M + V_s$ ($K_d = 1$), which is roughly $2.5 \times V_M$. Fewer solute peaks can fit into this limited retention range so that with a column of similar dimensions and theoretical plates, the peak capacity is reduced about four times compared to GC and LC. For complex separations, GPC columns must clearly be operated under conditions leading to high plate numbers (e.g., increased column length; recycle), and since the elution range of GPC is limited as explained above, such required conditions can still allow reasonably fast separation times. The most efficient column packing and the optimum packing procedure must be employed.

Semilog calibration curves (molecular size *vs* elution volume) for exclusion packings are characterized by a straight line with a greater or lesser slope in the fractionation range (between V_M and $V_M + V_s$). Gels with a flat slope give better separation of molecules of similar size but cover a small molecular weight range. Gels with a steeper calibration curve cover a larger range but result in poorer separation of adjacent bands. For broad range samples, several different columns are combined to provide the average slope of the individual gels.

2. *Column Packings* (see Section II.III, Table 4).

Gel permeation and filtration column packings function as nonionic molecular sieves, the average pore size of the packing determining which molecules are excluded from entering the gel. A partial description of some packings which have been used follows:

a. *Polystyrene* (Poragel A, Styragel, Bio-Beads). Polymers prepared by cross-linking styrene with divinylbenzene are analogous to polystyrene ion exchange resins (Section III.D) without the ionic exchange groups. They are used for size separations of low molecular weight (ca. 600–50,000) hydrophobic materials with organic solvents. Also available is a Poragel P series containing different functional groups (aryl N, aryl O, hydroxyl and keto) for adsorption separations with aqueous and organic solvents, and Aquapak, a lightly sulfonated polystyrene for size separations with aqueous solvents.

b. *Porous silica* (Porasil). Spherical silica beads with controlled pore sizes and surface areas; can also be used as an adsorbent for LSCC or a support for LLCC. For GPC, deactivation of the silica beads is often necessary so that certain solutes [e.g., poly(vinyl alcohol)] are not adsorbed. Polystyrene is more efficient (by a factor of 4 or 5) than silica.

c. *Porous glass* (Bio-Glas and Corning CPG-10 LC packing). These are rigid glass beads with pore size ranges from ca. 200 to 2500 Å. They are quite inert and stable and are especially useful for separations at elevated temperature or where possible contamination of the sample is a problem.

d. *Polyacrylamide* (Bio-Gel P). Designed for the separation of aqueous macromolecules below 400,000 molecular weight. They are prepared by polymerizing different amounts of acrylamide and methylene bisacrylamide.

e. *Agarose* (Bio-Gel A and Sepharose). For the separation of very high molecular weight aqueous macromolecules such as nucleic acids, proteins, polysaccharides, certain subnuclear particles and viruses.

f. *Polydextran* (Sephadex). Spherical beads of Sephadex are produced by cross-linking the polysaccharide dextran with epichlorohydrin to produce a highly porous, hydrophilic, sponge-like gel (Figure 21). The degree of cross-linking is controlled by regulating the amount of epichlorohydrin used during formation of the polymer, and this in turn determines the amount of water absorbed per gram (the swelling) and influences the size of the pores in the molecule. Hydrophilic Sephadex gels preferentially adsorb aromatic compounds and contain some carboxylic acid groups (10–20 μeq/dry g) which can interact with various molecules so as to distort gel filtration chromatograms.

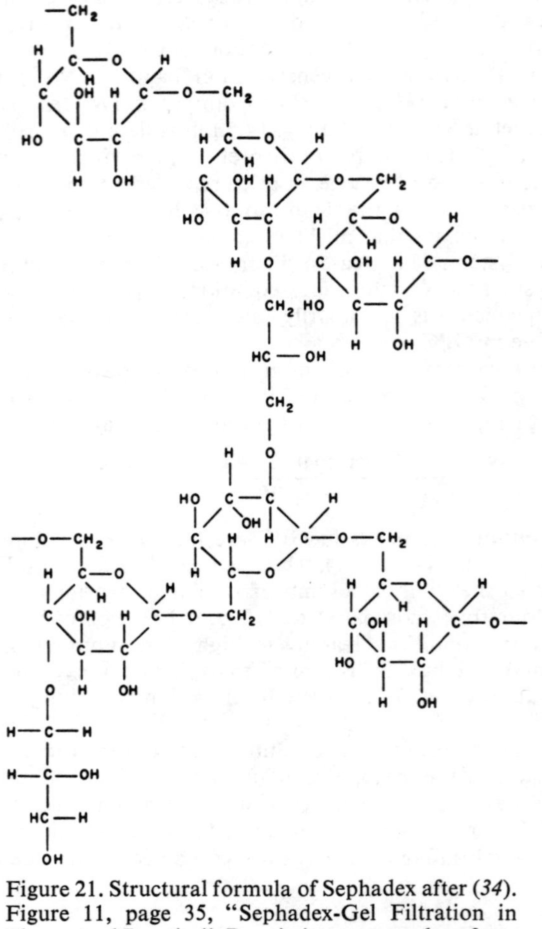

Figure 21. Structural formula of Sephadex after (*34*). Figure 11, page 35, "Sephadex-Gel Filtration in Theory and Practice". Permission to reproduce from Pharmacia Fine Chemicals, Inc., Piscataway, N.J. and American Laboratory, International Scientific Communications, Inc.

The Sephadex G series is used for gel filtration in aqueous media. The LH-20 series is a lipophilic derivative of Sephadex (obtained by alkylation of most of the hydroxyl groups) useful for GFC in polar organic solvents (DMF, methanol, acetone, dioxane, etc.) and these solvents mixed with water for the separation of materials such as steroids, petroleum hydrocarbons, and other organic molecules. Superfine grades (10–40 μ) of the G series are available for TLC, as are Sephadex ion exchangers for the separation of various labile macromolecules (enzymes, hormones).

g. *Other packings*. Starch, vulcanized natural rubber and polyvinylacetate (Merckogel OR) have also been used for separations based on size.

3. *Equipment and Procedures*

Equipment can range from a simple open column to a modern, high temperature, pressurized LC instrument. Since gels for gel filtration are relatively soft, separations are generally carried out in rather simple glass columns with the flow of liquid produced by a difference in hydrostatic pressure. Gel permeation, which employs harder gels, is usually performed in a high pressure commercial instrument of the type shown in Figure 13. Major differences between GPC and general liquid chromatography are the use of loop injection and recycle techniques, and the absence of solvent programming (see Section h). Multiple columns are often used (Figures 28 and 29).

a. *Packing the bed* (see also Section II.III, Table 4). To pack Sephadex G-75-G-200, the tube (generally ranging from 0.9 × 15 cm to 10.0 × 100 cm) is mounted vertically and the outlet is fitted with a narrow piece of tubing (Figure 22a). A small amount of liquid is poured into the tube and the outlet is closed.

The gel is mixed with an appropriate solution to swell the beads. Sephadex gels are hydrated in the buffer solution which will serve as the eluant according to the following table:

Type of Sephadex	Minimum swelling time at room temperature	Minimum swelling time on boiling water bath
G-10, G-15, G-25, G-50	3 hours	1 hour
G-75	24 hours	3 hours
G-100, G-150, G-200	3 days	5 hours
LH-20	3 hours	—

(From "Sephadex-Gel Filtration in Theory and Practice," Table 3, p. 31, Pharmacia Fine Chemicals, Inc.)

A recent report (*24*) indicates that boiling Sephadex G-15 in 1 *N* HCl for 2 hr and washing with water before packing the column improves the chromatographic properties of the gel by increasing the number of theoretical plates, the internal volume and the effective pore size without any deterioration of the gel.

The buffer is chosen so as to be inert toward the sample and should not contain oxidizing agents or strong acids which could hydrolyze the gel matrix. The ionic strength of the buffer should be >0.02 to obviate the possible ion exchange effects due to the carboxylic content of the matrix. After hydration, fine particles are poured off from the slurry, and the buffer and slurry are degassed.

The slurry is poured down a glass rod into the tube. If possible, all the slurry required for the whole bed is added at once; an extension tube can be attached to the top of the chromatography tube if necessary. The slurry is stirred to remove air bubbles.

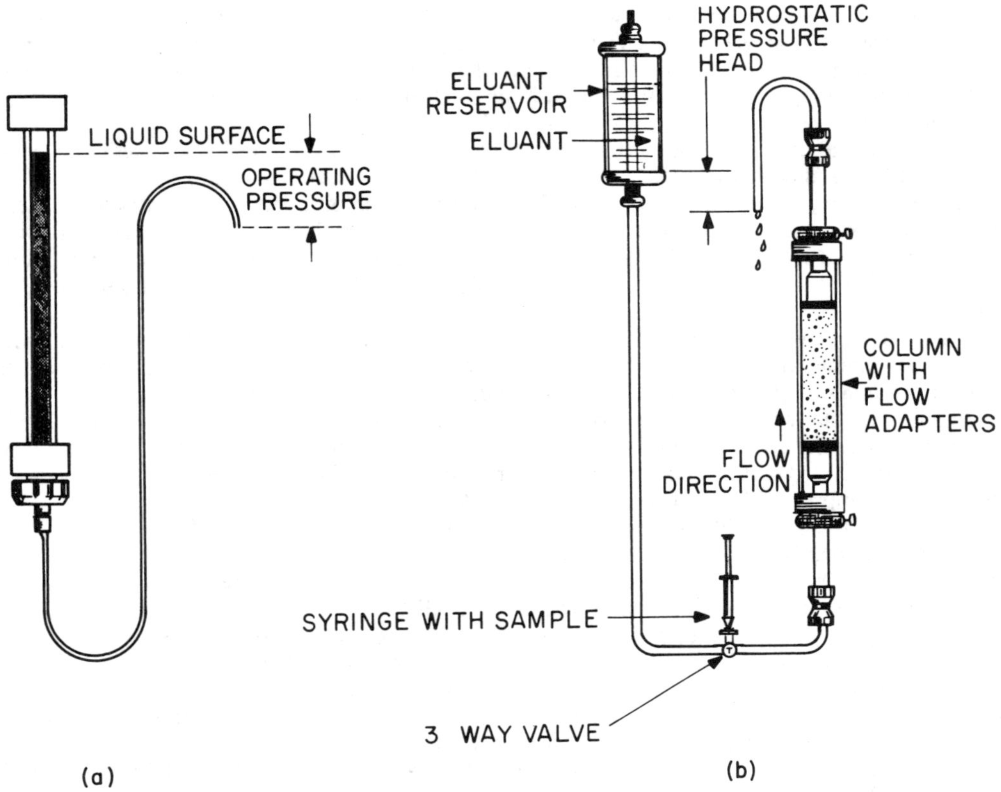

Figure 22. (a) Sephadex gel filtration column for use with downward flow of solvent; (b) a Sephadex closed-system setup for use with upward flow of solvent.

The outlet tube is positioned as shown in Figure 22a and opened to let solvent flow out. If necessary, additional slurry is added as the solvent flows out, the gel settles and the column level rises. The tubing is finally lowered until the pressure to be used for elution is obtained (for Sephadex G-200, 100–150 mm pressure maximum is recommended). Sephadex G-10 to G-50 beds are easier to pack than beds of G-75 to G-100. The operating pressure can be higher so the exit tubing need not be so long. Columns of Sephadex LH-20 are packed as just described. Since the beads float in chloroform, a high flow rate is applied as soon as the slurry is poured into the tube, and a tube with a plunger-type flow adaptor is needed to keep the bed in position after the flow is stopped. Figure 22b shows a Sephadex column with two flow adaptors for use with gels that float or for upward flow or recycling chromatography.

A circular piece of filter paper or some other material is placed on top of the bed to stabilize it. Two or three column volumes of the eluant are passed through to equilibrate the bed, and then a sample of blue dextran 2000 is chromatographed to determine V_M and to check the quality of the packing by watching the colored zone move through the bed.

For GPC, polystyrene beads are first swollen in an organic solvent, packed into a tube with a slurry-pressure technique, and washed with the solvent in which they were swollen. Columns are made of glass or metal, are uniform and not coiled. The slurry-pressure technique of packing is difficult for a beginner and hard to apply reproducibly. It may be best to purchase these columns prepacked because efficiency is so vital in GPC. Waters Associates sells prepacked columns and also a column-packing unit which comes with a detailed description for this technique.

Excellent, reproducible columns containing controlled-pore glass material for exclusion chromatography may be packed by either a dry or wet (slurry) technique. With either method, it is most important that all pores be completely filled with the mobile phase. Correct procedures for packing and maintaining such columns have been provided by Pidacks (*25*).

b. *Sample application.* For analytical separations, a few mg of sample is applied as a dilute solution (ca. 0.5%) in the eluant. In gel filtration, application can be with a pipette after lowering the level of liquid in the column just to the top of the bed. Or, if the sample is more dense than the eluant, it may be applied with a pipette or syringe beneath a layer of eluant which is allowed to remain on top of the bed. Syringe injection can also be used (Figure 22b). Typical sample sizes are 0.4 ml for 15 mm columns and 1–2 ml for 25 mm columns. Applying the sample at a density above that of the solvent is a common technique in GFC so that there is a sharp boundary between the sample and the solvent. This is achieved by addition of a neutral salt or sucrose. Sample solutions with a high viscosity relative to the eluant can lead to skewed peaks with tailing or heading.

Sample injection with a syringe through a septum into the solvent stream and loop injection are used in GPC. Loop injection is performed as follows: a four-port valve is set to "fill" and the sample is introduced into the sample loop from a syringe; the valve is changed to "empty" and the sample is discharged as the loop becomes part of the eluant stream. The amount of sample loaded on the column is controlled by the concentration of the sample solution and the amount of time the valve is open. The sample should be injected as quickly as possible at a point just ahead of the column.

c. *Solvents.* Typical eluants for gel filtration include water (for uncharged substances), 0.025 *M* phosphate buffer (pH 7.0) and 0.1 *M* tris-HCl + 1 *M* NaCl (pH 8.0).

For gel permeation, tetrahydrofuran, *o*-dichlorobenzene, trichlorobenzene, perchloroethylene, chloroform, methylene chloride, carbon tetrachloride, toluene, benzene, cyclohexanone and others have been used. The eluting solvent and the gel should have similar polarity, and, of course, the solvent must completely dissolve the sample. The solvent should have low viscosity, a high boiling point, and should be compatible with the detector.

Solvents should be degassed prior to entering a heated column so that bubbles do not form within the bed. In GPC instruments, this can be done by passing the solvent through a vented heater placed just ahead of the solvent pump and held at a temperature just under the boiling point of the solvent.

d. *Elution.* A constant pressure closed-system set up for gel filtration is shown in Figure 22b. Upward flow is often used with Sephadex, and this sometimes allows higher flow rates than possible with downward flow of solvent. Downward elution in an open tube can also be used. Improved resolution has been obtained in one study with compressed beds of Sephadex G-50 (*26*).

e. *Temperature.* In some GPC separations, the solubility characteristics of the sample require the use of elevated temperatures. Increased temperature will improve efficiency if a viscous solvent is being used or if the sample solution is concentrated and therefore viscous. Temperature programming is not a generally fruitful experimental approach for increasing resolution in GPC.

f. *Flow rate.* Low flow rates and small gel particles lead to peaks with decreased widths in both gel permeation and gel filtration. Elution volumes are normally independent of flow rate.

g. *Recycle chromatography.* The effective length of the column can be increased without requiring large pressure increases by passing the column effluent back through the column both in gel permeation and gel filtration. Peaks well separated in the first cycle are taken off so that they do not remix with other peaks during later cycles. Recycle GPC can be carried out with a Waters ALC-100 LC (Figure 13) modified as shown in Figure 23.

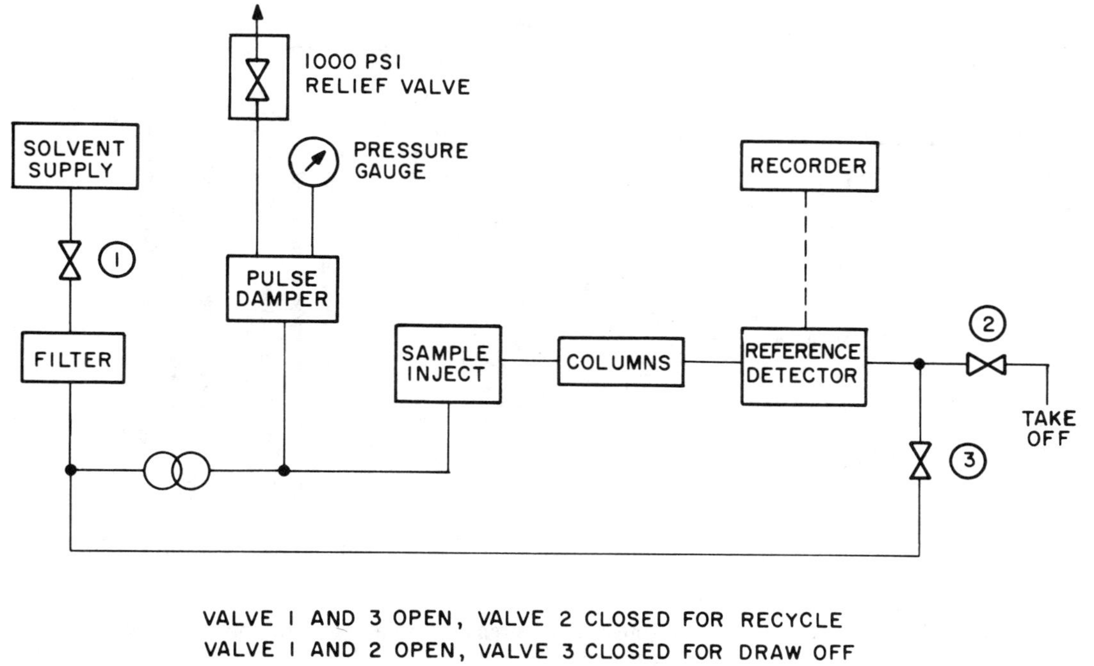

Figure 23. Schematic diagram of a recycle system [after (*23*)]. From *J. Chromatogr. Sci.* 7, 43 (1969). Permission to reproduce from Journal of Chromatographic Science, Evanston, Illinois.

h. *Programmed exclusion chromatography.* Giddings and Dahlgren (*27*) have proposed a method for the continuous control of retention which substitutes for the techniques of solvent and temperature programming which are widely used in LC and GC, respectively, but are not effective in exclusion chromatography. Control is gained by adding to the incoming solvent a certain percentage level of a high-molecular-weight polymer whose molecules are too large to penetrate the pores of the gel. The added polymer will selectively alter the thermodynamic properties of the mobile phase because of interactions with the solute species. Solutes will be selectively excluded from the mobile phase based upon their molecular dimensions, leading to altered equilibrium constants and improved size-dependent separations.

i. *Detection and analysis.* Solutes are detected and estimated either continuously or by collecting fractions.

Continuous detectors are of the same type as for other kinds of liquid chromatography. These include refractive index (by far the most widely used for GPC), moving wire, infra-red, conductivity, radioactivity and ultraviolet detectors. These are used in conjunction with a recorder and integrator as described before.

Fraction collectors which measure volume rather than time are desirable because timing devices will not take account of changes in flow rate which will change the elution time but not the elution volume of a given solute.

A fully automated gel filtration system employing the Technicon Autoanalyzer for the continuous detection of eluted polysaccharides with the orcinol-H_2SO_4 reagent has been described (*28*).

j. *Regeneration and repacking.* Usually no regeneration of the bed is required between runs. Flow rates through beds of soft gels may be reduced with time as the particles compress. It may then be desirable to backwash or repack the column.

k. *Commercial equipment.* Suitable tubes for gel filtration can be purchased from commercial sources (e.g., Pharmacia Fine Chemicals, Inc., Figure 22) or can be constructed as described by Varley (*29*). These tubes should have a Terylene or Nylon support for the bed rather than sintered glass discs which can adsorb solutes (e.g., lipoproteins) and easily clog. Columns must also have a minimum dead volume at the exit to prevent remixing of the separated components. Columns for GFC are typically 1–5 cm diameter and 20–200 cm length.

Commercial chromatographs for GPC are manufactured by Waters Associates. Their ALC-100 is a general liquid chromatograph useful for molecular size separations at room temperature (Figure 13). The Waters Model 200 gel permeation chromatograph (Figure 24) is a high temperature, wide range GPC instrument. The operating procedure for the GPC-200 for determining molecular weight distribution curves, as taken from Waters' literature, is as follows:

A sample is prepared by weighing out a sufficient quantity of the polymer to make up a 0.25 or 0.50% mixture in a suitable solvent. The sample is dissolved in the solvent in an oven. A hypodermic syringe is then filled with 5 ml of the sample in the solvent and the valve loop flushed with this sample. The solvent reservoir

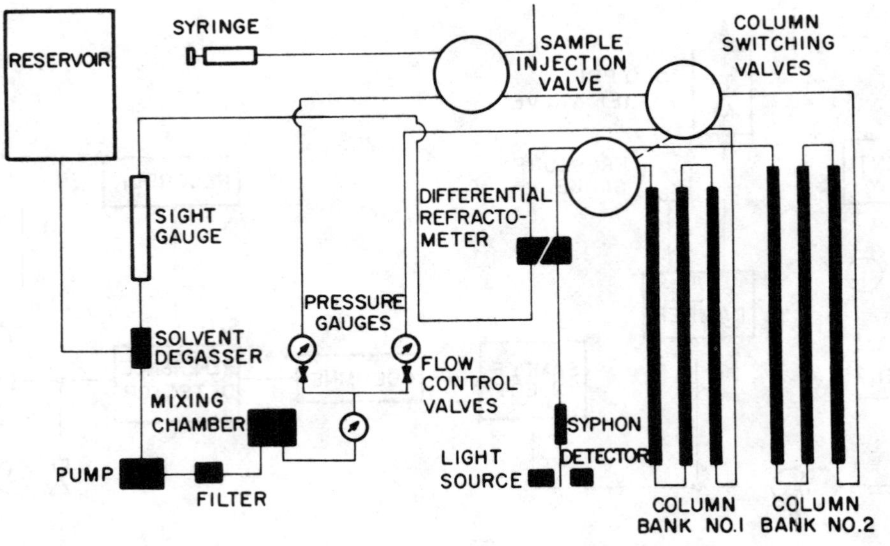

Figure 24. Flow diagram of Waters Model 200 Gel Permeation Chromatograph.
Permission to reproduce from Waters Associates, Inc.

has been previously filled with the same solvent used to prepare the sample. The solvent is pumped from the reservoir through a heater to degas the solvent and then a filter to the columns. The solvent flow is controlled by means of control valves in each line. Flow rate through each bank of sample columns is set at 1 ml per min. The column switching valves are set to direct the sample flow through the desired set of columns.

When ready to place the sample on the column the valve is turned 90° to place the sample loop in the solvent line. The solvent then carries the sample from the valve loop on to the packed sample column. The valve is returned to its original position and solvent continues to elute the column. Depending upon the length of the column a molecular-weight-distribution curve will be obtained within one to three hours.

The effluent from the columns passes through the sample and reference cell to a differential refractometer. Since no solvent gradient is necessary for separation, the difference in the refractive indices between sample and reference cells of the refractometer is used to detect each fraction of the sample as it leaves the column. The solvent after passing through the reference side of the refractometer returns to the solvent reservoir. The sample passes to a 5 ml syphon and then to a fraction collector or suitable waste collector. When each 5 ml fraction is dumped by the syphon, the light beam through the syphon tube is interrupted and a pulse occurs on the recorder chart. In this fashion each 5 ml fraction is itemized on the recorder.

Gilding (*15*) summarizes typical experimental conditions for GPC as follows:

Three or four columns, each 4 ft × $\frac{3}{8}$ in. diameter.
Sample injections of 3–5 mg.
Flow rate—1 ml/min.
Pressure drop—100–120 psi/16 ft of column bed.
Time of run—2.5–3 hr.
Mixtures of MW $> 10^3$ handled most efficiently.

The approximate molecular weight ranges normally handled by the various methods are <100 to 400 for GC, 7500 to >100,000 for GPC and 200 to 10,000 for LSCC and LLCC.

4. *Applications*

a. *Desalting*. Macromolecules are eluted in the interstitial volume and are separated from salts and other low-molecular-weight compounds which are eluted later. Examples are the removal of salts from proteins and phenol from nucleic acids. Gel filtration is faster and more efficient than dialysis for desalting, and denaturation of labile substances (nucleic acids, enzymes) is less likely. Centrifugal desalting with Sephadex is also useful for highly viscous polymer solutions.

b. *Separation of multicomponent mixtures*. Complex mixtures of substances with different molecular weights are separated by exclusion chromatography (Figures 25–28). Substances with similar molecular weights can be separated if there is preferential adsorption for one or more of the compounds (e.g., aromatic compounds).

c. *Molecular-weight determination*. Chromatography on Sephadex can be used to determine the molecular weights of unknown proteins. A plot of log molecular weight *vs* elution volume for a series of known proteins approximates a straight line. The unknowns are chromatographed under the same conditions and their molecular weights estimated from the standard curve based on their elution volumes.

GPC is used extensively to determine molecular-weight averages and distributions of polymers (Figure 29). The column is first calibrated with known molecular-weight standards. Polystyrene standards can be

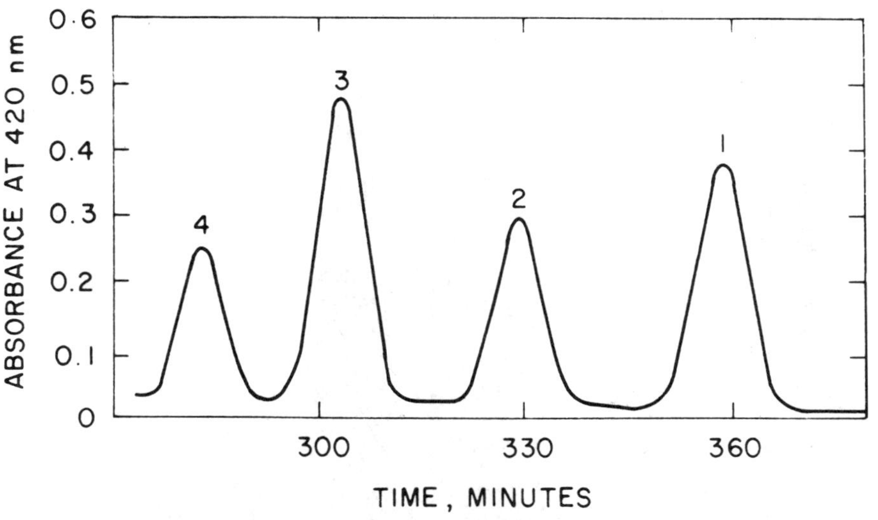

Figure 25. Gel filtration chromatography of glucose (1), lactose (2), raffinose (3) and stachyose (4) on Bio-Gel P-2, at 65 °C. Column 2.5 × 100 cm. Flow rate, 58 ml per hour. Eluant, water. 20 μl of a solution containing glucose, 320 μg; lactose, 240 μg; raffinose, 360 μg; stachyose, 200 μg, was applied to the column. After (*35*); see *J. Chromatogr.* **42**, 476 (1969) for later, improved separations of a similar nature.

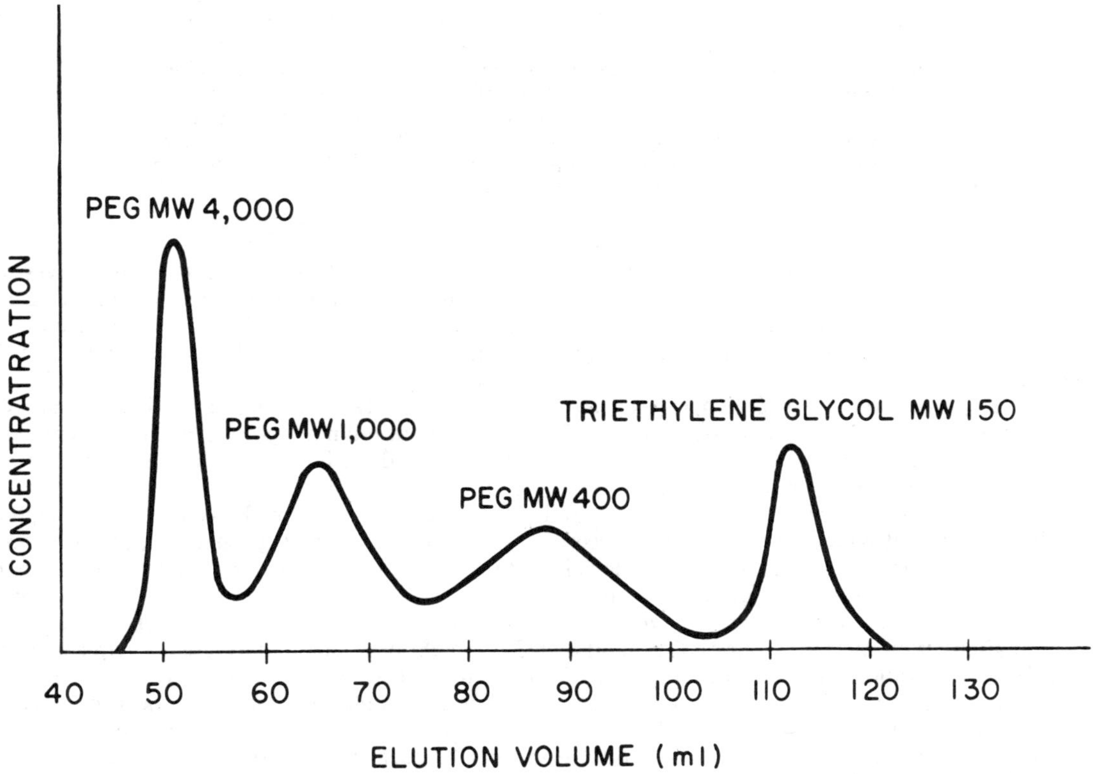

Figure 26. Elution diagram of a mixture of polyethylene glycols (PEG) on Sephadex LH-20. Solvent: ethanol. Bed dimensions: 1 in. × 30 cm. Sample: 2 ml containing 4 mg of each substance. Flow rate: 0.8 ml/min. [From (*36*).] From LH-20 booklet, page 4. Permission received to reproduce from Pharmacia Fine Chemicals, Inc., Piscataway, N.J.

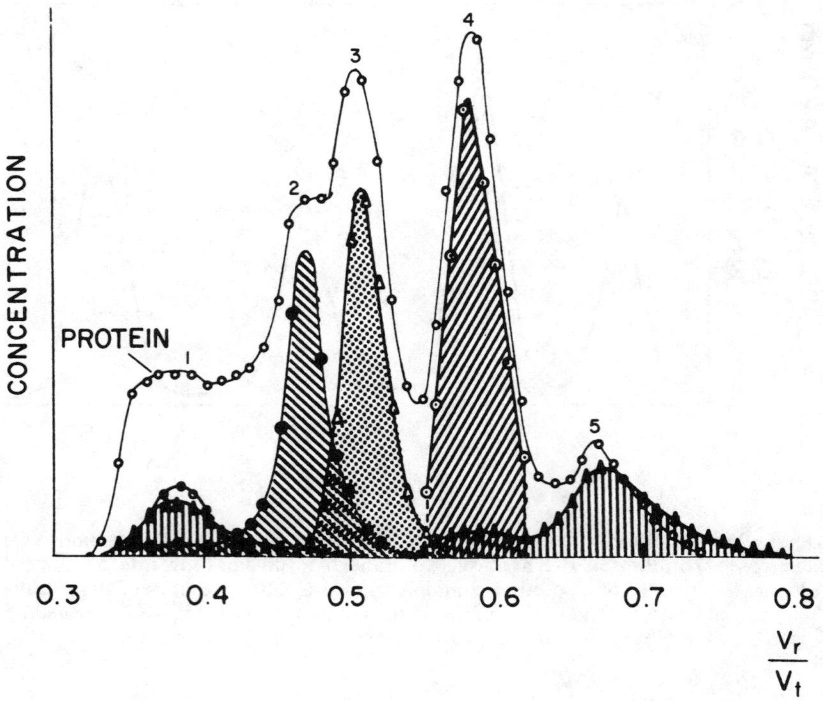

Figure 27. Fractionation by gel filtration of human serum proteins and hemoglobin on Sephadex G-200. Bed dimensions: 4.2 × 73.5 cm. Flow rate: 10–20 ml/h. Eluant: 0.1 *M* tris-HCl buffer, pH 8.0 and 1 *M* NaCl. V_r = elution volume, designated V_R in text. Peaks: 1. haptoglobin-hemoglobin complex, 2. γ-globulins, 3. ceruloplasmin, 4. albumin, 5. free hemoglobin; total protein concentration of the eluate is indicated by open circles [after (*34*)]. Reprinted with permission from American Laboratory, International Scientific Communications, Inc. and Pharmacia Fine Chemicals, Inc.

used in the determination of other polymers, or for more accurate work separate calibration curves must be made for each polymer. After calibration, the unknown sample is chromatographed, the resulting chromatogram is divided into equal sections by drawing vertical lines every 5 ml, and the average molecular weight of each section is obtained from the height of each line by referring to the calibration curve. The weight-average and number-average molecular weight of the polymer is then calculated. Applications include the characterization of polymers prepared under different reaction conditions, the comparison of two identical samples of a polymer after being subjected to different milling processes, and the differentiation of motor oils in order to relate performance and properties. A paper describing the molecular characterization of silicones by GPC has appeared (*30*).

d. *Separation of inorganic salts.* Inorganic salts have been separated on Bio-Gel P-2 and Sephadex G-10 by Pecsok and Saunders (*31*). Sorption isotherms, retention data and mechanisms of retention are discussed. A combination of adsorption on the gel, exclusion from internal water bound to the gel matrix, and Donnan exclusion of anions are all operative factors.

e. *Studies of molecular structure.* Cazes (*32*) has pointed out that adsorption between solutes and the substrate often retard migration during GPC and that GPC might be applied, therefore, to help characterize molecular configurations and stereochemical conformations of unknown structures. Molecules with permanent dipoles are often eluted earlier than expected based on their molecular volumes because of associative forces (solute-solute or solute-solvent). These attractive forces were studied for hydrocarbons, alcohols and other compounds by GPC. Molecular association has also been studied using GFC (*33*).

f. *Adsorption and ion-exchange chromatography.* Examples of the effects of adsorption or ion exchange in GFC include the retardation of aromatic compounds on Sephadex, fractionation of amino acids, fractionation of humic acid, separation of nucleic acid components, and partial resolution of stereoisomers on Sephadex (*33*). In most instances of exclusion chromatography, these effects are neither observed nor are desirable.

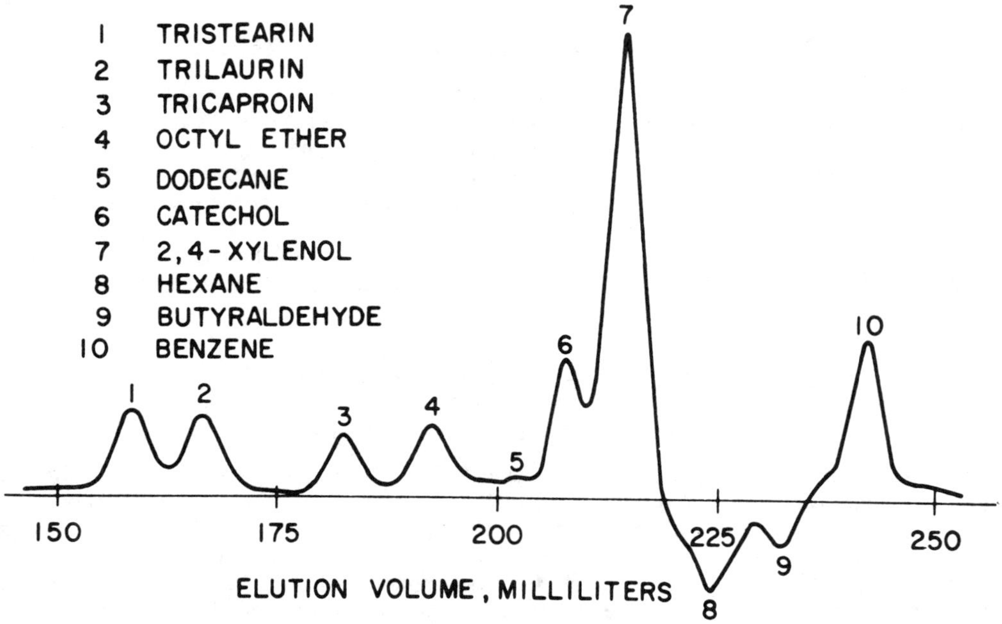

Figure 28. Molecular size separation of ten-component mixture, 78-891 molecular weight, on the Waters ALC-100 instrument with a differential refractometer detector; eight 3 ft Poragel A columns: 3-A1, 3-A3, 2-A25; 10 mg sample; tetrahydrofuran solvent at 1 ml/minute. Reproduced with permission from Waters Associates Inc. [After (*37*)].

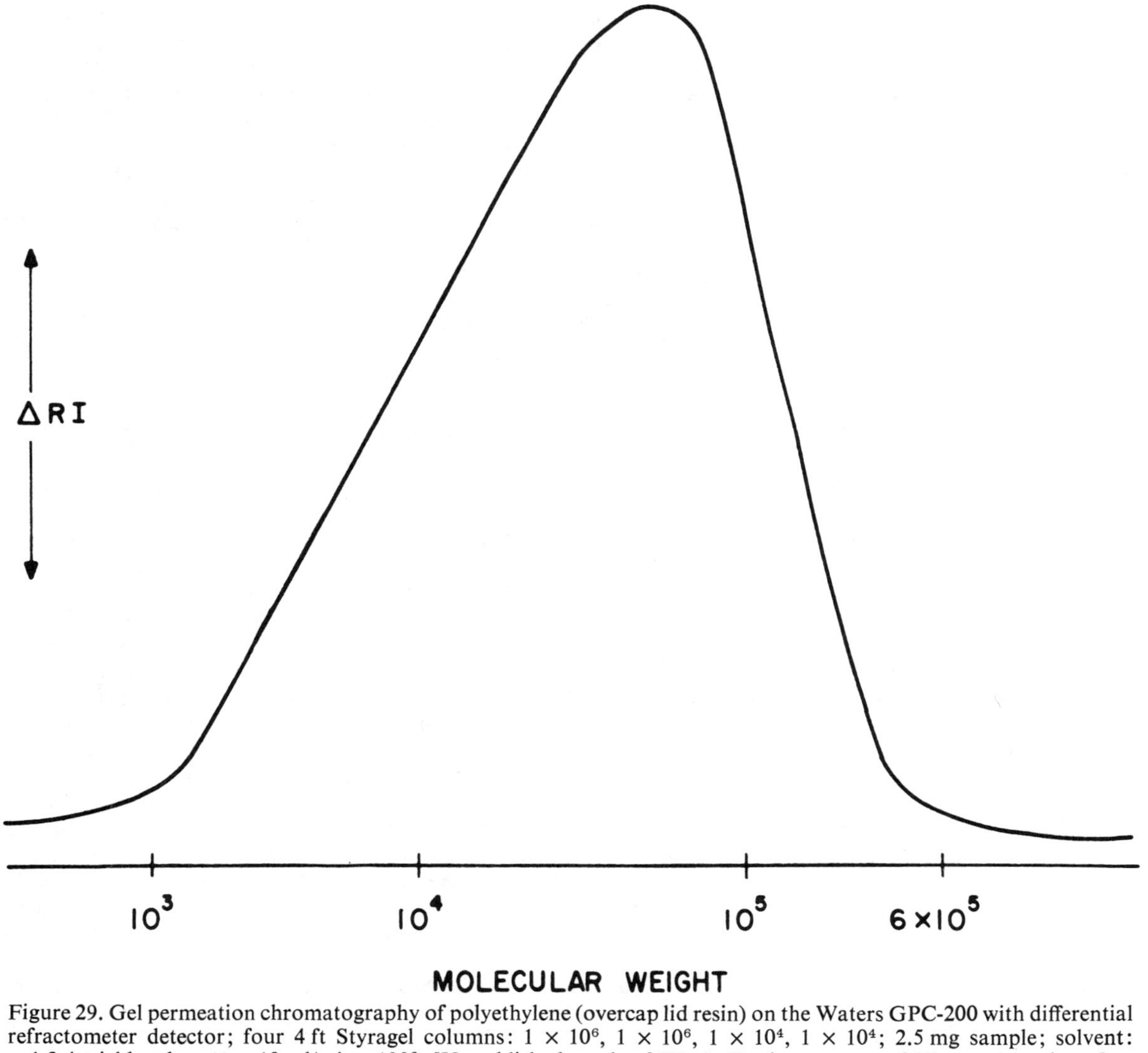

Figure 29. Gel permeation chromatography of polyethylene (overcap lid resin) on the Waters GPC-200 with differential refractometer detector; four 4 ft Styragel columns: 1×10^6, 1×10^6, 1×10^4, 1×10^4; 2.5 mg sample; solvent: 1,2,4-trichlorobenzene, 10 ml/min., 130°. [Unpublished work of W. A. Dark, courtesy of Waters Associates.]

D. ION EXCHANGE COLUMN CHROMATOGRAPHY (IXCC)

In ion-exchange chromatography, the column is packed with an insoluble solid phase containing ionic groups which can reversibly exchange either cations or anions with a solution. A mixture of ions is sorbed on top of the column and is developed with an appropriate ionic wash liquid. The ions in the mixture, which are attracted to the stationary phase by electrostatic forces, are displaced by the developer and move down the column at different rates depending upon their relative affinities for the resin. Those most attracted to the resin will move the slowest and those least attracted the fastest.

An example of a simple ion-exchange procedure is the separation of the halides Cl^-, Br^- and I^-. The mixture, dissolved in a few ml of water, is poured onto a nitrate-form anion-exchange column and the following equilibria are established:

$$Cl^- + R^+\text{–}NO_3^- \rightleftharpoons R^+\text{–}Cl^- + NO_3^-$$
$$Br^- + R^+\text{–}NO_3^- \rightleftharpoons R^+\text{–}Br^- + NO_3^-$$
$$I^- + R^+\text{–}NO_3^- \rightleftharpoons R^+\text{–}I^- + NO_3^-$$

(R represents the non-mobile resin matrix)

The arrow lengths indicate that the resin binds iodide most strongly and chloride least strongly. The flowing nitrate eluant carries only free ions and not those combined with the resin. Each halide as it moves down the column will be sorbed by the reactions to the right but desorbed by the reverse reactions. Since the reaction for chloride lies mostly to the left, the chloride ions will be bound the least and will be eluted first; iodide ions will spend relatively the most time on the resin and will be eluted last. (See Figure 34.)

The differential attraction of the three ions to the resin is due to the *selectivity* (see below) of the resin. Very small differences in selectivity can be exploited by employing column procedures to yield many valuable analytical separations.

1. *Ion-Exchange Materials*

a. *Ion-Exchange resins* (see Section II.III, Table 5). By far the ion-exchange resins most used are those prepared by chemically adding functional groups to spherical beads of styrene which have been copolymerized with divinylbenzene. Reaction of the copolymer beads with a sulfonating agent (H_2SO_4) yields a resin with an average of about one —SO_3H group per benzene ring, primarily in the para position. This product functions as a strongly acidic cation-exchange resin. Strong-base anion-exchange resins (Type I) are quaternary ammonium derivatives of cross-linked styrene. These are synthesized by chloromethylation and then amination of the styrene copolymer. The size of the beads is controlled by the rate of agitation during the preparation by suspension polymerization and the degree of cross-linking by the percentage of divinylbenzene mixed with the styrene. Figure 30(a,b) shows the chemical structures and preparation methods of these polystyrene-based resins. If amination is carried out with dimethylethanolamine instead of trimethylamine, a strong-base resin (Type II) with the functional group

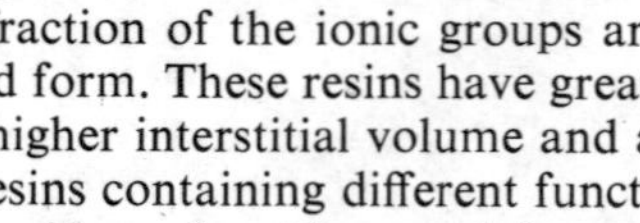

will result. Type II resins are less basic than Type I resins and are recommended when a strong base resin in the hydroxide form is required (i.e., the Type II resins have greater affinity for hydroxide ion).

These ion-exchange resins behave like tiny beaded, porous sponges which shrink or swell when placed in various aqueous solutions. Exchange between ions associated with the resin and other ions occurs mostly inside the beads since only a small fraction of the ionic groups are on the bead surface. Some resins are produced in granular rather than bead form. These resins have greater surface areas and pack less regularly, the latter leading to columns with a higher interstitial volume and a lower pressure drop.

Other cross-linked polystyrene resins containing different functional groups, and resins with a different type of copolymer matrix and strong acid, weak acid or weak base groups have also been made (see Section II.III, Table 5). Two of these are shown in Figure 30(c,d). Also available are electron-exchange resins (vinylhydroquinone-divinylbenzene copolymers), chelating resins [cross-linked polystyrene containing iminodiacetate, —$CH_2N(CH_2$—$COOH)_2$, groups], and snake-cage, ion-retardation resins [$RCH_2N^+(CH_3)_3$—$OOCR'$, see Section 5c].

Strong acid and strong base resins are most useful because they are, for practical purposes, completely ionized in aqueous media at all pH values, and they undergo a wide variety of exchange reactions which are generally rapid. The chemistry of weak acid and base resins is analogous to that of acetic acid and ammonia, respectively, leading to significant differences in behavior between strong and weak exchangers. For example, strong exchangers will split neutral salts (e.g., $R\text{—}SO_3^-H^+ + NaCl \rightleftharpoons R\text{—}SO_3^-Na^+ + HCl$) while weak exchangers will not. Strong base resins react with weak acids of silica and carbon dioxide while weak resins will not react with weak acids or bases. The alkali metal salt forms of weak acid resins and the acid forms of weak base resins (e.g., $R\text{—}NH_2 + HCl \rightleftharpoons R\text{—}NH_3Cl$) are readily hydrolyzed when washed with water and liberate free bases and acids respectively. The conversion of a weak resin to a salt form is accompanied

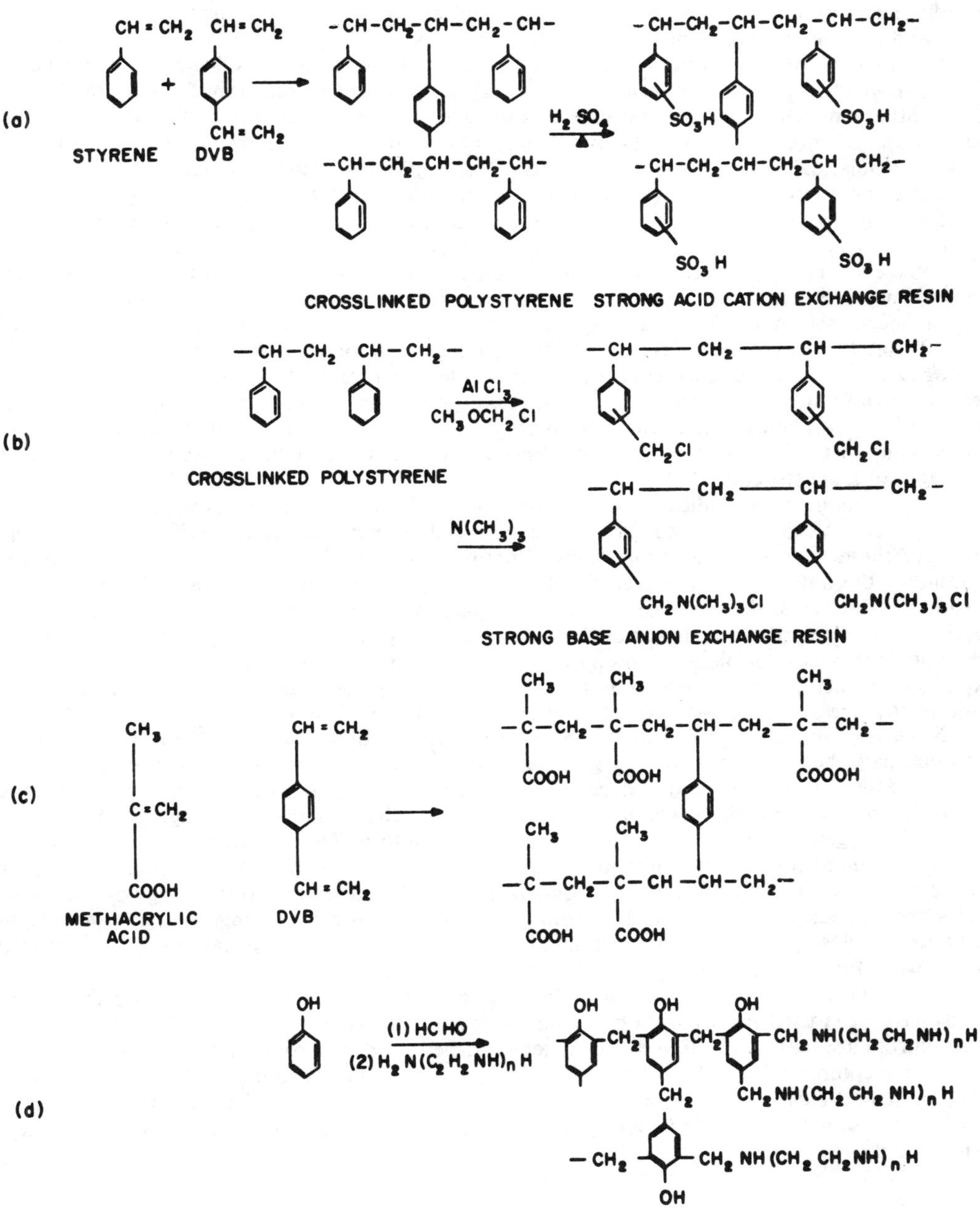

Figure 30. Examples of the preparation and structures of various exchange resins: (a) strong acid polystyrene cation exchange resin (e.g., Dowex® 50); (b) strong base polystyrene anion exchange resin (Dowex® 1); (c) weak acid crosslinked polymethacrylic acid resin (Amberlite® IRC-50); and (d) weak base phenol-formaldehyde condensation resin (Duolite A-7).

by considerable swelling not found with strong resins because the salt form is more ionic than the weakly ionized free-acid or free-base form and therefore the degree of hydration is greater.

Different polymerization techniques have led to the production of polystyrene copolymer resins with a rigid macroporous (or macroreticular) structure superimposed on the gel structure present in conventional gel resins. These macroreticular resins will therefore exchange with large molecules in nonaqueous media wherein gel resins will not swell and therefore will have negligible porosity. In aqueous solutions, gel resins with a relatively low degree of cross-linking will show a higher degree of porosity but low physical strength. Amberlyst resins (Rohm and Haas Co.) are macroreticular resins designed for use in nonaqueous or partly aqueous media, while Amberlite macroreticular resins are designed for improved stability in aqueous solutions (*38*).

Weak acid polymethacrylic acid resins (e.g., Amberlite® IRC-50, Figure 30c) are synthesized by a completely different method than the resins just described, yet these exhibit a high capacity for some large molecules and are therefore classified as macroporous resins (*39*).

b. *Inorganic exchangers.* Among the earliest exchangers were aluminosilicates such as leucite ($K_2O \cdot Al_2O_3 \cdot 4SiO_2$) which can reversibly and stoichiometrically exchange potassium for sodium, calcium, ammonium or other ions. Other inorganic exchangers include zinc or dipotassium cobalt hexacyanoferrate(II); hydrous oxides of zirconium, tin, thorium, etc.; phosphates, molybdates, tungstates and vanadates of tervalent metals; salts of heteropoly acids (e.g., ammonium phosphomolybdates); and some sulfides. Most of these materials are cation exchangers, although zirconium oxide can exchange either cations or anions depending upon the pH of operation (in acid solution it carries a plus charge and can exchange anions).

Inorganic exchangers are precipitated from aqueous solution in the form of granular, microcrystalline aggregates. They are useful for separations of some metal cations (usually of group I and II) for which they exhibit special selectivity. They cannot be used at extremes of pH, have low capacities, and are in most cases too soluble to be as valuable as polymer resins for general ion-exchange work.

c. *Cellulose exchangers.* Since almost all of the molecules present in living systems are ionic in nature, biochemists have found ion exchangers to be especially useful for the separation of such compounds. Conventional and macroreticular gel resins have proved unsuitable as media for the separation of the many large ions which are of biochemical interest. Exchangers based on cellulose, however, do not have the disadvantages of a gel structure.

Table 6 (Section II.III) indicates some types of cellulose ion exchangers which have been prepared by attaching fixed ionic groups to the hydroxyl groups of cellulose by oxidation, esterification, ether formation, etc. Some of these materials are prepared by Whatman in three forms: fibrous, improved fibrous, and microgranular, the latter being preferred for analytical separations. Because the exchange groups are on the outsides of the fibers, they are accessible to very large ions. The nominal capacities of these materials for small molecules are relatively low, but the realized capacity for large biopolymers is in many cases very high. Further, the release of biopolymers by these exchange materials is very fast.

Applications include the extraction and purification of enzymes, high resolution separations of nucleosides and nucleotides, the analysis and preparation of γ-globulins from serum, etc.

d. *Sephadex ion exchangers.* Table 4 (Section II.III) lists Sephadex gel filtration materials in which ionic groups have been attached to the glucose units of the cross-linked polydextran matrix. They are available as beads which have good hydrodynamic properties and possess a certain pore size characteristic of gel filtration media. Sephadex exchangers are more porous than cellulose exchangers so that biopolymers can penetrate the gel as opposed to surface binding on cellulose. This means that somewhat higher ionic strengths are required for elutions compared to cellulose. This is an advantage for proteins which are more labile at low ionic strengths but will cause problems if the salt eluants lead to shrinkage of the pores so that molecules are trapped inside the gel. The nominal capacity of these exchangers is generally higher than ion-exchange celluloses, and they exhibit minimal nonionic interaction. Applications have been in the field of biochemistry, for example the chromatography of tissue nucleotides.

e. *Liquid ion exchangers.* Water insoluble liquid materials which resemble ion-exchange resins in properties have been used for separations by liquid-liquid extraction or reversed phase column, paper and thin-layer chromatography. The liquid exchanger is sorbed onto a porous support (a paper sheet, a silica thin layer, or a column of cellulose or an adsorbent), and an aqueous solution of an inorganic compound (usually a mineral acid) is used as the mobile phase. Examples are long-chain amines (tri-*n*-octylamine), quaternary ammonium compounds (Aliquat 336) and alkyl acid phosphates [di-(2-ethylhexyl)orthophosphoric acid].

2. *Resin Properties*

a. *Particle size and shape.* The particle size of the resin affects the flow rate (slower for finer particles at a given pressure), the rate of equilibrium (faster for finer particles), and therefore the shape of the chromatogram (sharper and more narrow for finer particles). The range and distribution of the particle sizes also affects the interstitial (void) volume and the wet capacity of the resin. Resins are commercially available in various mesh-size ranges depending upon the particular application. Products of 50–100, 100–200 and 200–400 mesh are generally used for analytical separations and coarser products (10–40 mesh) for industrial applications. For very difficult separations, small, uniform particles are required.

Most commercial resins are now manufactured in the form of spheres by suspension polymerization. Phenol-formaldehyde condensation resins are produced as granules by a process that yields resins with a high degree of porosity. Columns of granular resins pack less regularly and therefore have a greater void volume and pressure drop than columns of spherical resins with the same particle size distribution.

b. *Cross-linking.* Resins are three dimensional polymer networks tied together by the cross-linking agent. The weight percentage of divinylbenzene (ca. 1–16%) used in the preparation of polystyrene-based resins determines the cross-linking and many of the properties of the resin. A high degree of cross-linking lowers diffusion rates inside the beads and increases the time necessary for equilibrium to be reached. Lightly cross-linked resins imbibe much water and are therefore gelatinous, have a lower capacity per volume (i.e., the "wet capacity" is lower and the "dry capacity" is higher), allow larger ions to enter the resin, and are less selective. Resins with 4–8% DVB are generally used for analytical work. The density of ionic groups in a resin with 8% cross-linking is such that the insides of the beads have the properties of a solution 6–8 molar in the counter ion.

c. *Swelling.* When a dry resin bead is placed in water or a dilute aqueous solution of an electrolyte, the resin will swell primarily due to hydration of the fixed ionic groups. The degree of swelling is an equilibrium quantity which is a function of the kind and concentration of the external solution; the degree of cross-linking, the capacity, and the ionic form of the resin; and the temperature and humidity. For a given resin, maximum swelling occurs when the resin is placed in pure water, and shrinking will occur if the resin is transferred to a concentrated salt solution. Resins with low cross-linking show the greatest volume change when the surrounding solution is changed. Volume changes accompanying an exchange of ions reflect their degree of hydration and the selectivity of the resin for the ion. For a sulfonic acid cation-exchange resin, the volume order for alkali metal forms of the resin is $Li^+ > Na^+ > K^+$ and for alkaline-earth forms $Mg^{+2} > Ca^{+2} > Ba^{+2}$. These orders of swelling are the same as the orders of ionic hydration and inverse to the order of selectivity [i.e., among the alkali metals, Li^+ is the most hydrated (largest) ion and has the least attraction for the resin]. Carboxylic resins swell greatly on conversion from the acid form to the sodium form. The selectivity orders of carboxylic resins are not simply the reverse of the hydration orders.

d. *Donnan equilibrium.* If a sulfonic acid resin is transferred from pure water to a dilute salt solution of a nonexchange ion (e.g., a sodium form resin is put into a solution of NaCl), the resin would shrink because of osmotic forces and there would be only a *slight* penetration of ions into the resin bead according to the Donnan equilibrium equation

$$[(a_{Na^+})(a_{Cl^-})]_{resin} = [(a_{Na^+})(a_{Cl^-})]_{solution} \qquad [33]$$

where a = activity. Because the activity of sodium ions inside the resin is very high relative to that outside, there is no driving force for the sodium ions to enter the resin phase; since the sodium-ion concentration in the resin is so high, the chloride-ion concentration must be low [recall that for electroneutrality, $(Na^+)_r = (—SO_3^-)_r + (Cl^-)_r$]. As the concentration of the external solution increases the Donnan penetration increases, the rate of increase being greater for resins with lower cross-linking.

The Donnan equilibrium concept explains the exclusion of dilute electrolytes by resins in a non-exchange form which is the basis for the separation of electrolytes from nonelectrolytes by the process of ion exclusion (see Section 5c).

e. *Capacity.* The capacity of a resin is a measure of the amount of exchangeable ion (milliequivalents) per dry gram or per unit volume of swelled resin. On a dry basis, the capacity of hydrogen form sulfonic acid cation-exchange resin is about 5 meq/g and the capacity of the chloride form quaternary ammonium anion-exchange resin is 3–3.5 meq/g.

f. *Equilibria and selectivity.* A fundamental property of ion-exchange reactions is that exchange occurs in equivalent quantities. Thus, if a solution of sodium ions is passed into a resin bed in the hydrogen form, the number of equivalents of sodium taken up by the resin exactly equals the number of equivalents of hydrogen released to the solution. The amount of sodium (or any other salt) added to the bed can be measured indirectly by washing the released hydrogen ions from the column with distilled water and titrating the effluent with standard base. The determination of salt content of a solution in this way is one important non-chromatographic application of ion exchange.

Ion-exchange reactions are reversible so that the law of mass action can be applied. For the reaction

$$R^-—H^+ + Na^+ \rightleftarrows R^-—Na^+ + H^+$$

(where R = the resin matrix plus the nondiffusible ionic functional group),

$$K_H^{Na} = \frac{[RNa]\gamma_{RNa}[H^+]\gamma_{H^+}}{[RH]\gamma_{RH}[Na^+]\gamma_{Na^+}}. \qquad [34]$$

This equilibrium constant is a true, thermodynamic constant which is virtually impossible to evaluate because the activity coefficients (γ) inside the resin phase are unknown. In addition

$$K_H^{Na} = \frac{[RNa][H^+]}{[RH][Na^+]} \cdot \frac{\gamma_{RNa}\gamma_{H^+}}{\gamma_{RH}\gamma_{Na^+}} \qquad [35]$$

$$= E_H^{Na} \cdot \frac{\gamma_{RNa}\gamma_{H^+}}{\gamma_{RH}\gamma_{Na^+}} \qquad [36]$$

where E (sometimes termed K, K_c, K_d or Q) is the selectivity coefficient or selectivity quotient.

E values vary with the composition of the resin phase (so as to favor the sorption of the ion which is in the minority in the resin), and with the concentration of the solution if the exchanging ions are of unequal charge (concentrated solutions favor the exchange of univalent ions for polyvalent ions). Equation [36] shows that the E value varies primarily with the ratio of activity coefficients for the ions in the resin phase (assuming the ratio in the dilute solution phase is about 1). Resins with lower cross-linking are more "dilute" (more water is absorbed), the ratio of activity coefficients approaches one, and therefore such resins are less specific than resins with a higher degree of cross-linking.

Even though E values are variable, some generalities and selectivity orders can be stated:

1. For sulfonic acid polystyrene cation-exchange resins, cations with a higher charge are most strongly bound (e.g., $Th^{+4} > Ce^{+3} > Ca^{+2} > Na^{+1}$). If the charges are the same, the ion with the smallest radius is most tightly bound:

(*+1 ions*) Li (least bound) < H < Na < NH_4^+ < K< Rb < Cs < Cu < Ag < Tl.

(*+2 ions*) Be < Mn = Fe < Mg = Zn < Co < Cu < Cd < Ni < Ca < Sr < Hg < Pb < Ba < Ra.

(*rare earths and actinides*) selectivity coefficients decrease as the atomic number increases.

2. With weak acid resins, the order may be different. For example K^+ is less strongly held than Na^+ by carboxylic acid cation exchangers, and H^+ is very strongly bound by these resins.

3. The differences in selectivities are greater for anions than for cations. For type I polystyrene strong base anion-exchange resins, the order is OH^- (least sorbed) < F^- < acetate < formate < iodate < HCO_3^- < Cl^- < nitrate < bromate < Br^- < NO_3^- < chlorate < HSO_4^- < phenoxide < I^- < citrate < salicylate < benzenesulfonate. As with cation resins, there is a general increase in affinity with increasing valence and atomic number.

Ions containing aromatic rings (e.g., benzenesulfonate anion and benzylammonium cation) are strongly held by polystyrene resins because of adsorption on the resin matrix in addition to normal electrostatic forces. Many other cases of anomalous sorption have been reported wherein complex anions are strongly bound to cation exchangers in concentrated electrolytic mobile phases. Examples are the strong adsorption of anionic complexes of thallium (TlX_4^-) on Dowex 50-X8 in 5 *M* $NaClO_4$ and of palladiazo (a structural isomer of arsenazo III reagent: $[H_4L]^{-4}$ and $[H_5L]^{-3}$) on Dowex® 50W resin in 9–12 *M* $NaClO_4$, pH 6.5. Kraus and coworkers have found that some negatively charged inorganic complexes are quantitatively sorbed on cation-exchange resins in concentrated neutral saline media, while cationic species are unsorbed under these conditions. Nonionic molecules are sometimes sorbed by resin matrices (see section 5b).

When differences in their relative affinities are sufficiently great, ions may be separated by elution chromatography on a column of resin originally combined with the eluting ion. The eluting ion usually, but not always, has a smaller E value than any ion of the mixture. Thus, sodium and cesium are separated in this order on a column of hydrogen-form sulfonic acid resin by elution with 0.7 *M* HCl. Another example is the separation of halides on nitrate-form quaternary ammonium resin with 0.5 *M* $NaNO_3$, described in the introduction to this section D. If selectivity differences are not sufficiently great, eluants containing complexing or chelating agents and organic solvents can be used to enhance separation (alter distribution coefficients) by superimposing selective complexation and solvent extraction effects upon normal ion exchange. One example is the separation of the alkaline earth metals on a sulfonic acid resin by elution with citrate or lactate buffers (see Section 3c).

If a mixture is eluted with an ion having a stronger affinity for the resin than the ions in the sample, the process becomes displacement, rather than elution, chromatography. Development of a mixture of sodium and potassium ions on a hydrogen-form resin with cesium ion as the eluant yields overlapping zones in the order H^+, Na^+, K^+, Cs^+. This procedure is useful for preparative work rather than for analytical separations.

g. *Theories of selectivity*. It is beyond the scope of this treatise to describe the many theories proposed to explain and thermodynamically interpret the relative selectivities of ions for resins. Donnan equilibria between the beads and the solution have been considered, in addition to ion-pair formation, ion-sieve effects, swelling effects, activity coefficients, solubilization and salting-out effects, and the influence of non-exchange ions, neutral molecules, and water upon the exchanging ion.

h. *Kinetics*. The ion-exchange process involves: diffusion of the exchanging ions through the liquid layer around the resin bead, diffusion within the bead, the exchange reaction, diffusion of the displaced ion through the bead and finally through the liquid film. Diffusion into and out of the exchanger is not necessarily of equal speed. It is generally conceded that the actual ion-exchange reaction is usually fast and does not control the kinetics. For typical chromatographic systems with high (> ca. 0.1 *M*) external solution concentration, the slow step is particle diffusion; in very dilute solutions, film diffusion is the slow step for small ions. In either case, equilibrium is speeded up by the use of small beads, resins with low cross-linking, and a high temperature. Small, single-valent ions have the fastest exchange rates. Singly-charged ions also have higher diffusion coefficients than doubly-charged ions in the resin. Exchange rates are fastest in water systems and become slower with less polar solvents.

Weak resins are not completely ionized or fully swollen, and diffusion in them is slow. Conversion of these resins to a salt form is slow, but conversion from one salt form to another is as fast as with strong resins.

i. *Resin stability*. In salt forms, sulfonic acid resins are stable up to about 120°–200°, but in the hydrogen form, they lose sulfuric acid when heated with water above about 100°–150°. Quaternary amine resins are stable up to about 100° in most salt forms but only to about 30°–60° when in the hydroxide form. Tertiary amine resins are stable up to about 100° in the hydroxide form. Operation above these limits for a brief period may not cause appreciable decomposition. Exposure of resins to strong oxidizing agents (Cl_2, H_2O_2, HNO_3, chromic-nitric acid mixtures, dissolved oxygen plus a metal catalyst) causes degradation of the polymer matrix. Continued exposure of resins to solutions of high and low concentration can cause cracking and breakage due to osmotic shock. Most resins have sufficient physical stability to resist attrition losses in normal analytical column operation, although unusual conditions (e.g., deep, small-diameter beds; very high flow rates; frequent agitation or pumping) can cause breakage.

3. *Theory of Ion-Exchange*

The concept of the theoretical plate was introduced in the section on GC. The size of a theoretical plate is calculated from the experimental chromatogram, and, although true equilibrium is never achieved, the narrower the plate the closer the approach to equilibrium is assumed to be.

To increase the number of plates (N), the particle size and flow rate should be decreased and the length of the column increased. As stated above, however, resolution between zones increases only as the $\sqrt{N}$. Plate thicknesses are typically 100 times the average radius of the resin particles, and flow rates are 0.2–2.5 ml/cm²/min.

The distribution ration or coefficient (usually designated D or C) is equivalent to the partition coefficient (K) defined above for GC:

$$D = \frac{\text{amount of ion in the resin of any plate}}{\text{amount of ion in the free solution of any plate}}. \qquad [37]$$

The volume distribution coefficient (D_v) is the amount of ion in 1 ml of resin bed divided by the amount in 1 ml of interstitial solution at equilibrium. The weight distribution coefficient (D_w) states the ratio in terms of grams of dry resin and mls of solution. Many authors use D for D_w as defined here. $D_v = dD_w$, where d is the density of the resin bed. The solute need not necessarily be an ion. One relationship between the elution volume of the peak and D is

$$D = \frac{V_R - V_M}{V_M} \qquad [38]$$

where V_R is the volume needed to elute the peak of the zone and V_M is the void or interstitial volume, the volume of solution between the resin particles (see Figure 6) equation [38] is identical to [24], so that the distribution coefficient as defined here is an expression of retention measured in column void volumes, and is identical to the capacity ratio K' as defined in equation [24]. An alternate equation for the volume distribution coefficient D_v is

$$D_v = V_{max} - i \qquad [39]$$

where V_{max} is the number of column volumes of effluent at the elution maximum and i is the fractional interstitial volume (usually about 0.40) (*40*). D_v as defined in equation [39] and D as defined in [38] are related as follows:

$$D_v = \frac{DV_M}{\text{total column volume}} = Di.$$

D values can also be calculated (*41*) from elution data using the expression

$$D = \frac{V_R - V_M}{m} \qquad [40]$$

where m is the mass of the resin in grams.

Rieman and coworkers have modified and simplified the plate theory of Martin and Synge, and Mayer and Tompkins, to provide a practical guide for changing operational conditions in order to obtain improved separations by ion-exchange. This treatment assumes that equilibrium between the resin and solution exists in each plate during the elution (in fact, true equilibrium is never reached) and that the concentration of the sample ion in the interstitial volume and on the resin is negligible compared to the eluant ion concentration.

a. *Effect of eluant concentration.* It has been derived from equation [37] that for a simple ion-exchange system governed by the following equilibrium

$$zREL + B^{\pm z} \rightleftarrows R_zB + zEL^{\pm}$$

where R represents the resin matrix, EL a univalent eluant ion, and $B^{\pm z}$ a sample ion which does not complex with the eluant or combine with H^+,

$$D = \frac{WQE}{V_M[EL^{\pm}]^z} \qquad [41]$$

where W is the weight of resin in a plate, Q is the exchange capacity of the resin in meq/g, and E is the selectivity coefficient (Section 2f).

Combination of equations [41] and [38] yields

$$V_R = \frac{WQE}{[EL^{\pm}]^z} + V_M. \quad [42]$$

This equation allows one to calculate the effect of a change in eluant concentration on the position of elution peaks, since for a given ion on a given column

$$(V_R)_{C_1} = (V_R)_{C_2}\left(\frac{[EL^{\pm}]_2}{[EL^{\pm}]_1}\right)^z \quad [43]$$

where c_1 and c_2 are two different eluant concentrations. The fact that the eluant concentrations are raised to the power numerically equal to the valence of the sample ion means that changing the concentration of the eluant is effective for improving the resolution of ions with different valences. If the ion of higher valence follows but overlaps the ion of lower valence, the eluant concentration should be decreased to increase the relative displacement of the higher-valent ion and improve the separation.

b. *Effect of eluant pH.* Equations [41] and [42] may be modified to yield an expression for the elution volume of a weak monoprotic acid or its anion

$$V_R = \left(\frac{WQE}{[EL^{\pm}]^z}\right)\left(\frac{K}{K + [H^+]}\right) + V_M \quad [44]$$

where K is the ionization constant of the acid. For a diprotic acid

$$V_R = \left(\frac{WQ}{V_M}\right)\frac{(E_1K_1[H^+]/[EL^{\pm}]) + (E_2K_1K_2/[EL^{\pm}]^2)}{[H^+]^2 + K_2[H^+] + K_1K_2} \quad [45]$$

where K_1 and K_2 are the dissociation constants for the two ionization steps and E_1 and E_2 the respective selectivity coefficients.

Separations of acids with different K values can be improved by adjusting the pH of the eluant. Decreasing the $[H^+]$ increases the ionization and the values of D and V_R for an acid, causing it to be eluted later. Acids with different K values are displaced selectively. The elution of strong acids is independent of pH. Certain organic acids (e.g., alkyl esters of phosphoric acids) are adsorbed to the resin by Van der Waals' forces even in the unionized state and their elution may not follow the above equations.

Buffered eluants are used to control the pH during the elution of acid mixtures. So that the buffer ion does not displace the counter ions from the resin, it should have a low affinity for the resin and its concentration should be kept as low as possible consistent with adequately controlling the pH.

c. *Effect of complexing agents in the eluant.* The separation of Ca^{++} and Sr^{++} by elution with 1.2 M ammonium chloride through a column of ammonium-form cation-exchange resin is not complete because the selectivities of these ions for the resin are quite similar. Elution with 1.2 M ammonium lactate, however, provides a good separation. Both metal ions are complexed by lactate, but the smaller calcium ions form the more stable +1 complex and so are less sorbed and eluted before the Sr^{++}.

Kraus and coworkers have developed methods for separating metals on chloride-form anion-exchange resins in chloride media. Chloride complexes and oxyanions formed by the metals are sorbed on the anion-exchange resins to varying degrees, depending on the chloride ion concentration (Figure 35). The volume distribution coefficient for metals in such a system is given by

$$D_v = \frac{DV_M}{V_b} = \frac{V_R - V_M}{V_b} \quad [46]$$

where V_b is the bed volume. In the absence of chloride, the metals are not complexed and have no affinity (D_v or $D = 0$) for the anion exchanger.

d. *Effect of column length.* Rieman and coworkers have derived a Gaussian elution equation which in most cases allows the simple calculation of the ideal length of a column for a given "quantitative separation" (0.05% cross contamination):

$$\sqrt{H} = \frac{3.29}{D_2 - D_1}\left(\frac{D_2 + 0.5}{\sqrt{P_2}} + \frac{D_1 + 0.5}{\sqrt{P_1}}\right) \quad [47]$$

where H is the column length, P is the number of plates per cm of column, and the subscripts refer to the components to be separated. The total plate number for each peak (N) in a given column is calculated from

$$N = \left[\frac{2D}{(D + 1)}\right]\left[\frac{V_R}{V_a - V_R}\right]^2 \quad [48]$$

where V_a is the average of the volumes at $C = C_{max}/e$ (Figure 31). A separate elution of each ion through the column yields the data required to calculate N, P and H.

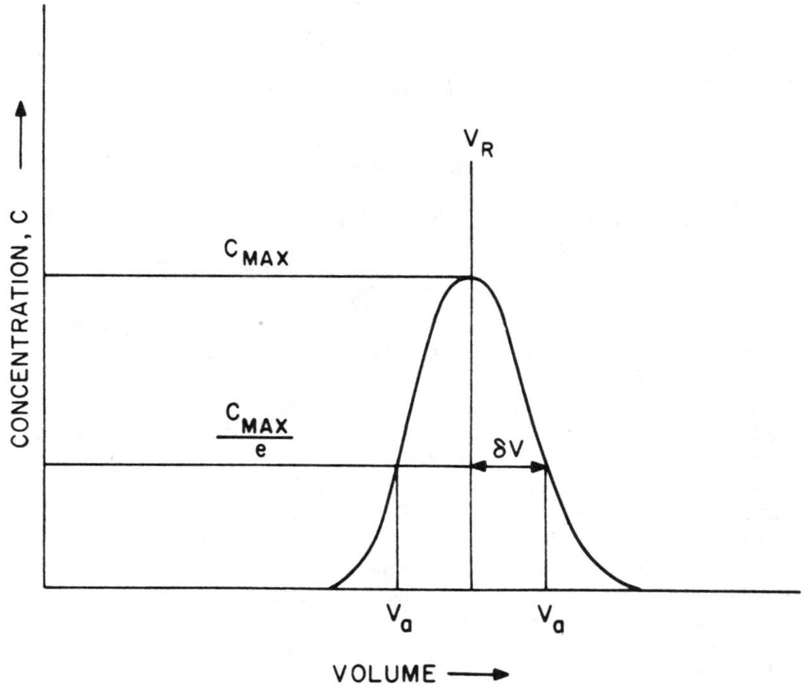

Figure 31. Ideal ion-exchange elution curve; e = the base of natural logarithms. The width of the band is defined here as the width for which $C = C_{max}/e$. Other ways of defining width are equally valid, e.g., the base of the equilateral triangle formed by the steepest tangents.

e. *Calculations of V_R with stepwise changes in the eluant.* The following equations may be used to calculate the elution volumes of peaks after stepwise eluant changes; if the distribution ratios of the solutes in a mixture are known from prior experiments for each concentration of eluant, an optimized separation can be easily designed. For a given solute in two eluants:

$$V_R = V_1 + V_M + D_2\left[V_M + \left(\frac{V_1}{D_1}\right)\right] \qquad [49]$$

where V_1 is the volume of eluant 1 used and D_1 and D_2 are the distribution ratios of the solute in the two eluants. For $n + 1$ eluants (n changes):

$$V_R = \Sigma_1^n V_1 + V_M + D_{n+1}\left[V_M + \Sigma_1^n\left(\frac{V_n}{D_n}\right)\right]. \qquad [50]$$

f. *The ideal elution curve.* Figure 31 shows the Gaussian shape of an ideal elution band. The width of the band (δ_v) is a function of the number of plates (N) according to the equation

$$\delta_v = V_R\sqrt{\left(\frac{2}{N}\right)}. \qquad [51]$$

The maximum concentration of the band is also related to N:

$$C_{max} = \frac{m}{V_R}\sqrt{\left(\frac{N}{2\pi}\right)} \qquad [52]$$

where m is the total mass of solute in the band.

4. *Experimental Procedures and Equipment*

a. *Columns.* Resin beds for analytical separations are usually about 15–20 cm long (or longer for more difficult separations) and 1 cm in diameter. A tube similar to that shown in Figure 22a can be used to hold the bed although backwashing during packing is facilitated if a bulb or other reservoir is at the top of the tube.

The conventional method of packing the column is to stir up the resin beads in an excess of the first eluant to be used, allow most of the resin to settle, and decant off the fines (the small particles). The stirring, settling and pouring-off are repeated once or twice. The remaining resin is slurried into the column and allowed to settle by gravity to form the packed bed. While the resin settles, the tube may be tapped gently with a small rubber mallet to expel air bubbles and improve the packing. Supernatant liquid is removed when necessary and additional slurry is added until the bed reaches the desired height. The column is then washed with several bed volumes of eluant (this is also done whenever a prepared column is not in use for 12 hours). The sample is added and washed into the resin after draining the supernate to the top level of the bed and adding a glass fiber or paper disk. The liquid level must never drop below the top of the bed or the column will have to be repacked or backwashed. A tube with outlet held above the top of the bed will prevent the bed from draining dry. Beds packed with small particles of resin exhibit capillary forces which prevent a water surface from sinking more than a few millimeters below the top of the bed.

Backwashing is accomplished by attaching a distilled water line to the bottom of the column and slowly introducing and increasing the upflow of water until the resin expands into the upper part of the tube. The water flow is maintained until all air pockets are removed and all particles are freely floating. The water flow is then stopped and the resin settles uniformly by gravity according to particle size: the larger beads will settle to the bottom and the smaller will be on the top. Some workers backwash every column after slurry packing in order to insure as regular a particle classification and eluant flow as possible. Backwashing must be performed if gas bubbles form in the bed. For difficult separations it may be necessary to screen the resin initially so that the entire column is of very uniform particle size.

With the conventional packing method described above, it is difficult to pack reproducible columns when the particle-size range of the resin is large, and it requires considerable time to pack columns of small resin particles ($< 20\ \mu$) which settle quite slowly. These problems are overcome by using two dynamic packing procedures recently described (*42*). In the first, a chamber or reservoir filled with a thick slurry (25–50 vol.% solids) of resin is connected to the chromatographic tube filled with clear liquid, and the slurry is displaced into the column with a liquid that is pumped into the top of the chamber with a linear velocity greater than the settling velocity of the largest particles. For packing small diameter columns of appreciable length or coiled columns, it is better to first pack a fixed bed into a reservoir of larger diameter and then extrude that bed into the smaller tube by displacing it with liquid.

b. *Choice and treatment of the resin.* Polystyrene strong acid and strong base resins, 4–8% divinylbenzene, 50–100 or 200–400 mesh, have been used for a vast majority of analytical applications. Other resins may be chosen for particular separations, e.g., carboxylic acid resins for separating organic bases, macroreticular resins for large molecules and/or nonaqueous solutions, and cellulose exchangers for large molecules of biochemical interest. Specially purified resins can be purchased from certain suppliers (e.g., Bio Rad, Inc.), or commercial-grade resins should be treated before use by repeated cycles of washing with 1–2 *N* HCl, 0.5–1.0 *N* NaOH and ethanol (with a water rinse following each) to remove metallic and organic impurities.

The ionic form of the resin should correspond to one ion of the eluant. For example, if the eluant is an aqueous solution of ammonium chloride, a cation exchanger would be used in the ammonium form or an anion exchanger in the chloride form. Resins are converted to a desired form by passing an appropriate salt, acid or base through the column until the effluent gives a negative test for the ion being replaced. For replacement of one univalent ion by another or a higher valent ion by one of lower valence on a strong acid or base resin, 1 *M* solutions are satisfactory. For replacement of a univalent ion by a polyvalent ion, 0.010 *M* solutions are better. Salt forms of weak acid or base resins are converted to the free acid or base form with 1 *M* HCl or 1 *M* NH_3. After the conversion is complete the bed is washed with distilled water to remove the excess conversion solution. If necessary, the resin is then extruded and repacked, or backwashed, before performing the separation.

If all the sample is eluted from the resin during the chromatographic run, the column can be used again for another sample without treatment. Any residue remaining on the column after the elution must be stripped off with an appropriate solution before the next addition of sample. If the ionic form of the resin is altered during the elution (e.g., the eluant contains more than one type of ion), it may be necessary to regenerate the column (convert it back to its original form) by passage of an appropriate solution.

c. *Column operation.* HETP increases with an increase in flow rate, since the ions are carried at a faster rate down the column and have less time to diffuse into the resin and reach all the exchange groups. Since peak widths (but not elution volumes) are proportional to HETP, good separations are favored by a slow flow of eluant. Flow rates commonly used in ion-exchange chromatography range from about 0.2–2.5 ml/cm²/min. Gravity flow or operation under the pressure of a column of liquid have traditionally been used in this field. In modern instruments with columns containing fine resin particles, eluants are forced through the column with a pump.

Elevated temperatures (which lower HETP) and temperature programming (which changes distribution ratios) are sometimes used, especially in conjunction with solvent programming (e.g., aqueous buffers with pH and ionic strength gradients) to improve the resolution of complex mixtures (see Figure 16). These methods require the use of much more complicated equipment than is required for separations at room temperature.

High efficiency column packings consisting of an impervious core with thin coatings of ion-exchange resin have recently been introduced. Kirkland has found that columns of his controlled surface porosity ion-exchange packings (now commercially available from Dupont as "Zipax" supports) exhibited 3.5 (cation) and 8 (anion) theoretical plates per second at the highest velocities tested compared to 0.1 to 0.5

theoretical plates per second for conventional gel resins. The high speed capabilities are due to improved mass transfer effects. Their hard, spherical nature permits operation at high column inlet pressures and carrier velocities (e.g., > 3 cm/sec) in narrow (2–3 mm I.D.) analytical columns loaded with small samples and connected to a continuous detector.

Figure 32 shows the flow diagram of the Technicon sequential multisample (TSM) amino acid analyzer. This is a dual column instrument capable of the totally automated, high speed separation and quantitative analysis of amino acids accurate to ca. ±3% at the 0.050 μmole level. The operation of this instrument

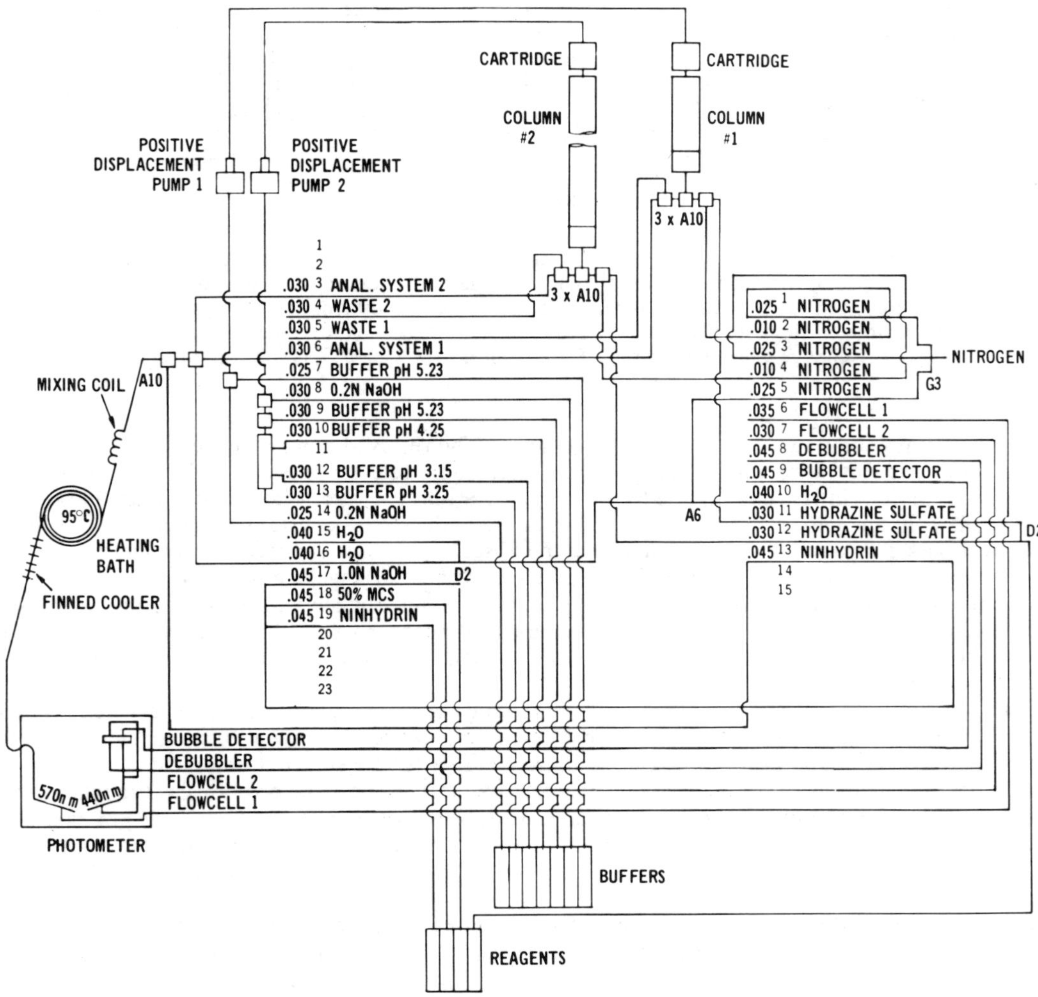

Figure 32. Complete flow diagram of the Technicon TSM Amino Acid Analyzer; the internal diameter of the pump tubes is given in inches. (Photograph courtesy of Harvey Adler, Technicon Corp., Tarrytown, N.Y.; reprinted from G. Ertingshausen and H. J. Adler, a New Accelerated Fully Automated System for Amino Acid Analysis by Ion-Exchange Chromatography, *J. Chromatogr.* **44**, 620–623 (1969) Figure 1.

has been described in two recent papers (*43, 44*); Figure 33 shows a one-hour protein hydrolysate chromatogram obtained with it. The resin used in the columns (220 mm × 5 mm I.D. for the acidic and neutral amino acid column and 40 mm × 4 mm for the basic column) is a specially hardened, spherical, sulfonated polystyrene resin with 8% divinylbenzene which does not pack after loading. Samples are preloaded into resin-filled cartridges, up to 40 of which can be fitted into a sequential sampling device. When the instrument is in operation, the samples are presented in turn to the columns and analyzed with no further handling.

Amino acid analyzers are also available from other companies [e.g., Beckman (Spinco Div.) and Phoenix Precision Instr. Co.]. In addition, Technicon offers automated systems for the ion-exchange separation of sugars and peptides. The operation of an amino acid analyzer is in general as follows: The sample is introduced at the top of the column, and buffer is supplied to the column at a selected rate from reservoirs by a metering pump. Before the buffer enters the pump, trapped air is eliminated with a deaerator to insure constant-volume delivery. The columns are enclosed in thermostated circulating water jackets, and temperature changes can be made automatically during a run. As the buffer and sample are pumped through a

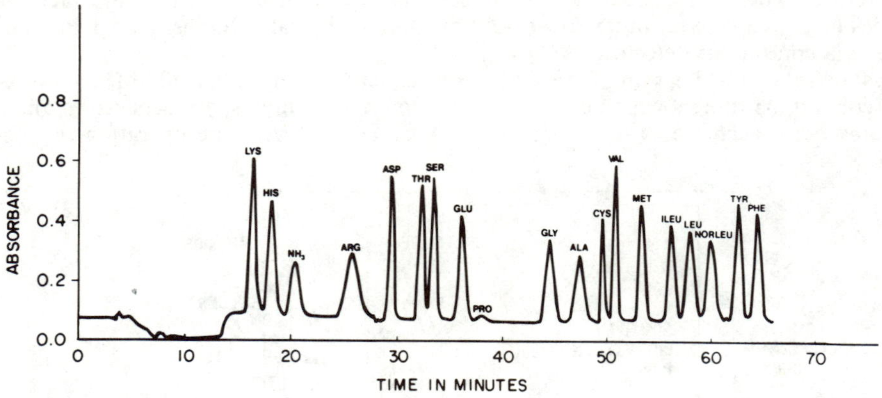

Figure 33. Chromatogram of an amino acid standard representing one complete automatic cycle of the Technicon TSM Analyzer. The sample contained 0.03 μmoles of each amino acid; the absorbance was read at 570 nm. (Reprinted from G. Ertingshausen and H. J. Adler, a New Accelerated Fully Automated System for Amino Acid Analysis by Ion-Exchange Chromatography, *J. Chromatogr.* **44**, 620–623, (1969) Figure 2.

column, the amino compounds in the mixture separate. The resolved compounds emerge from the bottom of the column and flow through capillary tubing to a column selector manifold. Here the column effluent is mixed with ninhydrin reagent supplied by a pump at a selected rate. The mixture then flows through a reaction coil contained in a reaction bath which is maintained at a constant temperature of 100 °C. The stream then passes through a photometer where the absorbance values at wavelengths 440 nm and 570 nm are measured for each reaction product. One or the other of these wavelengths is the absorption maximum of the ninhydrin reaction product for all amino acids. The absorbance values are monitored by sensitive photo-detectors which transmit the signals to a strip-chart recorder where the peaks are drawn. The instrument can be adjusted to automatically conclude an analysis, flush the lines, and put itself in stand-by condition for the next run.

Since all amino acids and many related compounds react with ninhydrin, a persistent problem in automatic ion-exchange chromatography of biological specimens is the identification of unknown peaks on the chromatogram. One procedure is to add standards of the suspected amino acids to the sample and then to repeat the analysis to see if the added standards appear in the same positions as the unknown peaks. Another is to use tracer amounts of marker amino acids labeled with carbon-14 to provide points of reference along the elution curve. The effluent stream is split before reaction with ninhydrin and one part diverted to a fraction collector. The labeled amino acids are detected in the fractions by liquid scintillation or gas flow systems.

In addition to the automated detection of compounds in the effluent by colorimetry, ion-exchange effluents can be continuously monitored by measuring refractive index, radioactivity, electrical conductivity, etc. Alternatively, fractions can be collected and subjected to analysis by chemical or physical means.

d. *Solvent* (*eluant*) *systems*. As mentioned above, simple salts, buffers or solutions of various inorganic or organic complexing agents can be used as eluants for various ion-exchange separations. Recently, eluants composed of aqueous-organic solvent mixtures have led to very selective separations of metal ions on both cation and anion exchangers. Typical solvents include an organic solvent such as methanol, ethanol, tetrahydrofuran or dioxane mixed with an aqueous solution of an inorganic complexing agent such as the acids HF, HCl or HNO_3; an organic agent such as tri-*n*-butylphosphine oxide or dithizone can also be added to the solvent.

Systems such as these are theoretically complex and the reasons for increased selectivities are not fully understood. Korkish has suggested that a bidimensional ion-exchange competition exists between a liquid exchanger in the outside phase and the solid resin phase, and he has termed methods using mixed solvents "combined ion-exchange-solvent extraction" (CIESE). Other factors which must be considered include changes in cation solvation (organic solvents in general make it easier to strip coordinated water from a metal cation to form a metal-chloride complex, so that many metals are strongly sorbed by anion-exchange resins that contain a much lower concentration of chloride than is required for their uptake from aqueous solution), altered electrostatic interaction between the fixed ionic groups and counter ions due to changes in the internal dielectric constant, and liquid-liquid partition effects due to the nonuniform distribution of solvent components between the resin and external phases.

The last factor explains why *D* values for metals increase in mixed solvents (except at very high organic constituent concentrations) for both cation and anion exchangers: the resin preferentially takes up the water from a mixed solvent so that the relative amount of water inside is greater than outside; since the resin phase is more aqueous, the inorganic complexing agent will prefer to go inside leading to increased complexing of the metal and higher D values. This type of partition effect, in addition to adsorption effects between the solutes and the resin, is also responsible for the separations of nonionic organic compounds by salting-out and solubilization chromatography illustrated in section 5b.

e. *Determination of distribution ratios.* Distribution ratios (D values) can be determined either by batch equilibration techniques or by elution of the compound through a column. In the former method, a weighed amount of resin is shaken with a known amount of a standard solution of the solute until equilibrium is reached (e.g., overnight). The phases are separated by filtration and either the solution phase, the resin phase or both are then analyzed, and, from the amounts of solute found in each, the distribution ratio is computed.

$$D_w = \frac{\text{amount of solute in resin phase}}{\text{amount of solute in solution phase}} \times \frac{\text{ml of solution}}{\text{g of dry resin}}. \quad [53]$$

For determination of D values on a column, the elution volume of the chromatographic peak is determined and equation [38], [39], or [40] is employed. If columns containing exactly one gram of resin are used, the interstitial volume (V_M) is relatively small (< 1 ml) and the volume at the elution peak can be taken as the D value (i.e., $m = 1$ in equation [40]). Any error involved in neglecting V_M will be small and of no concern when comparing D values, i.e., when calculating separation factors. (A separation factor is the ratio of D values for the substances of interest; the largest D value is put into the numerator so that a large factor indicates good separability.)

An advantage of the column method is that the elution peaks of the solutes will be available for calculating the column height necessary for any desired separation using equations [47] and [48].

A method for determining very high distribution ratios is the preloaded column technique used by Kraus and coworkers: a tracer of the element is uniformly adsorbed on a weighed amount of resin and a column is prepared from the loaded resin and eluted; D values are computed from the tracer concentration in the effluent and its known concentration on the preloaded bed.

f. *Determination of the interstitial or void volume* (V_M). The external volume surrounding the resin is determined by filling the interstices of the column with a solution, washing out that solution completely with water and determining the amount that was washed off. Care must be taken to first remove and discard all of the solution above or below the resin in the tube. The solution used can be an electrolyte such as 0.01 M HCl (with a hydrogen or chloride-form resin), but a positive error will occur due to the Donnan penetration of the acid into the resin phase, especially with low cross-linked resins (< 4% DVB). A polyelectrolyte (e.g., sodium polyphosphate) which is excluded from the resin because of its size can be successfully used without correction. Cyclohexane can be used by filling the interstices with this liquid, which is then displaced from the column either by a water wash or by blowing with air and measured.

The theoretical interstitial volume, obtained from experiments with glass beads similar in size to resin particles, is 37% of the bed volume. Experimental values which have been obtained with polystyrene cation and anion exchangers (8% DVB) are 38% and 41%, respectively. Interstitial volumes decrease as the degree of cross-linking decreases and increase for beds of irregular particles.

g. *Determination of the selectivity coefficient* (E) *and total exchange capacity* (WQ). Selectivity coefficients are determined from batch experiments by analyzing systems in which the ion-exchange reaction of interest has come to equilibrium. Equation [42] can be used to evaluate E from an elution experiment if W, Q and V_M have been determined. WQ, the total exchange capacity, is determined by converting a column to the hydrogen (cation exchanger) or chloride (anion exchanger) form with approximately 0.1 M HCl. The excess acid is washed out with water. Approximately 0.1 M KNO_3 is then passed through to displace all the H^+ or Cl^-, and the column is again rinsed with water. An aliquot of the combined effluent and rinse, containing all the displaced ions, is titrated with standard NaOH (for H^+) or $AgNO_3$ (for Cl^-).

5. *Applications*

a. *Inorganic ions.* Figures 34–41 illustrate various separations by chromatography on ion-exchange resins under different conditions. Figure 34 shows the separation of three halides by elution with the simple salt $NaNO_3$. The change to a higher eluant concentration is made so that the iodide is eluted in a small enough volume for an accurate titration; if the elution is begun with 2.0 M $NaNO_3$, the chloride and bromide are not resolved.

Figure 35 illustrates the effect of complexing agents on the separation of metal ions on an anion exchanger. The metals are initially sorbed in concentrated HCl where all except Ni^{+2} are complexed as anions and distribution coefficients are maximal, Figure 35(a). Elution then proceeds with solutions of progressively lower concentration so that the distribution coefficient of one element at a time is lowered to about 1 or below and it is eluted. Figure 35a shows that the sorption (log D) of Mn is essentially zero below 10 M HCl, Co below 6 M, Cu below 3 M, Fe at 0.5 M and Zn in H_2O. Hence the eluant changes shown in 35b.

Figures 36 and 37 show the separation of metal ions achieved by cation exchange with concentrated electrolyte solutions and mixed aqueous-organic solutions, respectively, as eluants. In each case a stepwise change of eluants was made at appropriate points during the separation.

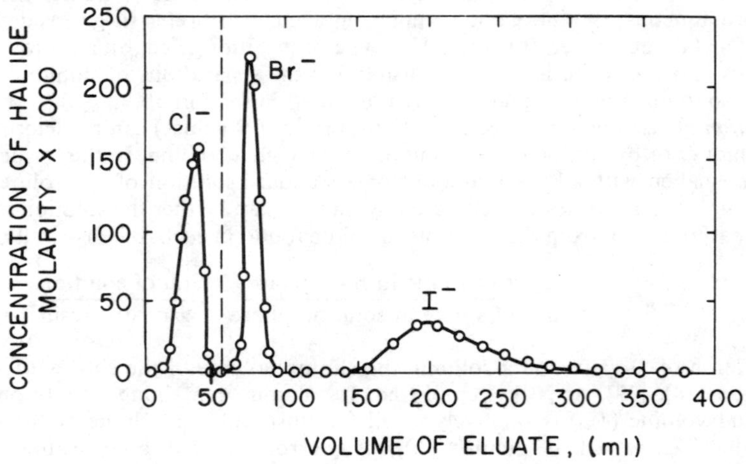

Figure 34. Separation of halides on Dowex 1-X10 nitrate form anion-exchange resin, 100–200 mesh, 6.7 cm × 3.4 cm^2 (2 cm diameter) column with 55 ml 0.50 *M* $NaNO_3$ and then 2.0 *M* $NaNO_3$ (starting at 50 ml) as the eluant at a flow rate of 1.0 cm per minute [after (*46*)]. Permission received to reproduce Figure 4, p. 89, vol. 15, No. 3 (1954), from Record of Chemical Progress, Wayne St. University Press, Detroit, Michigan.

b. *Organic compounds*. Organic substances can be separated by ion-exchange chromatography, an example of which is the separation of aldehyde compounds on bisulfite form anion-exchange resins with sodium bisulfite solutions of increasing concentrations used as eluants (Figure 38). The aldehyde which forms the most stable bisulfite addition compound is attracted most strongly by the resin, e.g.,

$$R-N^+(CH_3)_3HSO_3^- + HCHO \rightleftarrows R-N^+(CH_3)_3\overline{S}O_3(OH)HCH.$$

Nonionic organic compounds may also be separated by partition chromatography on ion-exchange resins. In salting-out chromatography (Figure 39), water soluble nonelectrolytes are separated by elution with an aqueous salt solution through a resin in a nonexchange form. The compounds are selectively salted into the resin phase and are separated because of their differential distributions between the two phases. In solubilization chromatography (Figure 40), water insoluble compounds are separated by elution with a mixed solvent through a resin in a nonexchange form. Separations are based upon differential dissolving of the compounds from the resin to which they are strongly attracted by London dispersion forces.

Figure 41 shows a separation of amines by ligand-exchange chromatography: a column of cation-exchange resin is loaded with a metal-ammonia complex (e.g., nickel–ammonia) and the mixture of amines is added to the top. The amines coordinate to different degrees with nickel by displacing the ammonia and are selectively eluted with aqueous NH_3.

Already shown in earlier figures were the separation of amino acids with stepwise temperature, pH and ionic strength gradients (Figure 16) and with solvent programming in an automated analyzer (Figure 33). Amino acids are amphoteric compounds which contain both acidic and basic groups. Depending upon the pH of the solution, these substances will be positively or negatively charged or have no net charge and therefore will be more or less attracted to the cation-exchange resin. However, the separation of the amino acids shown in Figure 16, for example, is not due solely to differences in their ionic nature. The rate of travel on the column of resin is a function both of the charge possessed by the acid and the nature of its side group. The electrostatic attraction of the ionic part of the molecule and the physical attraction of the nonionic part are involved, and the rate of movement is determined by the pH and ionic strength of the eluant and its temperature.

The identification and detection of nanogram amounts of adenine and metabolites (including guanine) in body fluids has been carried out by high performance ion-exchange chromatography (*45*) on a 300 cm × 1 mm column of a pellicular cation-exchange resin, with 0.01 *M* $NH_4H_2PO_4$ as eluant, pH 2.40, flowing at 60 ml/hr (3000 psi) at 70 °C (15 minutes analysis time). This paper clearly illustrates how chromatographic conditions can be systematically varied to obtain optimized resolution of the compounds of interest.

c. *Ion exclusion and ion retardation*. Two methods for the separation of electrolytes from nonelectrolytes have been developed by the Dow Chemical Co. In ion exclusion, a mixture of, for example, sodium chloride and ethanol is added to a column of strong acid resin in the sodium form or strong base resin in the chloride form and eluted with water. The sodium chloride is excluded from the resin by the Donnan equilibrium principle described above and is eluted first while the ethanol can distribute between both phases and is eluted later. Since no ion exchange occurs, no column regeneration is required after the

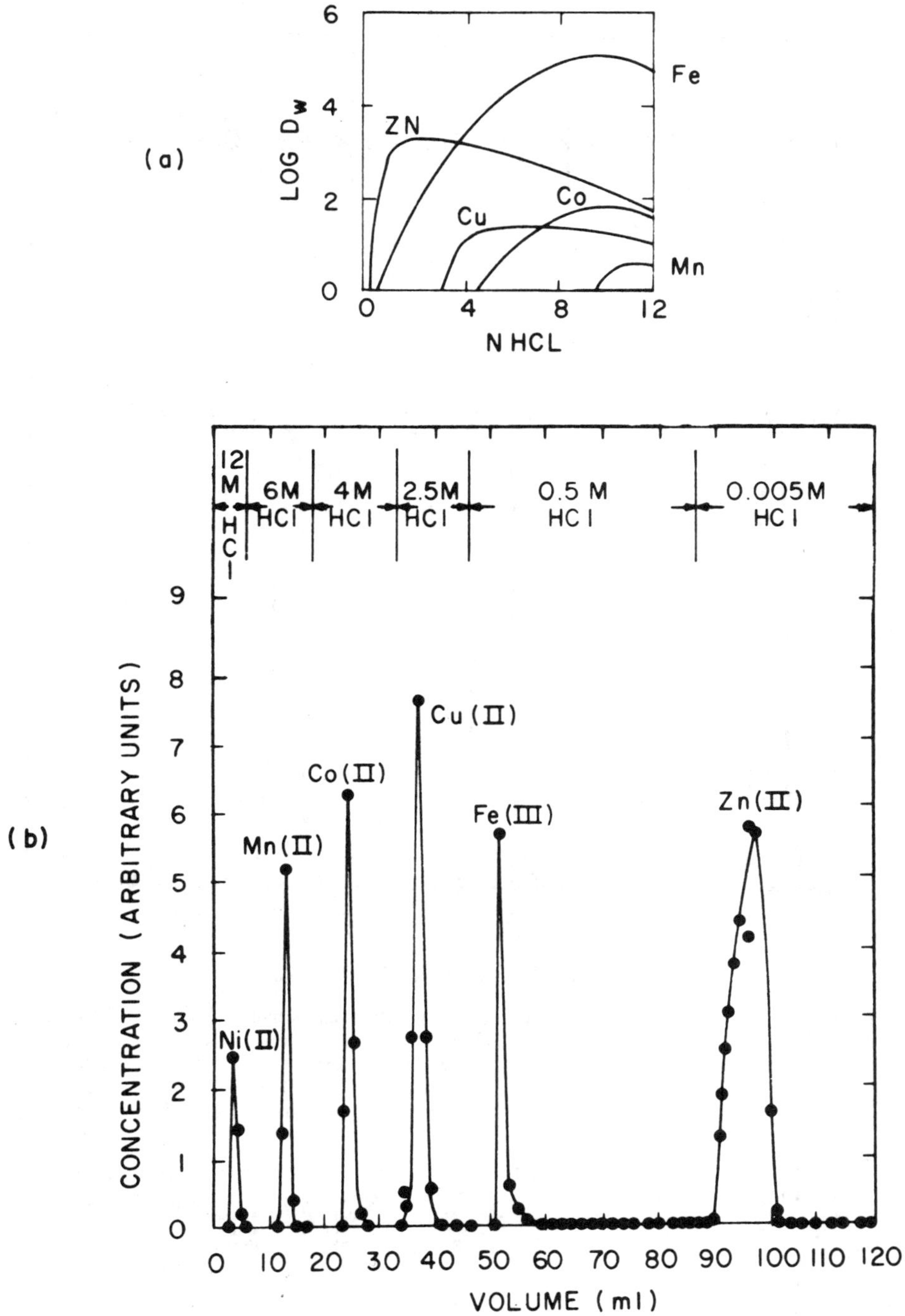

Figure 35. (a) Effect of HCl concentration on the distribution coefficients of various transition metal ions, and (b) anion-exchange separation of these metals on a Dowex® 1 column, 26 cm × 0.29 cm, flow rate 0.5 cm/min [after (*47*)]. Permission to reproduce received from American Society for Testing and Materials.

separation. In theory, if the electrolyte is completely excluded, it will be eluted by a volume of water equal to the interstitial volume. If the nonelectrolyte has a D value of 1 (is not adsorbed by the resin matrix), it will be eluted with a volume of water equal to the interstitial volume plus the solvent volume inside the resin particles (compare to gel chromatography). Other mixtures well separated by ion exclusion include (most ionic listed first): HCl from acetic, chloroacetic or dichloroacetic acid; trichloroacetic acid from acetic, chloroacetic or dichloroacetic acid; NaCl from ethylene glycol or formaldehyde.

As explained before, many nonionic organic compounds are sorbed by the resin matrix, so that these compounds will have D values > 1. If the D values among a group of compounds are sufficiently different, they will be separated by elution through a resin with water. An example is the separation of sucrose (D = 0.24), glycerine (0.49), triethylene glycol (0.74) and phenol (3.08) on sodium form Dowex® 50-X8.

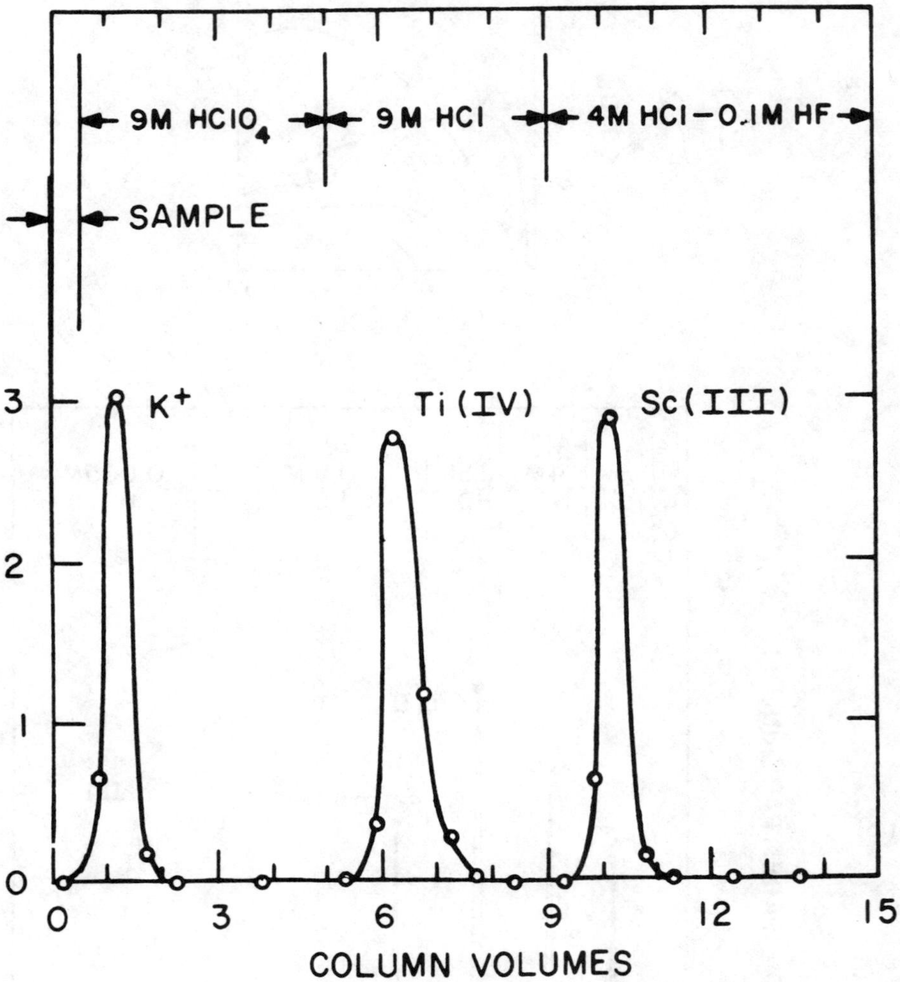

Figure 36. Separation of K^+, Sc(III) and Ti(IV) by cation exchange at high ionic strength; Dowex® 50-X4 pretreated with 9 *M* $HClO_4$, 3 cm × 0.2 cm^2 column. (Reproduced from F. Nelson, T. Murase, and K. A. Kraus, Ion Exchange Procedures I. Cation Exchange in concentrated HCl and $HCLO_4$ Solutions, *J. Chromatogr.* **13**, 503–535 (1964), Figure 11.) Permission to reproduce from Elsevier Publishing Co., Amsterdam, The Netherlands.

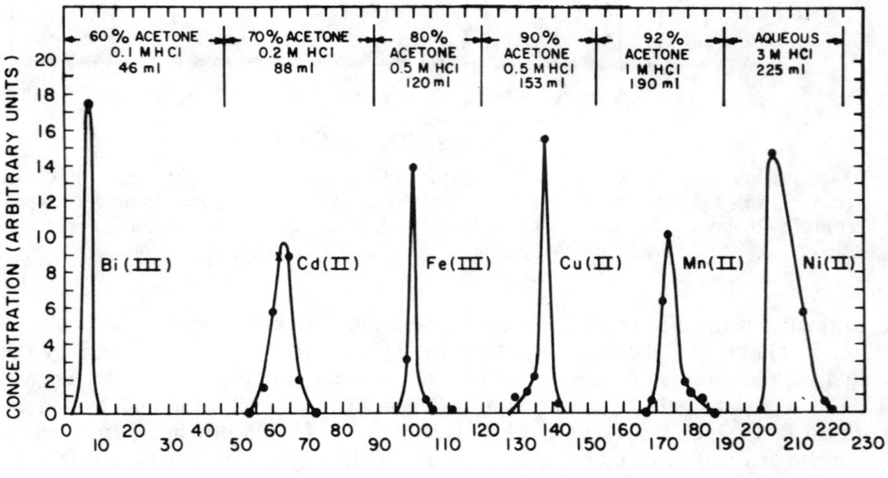

Figure 37. Separation of six metals by cation exchange in mixed solvents; Dowex® 50W-X8, hydrogen form, 100–200 mesh, 12.5 cm × 1.2 cm [after (*48*)].

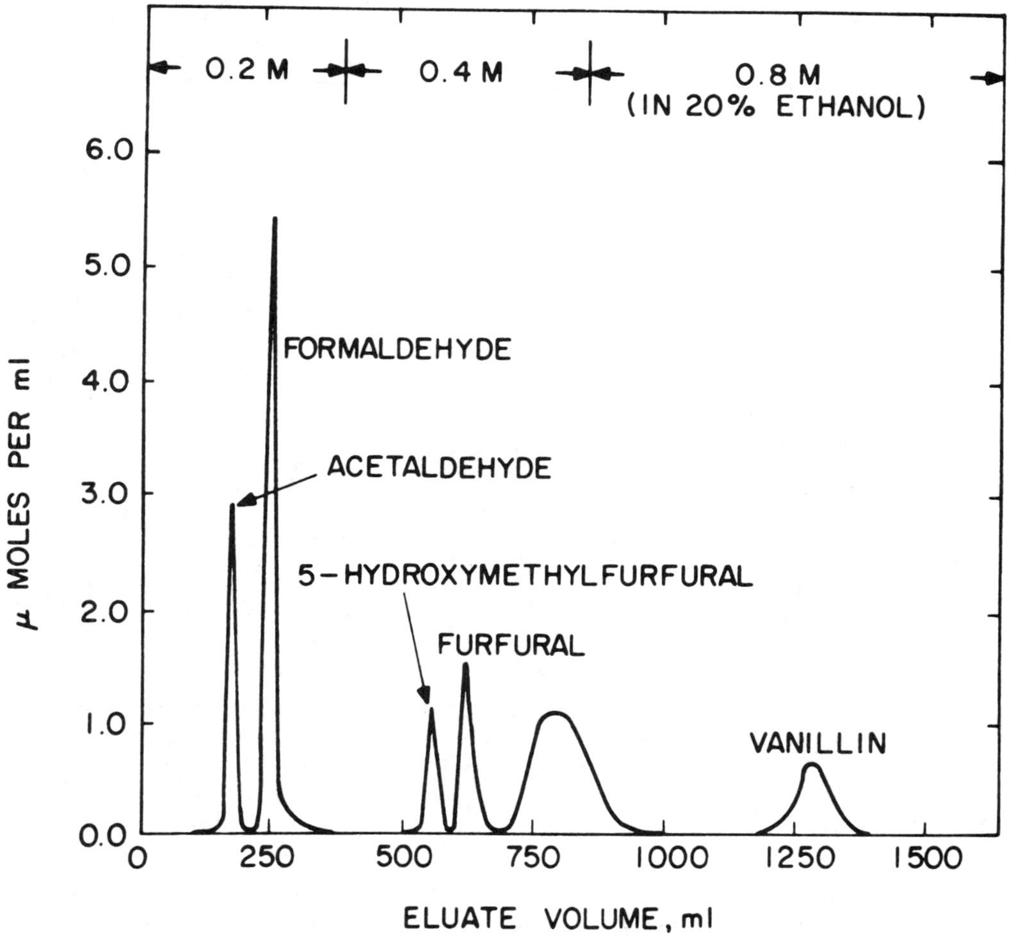

Figure 38. Separation of aldehydes by anion-exchange on bisulfite form Dowex® 1-X8, 150–300 mesh, 410 × 11 mm column, with $NaHSO_3$ eluants of different concentrations in 20% ethanol, flow rates 0.27, 0.27 and 0.52 ml/cm²/min [after (*49*)]; *Anal. Chim. Acta*, **33**, 285 (1965). Reproduced with permission from Elsevier Publishing Co., Amsterdam, The Netherlands.

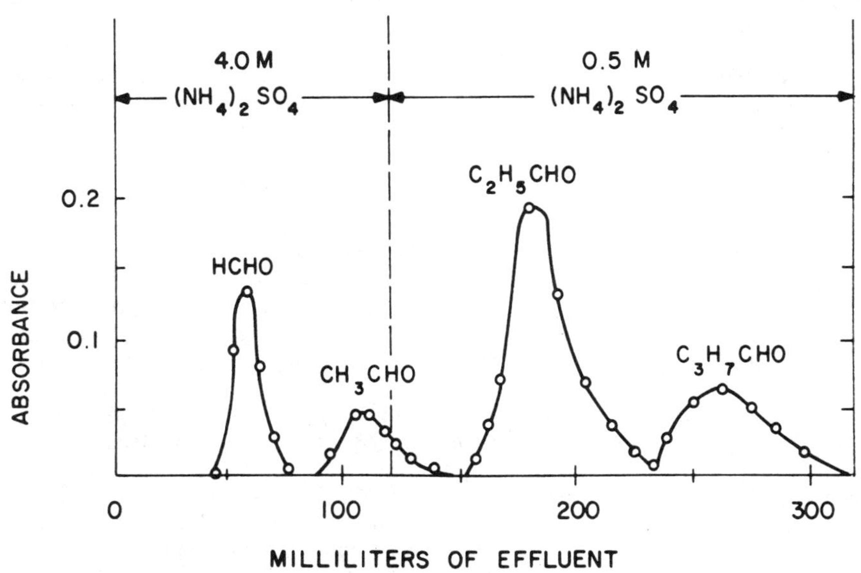

Figure 39. Salting-out chromatography of aldehydes on Dowex® 1-X8, 200–400 mesh, sulfate form, 30 cm × 3.88 cm², 0.5 cm/minute [after (*50*)]; *Anal. Chim. Acta*, **18**, 204 (1958). Reproduced with permission from Elsevier Publishing Co., Amsterdam, The Netherlands.

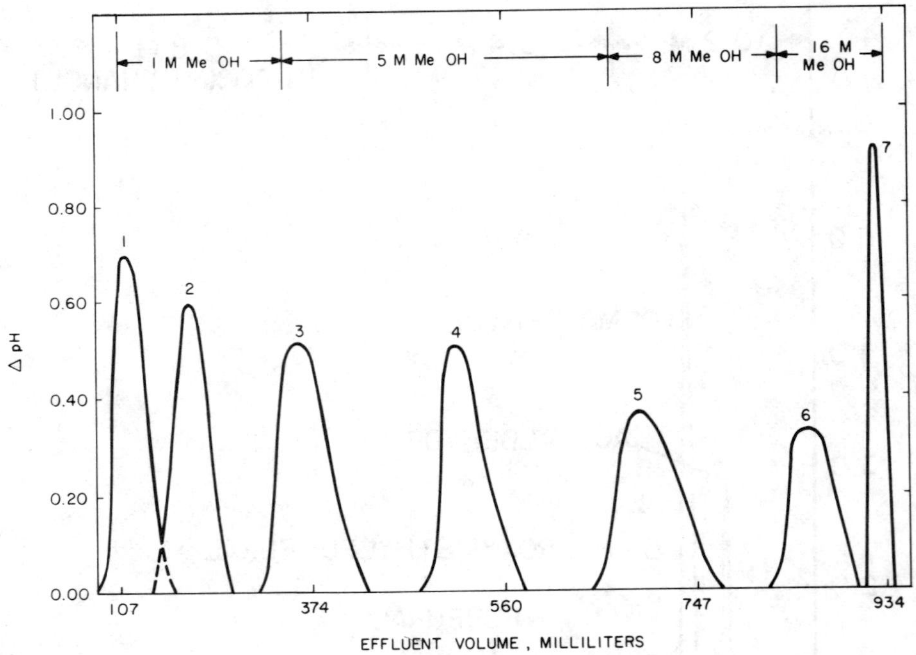

Figure 40. Solubilization chromatography of methyl ketones on Dowex® 50-X8, 200–400 mesh, hydrogen form, 54.5 cm × 2.28 cm^2, aqueous methanol eluants, 0.28 cm/min. 1. methyl iso-butyl ketone, 2. *n*-butyl, 3. *n*-amyl, 4. *n*-hexyl, 5. *n*-heptyl, 6. *n*-octyl, 7. *n*-nonyl [after (*51*)]; *Anal. Chim. Acta*, **33**, 84 (1965). Reproduced with permission from Elsevier Publishing Co., Amsterdam, The Netherlands.

By using special ion-retardation resins (Dowex® 11A8), nonelectrolytes are eluted with water before electrolytes. This resin has both anionic and cationic sites which interact with the electrolyte and "retard" its migration while the nonelectrolyte is partitioned between the phases and is eluted earlier. Examples are the separation of sucrose from NaCl, and glycerine and polyglycerides from NaCl. Two electrolytes may interact with the resin to different degrees and therefore be separable by ion retardation. Examples are the separation of Fe^{+2} from Zn^{+2} and Na_2SO_4 from NaCl. Again, no regeneration of the resin is required. By methods analogous to ion retardation, salts or water-soluble nonionic substances may be separated from strong acids by water elution (acid retardation).

d. *Ion exchange.* Ion-exchange procedures (as contrasted to ion-exchange chromatography) make use of the ability of resins to exchange ions, but chromatographic separations are not involved. These applications are extremely important but since they are not chromatographic in nature they will only be listed: determination of total electrolyte concentration, water softening, separation of interfering ions, concentration of traces, and chemical conversions. Resins are also useful as catalysts for many chemical reactions.

6. *Selection of a Particular LC Method*.

Some factors to be considered in choosing an LC method include:

a. Sample solubility—ion-exchange and partition work best with water-soluble samples, adsorption chromatography with fat-soluble samples. Exclusion chromatography has been applied to both.

b. Ionic nature—ion exchange is the first choice for ionic or ionizable compounds, and partition chromatography can also be used for these. Gel chromatography and adsorption chromatography are generally not used for ionic materials.

c. Molecular weight—very low-molecular-weight compounds are best handled by GC and very high-molecular-weight compounds by exclusion chromatography. Intermediate-molecular-weight compounds can be successfully separated by all four LC methods.

The following general scheme has been proposed by Kirkland [Chapter 5 in *Modern Liquid Chromatography*, L. R. Snyder and J. J. Kirkland, American Chemical Society, 1971] as a guide in selecting a mode of LC and a column type. Products mentioned are merely illustrative of types that would successfully be used.

a. Molecular-Weight Range of Sample greater than 2000.

1. Aqueous system—use gel filtration on Sephadex, Biogel, porous glass, etc.
2. Nonaqueous system—use gel permeation chromatography on Poragel, porous glass, Porasil, etc.

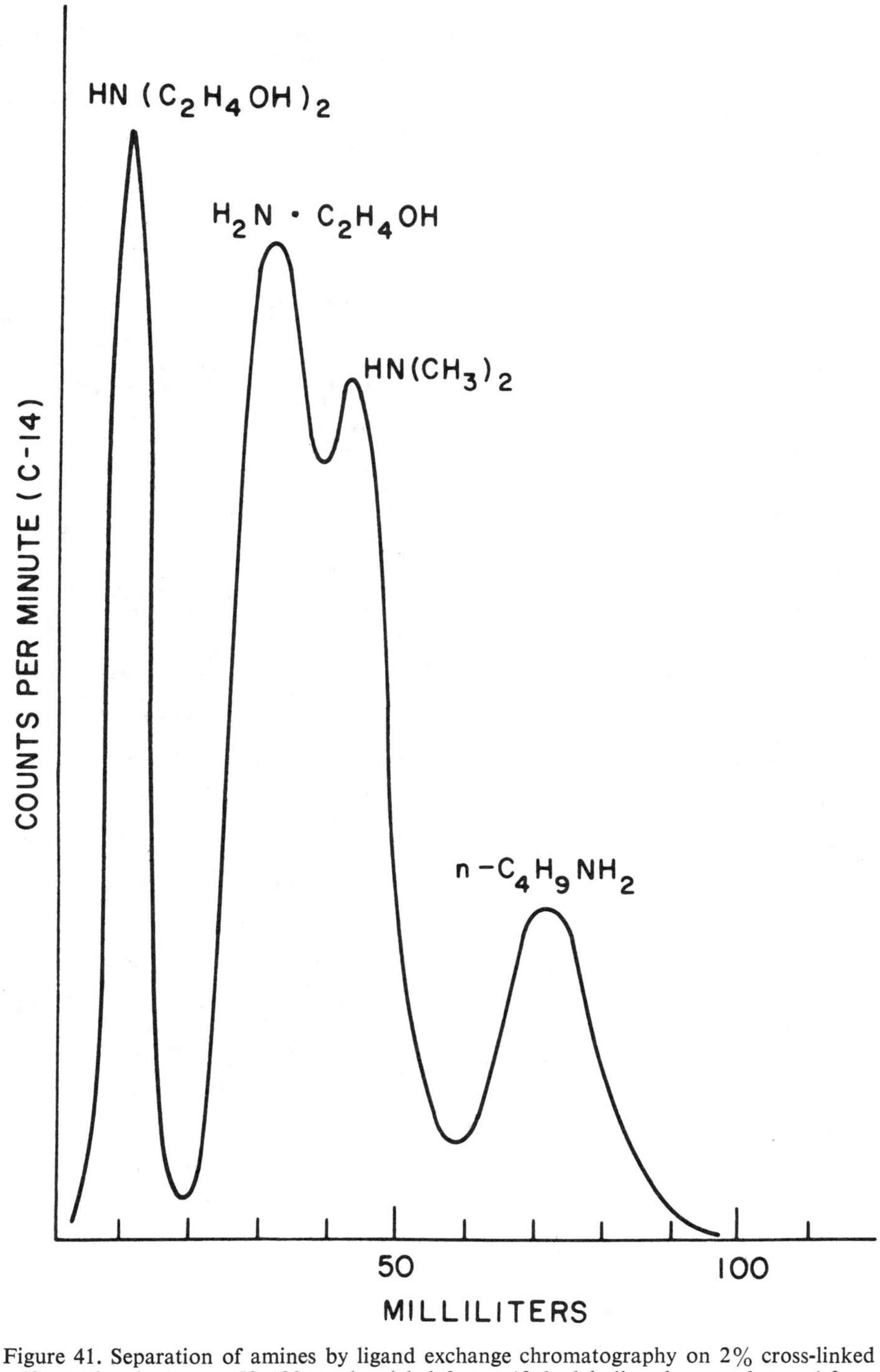

Figure 41. Separation of amines by ligand exchange chromatography on 2% cross-linked sulfonated polystyrene, 50–100 mesh, nickel form; 10.6 ml bulk column volume, 1.0 cm diam.; eluant, 0.94 *M* NH_3 to 50 ml, 1.8 *M* after that, 0.3 ml/min [after (*52*)]; *Anal. Chim. Acta*, **33**, 84 (1965). Reproduced with permission from Elsevier Publishing Co., Amsterdam, The Netherlands.

b. Molecular Weight less than 2000.

1. Aqueous system—use gel filtration on low porosity Sephadex or ion exchange on a gel or pellicular cation-exchange resin for basic compounds or on a gel or pellicular anion-exchange resin for acidic compounds.
2. Nonaqueous system—if size differences are significant, gel permeation chromatography on low porosity polystyrene beads or Poragel is used. For non-labile systems or isomer separations, use adsorption chromatography on silica gel, alumina, Porasil or Corasil II. For labile systems

and different compound types, use partition chromatography in the normal mode for polar compounds and in the reversed-phase mode for non-polar compounds.

LC methods can be readily combined for the separation of complex mixtures. A good general approach is separation first by exclusion chromatography followed by further separation of separated fractions by one of the other three high resolution methods.

REFERENCES

1. Snyder, L. R., *J. Chromatogr. Sci.* **7**, 359 (1969).
2. Knox, J. H. and M. Saleem, *J. Chromatogr. Sci.* **7**, 745 (1969).
3. Stewart, H. N. M., Amos, R., and S. G. Perry, *J. Chromatogr.* **38**, 209 (1968).
4. Nota, G., Marino, G., Buonocore, V., and A. Ballio, *J. Chromatogr.* **46**, 103 (1970).
5. Snyder, L. R., *J. Chromatogr. Sci.* **8**, 692 (1970).
6. Conlon, R. D., *Anal. Chem.* **41**, 107A April, 1969.
7. Bakalyar, S. R., *American Laboratory*, p. 21, June 1971.
8. Scott, R. P. W. and J. G. Lawrence, *J. Chromatogr. Sci.* **8**, 65 (1970).
9. McGuinness, E. T. and M. C. Cullen, *J. Chem. Educ.* **47**, A9 (1970).
10. Netting, A. G., *J. Chromatogr.* **53**, 507 (1970).
11. Keller, R. A. and J. C. Giddings, in "Chromatography", E. Heftmann, ed., Reinhold Publishing Co., N.Y. Chapter 6, 2nd Edition, 1967.
12. Karger, B. L., Conroe, K., and H. Engelhardt, *J. Chromatogr. Sci.* **8**, 242 (1970).
13. Hildebrand, J. H. and R. S. Scott, "The Solubility of Nonelectrolytes", Dover Publications, N.Y., 3rd edition, 1964, p. 435.
14. Freeman, G. G., *J. Chromatogr.* **28**, 338 (1967).
15. Gilding, D. K., *American Laboratory*, October 1969, pp. 36–46.
16. Bidlingmeyer, B. A., Hooker, R. P., Lochmuller, C. H., and L. B. Rogers, *Separ. Science*, **4**, 439 (1969).
17. Bombaugh, K. J., *American Laboratory*, July 1969, pp. 43–52.
18. Bombaugh, K. J., King, R. N., and A. J. Cohen, *J. Chromatogr.* **43**, 332 (1969).
19. Gaucher, C. M., *J. Chem. Educ.* **46**, 733 (1969).
20. Moore, S. and W. H. Stein, *J. Biol. Chem.* **211**, 893 (1954).
21. Bombaugh, K. J., Dark, W. A., and R. N. King, *Res/Dev.* **9**, 28 (1968).
22. Marshall, J. J., *J. Chromatogr.* **53**, 379 (1970).
23. Bombaugh, K. J., Dark, W. A., and R. F. Levangie, *J. Chromatogr. Sci.* **7**, 42 (1969).
24. Goodson, J. M. and V. DiStefano, *J. Chromatogr.* **45**, 139 (1969).
25. Pidacks, C., *J. Chromatogr. Sci.* **8**, 618 (1970).
26. Edwards, V. H. and J. M. Helft, *J. Chromatogr.* **47**, 490 (1970).
27. Giddings, J. C. and K. Dahlgren, *Separ. Science* **5**, 717 (1970).
28. Bathgate, G. N., *J. Chromatogr.* **47**, 92 (1970).
29. "Practical Clinical Biochemistry" (4th edition), Interscience Publishers (Division of John Wiley and Sons, Inc.), N.Y., 1967, p. 265.
30. Larsen, F. N., *American Laboratory*, October 1969, pp. 10–16.
31. Saunders, D. and R. L., Pecsok, *Anal. Chem.* **40**, 44 (1968); Pecsok, R. L. and D. Saunders *Separ. Sci.* **3**, 325 (1968).
32. Cazes, J., *Separ. Sci.* **4**, 15 (1969).
33. Cameron, B. F., *Separ. Sci.* **6**, 229 (1971).
34. Reiland, J., *American Laboratory*, October 1969, p. 29.
35. Trennel, G., John, M., and H. Dellweg, *FEBS Letters*, **2**, 74 (1968).
36. "Sephadex LH-20 for Gel Filtration in Organic Solvents", p. 4, Pharmacia Fine Chemicals, Inc.
37. Bombaugh, K. J., Dark, W. A., and R. F. Levangie, *Z. Anal. Chem.* **236**, 443 (1968).
38. Kunin, R., *Amber-Hi-Lites* **No. 78**, Rohn and Haas Co., Philadelphia, Pa., November 1963.
39. Kunin, R., *Amber-Hi-Lites* **No. 83**, Rohm and Haas Co., Philadelphia, Pa., September 1964.
40. Kraus, K. A. and F. Nelson, *ASTM Special Tech. Publ.* **195**, p. 34, 1958.
41. Faris, J. P., *J. Chromatogr.* **32**, 795, 1968.
42. Scott, C. D. and N. E. Lee, *J. Chromatogr.* **42**, 263 (1969).
43. Ertingshausen, G., Adler, H. J., and A. S. Reichler, *J. Chromatogr.* **42**, 355 (1969).
44. Ertingshausen, G. and H. J. Adler, *J. Chromatogr.* **44**, 620 (1969).
45. Gere, D. R., Stevenson, R. L. and S. Mutha, *American Laboratory*, p. 45, July 1971.
46. Riemann, W., III, *Record of Chemical Progress*, **15**, 89 (1954).
47. Kraus, K. A. and F. A. Nelson, *ASTM Special Technical Publication* **No. 195**, pp. 36 and 38, 1958.
48. Fritz, J. S. and T. A. Rettig, *Anal. Chem.* **34**, 1565 (1962).
49. Christofferson, K., *Anal. Chim. Acta*, **33**, 285 (1965).
50. Breyer, A. and W. Rieman III., *Anal. Chim. Acta*, **18**, 204 (1958).
51. Sherma, J. and W. Rieman III, *Anal. Chim. Acta*, **19**, 137 (1958).
52. Walton, H., *Anal. Chim. Acta*, **33**, 84 (1965).

VOLUME TWO
SECTION I

PRINCIPLES AND TECHNIQUES

I.IV Paper Chromatography

Section I.IV

PAPER CHROMATOGRAPHY (PC)

In paper chromatography, one spots a drop of sample near one end of a sheet or strip of filter paper. The paper edge nearest the spot is immersed in a suitable solvent contained in a tank. The spot must not be covered by the solvent. In the tank, the solvent moves along (up or down) the paper by capillarity carrying the components along at different rates. When the solvent front approaches the opposite end of the paper, it is removed from the tank and the zones are observed. In many cases, the complexity of the mixture makes for incomplete separation of its components in a single solvent. Two-dimensional chromatography is more effective because it utilizes the differential separating power of two solvents, run in two directions at right angles to each other, and because development occurs over twice the length of paper.

Differential migration occurs because the components of the mixture are selectively distributed between the stationary phase containing cellulose or attached to it and the solvent, which can be organic, aqueous or a mixture of these. For many applications, ordinary cellulose paper can be modified so that resolution is increased. The equipment for paper chromatography is inexpensive, the techniques are simple, and virtually every class of compounds can be separated.

A. FUNDAMENTALS OF PAPER CHROMATOGRAPHY

Cellulose paper consists of a partially oriented collection of cellulose fibers. These fibers are composed of approximately parallel carbohydrate chains strongly cross-linked together by hydrogen bonding in some regions to give a partly crystalline and partly amorphous structure. In the amorphous regions, water or other hydrophilic solvents are absorbed by the cellulose. This leads to the formation of pools of liquid connected by crystallite bridges. Water in these regions is of two types, one being chemically bonded to the cellulose fibers and the other being more loosely bound and available for partitioning the solutes.

1. *Theory and Mechanism*

As stated in Section I.IIIB3e, paper chromatography in systems with stationary water involves a combination of mechanisms, namely adsorption, partition and ion-exchange. Ordinary chromatography papers have ion-exchange properties due to the presence of a small number of carboxyl groups, and under certain conditions this effect can explain the retention of cations, the frontal analysis (demixing) of developers and the formation of multiple solute zones. Paper can be impregnated with various adsorbents, liquids, or ion exchangers to make the interactions with the solutes more selective.

Considerations discussed in earlier sections are valid in relation to the performance of paper chromatographic systems: a good system is one which has the ability to separate the centers of the solute spots and to keep the spots compact; three factors responsible for spot spreading are molecular diffusion (both in the mobile and stationary phases), eddy diffusion and resistance to mass transfer; and an average plate height over the distance of development can be calculated by an equation similar to the van Deemter equation for GC (*1*). Based on theoretical studies, a velocity of development near 1×10^{-3} cm/sec has been recommended by Stewart as being optimum for systems with stationary water. In practice, it is much more difficult to control the velocity of solvent flow in PC than in column chromatography. Some methods include location of the initial spot farther from the solvent reservoir, use of solvents of different viscosities, and wick-feeding of the solvent to the paper. Another problem is that there is usually considerable variation in the solvent velocity during the run, from the initial, rapid penetration into the paper to the final, slower arrival of the front some distance along the length of the paper.

Thoma (*2*) has made simulation studies of the chromatographic behavior of model, polar systems in order to devise general guidelines for systematically optimizing operating conditions. He stresses that chromatographic theory cannot be used quantitatively as a predictive tool in system design even though the effects of many individual factors (e.g., particle size and solvent velocity) on chromatographic behavior are well understood. The problem lies in the complexity of the overall chromatographic system which causes many parameters to change when only one experimental condition is altered. Qualitatively, the following are recommended: small sample loads should be developed on a finely-divided stationary phase with a solvent migrating as rapidly as permitted by the velocity at which distribution equilibrium is obtained; the solvent and sorbent should be chosen to provide specific interactions with the solutes; solvent proportions are chosen by trial-and-error to carry the spots $\frac{1}{4}$–$\frac{1}{2}$ the distance along the support for single development; development may be improved by altering the solvent, lengthening the support or employing multiple development in the same direction with the same or different solvents.

2. *R Values*

With one-way or radial development, the migration behavior of a substance is described relative to the solvent front (R_F values) or a standard substance X (R_X values) (Figure 42). The migration distance of the solute can be measured to the geometric center of the zone, the point of maximum concentration, or to both

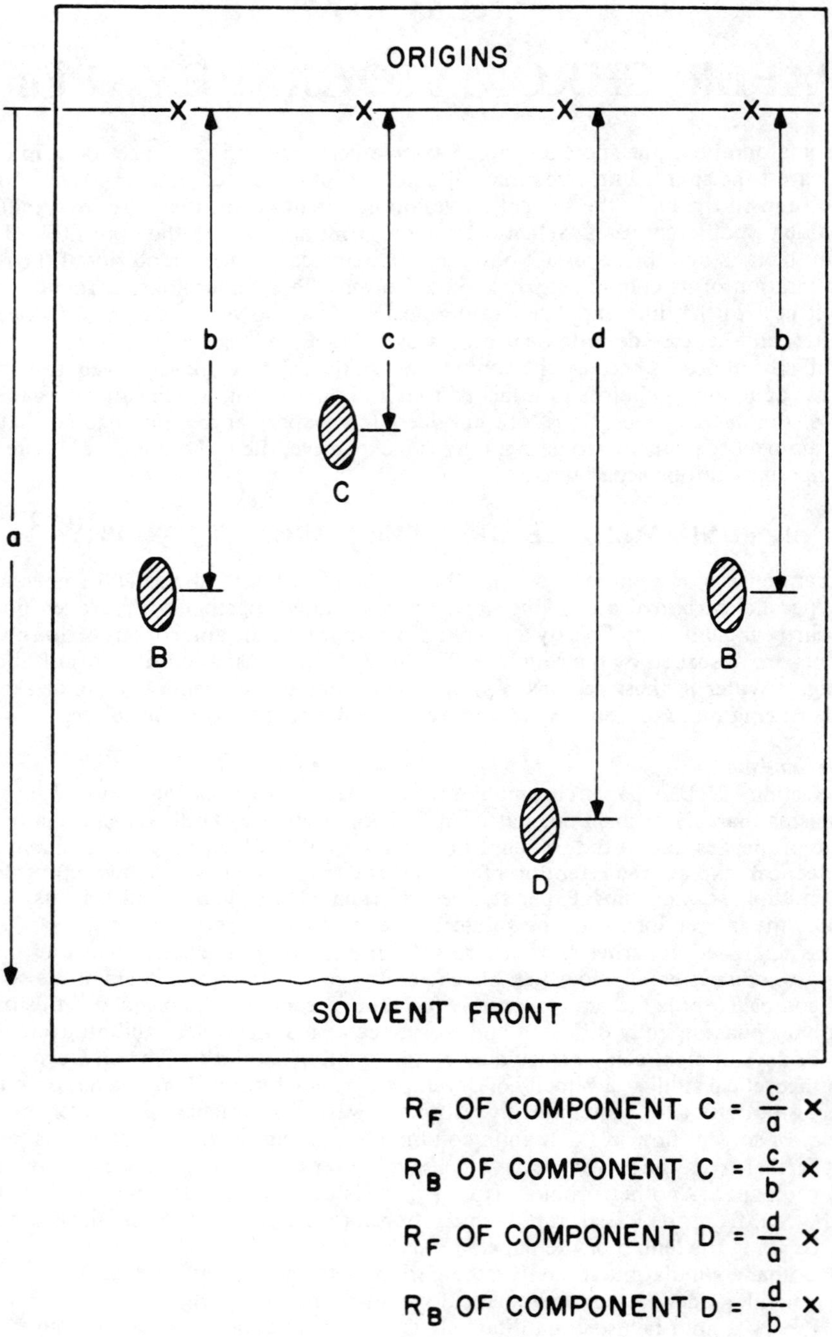

R_F OF COMPONENT C = $\frac{c}{a}$ × 100

R_B OF COMPONENT C = $\frac{c}{b}$ × 100

R_F OF COMPONENT D = $\frac{d}{a}$ × 100

R_B OF COMPONENT D = $\frac{d}{b}$ × 100

Figure 42. Method for calculating R_F values and R values relative to standard B (R_B values) of components C and D on a descending chromatogram.

the leading and tailing boundaries of the zone. The results of two-dimensional chromatography are best reported by listing the R values in each solvent and also presenting a drawing or photograph of the final chromatogram. Results can be reported without R values if sequences and separations are listed.

R_M values, where

$$R_M = \log\left[\left(\frac{1}{R_F}\right) - 1\right] \quad [54]$$

are used in studies of the relation between solute structure and chromatographic behavior [see, for example, Reference (*3*)].

3. *Reproducibility of* R_F *Values*

R values vary significantly depending upon the experimental conditions and are not sufficient alone for the certain identification of an unknown substance. Factors which influence R_F values are the following: composition and aging of the solvent; nature, humidity and treatment of the paper; concentration of the solute; shape of the paper; direction, length and method of development; distance of the origin from the solvent reservoir; volume of solvent in the reservoir; air flow about the chamber; temperature; conditions of equilibration; change in composition of the solvent as it flows over the paper; irregular solvent flow; dimensions of the developing chamber; and impurities in the solvent, paper, or sample. R_X values are less affected by many of these variables and are more reproducible.

It is seldom necessary to sacrifice the inherent simplicity of paper chromatography in order to attempt to rigidly standardize operating conditions. R_F and R_X values should be considered as guides to possible separations whose numerical values cannot be exactly reproduced. Sequences and differences between these values are more significant than the actual numbers.

4. *Artifacts and Anomalous Zones*

Each solute should ideally be found in one compact, round or oval spot after development. In practice, zones may have double tails (Figure 43) or be diffused, streaked, flattened, swerved, or otherwise distorted,

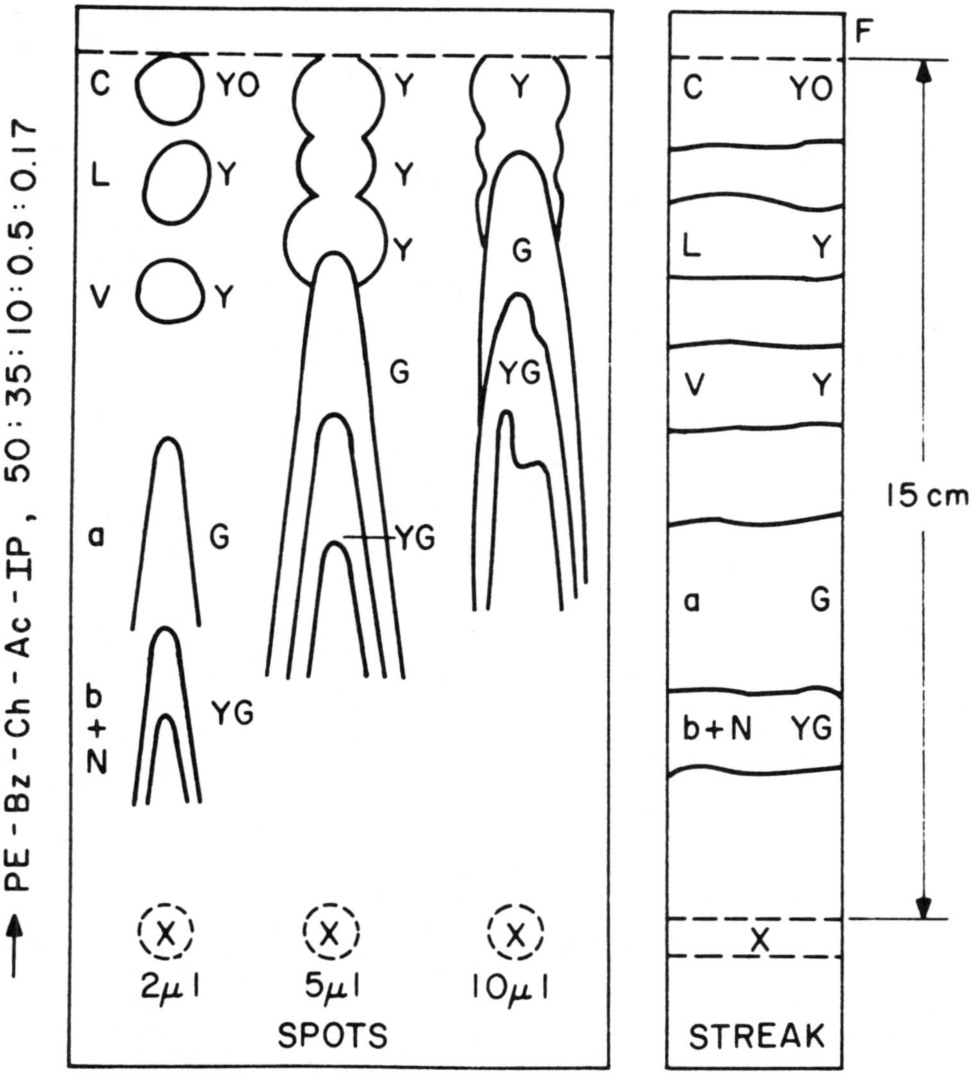

Figure 43. Pigments in various amounts of leaf extract separated by one-dimensional migration on Whatman No. 1 paper from initial zones formed as a spot and as a streak; PE = petroleum ether, Bz = benzene, Ch = chloroform, Ac = acetone, IP = isopropanol, C = carotene, L = lutein, V = violaxanthin, a = chlorophyll *a*, b = chlorophyll *b*, N = neoxanthin, Y = yellow, O = orange, G = green [after (*10*)]. Figure 6, p. 481, *J. Chem. Educ.*, 46 (1969). Reproduced with permission from Division of Chemical Education, American Chemical Society.

and a single substance may yield two or more distinct spots (multiple zonation). Even if the spots formed are not of ideal size and shape, the chromatographic system may be useful if it reproducibly provides a desired separation. Reasons for the formation of distorted zones are varied and not always understood. Interested readers may consult books on paper chromatography listed in the bibliography for detailed discussions of these topics.

B. THE PAPER

1. *Pure Cellulose Paper*

Various manufacturers provide commercial chromatography papers with a wide range of properties. Whatman Chroma Papers, especially manufactured for chromatography, are low in organic and inorganic impurities and uniform in physical characteristics. Whatman and other manufacturers supply various grades of filter papers "selected for chromatography", and the user should always specify that he desires such grades when placing an order.

Some workers prefer to personally pretreat commercial paper by an overnight descending development with a dilute solution of HCl, EDTA, diethyl ether, or the first development solvent they plan to use. This should be followed by a distilled-water wash and drying.

Many grades of paper are commercially available in a variety of sizes and shapes: rectangular, circular and other special shapes for certain procedures and apparatuses.

Table 7 (Section II.III) shows the types of pure cellulose and other papers available from selected commercial sources. As a general rule, Whatman No. 1 paper or an equivalent grade is suitable for general analytical work and the thicker Whatman No. 3 MM for preparative work.

2. *Chemically Modified Paper*

Partially acetylated paper, prepared in the laboratory or purchased commercially, is useful for separating hydrophobic substances. Papers with the carboxyl group content increased by chemical reactions have been used to separate various classes of polar compounds.

Copolymerized cellulose has been used as a support for reversed-phase chromatography. Wedge-compressed nitrocellulose membrane filters, either intact or impregnated with nonionic detergents or proteins, are a convenient medium for small-scale chromatographic separations or deproteinizations.

3. *Impregnated Papers*

Papers have been impregnated with hydrophilic liquids to facilitate separations of moderately hydrophilic substances (partition paper chromatography) and with olive oil, silicone oil, paraffin, rubber latex, etc., for the separation of hydrophobic solutes (reversed-phase partition paper chromatography). Papers impregnated with high-molecular-weight amine liquid anion exchangers, high-molecular-weight acid liquid cation exchangers, or neutral organophosphorus compounds serve for the separation of metal ions when developed with aqueous solutions of mineral acids. Chromatography on papers containing complexing or precipitating agents (e.g., 8-hydroxyquinoline, dithizone, CdS, quinalizarin, etc.) with various aqueous and aqueous-organic two- and three-component solvents also separates metal ions.

4. *Loaded Papers*

Loaded papers consist of a dispersion of powder, fiber or resin in a normal cellulosic paper network.

a. *Papers loaded with adsorbent powders.* These papers are used to separate less polar substances by adsorption chromatography using solvents similar to those used with thin layers of the same adsorbent. The presence of the cellulose along with the adsorbent may, however, lead to separations different than on a layer of adsorbent alone. Papers containing silica gel, alumina and kieselguhr are commercially available.

Polar compounds such as sugars and amino acids are separated on silica-gel papers using normal partition solvents developed for pure cellulose paper. By the proper choice of solvents, two-dimensional separations with an adsorption mechanism in one direction and partition in the other can be performed on silica paper.

b. *Papers loaded with ion-exchange celluloses.* Cellulose phosphate and carboxymethyl cellulose cation-exchange papers and aminoethyl, diethylaminoethyl and Ecteola cellulose anion-exchange papers are commercially available. Some properties of these papers are listed in Section II.III, Table 7. They have proven to be useful for a wide range of inorganic separations and applications in the biochemical field.

Knight (*4*) has pointed out that normal chromatographic techniques are often modified for use with ion-exchange cellulose papers. The papers are generally converted to the required ionic form by a descending wash with the developing solvent. Only with the "strong" cellulose phosphate exchanger can the treated paper be washed free of excess electrolyte after conversion, dried, and used in the normal "dry-start" manner without disturbing the established equilibrium. In other cases, the paper must be used with a "wet-start" technique in which the sample is applied directly to the wet, equilibrated paper as it hangs in the chamber. After application of the spots, descending development is carried out for a timed period since no solvent front will be visible. Ion-exchange papers are generally used with aqueous solvents and so are less sensitive to changes in conditions (e.g., temperature, humidity) during the development. All operations after development are the same as with ordinary paper.

Amino acids exhibit both ionic and nonionic interactions with ion-exchange celluloses, and both influences are important in determining the sequence and resolution of the compounds. By the proper choice of solvents, two-dimensional amino-acid separations, in which ion exchange predominates in one direction (ionic solvent) and partition ± adsorption in the other (nonionic solvent), have been obtained on ion-exchange papers.

c. *Papers loaded with synthetic organic ion-exchange resins.* Commercial papers containing polystyrene strong and weak anion- and cation-exchange resins are available. Conversion of the resin to the same ionic form as the developing solution is obtained by a descending wash with, or soaking in, an appropriate electrolyte, followed by a distilled water rinse and drying. The normal "dry-start" development technique is used unless solvent demixing occurs during development, in which case the sample is applied, if possible, after the *bulk* solvent front has been allowed to migrate a few cm past the origin.

Development can be with various types of solvents: simple electrolytes, aqueous solutions of complexing agents, or mixed solvents with two or more components. The papers can be impregnated with various precipitating or complexing agents to improve resolutions.

Results obtained on ion-exchange papers are not necessarily equivalent to results obtained in batch equilibrium and column experiments employing the same resin and solvent because of basic differences in the techniques and the presence of the cellulose plus resin in the ion-exchange paper.

d. *Papers loaded with inorganic ion exchangers.* Papers may be impregnated with inorganic exchangers such as zirconium phosphate, hydrous oxides and ammonium molybdophosphate. Support-free cerium(IV) phosphate sheets have provided selective metal-ion separations when developed with aqueous solutions of $HClO_4$.

5. *Glass Fiber Papers*

These papers are useful in extreme conditions of temperature and acidity where cellulose papers are unsuitable. Corrosive detection reagents (e.g., chromic-sulfuric acid charring solutions) can be employed with these papers. Glass papers can be used untreated, or more often after impregnation with aqueous salt solutions, silica gel or alumina. Glass fiber papers already impregnated with silica gel and silicic acid are commercially available from The Gelman Corporation as ITLC media (see Table 8 in Section II.III).

C. SOLVENT SYSTEMS

The most important variable in paper chromatography is the solvent, the choice of which depends upon the nature of the substances to be separated. Solvent systems have been devised for separating members of virtually every class of compounds as can be seen from inspecting the data presented in Part III of this Handbook.

Solvents can be composed of two phases, the atmosphere of the chamber being saturated with the aqueous phase (or both phases), while the immiscible organic phase is used as the developer. Separations obtained in these systems are due primarily to the selective partitioning of the solutes between the two liquids. The phases can be reversed so that the more-polar layer is used as the solvent and the paper is impregnated with the less-polar layer (often an oil). In addition to two-phase solvents, "direct-phase" solvents consisting of an organic liquid saturated with a more-polar substance (e.g., phenol or *n*-butanol saturated with water), water-miscible solvents and even pure water have been used as the mobile phase. In general, polar solutes are separated in a polar solvent on cellulose which is unmodified or impregnated with a polar liquid; hydrophobic solutes are separated in reversed-phase systems (see Table 1).

1. *Aqueous Stationary Phase*

The paper is saturated with water by soaking and then blotting the excess, or water is taken up from the atmosphere by equilibrating hanging paper in a sealed chamber saturated with water vapor. Aqueous buffer or salt solutions are applied by dipping the paper, drying it, and then allowing it to equilibrate with water vapor in a chamber as just described.

Hydrophilic (e.g., sugars, amino acids) and some medium-polarity substances (e.g., ketonic, nitro) are separated on these papers by developing with solvents such as isopropanol-ammonia-water (9 : 1 : 2 v/v), *n*-butanol-acetic acid-water (4 : 1 : 5 v/v, organic layer) or phenol saturated with water. When two-phase solvents are employed, the chamber is saturated with both phases.

2. *Stationary Polar (Hydrophilic) Organic Solvent*

For volatile organic liquids (e.g., methanol), the paper is saturated from the atmosphere of the chamber and developed with an immiscible organic solvent. For less volatile liquids (e.g., dimethylformamide), the paper is drawn through the liquid dissolved in a volatile solvent (e.g., ethyl acetate), and the excess liquid is removed by blotting between two thick filter papers, squeezing the paper between rollers, or by simply holding the paper and letting the excess drip back into the vessel containing the impregnation solution. The paper is then hung in air until the solvent has evaporated (5–10 min). Many workers recommend saturating the mobile phase with the stationary liquid, but others suggest that this is not always necessary (if the two phases have very low mutual solubility) or even desirable (because the paper may extract additional impregnating liquid from the mobile phase, becoming overloaded and thereby causing lowered R_F values).

TABLE 1

SOLVENT SYSTEM ACCORDING TO SUBSTANCE GROUPS AFTER DECKER

Substance group	Solvent systems
1. Strongly hydrophilic substances, such as amino acids, sugar, more readily soluble in water than in alcohol, R_F values in water-free butanol about 0	Organic solvent mixtures that are miscible with water to an unlimited or limited extent, with 10–40% water content. Possibly addition of acids, bases, or salts, especially buffers. Addition of water increases R_F value.
2. Moderately hydrophilic substances, more readily soluble in alcohol than in water, R_F values in water-free butanol frequently 0, in water about 1	Same as 1. Moreover, mixtures with a lower percentage of water, which contain homopolar solvents, such as chloroform, benzene, petroleum ether, ethyl acetate.
3. Aromatic and heterocyclic substances, such as phenols, dyes; R_F values in water, possibly after addition of acids, salts, or ammonia, 0.05–0.9	Same as 1, and 2. Moreover, mixtures of solvents with water 1 : 1 or 2 : 1 and various additions, such as acids, alkalies, salts (e.g., Na_2SO_4), salts reduce the R_F values.
4. Lipids, soluble in petroleum ether, insoluble in water; R_F values with water >0, with water-saturated butanol about 1	I. Same as 1. (water content will here reduce the R_F values) Same as 2. (petroleum ether and other hydrocarbons will frequently reduce the R_F values), however, frequently useless because of "tail" formation. II. Solvent mixtures, where the water is completely or in part replaced by formamide, glycol, etc. If necessary, the paper should be impregnated with the stationary phase. III. Reverse-phase system. Paper hydrophobized with silicones, oils, rubber, chlorinated rubber, or through acetylation. Solvent aqueous phase.
5. Acids and bases	I. Same as 1. and 2. and addition of stronger acids or bases for repressing dissociation. II. Same as 1. and addition of bases or acids for conversion into the hydrophilic salts.

(Reprinted from "Filtrak Papers for Chromatography", VEB Spezialpapierfabrik Niederschlag, Niederschlag, Erzgebirge)

The Zaffaroni systems employ paper impregnated with formamide or propylene glycol and developed with benzene, $CHCl_3$, cyclohexane or mixtures of these. These types of systems are chosen for the separation of moderately-hydrophilic, medium-polarity solutes such as many steroids.

3. *Stationary Non-Polar (Hydrophobic) Solvent*

Reversed-phase systems are used for the separation of hydrophobic solutes. The paper is drawn through a solution of Vaseline, kerosene, paraffin oil, or silicone oil dissolved in hexane, petroleum ether or benzene, hung in air until the solvent evaporates, spotted and developed with an immiscible, more-polar solvent such as aqueous isopropanol (70%), dimethylformamide-methanol-H_2O (10 : 10 : 1 v/v), or aqueous acetic acid. The mobile phase is usually saturated with the stationary phase prior to development.

Another technique for impregnating the paper is to dip the top into the impregnating solution which rises up the paper toward the origin. If the mobile phase to be used for development carries the solutes at its front on nonimpregnated paper, the impregnating solution is halted just short of the origin line. After evaporating the solvent, the sample is spotted below the impregnated area. The mobile phase will rise through the sample and carry it into the impregnated area whereupon an ideal thin, transverse origin is produced spontaneously.

Acetylation makes cellulose less hydrophilic so that systems employing acetylated paper are essentially reversed-phase systems. Such paper preferentially takes up organic components from equilibrating solutions in the chamber.

D. TECHNIQUES OF PAPER CHROMATOGRAPHY

1. *Sample Preparation*

Samples are dissolved in a small volume of a suitable solvent (often a volatile, organic solvent such as acetone, ethanol or chloroform; not necessarily the same as the development solvent) at a concentration level high enough so that a small spot can be applied to the paper.

Extracts of animal or plant tissues and other biological samples are prepared by grinding or blending with a suitable solvent and removing insoluble residue by filtration or centrifugation. The extract must usually be purified and concentrated and often transferred to a different solvent before application to the paper. Removal of extraneous organic materials and inorganic salts, which can lead to anomalous results (e.g., streaking), is accomplished by solvent extraction, precipitation, electrolysis, or ion exchange.

Some chromatographic systems have been developed which allow biological samples to be directly applied to the paper without any preliminary clean-up. One example is the separation of amino acids by the development of untreated urine samples with three solvents in two directions on a 35 × 28 cm sheet of Whatman No. 1 paper (*5*).

Sometimes it is desirable to convert the substance of interest into a derivative before chromatography. This is true if the substance is more volatile or less easy to chromatograph, detect or to quantitate than the derivative.

Some methods for the preparation of samples suitable for chromatography are collected in Section II.II.

2. *Sample Application*

The amount of sample to be applied depends upon the sensitivity with which the solutes can be detected after migration and concomitant dilution. One to 20 μl of a solution containing 0.1–1 % (w/v) of each solute is typical, and this amount of sample can be manually applied to pencil-marked origins with a micropipette, a platinum loop or by a dab of a wood applicator stick. The origins are situated about 6 cm from the end of the paper for descending chromatography and 2–3 cm for ascending. The spot is dried after application, either in air or with a portable hair drier, and should be about 5 mm in diameter (15 mm at most). Larger volumes of samples are applied by successive applications of a small volume to the same area of paper with drying in between to keep the spot diameter small, or, alternatively, as a streak along the origin line across the paper.

Application of the sample in the form of a streak rather than as a single spot can be beneficial in eliminating the double tailing of chlorophyll zones separated from leaf extract (Figure 43). When the loadings are comparable, the separation from the streak and in the central regions of the migrating spots are identical in this case. Figure 43 also illustrates that higher loading causes all the pigment zones to be pushed forward resulting in poorer resolution of the leaf extract. Many workers state that dependence of R_F values on sample concentration indicates that the system is governed by an adsorption rather than a partition mechanism.

The two most important general guidelines are that initial zones be kept reasonably small and as uniform as possible, and that solutions of standards and of unknowns must be as similar as possible and they must be applied in exactly the same manner.

3. *Development Procedures*

a. *Descending development.* The end of the spotted paper nearest the origin is placed into a glass or plastic trough supported at the top of the developing chamber on wires or on glass rods. The paper is anchored in the trough by means of a glass rod and passes over a second, elevated rod which prevents siphoning of the solvent (Figure 44). Solvent is added carefully to the trough through a hole in the top of the chamber and flows through the origins and down the paper.

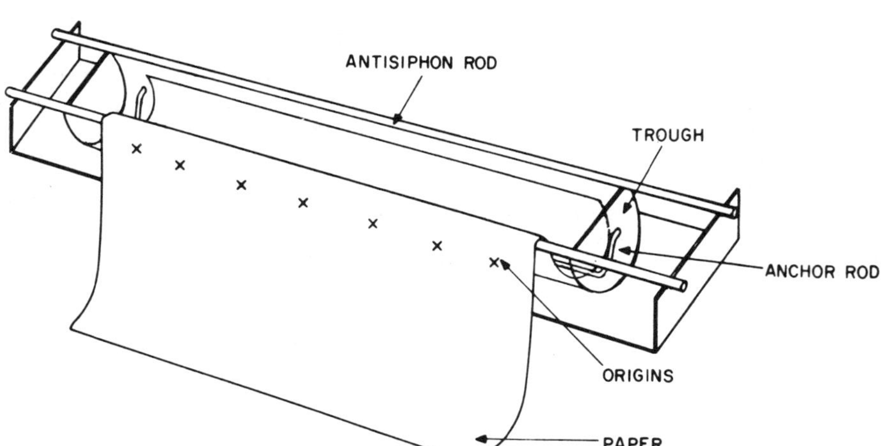

Figure 44. Arrangement of paper in a solvent trough for descending chromatography. A second piece of paper can be inserted under the anchor rod and over the second antisiphon rod for simultaneous development.

The chamber must be tightly closed in order to maintain its saturation with the vapors of the solvent components. This saturation is obtained by placing a small dish of the solvent (both phases when two-phase systems are used) at the bottom of the chamber, or by covering the bottom of the chamber with solvent and lining the walls with filter paper dipped into this solvent. Care must be taken that the paper being developed does not dip into this extra solvent or touch the paper lining the tank.

The paper may be saturated for a period in the tank after spotting but before the solvent is added to the trough. However, most workers now apply the initial spots to the paper and begin development at once (without pre-equilibration of the paper) in a tank pre-saturated with the solvent vapors. With this procedure, the paper is equilibrating with the solvent throughout the run.

At the end of development, the paper is removed and the solvent front marked at once so R_F values can be calculated. Glass chambers are convenient so the front can be observed during the run. For slow moving substances, better resolution may be achieved by permitting the solvent to drip off the lower end of the paper during development of several days duration. Migration must then be related to a standard compound rather than to the solvent front.

Various commercial chambers are available for the descending development of sheets up to 18 × 22 in. Apparatuses have been devised for automatically adding solvent to the troughs and stopping the solvent flow at a preselected distance from the origin.

b. *Ascending development*. In this method, solvent is placed in the bottom of the chamber, and the paper is suspended above it from a wire or glass rods (Figure 45a). Alternatively, the spotted paper can be clipped into the form of a cylinder and stood in the solvent (Figure 45b). The top of the solvent must be well below the level of the origin line on the sheet in each case. Again, the chamber may be lined with extra filter paper to improve vapor saturation.

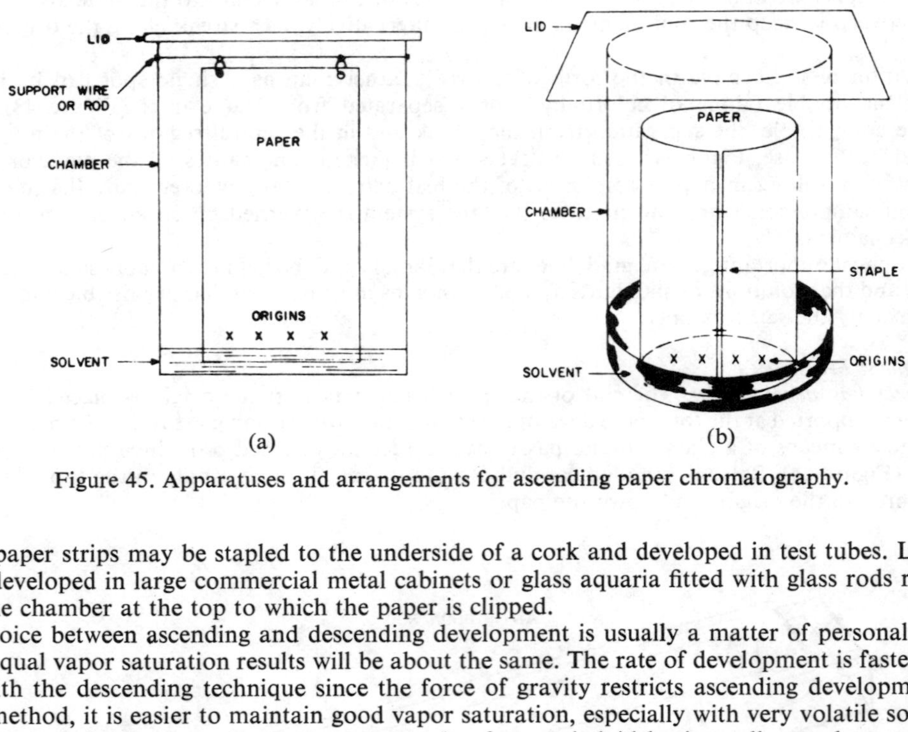

Figure 45. Apparatuses and arrangements for ascending paper chromatography.

Small paper strips may be stapled to the underside of a cork and developed in test tubes. Large paper sheets are developed in large commercial metal cabinets or glass aquaria fitted with glass rods running the length of the chamber at the top to which the paper is clipped.

The choice between ascending and descending development is usually a matter of personal preference since with equal vapor saturation results will be about the same. The rate of development is faster and more constant with the descending technique since the force of gravity restricts ascending development. In the ascending method, it is easier to maintain good vapor saturation, especially with very volatile solvents.

c. *Horizontal development*. A square or rectangle of paper is laid horizontally on glass rods or some other support, and the end nearest the origins is folded down and dipped into a solvent trough. Improved reproducibility of R_F values has been claimed for the horizontal method, and the chamber holding the support rods and trough can be made flat and quite compact so that it fits easily in an oven or refrigerator for development at elevated or reduced temperatures.

d. *Radial development*. In this method, the solutes are resolved into circular zones or arcs instead of the customary round or oval spots. Although circular zones are formed, circular paper is not required. The paper is usually developed in a horizontal position, but the method differs from that described directly above in that the solvent is fed to the paper through a wick or a restricted area of the paper. In one possible arrangement, horizontal, supported paper is in the shape of a square with a tab, which is bent down into the solvent, protruding from the center of one of the sides.

A simple apparatus for radial chromatography on a filter-paper disk consists of two equal-size Petri dishes slightly smaller than the paper. A narrow, parallel strip is cut from the center to the edge of the paper, and this is bent down at the center joint perpendicular to the paper to serve as a wick. The drop of mixture is placed on the paper disk at the joint of the wick, and the disk is placed between the two glass dishes, the lower containing the developing solvent. The rate of development is controlled by the width of the wick and the distance between the liquid surface and the paper. Dessicators can be used for larger tanks with the paper placed between the cover and the bottom part. Solvent is applied to the paper through a wick from a solvent reservoir below or fed to the paper by a pipette through a hole in the upper lid.

Multiple samples (e.g., standards and unknowns) can be applied as equidistant spots on a circle with a radius of 1–2 cm from the center of the paper disk; in this case, a series of segments results after radial development.

Resolution by radial chromatography is often superior to that by normal one-way ascending and descending chromatography because the arrangement leads to greater solvent flow at the trailing zone boundaries relative to the leading boundaries and therefore sharper zones.

e. *Overrun and unidimensional multiple development.* One method for gaining a greater effective distance of solvent flow without actually increasing the length of the paper is overrun development, where the solvent is allowed to continue flowing after the front has reached the end of the paper. This is accomplished by cutting drip points along the bottom of descending chromatograms or allowing the top of ascending chromatograms to protrude out of a slot in the chamber lid.

Another method is to develop the paper as usual by ascending or descending solvent flow, dry the paper, and repeat the development one or more times with the same, or a different solvent. The following equation is used to calculate the optimum number of developments with the same solvent in the same direction for obtaining the greatest separation between two substances

$$\eta_{opt} = \frac{\log[\log(1 - R_{F_2})/\log(1 - R_{F_1})]}{\log(1 - R_{F_1})/(1 - R_{F_2})} \qquad [55]$$

where R_{F_1} and R_{F_2} are the R_F values of the two compounds after one development, $R_{F_1} > R_{F_2}$.

f. *Two-dimensional development.* The mixture is placed in one corner of a square sheet of paper and developed in succession with two different solvents in transverse directions. Development is by ascending or descending flow as described above; the chromatogram is thoroughly dried in a hood or chromatographic oven between the runs in order to remove all traces of the first solvent. By judiciously choosing solvents with different characteristics, this procedure yields the maximum resolution of complex mixtures. Figure 46 illustrates the separation of amino acids in a protein hydrolysate by development with an acidic and basic solvent.

Two-dimensional chromatography with reaction of the solutes on the paper after the first run is used to assess the effect of an enzyme or reagent on the solute or to aid in their identification. The same or a different solvent is then used in the second direction. To improve resolution, spots can be transferred automatically from one type of paper to another type or to a thin layer by attaching the papers or the paper and the thin layer together for two-dimensional chromatography. Already mentioned in Section B were two-dimensional separations with a different mechanism operative in each direction on adsorbent and ion-exchange papers.

g. *Gradient development.* Various methods have been described for changing the composition of the solvent continuously during the run [e.g., Reference (*6*)]. This is a specialized method, which like centrifugal-paper chromatography and some others, has not been widely used.

4. *Detection Methods*

After development and marking of the solvent front, the paper is removed from the chamber and dried in a hood with the aid of a fan or electric hair drier or in a chromatography oven. The solutes, if they are not naturally colored, must then be located.

a. *Chemical methods.* A suitable chemical reagent which forms a colored or fluorescent derivative with the compounds of interest is applied by dipping the paper into a solution of the reagent in a shallow tray or by spraying the solution onto the paper by means of an atomizer or aerosol bomb. The paper must sometimes be heated to complete the reaction. In some cases, two or three reagents are sprayed on the paper in turn to give the desired reaction.

The dipping technique is considered by some workers to be superior although it is probably not as widely used as spraying. The solvent chosen for the reagent solution must be one in which the solutes and their derivatives have very low solubility so that the spots remain fixed on the paper. Spray reagents are applied lightly and as uniformly as possible over the entire surface of the paper.

Section II.I lists a large number of reagents suitable for the detection of many types of compounds. Limits of detection for most compounds range from about 50 μg to <0.1 μg with reagents of this type, depending upon the type of compound, the type of paper, the compactness of the spots, etc.

Maximum information is gained from a single chromatogram if a series of reagents are applied sequentially either by dipping or by spraying. One example is the use of ninhydrin to detect amino acids followed by Ehrlich reagent in acid solution to detect indoles and finally anisidine reagent to detect imidazoles and hydroxyindoles.

b. *Physical methods.* Many organic substances absorb ultraviolet light between 240–260 nm and show up as dark areas when illuminated with such light. In some cases the sensitivity is improved if the paper is sprayed with fluorescein. This provides a fluorescent background against which the absorbing spots contrast sharply.

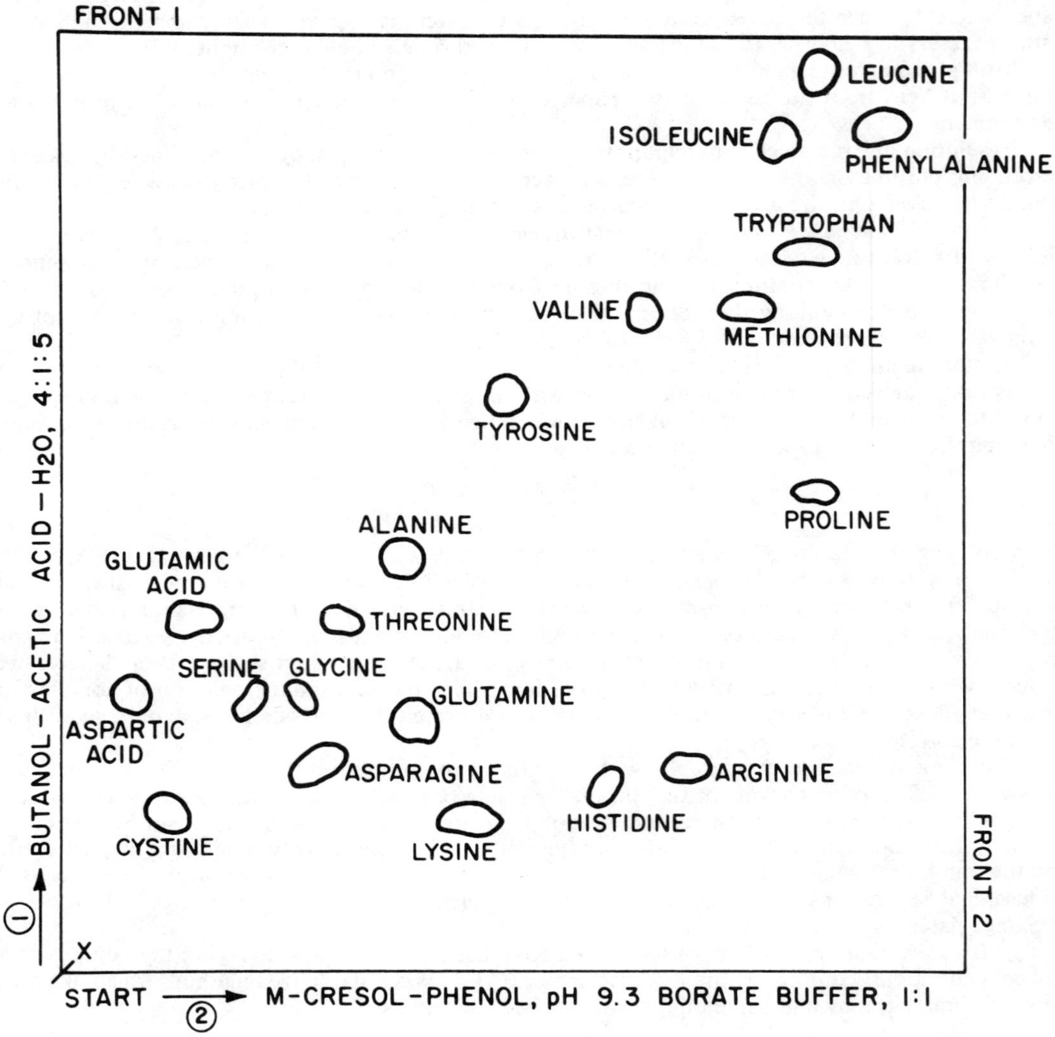

Figure 46. Two-dimensional paper chromatographic separation of amino acids [after (*11*)].

Other organic substances fluoresce when illuminated with light of about 360 nm (some only after heating or cooling the chromatogram) or phosphoresce when illuminated with 254 nm light (in some cases only in the wet state but not when present as dry spots on paper). Papers are conveniently examined in a darkened room under a long- or shortwave ultraviolet hand lamp or in a lighted room in a portable viewing cabinet.

c. *Radioactivity*. The positions of radioactive (labelled) substances can be determined by autoradiography or by scanning the paper with a hand-held counter or a mechanical scanner which graphically records peaks of radioactivity corresponding to the location of each zone. Both of these techniques are discussed in more detail in Section H.

d. *Biological methods*. Bioautographic methods of detection, based on the inhibition of growth of certain organisms, are specific for active antibiotics and do not detect biologically inactive artifacts, decomposition products or impurities. The procedure is to put the chromatogram on the surface of an agar plate which has been inoculated with a test organism (usually *Staphylococcus aureus* or *Bacillus subtilis*) which is sensitive to the antibiotic to be detected. After incubation for 15–20 hr at about 37°, clear zones become visible in the agar layer where the antibiotic has diffused in and inhibited the growth of the microorganism. The rest of the surface appears opaque. The time of incubation can be shortened and the growth-inhibition zones made more conspicuous by spraying the agar plate with a solution of 2,3,5-triphenyltetrazolium chloride and a solution of 2,6-dichlorophenol-indophenol after 4 hr incubation. After an additional 30 min incubation, inhibition zones are visible as blue spots on a colorless background.

Inhibitory zone diameters can be measured and related to concentration for the semi-quantitative estimation of antibiotics.

5. *Documentation of Results*

Chromatographic results can be recorded by means of R_F or R_X values as described above or by making drawings, Xerox copies, UV photocopies or photographs of the actual chromatograms.

In many cases, the papers themselves can be retained for future reference. Storage in the dark or spraying with a certain solution can help retard fading of the colored spots with time. For example, Zweig has recommended a copper nitrate-nitric acid dip followed by a clear acrylic spray for the preservation of amino acid chromatograms detected with ninhydrin.

E. IDENTIFICATION OF SUBSTANCES

Chromatography can be used in the following ways to aid in the identification of a substance. As more of these methods are employed to gain information, the degree of probability of the identification is greatly increased.

1. Co-chromatography—tentative identification is obtained if the unknown is mixed with an authentic standard and the two cannot be separated in several diverse systems.
2. Use of selective color-forming reagents after development.
3. Recording of visible, ultraviolet and infrared spectra after elution of the spots from the paper. UV and phosphorescence spectra can be recorded for substances directly on the paper, although the spectra may differ from those obtained for the same substances in solution.
4. Chemical reactions performed directly on the paper before one-way chromatography or between developments in two-way chromatography. [See Reference (7) for a review of diagonal techniques.]
5. Systematic analysis—R_F values are obtained for the unknown in a series of solvents under very reproducible conditions. The "chromatographic spectrum" (a plot of the R_F values in different solvents) of the unknown is compared to the spectra of reference compounds.

F. PREPARATIVE PAPER CHROMATOGRAPHY

Milligram to gram quantities of pure substances can be prepared by scaled-up descending chromatography using thick filter paper. The separated compounds are eluted from the paper with suitable solvents, the solvent evaporated and the compounds crystallized.

Samples are applied as streaks or adjacent spots to the origin of the paper. Commercial applicators especially designed for preparative chromatography are available. Spots of sample and/or standards are applied near the edges of the paper. After development, marginal guide strips are cut from the paper and sprayed to locate the bands containing the compounds of interest in the main sheet. The guide strips are fitted back on the paper, and horizontal areas of paper corresponding to the markers are cut from the paper and eluted by attaching a paper wick from a solvent reservoir and a drip point (Figure 47). The resultant paper strip is folded into a supported trough and placed in a chromatographic chamber for descending development.

In addition to free paper sheets, paper disks tightly compressed into a column, paper pressed into a block, paper wound into a roll, or a rotating paper cylinder can be used for preparative chromotography.

G. QUANTITATIVE PAPER CHROMATOGRAPHY

Quantitative paper chromatography involves the application of uniform, reproducible initial zones containing a known amount of solution; separation by development with a solvent that yields regular zones; formation, if necessary, of a colored derivative of the substance of interest; and measurement of the solute either after its elution from the paper or directly on the paper.

1. *Formation of the Colored Derivative*

The detection reagent must be applied in a concentration high enough to react completely with the greatest concentration of solute that will occur. This may require the use of higher-concentration reagents than are needed for qualitative work. The background areas usually serve as blanks and so should be kept as uniform as possible; dipping techniques for the application of reagents usually give better results than spraying in this regard. Rapid reactions are chosen, if possible, for detection of the spots. Slow reactions are allowed to occur for a timed period which will give maximum difference between the color of the zone and the background. It may be necessary to protect the paper from the light and laboratory atmosphere during the reaction period. Zones that fade badly may be photographed at the height of their intensity and the quantitation made from the photographs. Plots relating the derivative concentration to the concentration of the original compound may or may not be linear; nonlinear reactions can often be used for accurate analyses as long as they are reproducible.

2. *Estimation of the Spots*

Once the colored derivative has been formed, the chromatogram is quantitated by direct or elution methods. In either case appropriate standards are always analyzed along with the unknowns. The concen-

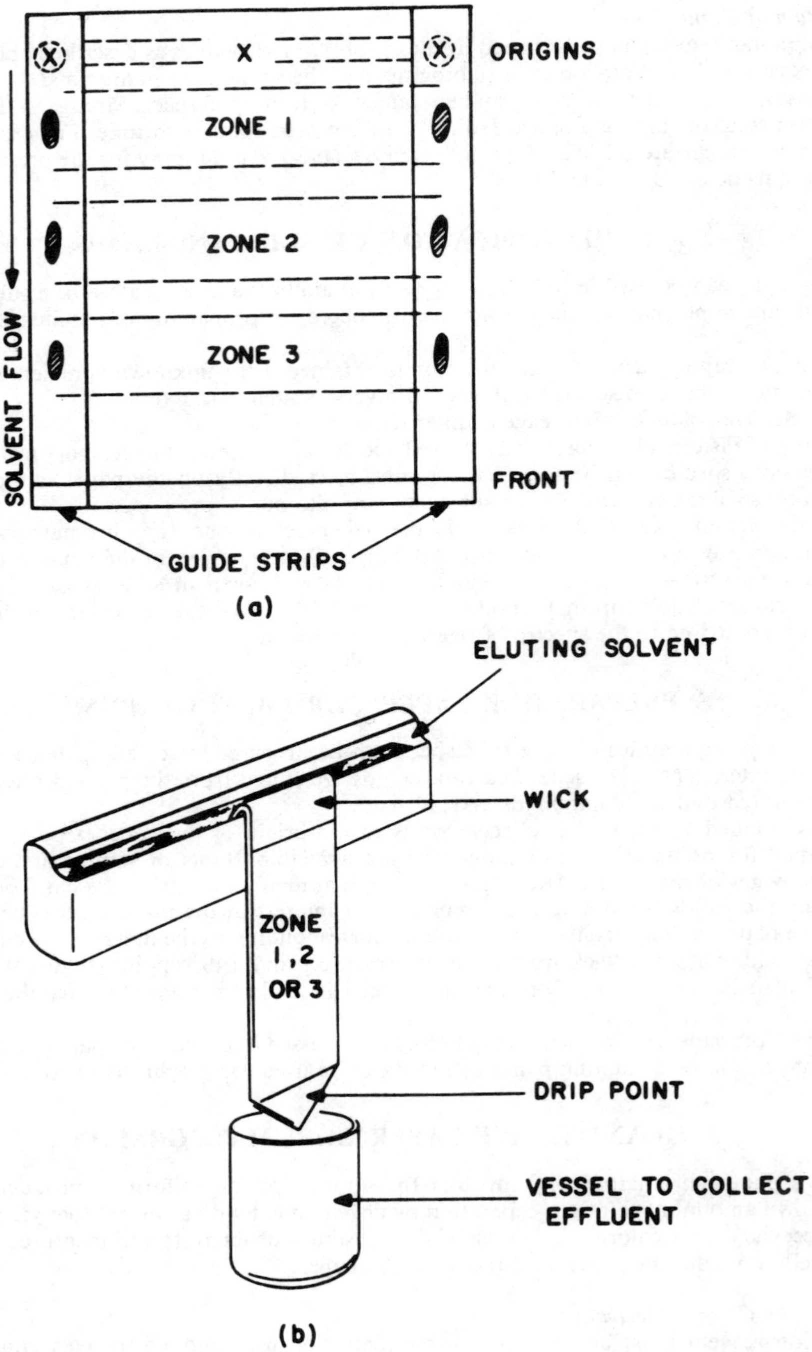

Figure 47. Arrangement of the paper sheet (a) and elution of the zones of substances from the paper (b) in preparative paper chromatography.

trations of standards are chosen so as to bracket the unknown, and the treatment of the unknown and the standards must be in all ways identical.

It is important for direct, comparative methods that the standard solutions be as similar as possible to the solution of the unknown so that the distribution of the compound of interest in all zones is the same. If the test solution contains impurities which could alter the zone distribution, the same impurities should be added to the knowns, or internal standardization should be employed.

a. *Visual estimation.* For many purposes, a rough estimation of the amount present in the unknown made by visual comparison with a series of standards is adequate. Some workers claim that optimum results are obtained when a range of standards of increasing concentration are spotted alternately with a range of dilutions of the unknown decreasing in concentration.

b. *Spot areas*. Another visual method involves measurement of the areas of spots after chromatography and plotting the areas *vs* the logarithm of the amount of substance present in the spots. If a series of standard spots of the same initial size, covering a short concentration range, is used, these quantities are linearly related and the concentration of an unknown can be read from the graph. If the sample is applied as a streak across a paper strip, the length of the developed zone is proportional to the log of the zone concentration in many cases.

c. *Elution methods*. The separated solutes can be eluted from the paper and determined in the eluate by any appropriate analytical method (e.g., spectrophotometry, microtitration, microgravimetry, etc.). If the solute is naturally colored or fluorescent, the areas of paper containing the solutes can be easily located. If not, guide strips (Section F) are treated with color-forming reagents to determine which region of paper to elute. In some cases, the locating reagent is applied to the chromatogram itself, and the colored derivative is eluted and measured by colorimetry. This variation is faster since guide strips are not required.

Miniaturized methods similar to that shown in Figure 47b have been developed for the elution of individual spots from paper in a very small volume of solvent. Commercial micro-Soxhlet extractors are also useful for the removal of solutes from areas of paper cut from chromatograms.

Errors of 1–2% or below have been claimed for elution methods, as compared to 10–20% for the visual methods described earlier. Recent work indicates that to obtain this high level of accuracy, automatic, machine spotting of samples is required.

If the elution step is not quantitative, it must be at least reproducible. Cellulose fibers appearing in the effluent can be removed, if necessary, by filtering through a small bed of Celite. Unstable solutes must be eluted and determined as quickly as possible.

d. *Direct photometric measurement of spots on the paper*. The instrumental analogue to visual comparison is photodensitometric measurement of the intensity of standard and unknown spots directly on the paper. Densitometry involves the manual or automatic scanning of the chromatogram with filtered light (e.g., visible light of 500 nm or light in the UV or IR regions) in order to measure the amount transmitted through (or reflected from) the paper. The machine is zeroed on a part of the paper free of any solute (the blank), and the strip is then moved slowly past a photocell (Figure 48). The readout consists of a series of peaks whose positions correspond to the spot locations and whose areas correspond to spot intensities.

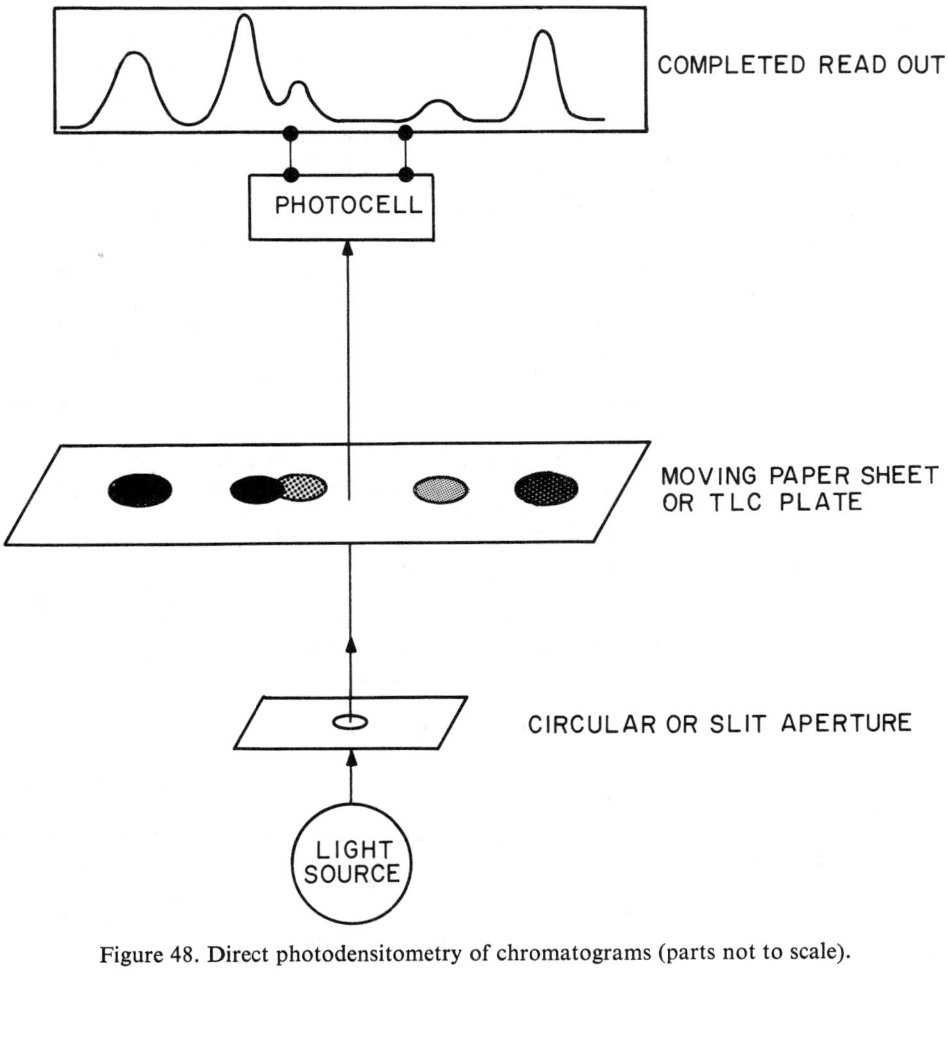

Figure 48. Direct photodensitometry of chromatograms (parts not to scale).

Commercial densitometry systems, available from several manufacturers, incorporate automatic and continuous integration of the areas of the peaks as well as ways of compensating for deviations from the Lambert–Beer Law in the spectroscopic process.

The colored spots are generally scanned through the spot centers along the line of development. Scanning perpendicular to the line of development may be desirable if the spots are poorly separated or if impurities are located between the spots so that there are no blank areas between the spots. When scanning a number of spots in a row, care must be taken to ensure that the center of each spot is being scanned. Instead of the chromatogram itself, a photographic negative can be evaluated by densitometry.

Densitometry is more convenient than methods involving elution and requires less sample for analysis. Most workers report errors of about 5–7% for photometric *in situ* procedures, indicating that elution methods are in general more accurate.

H. RADIOISOTOPE TECHNIQUES

Radioactivity can be exploited for the detection, identification and quantitation of compounds separated by paper chromatography. Various aspects of some of these procedures will be briefly described.

1. *Autoradiography*

The beta-emitting isotopes ^{14}C, ^{35}S and ^{32}P are detected by placing the chromatogram in direct contact with x-ray film. The exposed film, developed by usual darkroom methods, shows the exact self image of the radioactive spots. Radioactive spots may be identified by co-chromatography in which the radioactive regions are eluted from the chromatogram and rechromatographed together with non-radioactive carrier of the suspected compound. Coincidence for a given spot of radioactivity and color formed by a specific reagent is sufficient for tentative identification. Densitometric measurement of the degree of blackening of the film allows semiquantitative evaluation of the chromatogram.

For tritium, x-ray film without the usual protective gelatin layer (which will absorb the low energy beta rays) is used. Alternatively, the paper itself is impregnated with photographic emulsion and developed photographically, or with a liquid scintillator to convert the beta energy into light energy which causes exposure of the film.

A much faster, but lower resolution, method than conventional autoradiography for the evaluation of ^{14}C, ^{35}S, and ^{3}H chromatograms is the spark chamber technique. See Reference (*8*) for a complete discussion.

2. *Radiometric Methods*

Both elution and direct evaluation methods are used for the quantitation of radioactive zones. In the elution method, the spots are located by autoradiography or scanning of the paper with a ratemeter, cut from the paper and eluted into a counting planchet for measurement by conventional counting techniques (e.g., G-M, proportional, gas-flow, or liquid-scintillation counters). Direct measurement involves automatically scanning the chromatogram by drawing it in front of a counter. Commercial instruments of various degrees of sophistication are available for scanning one- and two-dimensional chromatograms.

Liquid scintillation spectrometry is used for counting tritium as well as for ^{35}S, ^{32}P and ^{14}C. The paper can be examined by cutting it into small, equal sections and inserting each into a counting vial to which phosphor solution is added. Or, the whole spot can be cut out (sometimes after application of a color-forming locating reagent) and counted. Corrections are made to reflect the counting efficiency for each isotope and for quenching effects due to substances adsorbed on the paper or to the solute-reagent complex and the excess reagent if a detection test is used.

a. *Isotope indicators.* Solutes, after chromatography, may be treated on the paper with a radioactive reagent to form a radioactive derivative which can be located by the methods described above. Examples are the detection of metal ions by $H_2{}^{35}S$ and reducing sugars with $^{110}AgNO_3$.

b. *Neutron activation analysis.* The finished chromatogram is placed in a nuclear reactor, where it undergoes nuclear bombardment. Some of the atoms in the separated compounds become radioactive, and these compounds are determined by comparing the activities to those of similarly treated standards. Time is usually required for the background activity of the paper to drop to a low level. Activation analysis methods are highly sensitive and convenient in that the sample preparation, development, drying, etc., can be performed without the problems associated with handling radioactive compounds.

I. SOURCES OF ERROR

Studies by Fairbairn have indicated that the major sources of error in quantitative paper chromatography are caused by the delivery of the initial spots and differences between the slopes of the regression lines (relating measurement of the final spot with quantities applied to the initial spots) from sheet to sheet. These were overcome by using machine spotting (The Chromaplot Machine by Burkard Mfg. Co., Hertfordshire, England, was specifically recommended by Fairbairn) and the use of standard and test solutions for each sheet. No additional error was caused by the development except where adjacent spots had very dissimilar quantities of solute leading to lateral diffusion and some slight errors.

For optimum results in densitometric methods, the volumes of the initial spots must be accurately measured, the initial spots should be of equal area, they should be dried in a current of cold air, tank conditions should be as constant as possible, and two quantities of the standard, one a multiple of the other, and two quantities of unknown, differing by the same factor, should be used for each assay. Color development is carried out by spraying on both sides of the paper or by dipping, depending upon which is most convenient for the particular reagent being used. Densitometry is always begun at exactly the same time after color development for each chromatogram. If these procedures are followed, errors of individual determinations are reduced to about $\pm 6\%$ (coefficient of variation about 2–3%; that is, 95% of the results will fall within 4–6% of the mean). If replicates are made, the limits of error are reduced by $1/\sqrt{n}$, where n is the number of replicates (*9*).

REFERENCES

1. Stewart, G. H., *Advances in Chromatography* **1**, 93 (1966).
2. Thoma, J. A., *Advances in Chromatography* **6**, 61 (1968).
3. Green J. and D. McHale, *Advances in Chromatography* **2**, 99 (1966).
4. Knight, C. S., *Advances in Chromatography* **4**, 98 (1967).
5. Singh, P. I., Bajaj, V. R., and A. S. Saini, *J. Chromatogr.* **43**, 554 (1969).
6. DeWachter, R., *J. Chromatogr.* **36**, 109 (1968).
7. Hais, I. M., *J. Chromatogr.* **48**, 200 (1970).
8. Hesselbo, T., *Chromatographic and Electrophoretic Techniques*, I. Smith, Ed., **Vol. 1**, Chapter 27, Interscience Publishers (Division of John Wiley & Sons, Inc.), N.Y., 1969.
9. Fairbairn, J. W., "Quantitative Paper and Thin Layer Chromatography," E. J. Shellard, Ed., Academic Press, New York, 1968, pp 1–14.
10. Strain, H. H. and J. Sherma, *J. Chem. Educ.* **46**, 479 (1969).
11. Levy, A. L. and D. Chung, *Anal. Chem.* **25**, 396 (1953).

VOLUME TWO
SECTION I

PRINCIPLES AND TECHNIQUES

I.V Thin-Layer Chromatography

Section I.V

THIN-LAYER CHROMATOGRAPHY (TLC)

Although paper chromatography had made valuable contributions to all fields of biology and chemistry, the sole use of cellulose as the stationary phase imposed a great limitation on the technique, because paper is not universally satisfactory for all separations (e.g., some classes of lipids). Scientists began, therefore, to wonder how they could employ the adsorbents which were so useful in the Tswett column method in a convenient sheet form, like paper. The present-day system of TLC was first introduced in 1951 by Kirchner *et al.* (*1*), and additional work on modifications and applications for the method was published by these authors in a series of papers during the years 1952–57. The method became popular after Ergon Stahl helped develop commercial equipment and adsorbents for TLC.

The adsorbent is mixed with a binder, often plaster of Paris, made into a slurry with water, and coated on a glass plate using a spreading device. After drying, a rugged thin layer of adsorbent, usually 0.25 mm thick, is bound to the glass plate. This layer can be used for chromatography in a manner similar to a paper sheet. However, separations now depend on the properties of the adsorbent surface much as if the adsorbent were packed in a column. For this reason, thin-layer chromatography is sometimes called open-column chromatography.

The technical aspects (sample application, development, detection, quantification, etc.) of paper and thin-layer chromatography are very closely related. With the present commercial availability of flexible cellulose thin layers on plastic film as well as adsorbent-loaded chromatography papers, the borderline between the two methods is indeed indistinct.

In addition to the traditional adsorbents, systems employing layers of ion exchangers, exclusion gels, liquid-coated supports, and combinations of these are now used in conjunction with many different varieties of solvents for the separation of all types of compounds. TLC is a highly sensitive, versatile analytical method, resulting in generally sharp and rapid separations.

Much of what is written in the preceding sections concerning theory, methods and materials applies to TLC. Depending upon the type of layer employed, the mechanism of separation can be adsorption, partition, ion exchange, exclusion or a combination of these. Many of the techniques are the same as those used in paper chromatography and most of the coating materials have already been described.

A. COATING MATERIALS

Table 8 (Section II.III) shows the TLC coating materials available from various manufacturers. These are similar to the sorbents used for column chromatography except that they are generally of a smaller particle size. Some of these contain a binder such as plaster of Paris ($CaSO_4$) or starch to improve the adherence of the film to the plate. An inert fluorescent indicator (e.g., zinc silicate) which fluoresces when illuminated with 2540 or 3660 Å UV light so as to aid in the detection of separated spots is also sometimes included. The presence of a binder may change the properties of the sorptive layer. Some materials (e.g., cellulose) are completely free of additives and still adhere well.

Silica gel is by far the most used adsorbent for TLC. In choosing a sorbent system, one is guided by the characteristics of the compounds to be separated such as the acidity or basicity, ionic character, solubility, and possibility of chemical reaction with the layer or the solvent. In general, lipophilic compounds are separated on aluminum oxide, silica gel, acetylated cellulose and polyamide. Hydrophilic substances are separated on cellulose, ion-exchange cellulose, kieselguhr and polyamide. This generalization is merely a rough guide since, for example, fat-soluble chloroplast pigments are successfully separated on cellulose as well as on alumina, magnesia and silica gel.

Activated silica gel is an acidic adsorptive medium especially suited to the separation of acidic and neutral compounds. Classes of compounds readily separated include aldehydes and ketones, alkaloids, sugars, phenols, steroids, and amino acids. Nonactivated silica gel contains enough water to permit separations based on a partition mechanism to be carried out. Aluminum oxide (alumina) is a basic adsorptive medium (acidic and neutral alumina are also available) useful for the resolution of basic and neutral compounds including polycyclic hydrocarbons, alkaloids, amines, fat-soluble vitamins, and aldehydes and ketones. Alumina may catalyze the decomposition of many organic compounds.

Kieselguhr is a neutral sorbent widely used as a support for partition separations. Cellulose powders for TLC are available in both fibrous and microcrystalline forms and can be used for all separations which can be done on paper. Magnesium oxide, the properties of which are strongly dependent upon the method of preparation, is selective for compounds with aromatic and conjugated double bonds.

Cellulose and resinous ion exchangers are used in thin-layer ion-exchange chromatography. The latter are also useful for thin-layer separations of organic compounds by a partition mechanism (section IIID5b). The resin can be bound to the plate with starch or can be mixed with cellulose powder prior to spreading. Silica gel and cellulose layers are impregnated with liquid ion exchangers (e.g., HDEHP, triisooctylamine) to achieve similar results.

Dextran gels are used for thin-layer gel-filtration chromatography with descending solvent flow only (no capillarity is operative). Development times are relatively long.

Polyamide powder is used for both column and thin-layer chromatography. Separations are usually based upon hydrogen bonding between the polymer chains and the solutes, although other factors are involved in some cases. Polyamide powders are prepared from Nylon 66 (polyhexamethyldiamine adipate), Nylon 11 (polyaminoundecanoic acid), Perlon (polycaprolactam) and acetylated Perlon. Classes of compounds separated include nitroanilines, benzophenones, phenols, flavonoids, amino acid derivatives, etc.

Alginic acid has been introduced as a support with ion exchange and complexing properties. Separations of various metal ions are possible by elution with aqueous acids (*2*).

Powdered glass (Corning) has been recently used as a successful adsorbent for TLC. The glass is ground to 200–250 mesh and mixed with plaster of Paris before spreading the layer. Polyacrylonitrile, polyacrylamide and poly(*N*-acetyl acrylamide) have been used for the separation of water soluble substances.

Layers can be modified in various ways to suit a particular separation: Two sorbents can be mixed prior to preparing the layer; adjacent layers of different sorbents can be placed on the same plate; buffers, precipitants (e.g., sulfide for the separation of metals), complexing agents (e.g., borate for sugars), chelating agents (for inorganic ions), $AgNO_3$ (for unsaturated compounds), hydrophobic materials, etc., can be incorporated; layers with activity gradients in various directions can be prepared [see References (*3*), (*4*)].

B. PREPARATION OF LAYERS

Various commercial apparatus are available for applying sorbent layers to glass plates (20 × 20 cm or 10 × 20 cm) or polyester film. As an example, Figure 49 shows the Kensco multi-thickness applicator which has interchangeable gates for producing layers of 250, 275, 500, 750, 1000, 1500 or 2000 μ thickness. An adjustable gate for layer thicknesses from 50 to 3000 μ in steps of 50 μ is also available. [It has been generally found that within a reasonably wide range of layer thicknesses (ca. 0.15 to 2.0 mm) R_F values are constant.] A gradient-thickness layering gate for producing a layer that gradually decreases in thickness allows heavy sample loading on the thicker part of the layer while the more rapidly moving trace components in the sample may be more easily visualized and recovered in the thinner portion. Adsorbent reservoir dividers allow the production of two to five parallel sections of different sorbent layers on the same plate; if sample development is carried out with the sections aligned horizontally, the sample will travel through each section in turn and fractionations not successful on one sorbent could occur on another. Or, the sections can be aligned vertically with samples being developed simultaneously on each for comparison under identical conditions.

The Camag plate coater (Figure 50) works in a different manner, such that the applicator is stationary and the plate is moved under the applicator. Layers of 300 and 500 μ thickness are produced, the 300 μ layer shrinking on drying to 250 μ.

Slurries are prepared by mixing the sorbent powder with an amount of water specified by the manufacturer (e.g., 30 g Mallinckrodt SilicAR TLC-7GF in 55 ml of water) in a mortar until the slurry is homogeneous and free of lumps or air bubbles. For the preparation of uniform layers of cellulose, homogenization of an aqueous suspension with an electric blender for 30–60 sec is often recommended. If a binder is present in the sorbent, coating must be carried out before the slurry hardens. Some workers prefer to use organic solvents in place of some or all of the water required to prepare the slurry, and basic silica gel layers for the separation of alkaloids can be produced by using dilute NaOH in place of water.

Layers of silica gel and alumina are first air-dried at room temperature for about 15 min without disturbing the support. They then may be dried vertically in a chromatography oven for 1–2 hr at 100–120 °C. Stahl recommends preliminary air-drying followed by 10 min drying by hot air in a vertical position and then 30 min at 110 °C. Truter states that air-drying overnight gives a layer activity about the same as drying at 100 °C. The temperature and time of drying are varied depending upon the activity required. Activity is determined by chromatographing a commercially available standard dye mixture. The plates are stored before use, if necessary, in a dessicator over silica gel. Convenient storage racks are commercially available.

Layers of cellulose, polyamide, and ion-exchange materials are thoroughly air-dried but are not usually oven heated. Sephadex gels are used at once in the swollen state.

Procedures for impregnating thin-layer plates with formamide, silicone, paraffin, etc., for partition separations are given as part of Table 8 (Section II.III).

If a commercial spreading device is not available, satisfactory layers can be produced in various other ways. Layers of masking tape may be placed on two opposite edges of a glass plate at a height equivalent to the desired layer thickness. The slurry is poured on the plate, a glass rod is drawn in a parallel direction over the taped edges to smooth out the layer, and the tape is later removed after the layer has set. Alternatively, tape can be put around the ends of the glass rod to raise it the required distance from the glass plate during the spreading operation. A slurry can be sprayed onto a horizontal glass plate with various laboratory spray devices, although the resulting layer will be nonuniform and of unknown thickness. Carefully cleaned microscope slides can be coated by dipping two slides back to back into a well-stirred nonaqueous slurry of sorbent. The slides are lifted out slowly, and excess adsorbent is drained. The slides dry

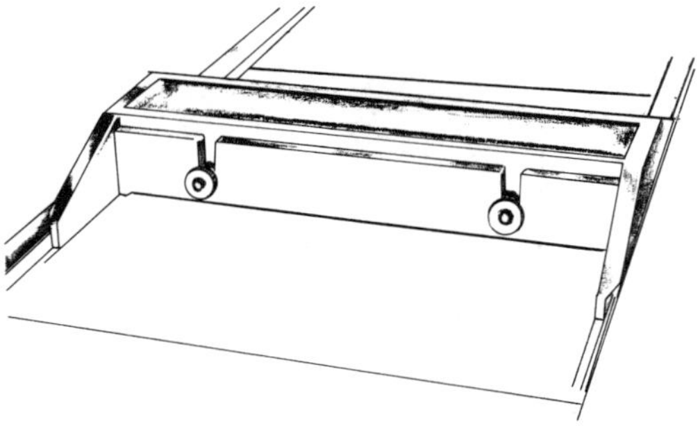

(a)

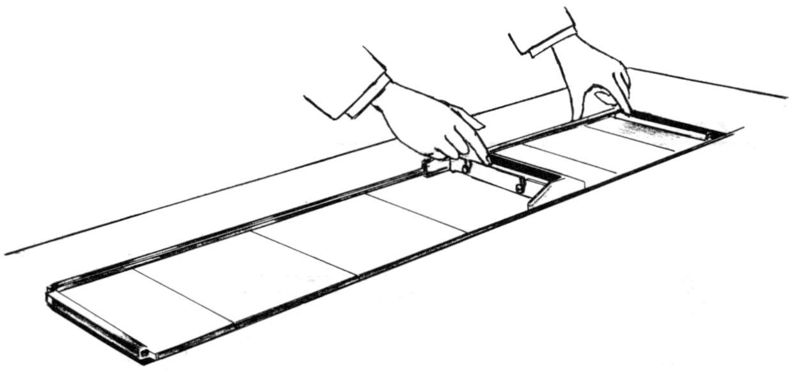

(b)

Figure 49. (a) Multi-thickness applicator with interchangeable gates. A choice of easily interchangeable gates is used with the multi-thickness applicator. Each gate has a different aperture which determines the layer thickness to be applied. When slipped into position on the applicator the gate moves freely in a vertical direction and produces a uniform layer across the plate by measuring from the surface of each successive plate. (b) Applying adsorbent layers with the multi-thickness applicator. Slurry is spread with a single smooth movement of the applicator along the guide bar. Matched glass plates are not required. Each plate receives the same adsorbent layer regardless of nominal variations in glass thickness or dimensional irregularities. The procedure for applying adsorbents to film is the same as coating glass. A single piece of film 48 inches long by 8 inches wide is coated with one continuous layer. After drying, sections of any dimension can be cut off with scissors, and the remaining film can be rolled without damage to the layer and stored. [Permission to reproduce from p. 4, Catalog K-400, Kensington Scientific Co., Oakland, Calif.]

rapidly. They are separated, the edges wiped clean with tissue, and, if necessary, the plates are steamed briefly to obtain a more strongly bound layer.

Precoated layers of many sorbents are available from various manufacturers (Section II.III, Table 8) on glass plates, plastic film and aluminum foils. The plastic films cannot be used with all organic solvents and not all brands will withstand corrosive, charring detection sprays. Coated glass tubes are also used.

Ultrathin liquid films and vacuum evaporated thin films (1 μ) of metal oxides provide some very rapid and sensitive separations [see References (*5*)–(*7*)].

C. CHROMATOGRAPHIC TECHNIQUES

1. *Sample Preparation and Application*

Samples are prepared for chromatography by procedures similar to those used for paper and liquid-column chromatography (Section II.II). Plates coated with a small strip of strong-acid ion exchanger in cellulose at the origin while the rest of the plate is covered with pure cellulose can be used to analyze the amino acids in urine without desalting the sample: The sample is spotted in the resin area and two develop-

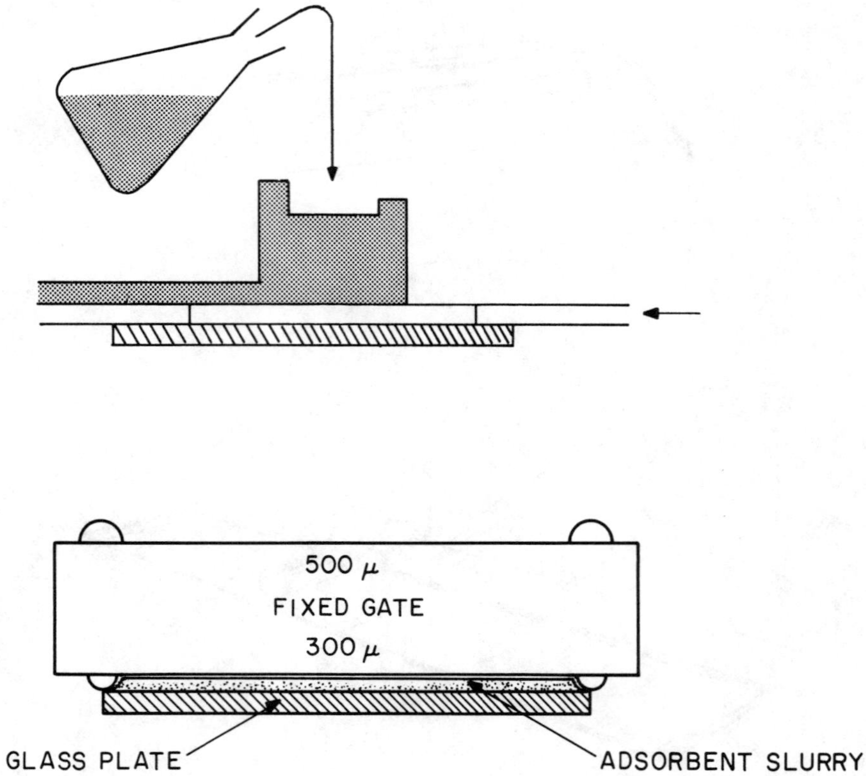

Figure 50. The Camag finger-tip plate coater. Reproduced with permission from Camag, Inc., New Berlin, Wisconsin.

ments in one dimension with water and a basic solvent, followed by an acid solvent in the second dimension, isolates the unwanted salts in the resin and separates the amino acids from each other on the cellulose.

Another method involving cleanup on the layer for drugs in blood is as follows:

First spot serum directly on a flexible, precoated, silica-gel thin-layer sheet. Then develop to a distance of 3 cm above the sample origin with a one-to-one mixture of ethyl alcohol-chloroform to denature and precipitate the protein and to extract the drug with the solvent front. Finally, remove the sheet. Dry it, cut off the first centimeter containing the protein residue, and remigrate the remainder of the sheet in a solvent system suitable for resolution of the drug and standard reference compounds. Application of reference materials in normal serum is particularly important in this case since matrix effects can be quite pronounced (*8*).

Substances can be changed to derivatives (e.g., trimethylsilylated carbohydrates) prior to chromatography to facilitate detection, identification or analysis.

Samples are usually applied as 0.1–1% solutions with a 1–25 μl micropipette or capillary tube. The spot size should be 1–3 mm d., and spots are kept 1–2 cm apart. Spotting templates are available as an aid in placing samples. For analytical separations, 1 μg to 0.5 mg of sample is generally applied, depending upon the layer material and the sensitivity of the detection method. The initial spots should be 15 mm from the lower end of the plate. Commercial sample applicators are available for the semi-automatic deposition of up to 12 similar or different samples onto a standard TLC plate [e.g., from Kensington Scientific Corp.; see also References (*9*), (*10*)].

Sample application can be directly made after the volatilization separation of substances from solid materials: The organic or inorganic mixture is put in a glass cartridge with a conical tip and heated in a furnace at a pre-set temperature. The emerging vapors, which can be pure substances or decomposition products (pyrolysis TLC), are deposited directly on the plate which is held one mm from the tip. GC fractions may be spotted directly on TLC plates in a similar manner.

2. *Choice of Solvent Systems*

Depending upon the sorbent, its activity, and the class of the solute compounds, a wide range of solvents can be used. Single solvents of the elutropic series, mixtures of solvents, totally aqueous, totally organic, aqueous-organic, and ionic solvents have all been used. The use of azeotropic mixtures reportedly (*11*) aids in the attainment of constant R_F values, for example methanol-chloroform-methyl acetate

(180 : 257 : 135 v/v) for the separation of sulfonamides or alkaloids on silica-gel layers. Molten salts have been used as developers for the separation of inorganic ions on silica gel. Table 1 gives a limited, selective listing of solvent systems successfully used for the TLC separation of various compounds.

TABLE 1

SELECTED SOLVENT-SORBENT SYSTEMS FOR THE TLC SEPARATION OF VARIOUS COMPOUNDS

1. *Chloroplast Pigments*
   a. Isooctane-acetone-ether (3 : 1 : 1)—silica gel and polyamide
   b. Petroleum ether-benzene-$CHCl_3$-acetone-isopropanol (50 : 35 : 10 : 5 : 0.17)—cellulose
   c. Petroleum ether-*n*-propanol (99.2 : 0.8) followed by 20% $CHCl_3$ in petroleum ether (2 dimensional)—sucrose
   d. Petroleum ether-acetone (4 : 6)—alumina
   e. Petroleum ether-*n*-propanol (199 : 1)—starch
   f. Petroleum ether-acetone (7 : 3)—magnesia-celite (1 : 1 w/w) and hydroxyapatite
   g. Petroleum ether-acetone (8 : 2)—calcium carbonate
   h. Methanol satd. with paraffin—Silica gel G—$Ca(OH)_2$ (1 : 4) impreg. with paraffin
2. *2,4-Dinitrophenylhydrazones of Aldehydes and Ketones*
   a. Hexane—ethyl acetate (4 : 1 or 3 : 2)—silica gel
   b. Benzene or $CHCl_3$ or ether or benzene-hexane (1 : 1)—alumina
   c. Petroleum ether-benzene mixtures containing small amounts of pyridine—$ZnCO_3$
3. *Alkaloids*
   a. Benzene-ethanol (9 : 1) or $CHCl_3$-acetone-diethylamine (5 : 4 : 1)—silical gel
   b. $CHCl_3$ or ethanol or cyclohexane-$CHCl_3$ (3 : 7) plus 0.05% diethylamine—alumina
   c. Benzene-heptane-$CHCl_3$-diethylamine (6 : 5 : 1 : 0.02)—cellulose impreg. with formamide
4. *Amines*
   a. Ethanol (95%)-NH_3 (25%) (4 : 1)—silical gel
   b. Acetone-heptane (1 : 1)—alumina
   c. Acetone-H_2O (99 : 1)—kieselguhr G
5. *Sugars*
   a. Benzene-acetic acid-methanol (1 : 1 : 3)—silica gel buffered with boric acid
   b. *n*-propanol-conc. NH_3-H_2O (6 : 2 : 1)—silica gel G
   c. Butanol-pyridine-H_2O (6 : 4 : 3) or ethyl acetate-pyridine-H_2O (2 : 1 : 2)—cellulose
   d. Ethyl acetate-isopropanol-H_2O (65 : 24 : 12 or 5 : 2 : 0.5)—kieselguhr G buffered with 0.02 *N* sodium acetate
   e. Ethyl acetate-benzene (3 : 7) (for sugar acetates)—starch-bound silicic acid
6. *Carboxylic Acids*
   a. Benzene-methanol-acetic acid (45 : 8 : 8)—silica gel
   b. Methanol or ethanol or ether—polyamide
   c. Isopropyl ether-formic acid-H_2O (90 : 7 : 3)—kieselguhr G-polyethylene glycol (M-1000) (2 : 1)
7. *Sulfonamides*
   a. $CHCl_3$-ethanol-heptane (1 : 1 : 1)—silica gel G
8. *Food Dyes*
   a. Methyl ethyl ketone-acetic acid-methanol (40 : 5 : 5)—silica gel G
   b. Butanol-ethanol-H_2O (9 : 1 : 1, 8 : 2 : 1, 7 : 3 : 3, 6 : 4 : 4 or 5 : 5 : 5)—alumina
   c. Aq. sodium citrate (2.5%)-NH_3 (25%) (4 : 1)—cellulose
9. *Essential Oils*
   a. Hexane—starch-bound silicic acid
   b. Benzene-$CHCl_3$ (1 : 1)—silical gel G
10. *Flavonoids and Coumarins*
    a. Ethyl acetate-Skellysolve B—starch-bound silicic acid
    b. Methanol-H_2O (8 : 2 or 6 : 4)—polyamide
    c. Toluene-ethyl formate-formic acid (5 : 4 : 1)—silica gel G + sodium acetate
    d. Petroleum ether-ethyl acetate (2 : 1)—silica gel G
11. *Metal Ions*
    a. Dilute HCl—starch-bound alumina—Celite
    b. Acetone-conc. HCl-2,5-hexanedione (100 : 1 : 0.5)—silical gel G
    c. 1 *M* aq. $NaNO_3$—Dowex 1 + cellulose
    d. Methanol—alumina
12. *Insecticides*
    a. Cyclohexane-hexane (1 : 1) or CCl_4-ethyl acetate (8 : 2)—silica gel G
    b. Hexane—alumina
    c. Heptane saturated with acetic acid—starch-bound silicic acid
    d. Chloroform—silica gel G + oxalic acid

TABLE 1—(Continued)

13. *Lipids*
    a. Petroleum ether-diethyl ether-acetic acid (90 : 10 : 1 or 70 : 20 : 4)—silica gel G
    b. Petroleum ether-diethyl ether (95 : 5)—alumina
    c. $CHCl_3$-methanol-H_2O (80 : 25 : 3)—silicic acid
14. *Fatty Acids*
    a. Petroleum ether-diethyl ether-acetic acid (70 : 30 : 1 or 2)—silica gel G
    b. Acetic acid-CH_3CN (1 : 1)—kieselguhr impreg. with undecane
    c. Benzene-diethyl ether (75 : 25 or 1 : 1)—starch-bound silicic acid
    d. CH_3CN-acetic acid-H_2O (70 : 10 : 25)—silica gel G impreg. with silicone oil
15. *Glycerides*
    a. $CHCl_3$-acetic acid (99.5 : 0.5)—silica gel G impreg. with $AgNO_3$
    b. $CHCl_3$-benzene (7 : 3)—silica gel G
    c. $CHCl_3$-methanol-H_2O (5 : 15 : 1)—silica gel G impreg. with undecane
    d. Petroleum ether-diethyl ether (9 : 1 to 4 : 6)—plaster-bound silicic acid
    e. Methyl isobutyl ketone—hydroxyapatite
    f. Acetone-CH_3CN (8 : 2 or 7 : 4)—kieselguhr G impreg. with petroleum
16. *Glycolipids*
    a. Propanol-12% NH_3 (4 : 1)—silica gel G
17. *Phospholipids*
    a. $CHCl_3$-methanol-H_2O (60 : 35 : 8 or 65 : 25 : 4)—silica gel G
18. *Nucleotides*
    a. 0.15 *M* NaCl or 0.01–0.06 *N* HCl—Ecteola cellulose
    b. Sat. aq. $(NH_4)_2SO_4$-1 *M* sodium acetate-2-propanol (80 : 18 : 2)—cellulose
    c. 0.02–0.04 *N* aq. HCl—DEAE cellulose
    d. Gradient elution: start with 1 *N* formic acid and add 10 *N* formic acid which is 2 *M* in ammonium formate—DEAE Sephadex A-25
    e. 1.0–1.6 *M* LiCl—cellulose PEI
19. *Phenols*
    a. Xylene, $CHCl_3$ or xylene-$CHCl_3$ (1 : 1, 3 : 1, 1 : 3)—starch-bound silicic acid or silicic acid-kieselguhr (1 : 1)
    b. Benzene—alumina plus acetic acid
    c. Benzene-1,4-dioxane-acetic acid (90 : 25 : 4)—silica gel G
    d. Diethyl ether—alumina
    e. Hexane-ethyl acetate (4 : 1 or 3 : 2)—silica gel plus oxalic acid
    f. Hexane or cyclohexane or benzene—δ-polycaprolactam
    g. Ethanol-H_2O (8 : 3) containing 4% boric acid and 2% sodium acetate—silica gel G plus boric acid
    h. CCl_4-acetic acid (9 : 1) or cyclohexane-acetic acid (93 : 7)—polyamide 6
20. *Amino Acids*
    a. Butanol-acetic acid-H_2O (3 or 4 : 1 : 1) or phenol-H_2O (75 : 25) or propanol-34% NH_3 (67 : 33)—silica gel G
    b. Butanol-acetic acid-H_2O (4 : 1 : 1)—cellulose
    c. Butanol-acetic acid-H_2O (3 : 1 : 1) or pyridine-H_2O (1 : 1 or 80 : 54)—alumina
    d. Ethanol-NH_3 (conc.)-H_2O (7 : 1 : 2)—silica gel G buffered with equal portions of 0.2 *M* KH_2PO_4 and 0.2 *M* Na_2HPO_4
    e. *n*-Butanol-acetone-NH_3-H_2O (10 : 10 : 5 : 2) followed by isopropanol-formic acid-H_2O (20 : 1 : 5) (2 dimensional)—cellulose
21. *Polypeptides and Proteins*
    a. $CHCl_3$-methanol or acetone (9 : 1)—silica gel G
    b. Potassium phosphate buffers, pH 6.5—polyamide-bound hydroxyapatite
    c. H_2O or 0.05 *M* NH_3—Sephadex G-25
    d. Phosphate buffers—DEAE Sephadex A-25
22. *Steroids and Sterols*
    a. Benzene or benzene-ethyl acetate (9 : 1 or 2 : 1)—silica gel G
    b. $CHCl_3$-ethanol (96 : 4)—alumina
    c. Ethyl acetate-cyclohexane mixtures—starch-bound silicic acid
    d. Benzene-isopropanol—silica gel plus NaOH
    e. Methanol-H_2O (95 : 5)—Celite impreg. with paraffin oil
    f. Cyclohexane-heptane (1 : 1)—silica gel G-kieselguhr G (1 : 1)
    g. Cyclohexane-ethyl acetate (99.5 : 0.5)—kieselguhr G
    h. Acetic acid-H_2O (92 : 8 or 90 : 10)—kieselguhr G impreg. with undecane
23. *Terpenoids*
    a. Hexane or hexane-ethyl acetate (85 : 15)—starch-bound silicic acid
    b. Benzene or benzene-petroleum ether or -ethanol mixtures—alumina
    c. Isopropyl ether or isopropyl ether-acetone (5 : 2 or 19 : 1)—silica gel G

TABLE 1—(Continued)

24. *Vitamins*
    a. Methanol, CCl_4, xylene, $CHCl_3$ or petroleum ether—alumina
    b. Methanol, propanol, or $CHCl_3$—silica gel G
    c. Acetone-paraffin (H_2O sat.) (9 : 1)—silica gel G impreg. with paraffin
25. *Barbiturates*
    a. $CHCl_3$-*n*-butanol-25% NH_3 (70 : 40 : 5)—silica gel
26. *Digitalis Compounds*
    a. $CHCl_3$-pyridine (6 : 1)—silica gel
27. *Polycyclic Hydrocarbons*
    a. CCl_4—alumina
28. *Purines*
    a. Acetone-$CHCl_3$-*n*-butanol-25% NH_3 (3 : 3 : 4 : 1)—silica gel

[This table was prepared with the help of information supplied by Dr. Fred Rabel, H. Reeve Angel & Co.]

3. *Development Methods*

Chromatograms are normally developed by the ascending method over a distance of 10-18 cm in glass tanks lined with filter paper to assure good vapor saturation (N or NS chamber) or in a sandwich chamber (S chamber) (Figure 51). The latter requires very little solvent and permits development under vapor-saturated conditions by using a pre-soaked cellulose-coated saturation plate (b) to achieve results which closely approximate those in the N chamber with most solvents. If the coated saturation plate is not used (c), saturation is not complete, and modestly improved separations may result due to the effects of solvent evaporation as the system approaches a steady state situation (*12*). The thin layer is inserted into the solvent to a depth of approximately 5 mm in all cases. It is difficult to predict in advance which chamber (N or S) will yield the best separation in any given case, and trial and error is usually necessary to find the best chamber environment. The mechanism of separations obtained with single and multicomponent solvents in various kinds of chambers with different environments is not clearly understood. See, for example, Reference (*13*).

Descending development is more difficult to achieve because the solvent must be fed to the top of an inclined layer through a wick arrangement. This method is seldom used except with Dextran gel layers or for eluting zones off the layer prior to analysis.

Horizontal development can be used with regular layers or with nonadherent (loose) layers. If spots of sample are applied at the end and solvent is fed to the edge of the horizontal plate through a wick, resolved spots will result. If the mixture is applied as a spot near a hole in the center of the plate and solvent is fed to the layer from below through the hole, ring-shaped zones result (circular method).

Continuous development is achieved by allowing the upper end of the plate to remain uncovered in the horizontal method (BN-chamber) or to protrude out the end of a slot in the cover of the chamber in the ascending method. In either case the solvent flows continually and evaporates from the uncovered area (which can be warmed).

It has been found that some separations can be improved by vapor not originating from the developing solvent. Two new chambers have been described for providing vapor control over the entire plate ("vapor-programmed TLC"). These are the Vario-KS-Chamber (Camag, Inc.) and the vapor programming chamber designed by de Zeeuw (*14*). Procedures have also been reported for producing gradient layers (with a systematic change in the composition of the adsorbent along the plate, either parallel or at right angles to the solvent flow) or gradient elution (a continuous change in the composition of the solvent). Although improved resolutions have been reported, these procedures detract from the inherent simplicity of normal TLC.

Sealed disposable plastic bags have been used in place of conventional chambers for the TLC of radioactive substances.

Development at temperatures higher or lower than ambient will change R_F values and may lead to improved resolution. Multiple development with one or more solvents and two-dimensional development with different solvents are also used. If mixtures of solvents are employed and the solvents are properly chosen, two dimensional separations governed by different mechanisms in each direction may be achieved.

Humidity variations can have a marked influence on R_F values obtained in TLC, and constant humidity is essential for reproducible results. Ideally, spots should be applied in a room with constant humidity. For alumina, silica gel and magnesium silicate, increasing humidity results in higher R_F values with nonpolar solvents; for cellulose, increasing humidity results in lower R_F values.

A new development technique is termed drum TLC by Saunders and Snyder (*15*). This method allows unlimited migration of a pair of sample bands along a TLC bed at constant, relatively high solvent flow rates, so that total resolution is increased relative to other TLC techniques by an order of magnitude, or equivalent separations can be carried out in a much shorter time. In its basic form, only a few bands of very limited

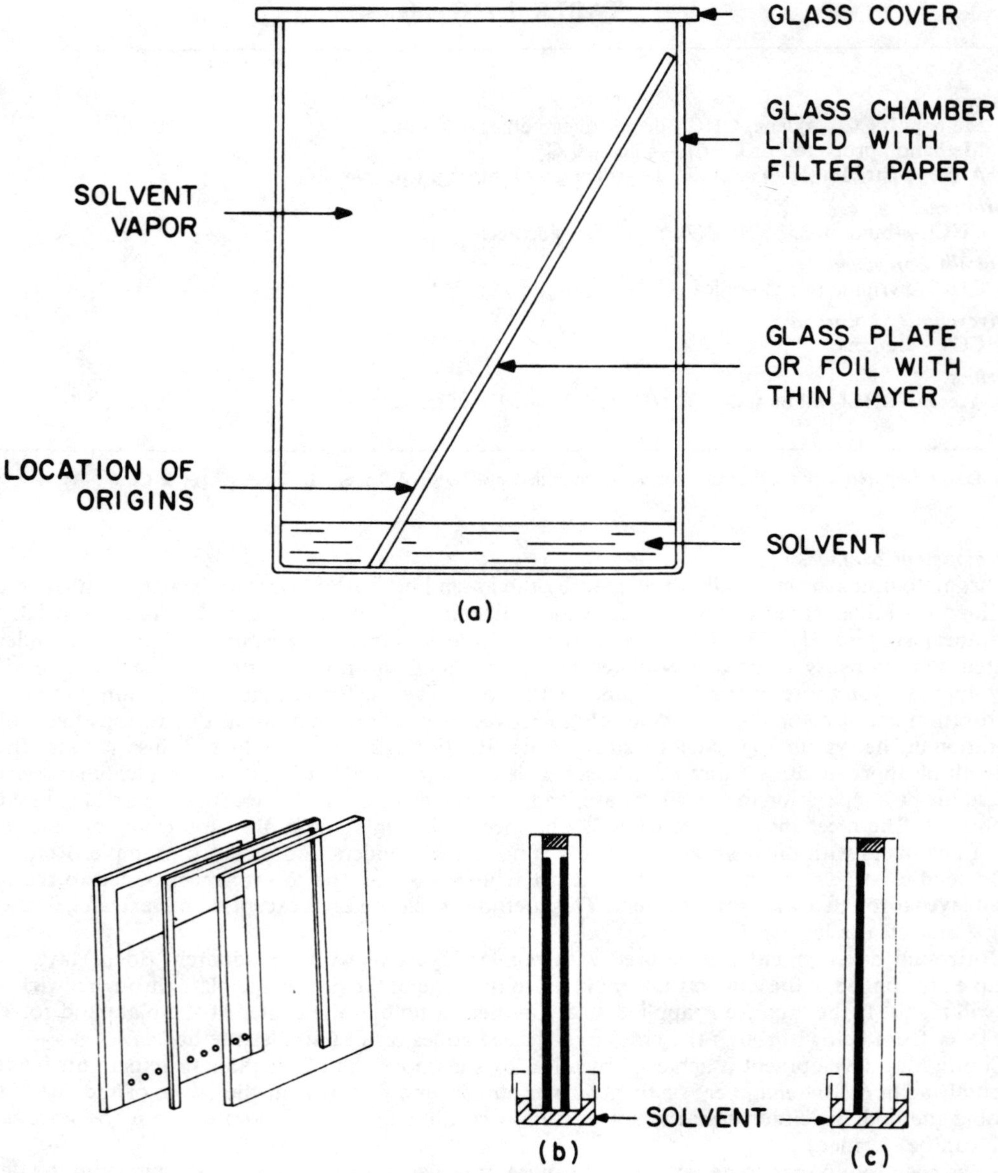

Figure 51. Developing chambers for ascending TLC: (a) rectangular developing tank; (b) sandwich chamber, saturated; (c) sandwich chamber, unsaturated. To use the sandwich plate, a TLC plate is prepared in the usual way. A strip of the adsorbent layer 10 mm wide is scraped off along the sides and upper edge of the plate. The ⊓-shaped cardboard frame is placed on the cleared strip and the cover plate (coated or uncoated) is placed on top of the frame. The sandwich thus formed is held together with clamps, two of which are firmly connected to the stand. Then the sandwich assembly, open end down, is placed through the slot in the cover into the solvent trough. Only 15 ml of solvent are required for development [available from Camag, Inc.]. Reproduced with permission from Camag, Inc., New Berlin, Wisc.

R_F range can be simultaneously resolved by this technique, but it is well suited for the analysis of two difficultly separable bands. Combined with inverse solvent programming, the separation of complex, multicomponent samples at high separation efficiency may be possible.

D. ZONE DETECTION, IDENTIFICATION AND DOCUMENTATION

1. *Detection*

After development, which may take from 20 minutes to over one hour depending upon the system, the plates are removed from the tank and dried after marking the front. Colorless substances are detected using the same types of color-forming reagents as for paper chromatography (Section II.I). In addition, corrosive and charring reagents detect nonvolatile, organic compounds. These reagents are, of course, destructive, and are used after nondestructive tests. Detection methods are generally more sensitive in TLC compared to PC.

Another charring detection procedure is the hot-line technique: An electrically heated glowing nichrome wire brought to within 1 mm of the plate chars organic material in a 1–2 mm wide strip.

Compounds which fluoresce are located by inspection of the layer under UV light. Nonfluorescent spots appear as dark areas against a fluorescent background when layers incorporating a fluorescing phosphor are employed.

Radioactive spots are located by scanning with a radiation detector or by autoradiography. Layers heavily loaded with a powdered scintillator (e.g., anthracene or zinc silicate) have been used for the detection of weak-energy radionuclides (e.g., tritium) by β-radioluminescence (scintillation fluorography on photographic film or direct photoelectric detection); interference with the separation is not necessarily caused by the presence of the scintillator (*16*, *17*). Bioautography is applicable to antibiotics.

2. *Identification*

Spots are identified in the usual ways as described in sections above, for example by comparison of migration with authentic reference compounds or by spectroscopy. A unique inlet system has been designed so that compounds separated by TLC can be directly exposed to a mass spectrometer source for rapid identification. Separated spots may be eluted from the support into KBr powder on the TLC plate with 100–150 μl of a dry, nonpolar solvent; the KBr powder is added to a KBr microdisk and pelletized for IR spectroscopy (*18*).

3. *Documentation*

TLC separations are recorded in various ways: The separated spots can be sketched onto tracing paper placed over the plate, or a photograph in black and white or color can be made upon illumination with visible light (transmitted or reflected) or long or shortwave UV radiation (a commercial TLC camera stand is supplied by Camag, Inc.). The thin-layer chromatogram can be copied on an office copying machine after treatment of the layer with paraffin to make it translucent. The layer can sometimes be pulled from glass intact with transparent adhesive tape; if the plate is sprayed with a plastic dispersion [e.g., Neatan (Merck)], the layer forms a flexible film which can be pulled from the glass and retained. Photodensitometer curves, which are used for quantitative analysis (below), also serve as a record of peak locations. Flexible layers on plastic or aluminum backing can be covered with Saran wrap and taped into a notebook for a permanent record.

E. QUANTITATIVE ANALYSIS

Methods of quantitative analysis are similar to those in paper chromatography, and readers interested in details are referred to the book edited by Shellard on this topic.

Photodensitometry of the layers (or alternatively of a photographic print, negative or autoradiograph) in transmitted or reflected light is often used. The methods of thin-layer densitometry have been reviewed (*19*). The flying spot densitometer for TLC has been described by Koopmans and Bouwmeester (*20*). This instrument attempts to eliminate the problem of uneven distribution of material in the spot by oscillating the TLC plate while it is being scanned.

Scanning of fluorescence is used where applicable and radiochromatograms are evaluated with radioscanners. In all of these *in situ* methods, quantitation is accomplished by measuring the areas under appropriate peaks, and comparisons are made between standards and unknowns treated in an identical manner.

Zones can be removed from glass plates by scraping and from flexible sheets by cutting prior to elution from the sorbent for quantitative analysis by weight determination, instrumental methods, chemical methods liquid scintillation counting, etc. Figure 52 shows a simple technique for zone extraction in TLC employing elution columns prepared from commercially available disposable capillary pipettes. A plug of glass wool is inserted into the top of a Pasteur disposable pipette, $5\frac{3}{4}$ in. long, until it completely covers the tip. Acetone is used to rinse the pipette and plug which dry before the tip is inserted inside vacuum tubing leading to a water aspirator. A plain dissecting probe allows finer outlining of the zone to be eluted and more exact scraping of the adsorbent powder from the supporting glass plate. Particles are sucked into the pipette and caught on the glass wool. The pipette is removed from the vacuum tubing; the tip is rinsed with acetone on the outside and dried; and then it is placed through a hole in a cork. The cork has been inserted into the top of a 15-ml conical centrifuge tube, as shown in Figure 52b. Solvent is slowly dropped into the pipette over the powdered adsorbent in the glass wool, and the compound is eluted through the capillary end into the centrifuge tube.

Elution is with a solvent polar enough to remove the compound of interest completely. To remove a very polar compound from a polar adsorbent, pyridine or another strongly adsorbed compound may be added to facilitate elution. Washing the layer with the elution solvent prior to activation and sample application will remove impurities which would also be eluted along with the separated zones (*8*).

The accuracy of the spot elution-spectrophotometry method will be affected by light scattering if silica gel particles which are too small to be removed by normal filtration are suspended in the eluate. The

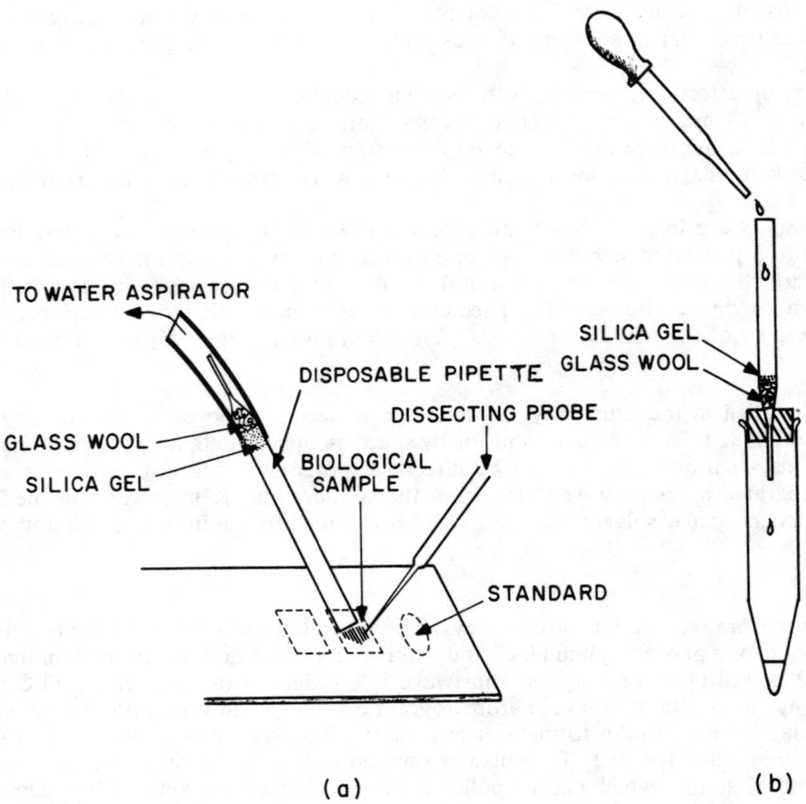

Figure 52. (a) Extraction of a zone from a thin-layer plate; (b) elution of the sample from the sorbent [after (*24*)]. Figure on elution and extraction from TLC plates, page 110, *J. Chem. Educ.*, **44** (1967). Permission to reproduce from Division of Chemical Education, American Chemical Society.

problem is particularly prevalent when polar solvents such as ketones, alcohols or water are used for elution. The contaminating particles can be removed by membrane filtration or by evaporating the polar solvents and redissolving the residue in a less-polar solvent, so that the silica gel particles remain precipitated and can be filtered off (see "The Brinkman Notebook", Fall issue, 1970, p. 5).

Novel methods recently applied to quantitative TLC include ultramicro carbon analysis, *in situ* X-ray emission spectrometry, the flame-ionization detector and neutral activation analysis.

The application of the sample is especially critical in both quantitative PC and TLC, and studies have been made of the variation between different techniques of application (*21*), and the variation between different workers using the same technique (*22*). Use of internal standards can remove the problem of quantitative sample application, but raises other problems, such as contamination of the sample.

F. PREPARATIVE TLC

Preparative separations are carried out on either regular 8 × 8 in. chromatoplates or on larger plates (e.g., 8 × 16 in.) coated with thick layers (0.5–2 mm or thicker) of an adsorbent. Many workers use normal slurries for preparing preparative layers while others recommend the use of slurries with less water (especially if layers >2 mm are used) and a longer period of air-drying before activation in an oven.

Samples up to 10 ml are manually applied with a streaking pipette (Shandon Scientific Co.). Automatic sample streakers are available for depositing long, narrow bands of solution quickly and reproducibly on preparative plates (e.g., from Applied Science Laboratories, or the Chromatocharger from Camag, Inc.).

Single plates are developed in large developing tanks, or up to five plates can be developed simultaneously in special chromatotanks (Shandon, Inc.) or in a regular tank by use of a multi-sandwich assembly (Camag, Inc.). Resolution on thick layers is sometimes not as good as on the thinner analytical layers so that multiple or stepwise development may be advantageous. Also, spots may be more diffuse on thicker layers. In many cases, however, solvent systems determined by TLC are directly applicable to preparative TLC with similar results. Preparative TLC is often faster and requires less solvent than would comparable separations by column chromatography. Development times are usually less than 3 hr.

At the end of the development, the locations of the bands of interest are determined by spraying guide strips (Figure 47) with an appropriate reagent. The adsorbent containing each zone is then scraped off, collected and eluted with an appropriate solvent. The solvent is evaporated for recovery of the solute.

Analytical TLC separations can be directly scaled-up for the separation of multigram amounts by use of dry-column chromatography in pre-packed columns (Quantum Industries, Inc.).

G. APPLICATIONS

TLC has been applied to the separation and analysis of many classes of compounds as indicated by the earlier table in this section and the data presented later in this Handbook. It is especially useful for substances which are either nonvolatile or too labile for GC analysis. As typical examples, Figures 53 and 54 show separations of vitamins and chloroplast pigments by TLC.

H. TLC *vs* PC

Many of the basic techniques in PC and TLC are essentially the same, for example sample spotting, ascending development, detection of the spots and quantification, especially directly on the chromatogram. Some techniques are simpler in PC than in TLC, namely circular, horizontal and descending solvent development methods (due to the ability to fold the paper) and methods for removing the spots from the

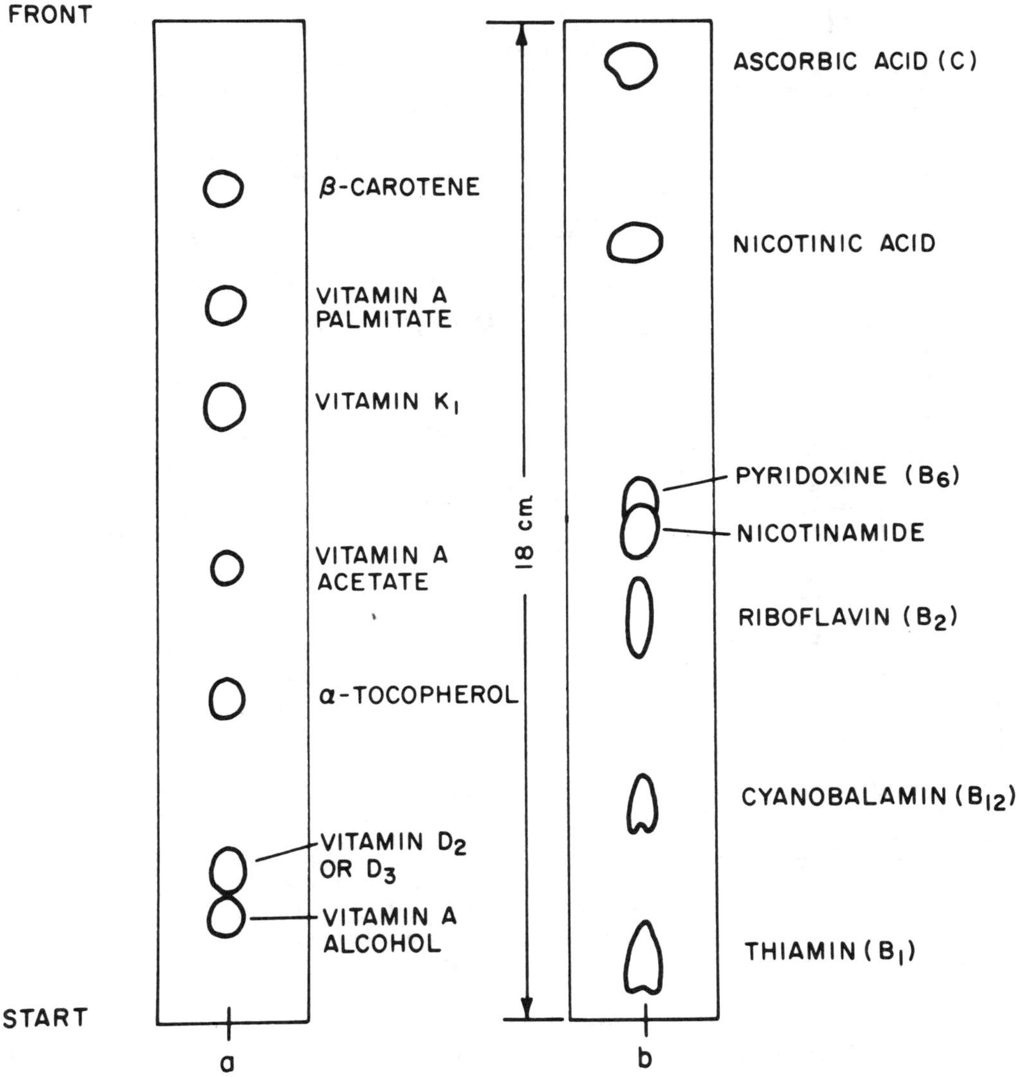

Figure 53. (a) Separation of 20–30 μg each of fat-soluble vitamins on a silica gel G layer containing a fluorescent indicator with cyclohexane-diethyl ether, 8 : 20. Time of run 60 min. (b) Separation of 3–30 μg each of water-soluble vitamins on silica gel G layer containing a fluorescent indicator with water as wash liquid. Time of run 40 min. [After (*25*)]. Part of Figure 115 and part of Figure 102 from Stahl, Thin Layer Chromatography, 1965. Permission received to reproduce from Springer-Verlag, Berlin, Germany.

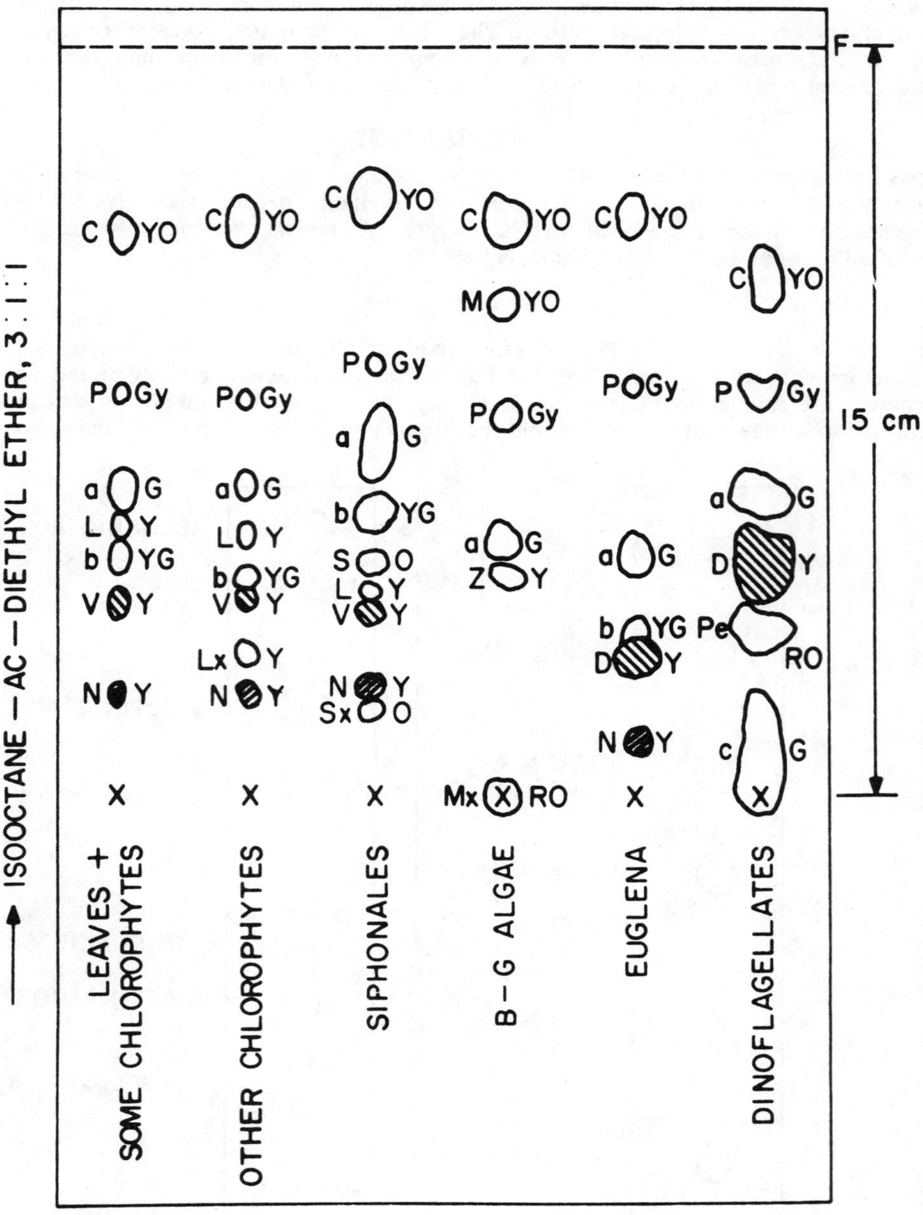

Figure 54. Pigments separated from 2–5 μl of extract of various plants by thin-layer chromatography in Eastman silica-gel Chromagram sheets. Abbreviations and symbols: a = chlorophyll *a*, AC = acetone, B = blue, b = chlorophyll *b*, C = carotene, c = chlorophyll *c*, D = diadinoxanthin, F = front, G = green, Gy = grey, L = lutein, Lx = loroxanthin, M = myxoxanthin, Mx = myxoxanthophyll, N = neoxanthin, O = orange, P = pheophytin, Pe = peridinin, R = red, S = siphonein, Sx = siphonaxanthin, V = violaxanthin, X = starting point, Y = yellow, Z = zeaxanthin, = blue by HCl vapors, = blue-green by HCl vapors [after (*26*)]. Figure 2, page 479, *J. Chem. Educ.*, **46** (1969). Permission to reproduce received from Division of Chemical Education, American Chemical Society.

chromatogram (the paper, as well as flexible thin layers, can be cut with scissors, while layers must be scraped from glass plates).

Chromatography paper is uniform and quite inexpensive; the latter is important if many experiments are to be performed. The casting of thin layers on glass plates is considered by some to be a chore, and it is not always possible to prepare uniform layers from day to day. Precoated glass plates and aluminum and plastic sheets are commercially available and are reasonably uniform, but they are expensive relative to paper. Not all adsorbents are commercially available as precoated layers (e.g., magnesia). Likewise, it is not especially convenient to prepare chromatography papers loaded with various materials when these are not commercially available.

Chromatographic theory predicts that TLC should be superior to PC both with respect to separation efficiency (resolution) and speed of solvent flow because the thin layers are composed of fine particles rather than fibers as in paper. The smaller particles of the layer material should lead to faster equilibria and sharper spots. Many studies have indicated such advantages for TLC but other work indicates that the differences in speed and resolution obtained in practice are sometimes only minor, for example when comparing certain separations on cellulose paper and thin layers. As another example, leaf pigments are separated with comparable speed and resolution on silica and alumina thin layers as compared with silica gel and aluminum hydroxide impregnated papers (*23*).

Another reason for increased speed and resolution in TLC is because TLC plates are thinner. Smaller spots are placed on them with smaller loadings, consequently the spots which are resolved are smaller and resolution is increased. This is related to the increased sensitivity often reported for TLC compared to PC. Turner and Redgwell reported, for example, that in one study the sensitivity of the ninhydrin reaction was 50 times greater on a mixed layer of cellulose and silica gel than on paper, and that the time required for autoradiography was about one-twentieth of that required for the same amount of extract separated by PC.

A large variety of sorbents have been used to prepare thin layers, but paper has been impregnated with an equally wide range of materials to provide selective separations. Many of these loaded papers are commercially available. In addition, glass fiber papers permit the use of corrosive charring solutions so popular for detecting spots on inorganic thin layers.

It is suggested that TLC is not likely to displace PC or column chromatography as suggested by some people even though it is a method of very great value. The various chromatographic methods are all important because each has its own peculiar advantages and limitations. Some separations can be performed with equal success by several separation methods, while in other situations one technique may stand out clearly as the method of choice. Careful comparative studies of different methods for the separation and analysis of all classes of compounds is a definite need. The different techniques of chromatography are in many cases complementary. For example, thin-layer and paper chromatography can be used to quickly scout for solvents which will provide successful separations on columns containing adsorbents or cellulose. Alternatively, one excellent way to monitor fractions collected during a liquid column separation is to develop a portion of each fraction by TLC or PC to check its purity.

REFERENCES

1. Kirchner, J. G., Miller, J. M., and J. G. Keller, *Anal. Chem.* **23**, 420 (1951).
2. Cozzi, D., Desideri, P. G., Lepri, L., and G. Ciantelli, *J. Chromatogr.* **35**, 396 (1968).
3. Niederwieser, A. and C. C. Honegger, *Advances in Chromatography*, **2**, 123 (1966).
4. Niederwieser, A., *Chromatographia* **2**, 23 (1969).
5. Cremer, E. and E. Seidl, *Chromatographia* **3**, 17 (1970).
6. Cremer, E. and H. Nau, *Naturwissenschaften* **12**, 651 (1968).
7. Cremer, E., Kraus, T., and H. Nau, *Z. Anal. Chem.* **245**, 37 (1969).
8. Tischer, T. N. and A. D. Baitsholts, *American Laboratory*, p. 69, May 1970.
9. Stahl, E. and E. Dumont, *J. Chromatogr.* **39**, 157 (1969).
10. Musil, F. and E. Fosslien, *J. Chromatogr.* **47**, 116 (1970).
11. Röder, E., Mutscheler, E., and A. Rochelmeyer, *J. Chromatogr.* **42**, 131 (1969).
12. Stewart, G. H. and T. D. Gierke, *J. Chromatog. Sci.* **8**, 133 (1970).
13. Geiss, F., *J. Chromatogr.* **53**, 620 (1970).
14. de Zeeuw, R. A., *Anal. Chem.* **40**, 2134 (1968).
15. Saunders, D. L. and L. R. Snyder, *J. Chromatogr. Sci.* **8**, 706 (1970).
16. Prydz, S., Melö, T. B., Koren, J. F., and E. L. Eriksen, *Anal. Chem.* **42**, 156 (1970).
17. Landmark, L. H., Hognestad, K., and S. Prydz, *J. Chromatogr.* **46**, 267 (1970).
18. de Klein, W. J., *Anal. Chem.* **41**, 667 (1969).
19. Lefar, M. S. and A. D. Lewis, *Anal. Chem.* **42**, 79A, March, 1970.
20. Koopmans, H. J. and P. C. Bouwmeester, *Chromatographia* **4**, 83 (1971).
21. Fairbairn, J. W. and S. J. Relph, *J. Chromatogr.* **33**, 494 (1968).
22. Brain, K. P. and T. D. Turner, *J. Chromatogr.* **61**, 157 (1971).
23. Sherma, J., *J. Chromatogr.* **61**, 202 (1971).
24. Ruchelman, M. W., *J. Chem. Educ.* **44**, 110 (1967).
25. Bolliger, H. R., "Thin Layer Chromatography", E. Stahl, Ed., Academic Press, N.Y. 1965, p. 20.
26. Strain, H. H. and J. Sherma, *J. Chem. Educ.* **46**, 476 (1969).

VOLUME TWO
SECTION II

PRACTICAL APPLICATIONS

II.I Detection Reagents for Paper- and/or Thin-Layer Chromatography

Section II.I

DETECTION REAGENTS FOR PAPER AND/OR THIN-LAYER CHROMATOGRAPHY

The color reagents listed in this section are suitable for detecting most of the specific compounds listed in Tables of Volume One.

NOTES

1. The editors recommend that the detection reagents may be tested for paper- and thin-layer chromatography without modification unless stated otherwise in the directions.
2. After spraying or dipping, chromatograms usually have to be treated in some other way. Unless stated otherwise, drying at room temperature is adequate. "Heating" steps are usually effected at 100–110 °C for up to 15 min.
3. For paper chromatography, location reagents can usually be applied either by dipping or by spraying. Although the latter method is probably more widely used, Dr. Ivor Smith enumerates the following advantages for dipping in his 1969 treatise (cited in the references at the end of this Section):
   a. Safety due to absence of noxious fumes.
   b. Economy of equipment, reagents and time.
   c. Uniform application of reagents.
   d. Uniform background and rapid drying.
   e. Spot colors often appear more rapidly.

   The preferred solvent for most dip reagents is acetone. It may be possible to apply dip reagents by spraying, depending upon the technique and apparatus employed. Dr. Smith recommends spraying from 9–12 in. to the paper or layer with a good power can sprayer. If necessary, a less volatile solvent such as ethanol or *n*-butanol is substituted for acetone. For thin-layer chromatography, spraying is almost always used for application of the reagent, although in some cases the reagent can be incorporated into the layer or the layer can be stabilized for dipping. Colors produced on thin layers may differ from those found on paper.
4. DANGER IN USING CERTAIN SPRAY REAGENTS!
   It is mandatory that spray reagents be used within well ventilated hoods or special spray cabinets since the aerosol droplets produced by the spray reagent may cause organ damage or in some cases even induce cancer, e.g. cyanide and butanol are highly toxic, and benzidine carcinogenic.
5. Sensitivities for specific color reagents are not always included in the directions. However, as a general rule, most reagents will detect in the order of 0.1 to 1 μg for TLC and 1–10 μg for most work in paper chromatography.
6. When observation under ultraviolet radiation is recommended in the directions, both short (254 nm) and long wavelengths (360 nm) should be tried for optimum results. As a general rule, chromatograms should be inspected under U.V. light before and after application of all reagents, and between reagents in multiple application sequences.
7. When percentages are given in the directions, solids in liquids will be specified as weight/volume, whereas for liquids in liquids the percentages are volume/volume.

Directions for Application of Reagents

1. Dipping is carried out in a shallow (e.g., 11 × 2 × 0.5 in.) special solvent-resistant plastic, metal or glass dip tray. The dry paper chromatogram is drawn rapidly through the reagent without touching the sides of the tray and then hung up for a few minutes to dry. Colors that appear at room temperature are then marked at once with a soft lead pencil. If necessary, the paper is then hung in a heating oven at an elevated temperature.
2. Spraying is accomplished by use of a glass spray apparatus attached to an air line, or a spray gun consisting of a metal canister containing an inert pressurized aerosol and a glass jar to hold the reagent. Both are commercially available. The spray is applied as uniformly and lightly as possible.
   Multiple dipping or spraying can be used to apply different reagents sequentially to the same chromatogram. Between reagents, the colored spots should be marked with a pencil and the chromatogram completely dried.

3. To silanize thin-layer plates before dipping, dry plates and place in a desiccator containing 5 ml dimethyldichlorosilane in a small beaker. Evacuate to 300 mm and leave 15 min. Transfer plates to a fume hood for 30 min. The plate can now be dipped or immersed in many detection reagents.

Index of Chemical Classes

DETECTION REAGENTS FOR PAPER AND/OR THIN-LAYER CHROMATOGRAPHY

ALPHABETICAL INDEX OF DETECTION REAGENTS FOR PAPER AND/OR THIN-LAYER CHROMATOGRAPHY

(Numbers refer to specific color reagents)

DETECTION REAGENTS

The detection reagents are arranged according to chemical classes, and within each class, tests are in alphabetic order. Other tests may be found under different sections, and numbers indicate where they may be found.

Alcohols
(aliphatic and aromatic alcohols, and glycols)

See Tests: 1–8, 16, 49, 258.

1. Ceric Ammonium Nitrate

Preparation: 6% ceric ammonium nitrate in 2*N* HNO_3.
Procedure: Dry chromatogram for 5 min. at 105 °C, cool, spray.
Results: Polyalcohols detected as brown spots on yellow background.

2. 3,5-Dinitrobenzoyl Chloride

Preparation:
Solution a. 2% 3,5-dinitrobenzoyl chloride in toluene.
Solution b. Aqueous 0.5% NaOH.
Solution c. Aqueous 0.002% rhodamine.
Procedure: Air-dried chromatogram (steamed for 2 min. if a butanol solvent was used) is sprayed with *a* and hung in air to dry overnight. Steam 2 min. and draw through *b* in a shallow dish for 30 sec. Rinse in a pan of water until the wash water dripping from the paper is not slippery. Draw wet paper through *c* in a dish for 15 sec., air-dry, examine under U.V. light.
Results: Detects primary aliphatic alcohols (0.2–17 μg), secondary aliphatic alcohols (1–50 μg), tertiary aliphatic alcohols (2 μg), glycols (2–6 μg), sugar alcohols (< 1 μg), polyhydroxy compounds (1–2 μg), phenols, monosaccharides, carbohydrate derivatives, hydroxy acids, esters, ketones, amino compounds.

3. Diphenylpicrylhydrazyl

Preparation: 15 mg 2,2-diphenyl-l-picrylhydrazyl in 25 ml chloroform.
Procedure: Spray and heat chromatogram 5–10 min. at 110 °C.
Results: Detects alcohols as yellow spots on purple background. Also detects terpene hydrocarbons, carbonyls, oxides, esters and ethers.

4. Hydrochloric Acid

Preparation: Mix one volume conc. HCl and 4 volumes ethanol.
Procedure: Spray and heat to 90 °C.
Results: Glycols appear as pink spots.
Comments: This reagent can be used as a general test for TLC.

5. 4,4′-Methylenebis(*N*,*N*-dimethylaniline)

Preparation:
Solution a. 0.25% 4,4′-methylenebis(*N*,*N*-dimethylaniline) in acetone.
Solution b. 1% diammonium ceric nitrate in 0.2*N* HNO_3.
Color reagent. Mix *a* and *b* (1 : 1).
Procedure: Spray with color reagent and heat at 105 °C for 5 min.
Results: Polyalcohols appear as light blue spots on a blue background.

6. *N*,*N*,*N*′,*N*′-Tetramethyl-4,4′-diaminodiphenylmethane-Diammonium Ceric Nitrate

Preparation:
Solution a. 0.25% *N*,*N*,*N*′,*N*′-tetramethyl-4,4′-diaminodiphenylmethane in acetone.
Solution b. 1% diammonium ceric nitrate in 0.2*N* nitric acid.
Procedure: Spray freshly prepared mixture of *a* and *b* (1 : 1). Heat for 5 min. at 105 °C.
Results: Polyalcohols detected as white to light blue on blue background.

7. Vanadium Oxinate

Preparation: Dissolve 0.40 g 8-hydroxyquinoline in a mixture of 25 ml xylene and 25 ml glacial acetic acid and heat on a steam bath to 55 °C. Add 0.20 g ammonium vanadate with stirring, cool the resultant solution and filter through paper. Solution is stable 3 days.
Results: Alcohols detected as light red spots on a blue-black background.

8. Vanillin-Sulfuric Acid

Preparation: Dissolve 3 g vanillin in 100 ml absolute ethanol and add 0.5 ml conc. H_2SO_4 to the solution.
Alternate preparation: Use 1.5 g *p*-toluenesulfonic acid instead of H_2SO_4.
Procedure: Spray chromatogram and heat to 120 °C.
Results: Green-blue spots; detects higher alcohols and ketones.

Alkaloids

See Tests: 9–28, 174, 177, 179, 180, 183.

9. Beam Reagent

Preparation: 5% KOH in 99% ethanol.
Procedure: Spray and heat 5 min. at 105 °C.
Results: Cannabidolic acid and cannabidiol detected as blue-violet spots.

10. Bromcresol Green

Preparation: 0.05% bromcresol green in alcohol.
Results: Many alkaloids give various shades of green or blue, at once or within 30 min.
Comments: Expose to NH_3 vapor if no reaction, after which the NH_3 is removed. As the blue background fades, some compounds may appear as blue spots. After alkaline solvents, a dark background may result.

11. Ceric Sulfate-Trichloroacetic Acid

Preparation: Boil 0.1 g ceric sulfate in 4 ml water containing 1 g trichloroacetic acid, adding conc. H_2SO_4 dropwise until the solution clarifies.
Procedure: Spray and heat to 110 °C.
Results: The reagent detects the alkaloids apomorphine, brucine, colchicine, papaverine and physostigmine. Also detects organic iodine compounds and tocopherol acetates.

12. Cinnamaldehyde-Acid

Preparation: 1 g cinnamaldehyde in 100 ml methanol. Prepare fresh before use.
Procedure: Spray chromatogram and place in a closed chamber which contains a beaker with a mixture of equal volumes of conc. HCl and conc. H_2SO_4.
Results: Detects curare alkaloids.

13. Cobalt Thiocyanate

Preparation: 2% cobalt thiocyanate in acetone; stable for several months.
Results: A few alkaloids can be differentiated by a green color and others by speed of development of color.

14. *p*-Dimethylaminobenzaldehyde

Preparation:
Solution a. 0.5% *p*-dimethylaminobenzaldehyde in ethyl alcohol.
Solution b. Conc. H_2SO_4.
Color reagent: Mix *a* and *b* (5 : 1).
Procedure: The paper is placed on a sheet of glass, and the reagent poured over it. After treatment, the paper is heated at 60 °C for a few seconds when a few alkaloids become visible as red or orange spots.
Alternate procedure: Spray or dip chromatogram using a solution of 0.5 g *p*-dimethylaminobenzaldehyde in 100 ml cyclohexane.
Results: Ergot alkaloids detected as blue spots.

15. Dragendorff Reagent (Theis and Reuther Modification, further modified by Vágújfalvi)

Preparation:
Solution a. Dissolve 2.6 g basic bismuth carbonate (dried for 24 hr. over conc. H_2SO_4) and 7.0 g sodium iodide in 25 ml boiling glacial acetic acid. Allow to stand 12 hr. and filter off precipitated sodium acetate.
Solution b. Add 8 ml ethyl acetate to filtered solution *a* (store in brown bottle).
Color reagent: Mix 10 ml solution *b*, 25 ml glacial acetic acid and 60 ml ethyl acetate.
Results: Alkaloids appear as orange spots, which are intensified by spraying with $0.05N$ H_2SO_4. Also detects adenine (specific) as yellow spot changing to red when sprayed with acid.

16. Dragendorff Reagent (Munier Modification)

Preparation:
Solution a. 17 g bismuth subnitrate plus 200 g tartaric acid in 800 ml water.
Solution b. 160 g potassium iodide in 400 ml water.
Color reagent: Mix 25 ml *a* and 25 ml *b*, add 500 ml water, and dissolve in this solution 100 g tartaric acid. The reagent solution is stable 1 week.
Results: Effective for detecting alkaloids on phosphate-buffered paper chromatograms. Also detects cyclohexylamines, polyethylene glycols and derivatives, polyethylene oxide compounds, lactams, lipids, and α,β-unsaturated steroids. Detects antihistamines.

17. Dragendorff Reagent (Munier and Macheboeuf Modification)

Preparation:
Solution a. Dissolve 0.85 g bismuth subnitrate in a mixture of 10 ml glacial acetic acid and 40 ml water.
Solution b. Dissolve 8 g potassium iodide in 20 ml water.
Color reagent: Mix 5 ml *a* with 5 ml *b*, add 20 ml glacial acetic acid, and dilute to 100 ml with water.
Results: Detects alkaloids. Alkaloids which do not react with Dragendorff reagent are sprayed on the dried paper chromatogram with 10% aqueous sodium carbonate. After drying, immerse in dimethyl sulfate, remove excess by blotting between filter papers, and heat for 10 min. at 90 °C. Spray finally with Dragendorff reagent.

18. Formic Acid Vapor

Procedure: Expose chromatogram to vapors of formic acid for 1 min. Inspect under U.V. light.
Results: Detects quinine and quinidine as intensely fluorescent (blue) spots.

19. Iodine

Preparation: 1% iodine in carbon tetrachloride.
Procedure: Dip papers and suspend in fume hood.
Results: Alkaloids give stable yellow and brown spots which intensify as solvent evaporates.
Comments: This test is unspecific, but is useful after inspection in U.V. light and before bromcresol green and iodoplatinate reagents or cobalt thiocyanate and iodoplatinate in multiple reagent sequences.

20. Iodoplatinate Reagent

Preparation:
Solution a. 5% platinic chloride in water.
Solution b. 10% potassium iodide in water.
Solution c. Water.
Color reagent: Mix 5 ml *a*, 45 ml *b*, 100 ml *c*. Stable for several months.
Procedure: The chromatogram is dipped and placed on clean blotting paper.
Results: Spots appear blue-black on a pink background. Some color differentiation is obtained with this reagent. It reacts with tertiary amines, but not with compounds having only primary and/or secondary amino groups. These compounds usually give a white to grey color and are therefore not visible on paper chromatograms unless present in excessive amounts.
Comments: The addition of conc. HCl (10 ml per 100 ml of reagent) before use makes this reagent more sensitive to some of this class of drugs especially methyl xanthines like caffeine. Pyrazalones (phenazone) are detected. Detects organic sulfur compounds with oxidizable S.
Alternate preparation: Immediately before use as spray for TLC plates, mix one volume conc. HCl with 10 volumes color reagent.
Results: Most basic drugs give blue or blue-violet spots which eventually turn to brownish-yellow but drugs containing only primary or secondary amine groups give bluish-white spots.

21. König Reagent (Cyanogen Bromide-*p*-Aminobenzoic Acid)

Preparation: Dissolve 2 g *p*-aminobenzoic acid in 75 ml of 0.75*N* HCl; dilute to 100 ml with 96% ethanol.
Procedure: Prior to spraying, store chromatogram for 1 hr. in a chamber containing a beaker of cyanogen bromide (toxic!).
Results: Detects alkaloids with pyridine ring. Detects nicotinic acid and related compounds.
Comments: Cyanogen bromide is toxic so proceed with care. Prepare cyanogen bromide solution from ice-cooled saturated bromine water to which is added sufficient 10% aqueous sodium cyanide solution to eliminate the bromine color.

22. Mercuric Chloride-Potassium Iodide (Meyer Reagent)

Preparation:
Solution a. Dissolve 13.55 g mercuric chloride in 20 ml of water.
Solution b. Dissolve 49.8 g potassium iodide in 20 ml water.
Solution c. Mix *a* and *b* and dilute to one liter with water.
Color reagent 1. 10 parts by volume of *c* and 1 part by volume of 17% HCl.
Color reagent 2. Dissolve 5 g zinc chloride in 80 ml water; add 15 ml conc. HCl to the solution.
Color reagent 3. 15% NH_4OH solution.
Procedure: Spray with reagent 1, rinse paper chromatogram with water for 10 min., blot or dry, spray with reagent 2 and then with reagent 3.
Results: Steroid alkaloids appear as faint yellow spots after spraying with reagent 1, and finally as dark brown spots that fade with time.

23. Nessler's Reagent

Preparation: Dissolve 50 g potassium iodide in 50 ml cold water; add saturated solution of mercuric chloride (about 22 g in 350 ml of water will be needed) until an excess is indicated by the formation of a precipitate. Then add 200 ml of 5*N* NaOH and dilute to one liter. Let settle and use clear liquid.
Results: Detects apomorphine, hydrastinine and physostigmine.

24. Nitric Acid

Preparation: Add 2 ml conc. HNO_3 to 100 ml absolute ethanol.
Procedure: Spray and inspect under U.V. light.
Results: Fluorescent spots for alkaloids and amines.
Comments: At this concentration or higher, other organic compounds may be detected. Frequently, fluorescent spots appear only after prolonged heating at 120 °C.

25. Paraformaldehyde-Phosphoric Acid

Preparation: 0.03 g paraformaldehyde in 100 ml conc. phosphoric acid. Stable for 1 week.
Results: Detects alkaloids.

26. Potassium Ferricyanide-Ferric Chloride (Kieffer's Reagent)

Preparation: Add 100 ml of ferric chloride to 10 ml of 1% aqueous potassium ferricyanide solution.
Procedure: Wash paper chromatogram briefly with water 2–3 min. after spraying or entire paper will turn blue.
Results: Alkaloids with free and phenolic hydroxyl groups appear as grey-blue spots under U.V. light.

27. Sodium Nitroprusside-Trichloroacetic Acid

Preparation: 3% solution of sodium nitroprusside in 50% trichloroacetic acid.
Results: Carboline alkaloids exhibit fluorescence in U.V. light.

28. Sulfuric Acid

Preparation: Add 2 ml conc. H_2SO_4 to 100 ml absolute ethanol.
Procedure: Spray and observe under U.V. light.
Results: Dehydration of alkaloids forms decomposition products that may fluoresce under U.V. light. Also detects glycosides and amines. Carboline alkaloids are detected by spraying with 90% H_2SO_4 and then with 9% sodium carbonate and viewing under U.V. light.

Amines
(aliphatic and aromatic amines, amino alcohols, choline, ethanolamines, adrenaline, urea and derivatives, hydrazines, guanidine derivatives)

See Tests: 16, 24, 28, 29–67, 148, 258, 262, 266, 269, 277, 302, 318, 330, 365, 369, 374, 377.

29. Acetoacetylphenol

Preparation: 1% solution of acetoacetylphenol in *n*-butanol.
Procedure: Spray and observe under U.V. light.
Results: Adrenaline and related compounds detected as fluorescent spots.

30. Acetylbenzoyl Reagent

Preparation:
Solution a. 1% α-naphthol in 8% aqueous NaOH.
Solution b. 0.1 ml acetylbenzoyl in 80% ethanol.
Color reagent. Mix equal volumes *a* and *b*.
Procedure: Follow directions for diacetyl reagent.
Results. Blue colors are obtained.

31. Alizarin

Preparation: 0.1% alizarin in ethanol.
Results: Bases such as aliphatic amines and amino alcohols are detected as violet spots on a light yellow background.

32. Calcium Nitrate

Preparation: 5% calcium nitrate in 95% ethanol.
Procedure: Spray and expose to U.V. light.
Results: Detects diphenylamine as yellow-green spot.

33. Csaky Reagent

Preparation:
Solution a. 1.3% solution of iodine in glacial acetic acid.
Solution b. 1% sulfanilic acid solution in 30% aqueous acetic acid.
Color reagent 1. Just before spraying, mix 20 ml *a* and 20 ml *b*.
Color reagent 2. 0.1% solution of *N*-(1-naphthyl)-ethylenediammonium dichloride in water.
Procedure: Spray the chromatogram consecutively with reagents 1 and 2.
Results: Detects hydroxylamine.

34. Diacetyl Monoxime-Nickel Chloride

Preparation:
Solution a. Dissolve 1.2 g diacetyl monoxime in 35 ml hot water and add 0.95 g nickel chloride hexahydrate to the hot solution. Cool and add 2 ml conc. NH_4OH.
Solution b. Dissolve 0.12 g hydroxylamine hydrochloride in 200 ml water.
Color reagent. Mix *a* and *b* and let stand for 1 day. Filter off precipitated nickel-dimethylglyoxime and use the red-brown filtrate.
Results: Detects amines.

35. Diacetyl Reagent

Preparation:
Solution a. 1 % α-naphthol in 8 % NaOH in water.
Solution b. 0.1 % diacetyl in water.
Procedure: Just before use equal volumes of the two reagents are mixed. the paper is dipped, placed flat on a second sheet of paper and heated for 3 min. at 100 °C. In order to lend extra wet strength to the paper it may be first placed on a sheet of polythene film and the two dipped together although the chromatogram must be transferred to another clean sheet of paper before heating.
Results: The paper is withdrawn from the oven and purple-red spots appear almost immediately; colors are stable for about a day and are obtained from mono- and *N,N*-disubstituted guanidines. Although many compounds react without heating, some do require heat. Creatine gives blue spot, streptomycin red spot. The unmixed reagents are stable for at least a month at room temperature.
Alternate preparation: The diacetyl reagent can be prepared as follows: 1.6 g of dimethylglyoxime is weighed into a 500 ml flask, 200 ml of 5*N* sulfuric acid is added and the first 50 ml of distillate is collected. This solution, which is stable indefinitely at room temperature in the absence of alkali, is diluted twenty times with water for use as above.

36. Diphenylamine-Palladium Chloride

Preparation:
Solution a. 1.5 % diphenylamine in ethanol.
Solution b. 0.1 % palladium chloride in 0.2 % saline solution.
Color reagent. A mixture of 5 parts *a* and 1 part *b*.
Procedure: Spray and expose moist chromatogram to 240 nm U.V. light.
Results: Nitrosamines detected as blue to violet spots on a colorless background.

37. Dipicrylamine

Preparation: Dissolve 0.2 g dipicrylamine in a mixture of 50 ml acetone and 50 ml redistilled water.
Results: Choline and derivatives detected as red spots on a yellow background.

38. Dragendorff Reagent (Bregoff-Delwiche Modification)

Preparation:
Solution a. Dissolve 8 g bismuth subnitrate in 20–25 ml of 25 % HNO_3.
Solution b. A slurry of 20 g potassium iodide, 1 ml 6*N* HCl and 5 ml water.
Solution c. Add *a* and *b* slowly with stirring. Add water until an orange-red color develops. The solution volume will be about 95 ml. Any solid residue is filtered off and the solution is diluted to 100 ml. Stable for several weeks in an amber bottle in the refrigerator.
Color reagent. Mix in this order: 20 ml of water, 5 ml of 6*N* HCl, 2 ml of *c* and 6 ml of 6*N* NaOH. If bismuth hydroxide is not completely dissolved by shaking, add several drops 6*N* HCl. Solution stable for 10 days in refrigerator.
Results: Detects quaternary bases, e.g., choline.

39. Ekman Reagent

Preparation:
Solution a. Mix 2*N* HCl, acetone and 5 % aqueous sodium nitrite (5 : 45 : 1) in this order. Prepare right before use.
Solution b. 5 % ethyl α-naphthylamine in ethanol.
Procedure: Dip through *a*, let stand a few minutes, and note colors. Dip through *b*.
Results: Diazotizable aromatic amines, including kynurenine and anthranilic acid, give intense and immediate magenta colors. 5-Hydroxyanthranilic acid gives a slow blue. The 3-isomer does not couple but gives a yellow-brown color at the diazotization stage. Some indoles give brown or pink colors similar to those from persulfate oxidation. Indolylacetonitrile does not react.

40. Fast Potassium Ferrocyanide B

Preparation:
Solution a. 0.5 % aqueous fast potassium ferrocyanide B, freshly prepared.
Solution b. 0.1*N* NaOH.
Procedure: Spray with *a* and then *b*.
Results: Detects coupling amines and phenols.

41. Glycine-Paraformaldehyde

Preparation: 5% glycine solution adjusted to pH 3 with HCl.

Procedure: Spray glycine solution onto the dried chromatogram, which is redried at 80 °C before being suspended in a sealed kilner jar containing paraformaldehyde (20 g) moistened with water (6 ml). The jar is then heated in an oven at 80 °C for 3 hours and the fluorescent spots which develop are viewed under U.V. light of wavelength 360 nm. The fluorescent compounds may be eluted from the paper with 0.1*N* HCl and measured in a spectrophotofluorimeter. The eluates are stable for several days at 0–5 °C.

Results: The fluorescence characteristics of catecholamines and related compounds after glycine-formaldehyde treatment are shown in the table below.

Compound	Minimum detectable amount (μg)	Color	max (nm) uncorrected	
			Activation	Fluorescence
Noradrenaline	0.03	Greenish-yellow	430	540
Adrenaline	1	Dull blue-grey		
Dopamine	0.03	Greenish yellow	430	525
DOPA	0.1	Buff orange	430	530
Metadrenaline	10	Dull olive green		
Normetadrenaline	1	Primrose		
3-Methoxytyramine	0.03	Bright yellow	440	520
3-Hydroxy-4-methoxyphenylethylamine	0.03	Bright ice blue	360	465
3,4-Dimethoxyphenylethylamine	0.03	Bright ice blue	360	470
Octopamine	10	Dull blue violet		
4-Hydroxy-3-methoxymandelic acid	10	Apple green		

42. Isatin

Preparation: 0.2% isatin in acetone.

Color reagent: Incorporate 2% pyridine before use.

Procedure: Dry chromatogram is dipped through the reagent and after the acetone evaporates off it is heated at 105 °C for 2–3 min.

Results: Prolines react to yield blue colors; derivatives of phenylalanine and certain sulfur amino acids yield light blue colors, but with lower sensitivities for these compounds.

Comments: Pyridine is incorporated in the reagent for the same reasons as in ninhydrin reagent. Isatin-pyridine is more valuable for hydroxyproline, but isatin containing 5% acetic acid yields stronger blue colors with phenylalanine, tyrosine and tryptophan.

To test for hydroxyproline, the isatin reagent is followed by Ehrlich reagent; in one minute, a purple-red spot appears with 0.1 μg/cm^2 sensitivity. Specific for hydroxyproline.

43. Jaffe Reagent

Preparation:

Solution a. 1% picric acid in 95% ethanol.

Solution b. 5% potassium hydroxide in 80% ethanol.

Procedure: The paper is dipped in *a*, allowed to dry and then dipped in *b*.

Results: Stable red spots are obtained on a yellow background. Creatinine, glycocyamidine and lactams of α-guanidino-acids react positively.

44. Mercuric Acetate-Hydrogen Sulfide

Preparation: 1% aqueous mercuric acetate containing 1% acetic acid.

Procedure: Spray paper chromatogram and after 30 min. remove excess reagent by washing paper for 3 hr. in running water. Dry paper and place in a chamber with 50 ml conc. HCl at the bottom, and introduce H_2S.

Results: Allyl urethane spots reach maximum color after 30 min.

45. 1-Naphthol-Bromine (Sakaguchi Reagent)

Preparation:

Solution a. 16% urea and 0.2% 1-naphthol in ethanol-water (5 : 1).

Solution b. Mixture of 500 ml 5% aqueous NaOH and 3.3 ml bromine.

Procedure: Spray with *a*, dry below 40 °C and then with *b*.

Comments: Detects arginine and other guanidine derivatives as pink or red spots. For detection of streptomycin, spray with a mixture of 50 ml aqueous sodium hypochlorite (13% of activated Cl) and 50 ml ethanol instead of with *b*.

46. Ninhydrin-Pyridine

Preparation:
Solution a. 0.2% ninhydrin in acetone. With very dry acetone, add 2–3% water.
Color reagent. Incorporate 2% pyridine in *a* before use.

Procedure: Dip paper through the reagent. Hang paper in the air or, after the acetone has evaporated, heat 2–3 min. at 105 °C. Inspect under U.V. light.

Results: All α-amino acids react in air usually within 3 hr. or certainly overnight giving purple spots with most compounds (asparagine, brown). If the chromatogram is heated 2–3 min. at 105 °C all compounds containing a primary or secondary amino group attached to an aliphatic carbon atom (including aliphatic amines, non-α-amino acids, nonaromatic nitrogen heterocyclic compounds such as piperidine-carboxylic acids) react to give mostly purple spots with some variations. A compound yielding a color on heating but not by standing overnight in air is almost certainly not an α-amino acid.

Incorporation of pyridine into the reagent nullifies the adverse effect of strong acid fumes on the spot colors. Pyridine causes the purple spot colors to have a blue tinge, and adversely affects the intensity of spot fluorescences.

Comments: To preserve chromatograms treated with ninhydrin, dip paper through a solution composed of 1 ml saturated aqueous copper nitrate in 100 ml ethanol plus 0.2 ml 10% HNO_3. Colors change to pinkish-red and are stable for many months.

O-DNP-tyrosine, *im*-DNP-histidine, and ε-DNP-lysine give colors with ninhydrin (grey-brown for first two, purple for latter). Iodoamino acids react to give purple-brown spots. Greater sensitivity is obtained if the colors are allowed to develop at room temperature.

C-(3-indolyl)glycine gives a bright yellow spot. Compounds of the tryptamine series react.

47. Nitraniline

Preparation:
Solution a. 0.25 g *p*-nitraniline in 2 ml conc. HCl and 98 ml water.
Solution b. 0.5% sodium nitrite in water.
Color reagent. Add *b* to 5 volumes *a* until decolorized, then dilute to 20 volumes with water.
Solution c. 10% sodium carbonate in water.

Procedure: Dry chromatogram, spray with *c*, dry in stream of warm air, spray with reagent.

Results: Detects methoxy catecholamines, other bases and hydroxycyclic acids with various colors.

48. Nitrosonaphthol Reagent

Preparation:
Solution a. 0.1% α-Nitroso-β-naphthol in ethanol.
Color reagent. Mix *a* and conc. HNO_3 (9 : 1).

Procedure: Prepare reagent and immediately dip paper and allow to damp-dry 2–3 min. at room temperature. Then heat paper 2 min. at 105 °C. Colors fade rapidly, but some can be stabilized by dipping through dilute NH_4OH.

Results: Many phenolic compounds containing a free ortho position, e.g., tyrosines and thyronines, give red colors; excess heating destroys these colors. A few indoles react to give stable grey or brown colors, but HNO_3 alone will give these colors.

Phenols containing an aliphatic sidechain such as an acetic, propionic or cinnamic acid residue react, but it is not a general reagent for phenolic acids.

p-Hydroxyphenylacetic acid, *p*-hydroxyphenylpyruvic acid, and *o*-hydroxyphenylpropionic acid react.

49. Periodic Acid-Pyridine-Ammonium Acetate

Preparation:
Solution a. 40 % periodic acid in water.
Solution b. Pyridine.
Solution c. Acetone.
Solution d. Dissolve 15 g ammonium acetate, 0.3 ml acetic acid, 1 ml acetyl acetone in 100 ml methanol.
Color reagent. Mix 2 ml *a*, 2 ml *b*, 100 ml *c*.

Procedure: Dip dry chromatogram through freshly prepared reagent, dry, and dip in *d*.

Results: Substances yielding formaldehyde on periodate oxidation give first a green-yellow fluorescence in 10–15 min. and a visible yellow color in 0.5–1 hr. Sensitivity $\sim 2\ \mu g/cm^2$, but less if phenol was the chromatographic solvent.

Serine, hydroxyserine, ethanolamines, 1,2-diols and 1-ols, 2-NH_2 compounds such as glycosamines, sugars, sialic acids react.

Alternate procedure: Dip in color reagent, dry, and dip in a 1 : 1 mixture of 5% sodium nitroprusside in methanol (fresh) and 20% piperidine in methanol.

Results: Threonine gives blue color on pale blue background within few minutes.

50. Phenanthrenequinone

Preparation:
Solution a. 0.02% phenanthrenequinone in absolute ethanol.
Solution b. 10% NaOH in 60% ethanol. (Both solutions stable in refrigerator).
Color reagent. Mix *a* and *b* (1 : 1).

Procedure: Spray or dip chromatogram and after 20 min. examine in 360 nm U.V. light.

Results: Arginine, arginine peptides and other monosubstituted guanidines detected as fluorescent spots, $10^{-4}\ \mu$mole sensitivity. Guanidoacetic acid gives positive test. 1,1-Dimethylguanidine and amino acids without guanido groups do not react.

51. Phenol-Hypochlorite

Preparation:
Solution a. 5% phenol in 95% ethanol.
Solution b. 5.2% sodium hypochlorite (Clorox®).
Results: Detects ureas, guanidine bases: urea—yellow-green, arginine—orange, chloride ions—blue, *p*-aminobenzoic acid—brown.

52. Phosphomolybdic Acid-Stannous Chloride (Chargaff's Reagent)

Preparation:
Solution a. Dissolve 1 g phosphomolybdic acid in 100 ml of ethanol-chloroform (1 : 1).
Solution b. Dissolve 1 g stannous chloride in 100 ml of 2–3*N* HCl. Prepare fresh before use.
Procedure: Spray with *a*, wash under running water, then dip into *b*. Thin layers are stablilized for washing before spraying with *a* by placing developed, dry chromatogram in a vacuum desiccator at 300 mm with 3–5 ml of dichlorodimethylsilane for 15 min. and then removing and exposing to air for 30 min.
Results: Detects choline and substances containing choline. Also detects phospholipids.

53. Potassium Ferricyanide-Ferric Chloride

Preparation: Equal parts of 0.1*M* ferric chloride and 0.1*M* potassium ferricyanide.
Results: Detects aromatic amines and tryptamine as blue spots.

54. Potassium Ferricyanide-Phosphate Buffer

Preparation: 0.44 g potassium ferricyanide in 100 ml 0.1*M* phosphate buffer, pH 7.4. Buffer is 0.1*M* potassium dihydrogen phosphate adjusted to pH 7.4 with 0.1*M* KOH.
Procedure: Dry chromatogram, spray, and view in daylight and U.V. light.
Results: Detects catecholamines with various colors. Noradrenaline—brown-red; adrenaline—light red; methyladrenaline—white on yellow-brown background.

55. Potassium Ferricyanide-Sodium Nitroprusside (Pentacyanoaquoferriate Reagent: PCF)

Preparation:
Solution a. 10% sodium hydroxide in water, 10% potassium ferricyanide in water, 10% sodium nitroprusside in water.
Procedure: Fresh solutions of the components of solution *a* are prepared and for the latter two components the crystals are first well washed by covering twice with water, shaking and decanting. Equal volumes of all three are then mixed and the immediate deep red color obtained changes to a light yellow or yellow-green in about 20 min., when it is diluted with 9 parts of water; this solution is stable for many months at 2–4 °C. Just prior to use, the dilute solution is mixed with an equal volume of acetone and the paper is then dipped.
Results: Immediate red or orange colors are obtained with mono-*N*,*N*-disubstituted and *N*-substituted 3-nitro guanidines but not with *N*,*N'*-dialkyl substituted compounds. Some aromatic amines, pyridine derivatives, etc., yield green-blue colors. Detects nicotinamide (yellow) and thiamine (fluorescent).

56. Potassium Ferrocyanide-Cobalt Chloride

Preparation:
Solution a. 1% aqueous potassium ferrocyanide (II) solution, freshly prepared.
Solution b. 0.5% aqueous cobaltous chloride solution.
Procedure: Spray with *a*, dry briefly, then spray with *b*.
Results: Choline detected as green spot.

57. Potassium Iodate

Preparation: 1% aqueous solution of potassium iodate.
Procedure: After treating chromatogram, heat for 2 min. at 110 °C.
Comments: Detects phenylethylamines (sympathomimetic amines).

58. Potassium Persulfate-Silver Nitrate

Preparation: 1.0% aqueous potassium persulfate containing 1×10^{-3} *M* silver nitrate.
Procedure: Spray and then heat at 45 °C if necessary.
Results: Many spots appear without heating; aromatic amines detected with various colored spots, e.g., *o*-toluidine, blue changing to yellow; benzidine, brown; *p*-anisidine, green; *p*-toluidine, pink; *p*-aminophenol, violet.

59. Quinone

Preparation: Dissolve 0.5 g of *p*-quinone (benzoquinone) in a mixture of 10 ml of pyridine and 40 ml of *n*-butanol.
Results: After spraying, red spots of ethanolamine will immediately appear. Choline does not react.

60. Sakaguchi Reagent

Preparation:

Solution a. 0.1% oxine in acetone.

Solution b. 0.3 ml liquid bromine in 100 ml 0.5*N* NaOH (stable 2–3 weeks).

Procedure: Dip chromatogram through *a* and allow acetone to evaporate completely. Then dip through *b*.

Results: Monosubstituted guanidines (arginine) give deep red to orange colors. Colors fade in 30 min. to 2–3 days. Cysteine, cystine, cysteic acid—pink-brown spots; agmatin—orange. DNP-arginine reacts in usual way.

Comments: 0.2 ml of water containing 0.1 g urea may be added to 100 ml solution to obtain permanent colors. This is omitted if this reagent follows Ehrlich reagent in multiple sequences.

61. Sodium Nitroprusside-Acetaldehyde

Preparation:

Solution a. 5% sodium nitroprusside in 10% aqueous acetaldehyde solution.

Solution b. 1–2% sodium carbonate.

Color reagent. A 1 : 1 mixture of *a* and *b*.

Results: Detects secondary aliphatic and alicyclic amines, morpholin and diethanolamine.

62. Sodium Nitroprusside-Potassium Ferricyanide

Preparation:

Solution a. 10% NaOH.

Solution b. 10% sodium nitroprusside.

Solution c. 10% potassium ferricyanide.

Color reagent. Mix equal volumes of *a*, *b* and *c* with 3 parts water. Allow solution to stand 30 min. before spraying. Stable several weeks under refrigeration.

Results: Cyanamide, violet spots; dicyanodiamide, carmine-red; guanylurea, yellow-orange; guanidine, red-orange; arginine, light red; creatine, carmine-red; creatinine, yellow-brown; agmatine, pink; guanidineacetic acid, carmine-red; thiourea, violet; urea, faintly pink.

63. Sodium Pentacyanoaminoferrate (II) (Fearon's Reaction)

Preparation: Dissolve 10 g of sodium nitroprusside in 40 ml of ammonia solution. Allow the solution to stand at 0 °C until all nitrose iron (III)-cyanide is decomposed. This is the case if several drops of the mixture, added to a solution of creatinine in 1*N* sodium carbonate solution, no longer produce any red color. Then filter and add ethanol to the clear filtrate until no further precipitate is formed. Filter off the resulting precipitate, wash with absolute ethanol and dry over sulfuric acid in a vacuum desiccator. The salt is stable when stored protected from light and moisture.

Color reagent. Add 15 ml of a 1% aqueous sodium pentacyanoaminoferrate (II) solution and 1 drop of 30% hydrogen peroxide to 5 ml of 20% NaOH. Stable for 24 hr.

Results: Detects urea, thiourea and guanidines.

64. Sulfanilic Acid

Preparation:

Solution a. 1 g sulfanilic acid in 10 ml conc. HCl and 90 ml water.

Solution b. 5% sodium nitrite in water.

Solution c. 10% sodium carbonate in water.

Color reagent. Mix *a* and *b* (1 : 1), and after standing at room temperature for 4–5 min., add 2 volumes *c*. Cooling not needed if room temperature < 20 °C. Stable for some time.

Procedure: Spray chromatogram; chromatograms developed with acidic solvents are presprayed with *c* and dried before applying diazo spray.

Results: Detects catecholamines, other bases, and hydroxycyclic acids with red to orange to yellow colors.

65. Sulfuric Acid-Potassium Dichromate

Preparation: Dissolve 5 g of potassium dichromate in 100 ml of 40% sulfuric acid.

Results: Detects amylamines with various colors.

66. 7,7,8,8-Tetracyanoquinodimethan (TCNQ)

Preparation: 0.3% TCNQ in pyridine-acetone (1 : 1).

Procedure: Spray paper or layer with dimethylsulfoxide, dry with gentle heat with a hairdryer and spray with TCNQ. Inspect the air-dried chromatogram in daylight and after 5 min. irradiation with U.V. light.

Comments: Also detects amino acids, mercaptans, prolines, carbazoles, acridines, thiosemicarbazones and polynuclear hydrocarbons.

67. Vanillin-Potassium Hydroxide

Preparation:

Solution a. Dissolve 2 g vanillin in 100 ml *n*-propanol.

Solution b. 1% ethanolic potassium hydroxide solution.

Procedure: Spray with *a*, heat chromatogram for 10 min. at 110 °C and view under U.V. light. Spray with *b* and heat again.
Results: Detects amines and amino acids. After spraying with *a*, ornithine shows green-yellow fluorescence and lysine faint green-yellow fluorescence. After spraying with *b*, ornithine first shows a salmon color and then fades, while proline, hydroxyproline, pipecolinic acid and sarcosine turn red after several hours. Glycine turns brown-green, the other amino acids faintly brown.

Amino Acids, Peptides, Proteins, Enzymes

See Tests: 42, 45, 46, 48, 49, 50, 60, 66, 67, 68–94, 262, 266, 269, 284, 375, 376, 377, 391

68. Bromphenol Blue (Stain for Proteins)

Preparation:
Solution a. 1 % bromphenol blue in ethanol saturated with mercuric chloride.
Solution b. 0.5 % acetic acid.
Procedure: The chromatogram is dipped for 5 min. in *a*. The still-wet chromatogram is then washed in *b* which should be replaced about 5 times in the course of 30 min. When the background has been thoroughly decolorized, the paper is dried between two filter papers. Before allowing the paper to dry completely, the yellow spots may be turned to more intense blue spots by exposing to ammonia vapor. Quantitative analysis can be performed either by the elution of the colored product with a 5 % solution of sodium carbonate in 50 % aqueous methanol and colorimetry, or directly by photometry *in situ*. Mercuric chloride is not necessary in the staining of serum proteins.
Comments: Proteins are detected most often based on their affinity for acidic dyes such as bromphenol blue. Other dyes which can be used include eosin plus methyl orange, Solway purple, azocarmine B and naphthalene black.

69. Butyl Chloride-Potassium Iodide-Starch-Mercuric Chloride

Preparation:
Solution a. 10 % *tert*-butyl chloride in acetic acid-1,2-dichloroethane (1 : 99).
Solution b. Aqueous solution containing 1 % potassium iodide, 1 % soluble starch, and 5 mg HgI_2.
Procedure: Spray with *a*, dry in air 5–10 min. in a hood, spray with *b*. Outline spots at once.
Results: Detects proteins (more sensitive than bromphenol blue) and amino acids.

70. Ceric-Arsenite Reagent

Preparation: Use glass-distilled water and reagent-grade chemicals.
Solution a. 10 % ceric sulfate tetrahydrate in $1N\ H_2SO_4$ previously cooled to 0 °C. The cloudy solution should be refrigerated and shaken intermittently, then filtered. Store in cold.
Solution b. Add 5 g sodium arsenite to 100 ml $1N\ H_2SO_4$, previously cooled to 0 °C, with vigorous stirring. Do not let temperature rise during preparation or arsenious oxide will precipitate.
Color reagent. Mix equal volumes of *a* and *b* just before use.
Procedure: Place a sheet of filter paper equal in size to the chromatogram on a clean glass plate. Use a small portion of reagent to wet the paper evenly. Cover the wetted paper with the chromatogram, and place a second glass plate on top and press firmly down. Leave for 30 min. Inspect under U.V. light.
Results: Iodine-containing amino acids appear as white spots on a yellow background and also fluoresce markedly. Other organic iodine compounds and iodide react. Sensitivity—0.1 μg for triiodothyronine and thyroxine and 0.01 μg for iodide.
Comments: Spraying reduces the sensitivity of the reagent and also exposes the washer to needless risk from the toxic reagent. Stained chromatograms are dried at room temperature in an iodine-free atmosphere.

71. Chloramine T

Preparation:
Solution a. Dissolve 560 mg *p*-toluenesulfochloramide sodium salt in 50 ml water and dilute to 50 ml with methanol.
Solution b. Dissolve 5 g *p*-dimethylaminobenzaldehyde in 70 ml *n*-propanol and 5 ml $6N\ H_2SO_4$.
Solution c. 10 % sodium carbonate.
Solution d. Suspend 5 g dry diazotized sulfanilic acid in 50 ml cold water.
Procedure 1: Spray lightly with *a* and after 10 min. with *b*. After 10 min. heat the chromatogram 3–5 min. at 65 °C.
Results: Hydroxyproline detected as violet spot.
Procedure 2: Spray with *a*, then after 60 min. spray lightly with *c*, and finally after an additional 5 min. with *d*.
Results: Aspartic acid detected as violet or orange-red spot. Histidine and tyrosine also react.

72. Chlorine-*o*-Tolidine

Preparation: Saturated solution of *o*-tolidine in acetic acid-water (1 : 49).
Procedure: Expose paper to chlorine gas and then dip into the reagent.
Results: Detects pipsyl derivatives of amino acids.

73. Dehydroascorbic Acid

Preparation: Dissolve 0.1 g dehydroascorbic acid in 5 ml water at 60 °C, dilute to 100 ml with butanol.
Procedure: Spray and heat at 100 °C for 5 min.
Results: Hydroxyproline—pale violet-blue, 25 μg; proline—pale yellow, 25 μg; phenylalanine, tyrosine, tryptophan—pale pink, 10 μg; other amino acids—pink to red, 1–3 μg.

74. *N*-Ethylmaleimide

Preparation:
Solution a. 0.05*M* *N*-methylmaleimide in absolute isopropanol.
Solution b. Dissolve 1.4 g potassium hydroxide in 100 ml water.
Procedure: Immerse paper chromatogram in *a*, dry for 15 min., then immerse in *b*.
Results: Detects amino acids with —SH groups.
Comments: This test detects mainly —SH compounds and their condensates at concentrations of 0.1 μg. At higher concentrations, the pink-red spot colors are preserved in the dark at 0 °C for several days. Also detects S-acetyl derivatives and thiolactones, but not disulfides.

75. Ferrichloride-Ferricyanide-Arsenious Acid (FFCA)

Preparation:
Solution a. 2.7 g $FeCl_3 \cdot 6H_2O$ in 100 ml 2*N* HCl.
Solution b. 3.5 g potassium ferricyanide in 100 ml water.
Solution c. 3.8 g sodium meta arsenite in 10 ml 21% aqueous NaOH. When required, cool and add 20 ml 6% aqueous NaOH and then 65 ml 2*N* HCl with vigorous stirring.
Color reagent. Mix *a*, *b* and *c* (5 : 5 : 1) just before use.
Results: Detects 0.001 μg iodide and 0.002 μg of iodothyronines and diiodotyrosine as blue spots.

76. *N*-Hydroxyphthalonimide

Preparation: 0.5% *N*-hydroxyphthalonimide in 96% ethanol.
Procedure: Spray, air-dry, heat 15 min. at 140 °C.
Results: Amino acids detected as blue, green and violet spots.

77. Iodine-Azide-Starch Reagent

Preparation:
Solution a. Dissolve 2.54 g iodine plus 8 g potassium iodide in 100 ml water.
Solution b. Mix 0.5 g soluble starch into a smooth paste with 3–4 ml cold water and then pour into 90 ml boiling water. Cool and add 1.5 g sodium azide, and then dilute to 100 ml.
Color reagent. Mix *a* and *b* (1 : 2).
Procedure: Dip in reagent.
Results: PTH-amino acids detected as stable white spots in about one minute on a dark blue background. Background changes to brown and white with time. PTH-proline and PTH-hydroxyproline react more slowly.

78. Iodoplatinate Reagent

Preparation:
Solution a. Chloroplatinic acid, 1 mg/ml, in water.
Solution b. Potassium iodide, 167 mg/ml, in water.
Solution c. 2*N* HCl.
Solution d. Acetone, reagent grade.
Color reagent. Mix 5 ml *a*, 0.3 ml *b*, 0.5 ml *c* and 25 ml *d* in order above.
Procedure: Dip chromatogram and lay flat.
Results: Most sulfur amino acids, except those oxidized, give white spots on purple background. Up to one hour may be required to develop the spot, depending upon the chromatography solvent.
Comments: Use reagent as soon as prepared.

79. Isatin-Zinc Acetate

Preparation: Warm on a water bath at 70–80 °C until solution takes place and then cool quickly.
Solution a. 1 g isatin and 1.5 g zinc acetate in 100 ml isopropanol and 1 ml pyridine.
Solution b. As in *a*, except use 1 ml acetic acid plus 95 ml isopropanol plus 5 ml water as the solvent.
Procedure: Spray heavily either with *a* or *b* and dry 30 min. at 90 °C. Better color differentiation is obtained by letting development take place at room temperature (20 hr.).
Results: Detects amino acids.

80. Morin (2′,3,4′,5,7-Pentahydroxyflavone)

Preparation: 0.005–0.05% morin in methanol.
Procedure: Spray, dry at 100 °C for 2 min. and examine under U.V. light immediately.
Results: Detects amino acids as yellow-green fluorescent or dark spots on a fluorescent background.
Comments: Useful as a general detection reagent for various classes of compounds.

81. Naphthalene Black (Stain for Sephadex Thin Layers)

Preparation: 1 g naphthalene black in 100 ml of a mixture of 50 ml methanol, 40 ml water, and 10 ml glacial acetic acid.
Procedure: Cover completed Sephadex plate with filter paper (Whatman No. 3 MM) taking care to exclude air bubbles. Dry for 30 min. at 80–90 °C. Immerse in dye bath for 30 min. then wash in same solvent mixture to remove excess dye.
Results: Detects proteins.

82. β-Naphthoquinone-4-sulfonic Acid, Sodium Salt (Folin Reagent)

Preparation: Spray solution. Dissolve 0.2 g *β*-naphthoquinone-4-sulfonic acid, sodium salt, in 100 ml 5% sodium carbonate solution.
Procedure: Spray 10–15 min. after preparing spray solution. No further treatment.
Preparation: Dip solution. Dissolve 0.3 g *β*-naphthoquinone-4-sulfonic acid, sodium salt, in 10 ml water. Dilute to 300 ml with acetone.
Procedure: Dip paper chromatogram and heat to 80–90 °C for 3–5 min.
Results: Pink-red spots.
Comments: The spots of amino acids change color differently if the chromatogram is dipped after drying for 1–1.5 min. into a freshly prepared solution made by diluting 4 ml aqueous 5*N* NaOH with 96% ethanol to 200 ml.

83. Ninhydrin-Cadmium Acetate

Preparation: Spray solution. Dissolve 1 g ninhydrin, 2.5 g cadmium acetate and 10 ml glacial acetic acid in 490 ml methanol.
Procedure: Spray and heat in oven at 120 °C.
Preparation: Dip solution. Dissolve 0.1 g cadmium acetate in 10 ml water, add 5 ml glacial acetic acid and 100 ml acetone, and finally 1 g ninhydrin.
Procedure: Draw through dip solution, then place chromatogram for 30 min. in closed vessel containing a dish of conc. H_2SO_4.
Results: Detects amino acids.

84. Ninhydrin-Collidine

Preparation: Spray solution. Dissolve 0.2–0.3 g ninhydrin in 95 ml isopropanol or *n*-butanol saturated with water. Add 5 ml s-collidine to the solution.

Alternate spray solutions. Add 5 ml acetic acid to the above solution, or use a solution of 95 ml of 0.2% ninhydrin in *n*-butanol plus 5 ml acetic acid.

Dip solution. Dissolve 0.2–0.3 g ninhydrin in 95 ml acetone and add 5 ml collidine.
Procedure: Spray or dip chromatogram and then heat for 30–60 min. at 80–90 °C.
Results: Blue spots.
Comments: For stabilization of ninhydrin-complex colors, spray with a solution containing 1 ml saturated aqueous copper nitrate, 0.2 ml of 1% HNO_3 and 4 ml of distilled water diluted to 100 ml with methanol, and then dry.

When ninhydrin is used on TLC plates, background discoloration can mask weak spots. This is minimized by heating TLC plates, after spraying, at 80 °C until just dry but before the color reaction is initiated. The dry plate is kept in the dark for 24 hr. (in a refrigerator, if possible) to slow down color development. Plates with fluorescent indicator (F-254) are not well suited to ninhydrin staining. Also detects amino sugars as blue spots.

85. Ninhydrin-Cupric Nitrate

Preparation:

Solution a. 0.2% ninhydrin in a mixture of 50 ml absolute ethanol, 10 ml glacial acetic acid and 2 ml of s-collidine.
Solution b. 1% cupric nitrate trihydrate in absolute ethanol.
Color reagent. A fresh mixture of 25 ml *a* and 1.5 ml *b*.

Procedure: Dry chromatogram, spray with reagent, and heat 1.5–2 min. at 105 °C.
Results: Detects amino acids.

86. Ninhydrin-Stannous Chloride

Preparation:

Solution a. Dissolve with heating 2 g ninhydrin in 40 ml water.
Solution b. Dissolve 80 mg stannous chloride in 50 ml water.
Solution c. Add *b* to *a* and allow to stand. Filter off precipitate and store in refrigerator.
Color reagent. Add 50 ml water and 450 ml isopropanol to 25 ml *c*.

Results: Detects amino acids.

87. *p*-Nitrobenzoyl Chloride Reagent

Preparation:

Solution a. 0.2% *p*-nitrobenzoyl chloride in benzene.
Solution b. Pyridine-petroleum ether (1 : 10).

Procedure: Dip in *a*, dry, dip in *b*.
Results: Orange colors, lasting only a few min. *N*-methyl-α-amino acids and ring compounds such as pipecolonic acid react positively. *N*-methyl-amines and other amino acids are negative.

88. Nitrophenylstearate

Preparation: 1% *p*-nitrophenylstearate.
Procedure: Spray with reagent and incubate in a humid chamber at 40 °C.
Results: Lipases detected as yellow spots which are intensified by treatment with NH_3.

89. Nitroprusside Reagent

Preparation:
Solution a. 2 g sodium cyanide is dissolved in 5 ml water and 95 ml ethanol is added. A precipitate immediately appears; use the supernatant without filtering.
Solution b. Dissolve 1.5 g sodium nitroprusside in 5 ml of 2*N* H_2SO_4 and add 95 ml methanol followed by 10 ml conc. NH_4OH. A copious precipitate appears, and the filtrate is stored in the cold.
Color reagent. Mix *a* and *b* in equal volumes as required.
Procedure: Dip chromatogram and lay flat.
Results: Purple spots, which fade after about 30 min., obtained with cysteamine, cysteine, cystine, meso cystine, homo cysteine, homo cystine.

90. *o*-Phthalaldehyde-Potassium Hydroxide

Preparation:
Solution a. 0.2% *o*-phthalaldehyde in acetone.
Solution b. 1% potassium hydroxide in 95% ethanol.
Procedure: Dip in *a*, heat at 100 °C for 2 min., dip in *b*, reheat up to 10 min. at 100 °C.
Results: Glycine yields a green color, taurine, brown-red. With larger quantities present, colors may appear after the first dip and even without heating. Histidine and tryptophan yield fluorescence reactions; most other common amino acids do not react.

91. Potassium Hypochlorite-*o*-Toluidine (Reindel-Hoppe Reagent modified according to Greig and Leaback)

Preparation:
Solution a. Dissolve 2 g potassium hypochlorite in 100 ml water.
Solution b. Saturated solution *o*-toluidine in 2% acetic acid–85% potassium iodide (1 : 1).
Procedure: Spray with *a* lightly, let stand 1–1.5 hr., spray with *b*.
Results: Amino acids give blue-black spots on white background. Detects proteins, peptides and other N- and NH-containing substances.

92. Sodium Nitroprusside-Sodium Cyanide

Preparation:
Solution a. Dissolve 1.5 g of sodium nitroprusside in 5 ml 2*N* HCl. Add 95 ml of methanol and 10 ml conc. NH_4OH and then filter.
Solution b. Dissolve 2 g sodium cyanide in 5 ml water and dilute to 100 ml with methanol. Care—Poison!
Procedure: Spray with *a* to detect S-H compounds as red spots. Spray with *b* to detect -S-S compounds as red spots on a yellow background.
Results: Arginine turns orange and later blue-grey after spraying with *a*.
Alternate method for -S-S linkage compounds:
Preparation:
Solution a. Dissolve 5 g sodium cyanide and 5 g sodium carbonate in 100 ml 25% ethanol.
Solution b. Dissolve 2 g sodium nitroprusside in 100 ml of 75% ethanol.
Procedure: Spray with *a*, air-dry briefly, spray with *b*.

93. Thymol Blue

Preparation: Dissolve 40 mg thymol blue in 100 ml of a mixture of 25 ml *n*-butanol, 25 ml ethanol and 50 ml of 0.01*N* H_2SO_4.
Results: Detects dimethylamino acids as yellow spots on a red background.

94. Ultraviolet Light

Procedure: Inspect dry chromatograms under U.V. light.
Results: DNP-amino acids absorb U.V. light and appear as dark spots. This compliments the location of these derivatives, all of which are yellow except O-DNP-tyrosine and *im*-DNP-histidine, in daylight.

PTH-amino acids absorb 250 nm U.V. light and are also detected as dark spots. Pyridine must first be removed by vigorous steaming. DNS-amino acids have intense fluorescence in U.V. light. The color is generally yellow, with a green tinge for very nonpolar amino acids and an orange tinge for the polar compounds. DNS-OH is present in all derivative samples and gives an intense blue fluorescence.

Iodotyrosines, iodothyronines and most derivatives absorb strongly—sensitivity is 20–30 μg. Long exposure can cause chemical changes.

Antibiotics

See Tests: 35, 45, 95, 96, 97, 300, 303.

95. Bioautography of Penicillin-Paper Chromatography

In penicillin assay, the agar and spore suspension may be prepared as follows: The nutrient medium consists of 1 g of glucose, 1.5 g of meat extract, 6 g of Bacto-peptone, 3 g of yeast extract, and 15 g of agar per liter of water. The *B. subtilis* spore suspension consists of 3 g of peptone and 3 g of meat extract per liter inoculated with *B. subtilis*, Marburg type, and incubated for 6 days on a shaker at 30 °C. The suspension is then pasteurized at 80 °C for 10 minutes and stored in the refrigerator until required. The agar medium is seeded just prior to pouring the plates by first heating to about 70 °C. Precautions should be taken to ensure uniformity of depth of seeded agar over the entire plate. When many plates are poured, an equal volume should be added to each so that the depth of medium is the same in each case. After pouring, all plates are stored in the cold room until needed.

After chromatography, the dried strips of paper are laid on the assay plates which are then returned to the cold room for 3 hours, after which they are incubated at 30 °C until the inhibition zones are well defined (about 12 hours).

96. Bioautography for Thin-Layer Chromatography

Principle. After development, the chromatographic plates are coated with a layer of agar containing a small amount of triphenyltetrazolium chloride (TTC) and a microorganism that is sensitive to the antibiotic in question. After some time, light yellow inhibition zones appear in the agar corresponding to the position of the antibiotic on the chromatogram. Where it is not in contact with the antibiotic, the agar is colored a deep reddish-brown due to the reduction of TTC to triphenylformazan.

Method. The medium contains 6 g peptone, 3 g yeast extract (DIFCO), 1.5 g meat extract (DIFCO), 4 g casein, 1 g glucose, 15 g agar and 1000 ml distilled water. The mixture is brought to the required pH by the addition of sodium carbonate and sterilized in the usual manner. The pH of the medium is 5.9 for *Sarcina lutea* and 7.0 for *Bacillus subtilis* and *Staphylococcus aureus*.

0.7 ml of a 5% solution of TTC in 50% methanol is added at 50 °C to 50 ml of medium in a 250 ml flask. The agar is then inoculated in the usual way with various bacterial suspensions of the following turbidities according to the antibiotic being detected: rifomycin, 0.3 ml of *Sarcina lutea* with 30–35% transmittance; penicillins, 0.5 ml of *Staph. aureus* of 70% transmittance; penicillins and tetracyclines, 0.5 ml of *B. subtilis* of 35% transmittance.

The yellowish-brown fluid is swirled round in the flask for 30 sec. and then slowly poured over the chromatogram* which is lying on a Plexiglas base. The medium is poured out in portions, starting at the upper end of the plate where there is no antibiotic. The agar spreads over the whole plate without disturbing the layer, which is then left to cool under sterile conditions at room temperature for 15 min. The agar forms an even, gelatinous yellow coating over the white chromatogram. As atmospheric oxygen would hinder the reduction of the TTC, the inoculated medium is protected by pouring on a further coating of 25 ml of sterile agar (15 g agar in 1000 ml distilled water) warmed to 50 °C. The multiple layer is allowed to cool for a further 15 min. and is then placed in a wide, well-closed Plexiglas container in the refrigerator at 0 °C for 1 hr. During this period the antibiotic diffuses out of the chromatogram into the agar above it, and the microorganisms do not multiply. The plates are then kept in an incubator at 37 °C for at least 16 hr.

Light yellow zones of inhibition are seen against a chestnut brown background. There is no simple relationship between the amount of antibiotic and the size of the inhibition zone; hence an exact quantitative determination is not possible.

* If an acidic solvent has been used for development, the plate is exposed to an atmosphere of ammonia for some time and then kept for 1 hr. in an evacuated desiccator to remove excess of ammonia, which would inhibit the growth of the bacteria.

97. Iodine-Azide-Starch

Preparation:

Solution a. 0.5% aqueous soluble starch.

Solution b. 1 g sodium azide in 10% aqueous 0.1*M* iodine solution.

Procedure: Spray with *a*, dry, spray with *b*.

Results: Detects penicillin, sensitivity 0.2 μg.

Comments: Penicillin and penicilloic acids also detected by starch-iodine-iodide reagents, as are cephalosporins.

Antioxidants and Preservatives

See Tests: 253, 377, 415.

Carbohydrates

(sugars, sugar alcohols, carbohydrate acids and lactones, deoxy sugars, methylated sugars, amino sugars, polysaccharides)

See Tests: 49, 84, 98–141, 145, 246, 268, 329, 374, 424.

See also Table 1 at the end of this section.

98. Aminobenzoic Acid

Preparation: Add 3 g *p*-aminobenzoic acid gradually with stirring to 5.0 ml hot H_3PO_4. When dissolved, add 300 ml *n*-butanol-acetone-water (10 : 5 : 2). (Stable below 25 °C for long periods).

Procedure: Treat chromatogram and heat at 105 °C for a few minutes.

Results: Pentoses—dark red, other sugars—dark brown.

99. *o*-Aminodiphenyl-Orthophosphoric Acid

Preparation: 0.3 g *o*-aminodiphenyl plus 5 ml conc. H_3PO_4 in 95 ml ethanol.
Procedure: Spray and heat at 110 °C for 15–20 min.
Results: Carbohydrates detected as brown spots, 0.1γ sensitivity.

100. Aminohippuric Acid

Preparation: Dissolve 0.3 g *p*-aminohippuric acid in 100 ml ethanol. Add 3% phthalic acid if reducing disaccharides are present.
Procedure: Spray, heat 8 min. at 140 °C, examine under U.V. light.
Results: Hexoses and pentoses give orange-red spots, seen more easily under U.V. light.

101. Aminophenol

Preparation: 0.15 g *o*- or *p*-aminophenol in 10 ml 50% H_3PO_4. (Prepare fresh).
Procedure: Spray and heat several minutes at 105 °C.
Results: 1–5 μg aldoses and ketoses detected.

102. Aniline-Diphenylamine Phosphate

Preparation:
Solution a. Mix 5 ml aniline, 5 g diphenylamine and 100 ml acetic acid.
Solution b. Acetone.
Solution c. 20 ml 85% phosphoric acid in 100 ml water.
Color reagent. Mix in order *a*, *b*, *c* (1 : 1 : 1).
Procedure: Dip papers, dry, and heat at 95–100 °C for few minutes.
Results: Reducing sugars react to give variety of colors; sensitivity lower than aniline phosphate. 1,4-Aldohexose-oligosaccharides give blue spots.
Alternate preparation: Mix 5 parts of 4% ethanolic aniline solution, 5 parts of 4% ethanolic diphenylamine solution and 1 part conc. H_3PO_4, prepared fresh.
Procedure: Spray, heat 10 min. at 80 °C, inspect under U.V. light.

103. Aniline Phosphate

Preparation:
Solution a. Mix in order 20 ml aniline, 200 ml water, 180 ml acetic acid and 10 ml phosphoric acid. Store at 4 °C.
Solution b. Acetone.
Color reagent. Mix *a* and *b* (2 : 3).
Procedure: Dip papers, dry and heat 2–5 min. at 100°C.
Results: Pentoses—red-brown; aldoses and sorbose—yellow or yellow-brown. Other ketoses do not react except in large amounts. Sensitivity greater than aniline phthalate reagent, but specificity lower.
Comments: *p*-Anisidine may be substituted for aniline, yielding bright yellow spots which fluoresce under U.V. light.

104. Aniline Phthalate

Preparation: Mix 0.93 g aniline hydrogen phthalate, 1.66 g phthalic acid and 100 ml water-saturated butanol.
Procedure: Spray and heat paper at 105–130 °C for 5 min. Inspect under U.V. light.
Results: Detects aldoses; weak positive reaction by ketoses and oligosaccharides; aldohexoses and methylpentoses—brown spots; aldopentoses—red spots.

105. Anisidine

Preparation: *Solution a.* Dissolve 1 g of *p*-anisidine hydrochloride in 10 ml of methanol, and dilute with *n*-butanol to 100 ml. Add 0.1 g of sodium dithionite and shake well.
Solution b. 3% *p*-anisidine hydrochloride in *n*-butanol.
Procedure: Spray with *a* and heat for 10 min. at 130 °C; or spray with *b* and heat for 2–10 min. at 100 °C.
Results: Aldohexoses—green-brown; ketohexoses—yellow; aldopentoses—green; uronic acids—red; 2-deoxy aldoses—grey-brown.

106. *p*-Anisidine-Phthalic Acid

Preparation: 1.23 g *p*-anisidine and 1.66 g phthalic acid in 100 ml methanol.
Results: Hexoses, green; pentoses, red-violet; methyl pentoses, yellow-green; uronic acids, brown. Sensitivity: methyl pentoses and hexoses, 0.5 μg; pentoses and uronic acids, 0.1–0.2 μg.

107. Anthrone Reagent

Preparation: Dissolve 0.3 g of anthrone in 10 ml of glacial acetic acid and add to the solution 20 ml of 96% by volume ethanol, 3 ml of conc. phosphoric acid and 1 ml of water. The solution is stable for several weeks in the refrigerator.

Procedure: After spraying, heat the chromatogram for 5–6 min. at a temperature of about 110 °C.
Results: Ketoses and oligosaccharides containing ketoses appear as yellow spots.
Comments: Paper chromatograms may be stored for a prolonged period of time after washing with water.

108. Benzidine

Preparation:
Solution a. Dissolve 1 g benzidine in 40 ml glacial acetic acid, warming if necessary. Dissolve 30 g trichloroacetic acid in 40 ml water, and mix the two solutions. (Stable in refrigerator; slowly darkens in color).
Solution b. Acetone.
Color reagent. Mix *a* and *b* (1 : 9) right before use.
Procedure: Treat chromatogram and heat at 100–110 °C.
Results: Almost all sugars give brown spots on light yellow background.
Comments: *Caution*! Benzidine is highly carcinogenic.
Alternate Preparation: Dissolve 0.5 g benzidine in 20 ml glacial acetic acid and 80 ml of ethanol.
Procedure: Spray and heat chromatogram for 15 min. at 100 °C. Note any colors in daylight, spray with dilute HCl and inspect under U.V. light.
Results: Detects carbohydrates, terpene aldehydes and flavonoids. Vanillin detected as yellow to orange spot. Sensitivity 0.1 μg.
Alternate preparation: Dissolve 50 mg benzidine in 100 ml 1*N* acetic acid.
Results: Persulfates detected as blue spots.

109. Boric Acid

Preparation: 1% boric acid in 90% aqueous methanol containing 1% HCl.
Procedure: Spray and heat at 100 °C for 1–3 min.
Results: Glycosides give blue-grey spots by daylight; deoxy sugars also detected as blue-grey spots by daylight, but also as a purple fluoresce in U.V. light.

110. Bromphenol Blue-Boric Acid

Preparation: Dissolve 40 mg bromphenol blue (or bromcresol green) in 10 ml ethanol. Add 100 mg boric acid and 7.5 ml of 1% sodium tetraborate and dilute to 100 ml with ethanol.
Results: Sugar alcohols detected as yellow spots on blue background.

111. 3,5-Diaminobenzoic Acid-Phosphoric Acid

Preparation: 1 g 3,5-diaminobenzoic acid dihydrochloride in a mixture of 25 ml 80% phosphoric acid and 60 ml water.
Procedure: Spray and heat plate to develop colors and observe in U.V.
Results: 2-Deoxysugars detected by green-yellow fluorescence.

112. *o*-Dianisidine Phosphate

Preparation:
Solution a. 0.15% *o*-dianisidine in acetone; prepare fresh.
Solution b. Mix 5 ml acetic acid, 5 ml water, 1 ml 85% phosphoric acid; stable in bulk.
Color reagent. Mix *a* and *b* (4 : 1).
Procedure: Dip paper, air-dry and then heat few minutes at 100 °C.
Results: Nearly all sugars give yellow spots on pale yellow background. The background darkens slowly.
Comments: Reagent useful for semiquantitative scanning procedures. *Caution—o*-dianisidine is carcinogenic.

113. *N,N*-Dimethyl-*p*-phenylaminediamine (*p*-Aminodimethylaniline)-Stannous Chloride

Preparation: Dissolve 0.34 g dimethyl-*p*-phenylamine diammonium dichloride and 0.76 g stannous chloride in 100 ml ethanol. Prepare fresh daily prior to use.
Procedure: Spray and heat chromatogram for 10 min. at 120 °C.
Results: Differentiates ketoses and aldoses.
Comments: 0.4% dimethyl-phenylenediamine in 2% aqueous trichloroacetic acid solution detects methyl sugars.

114. Dinitrosalicylic Acid (DNSA)

Preparation:
Solution a. 0.5% 3,5-DNSA in acetone.
Solution b. Dissolve 4 g NaOH in 15 ml water and dilute to 100 ml with ethanol.
Procedure: Dip in *a*, allow acetone to evaporate, dip in *b*, allow ethanol to evaporate, heat few minutes at 110 °C.
Results: Reducing sugars yield dark brown colors on a yellow background; care must be taken not to overheat the paper as the background then intensifies. Sensitivity *ca.* 1 μg. Reagent *a* is strongly acidic and may hydrolyze sugars, such as sucrose, if reagent *b* is not applied as soon as the acetone has evaporated off the paper. The colors are permanent.

115. Diphenylamine

Preparation: 2.3 g diphenylamine in 100 ml water saturated with *n*-butanol.
Procedure: Spray and then dry chromatogram in air and then at 130 °C for 20 min.
Results: Aldoses and ketoses appear as blue spots.

116. Elson-Morgan Reagent

Preparation:
Solution a. 25% potassium hydroxide in water (20 vols.) and 95% ethanol (80 vols.).
Solution b. 1% redistilled acetylacetone in 95% ethanol.
Solution c. 10% *p*-dimethylaminobenzaldehyde in conc. HCl.
Solution d. 95% ethanol.
Solution *b* is prepared immediately before use.
Procedure: The dried chromatogram is dipped through a mixture of 1 vol. *a* and 10 vols. *b* and heated at 110 °C for 5 min. It is then dipped through a mixture of equal volumes of *c* and *d* and dried in a stream of cold air.
Results: Transient purple spots indicate the presence of hexosamines. Heating to 80 °C fixes the spots with a permanent red color.

117. Fleur's Reagent

Preparation:
Solution a. Dissolve 10 g mercuric oxide in 10 g conc. HNO_3 and 200 ml water. Dilute 1 : 1 with water.
Solution b. Mix 1 part of 10% aqueous barium acetate and 10 parts glacial acetic acid.
Procedure: Spray with *a*, heat 10 min. at 95 °C, then spray with *b* and heat 10–30 min.
Results: Inositols detected as orange spots, other polyols are black spots.

118. β-Indolylacetic Acid-Trichloroacetic Acid

Preparation:
Solution a. 1 g β-indolylacetic acid in 50 ml *n*-propanol.
Solution b. 10 g trichloroacetic acid in 2 ml water (stir to dissolve).
Color reagent. Mix *a* and *b* (1 : 1); not stable.
Procedure: Spray, heat 10–15 min. at 100 °C.
Results: Ketoses detected specifically as violet spots.

119. Lead Tetraacetate

Preparation: 1% lead tetraacetate in benzene.
Results: Maroglycerides and reducing sugars detected as white spots on a brown background, sensitivity 50–100 μg.

120. Malonic Acid-Aniline

Preparation: 1g malonic acid plus 1 ml aniline in 100 ml absolute methanol.
Procedure: Draw chromatogram quickly through the reagent, air-dry, dry at 110 °C for 10 min. (longer for sucrose).
Results: Yellow, grey or brown spots for sugars, fluorescent in U.V. light.

121. *p*-Methoxybenzaldehyde

Preparation: Add 1 ml *p*-methoxybenzaldehyde and 1 ml conc. H_2SO_4 to 18 ml ethanol.
Procedure: Spray and heat at 110 °C.
Results: Sugar phenylhydrazones detected as yellow-green spots in 2–3 min.; sugars as green, blue or violet spots in 10 min.

122. Naphthoresorcinol

Preparation:
Solution a. 0.2% naphthoresorcinol in acetone.
Solution b. 9% H_3PO_4 in water (mix 1 volume 90% H_3PO_4 and 9 volumes water).
Color reagent. Mix *a* and *b* (5 : 1).
Procedure: Dip paper, place in oven at 95 °C in which a beaker of water has been standing.
Results: After a few minutes, ketopentoses yield green-brown colors, other ketoses yield red-browns and, in 5–8 minutes, uronic acids yield blues on a pale pink background; aldoses do not normally react although large quantities of glucose give a pale blue color. Residual pyridine interferes with the reaction but may be readily removed by steaming.
Alternate preparation: Dissolve 200 mg naphthoresorcinol in 100 ml ethanol and add 10 ml H_3PO_4.
Procedure: Dip, blot and hang in warm air 30–60 min. Then heat at 90 °C for 5 min.
Results: Glucuronides give blue spots at 10 $\mu g/cm^2$, glucuronic acid at 1 $\mu g/cm^2$.
Alternate preparation for spraying: 200 mg naphthoresorcinol in 100 ml ethanol plus 10 ml H_3PO_4.

123. β-Naphthylamine-Thymol

Preparation: Mix 0.1 g β-naphthylamine, 1 g thymol, 150 ml ethanol, 2 ml H_3PO_4.
Procedure: Spray and heat at 110 °C for a few minutes.
Results: Fructose and fructose oligosaccharides—yellow; aldohexoses—brown; aldopentoses—pink; uronic acids—red.

124. Ninhydrin

Preparation: 0.1 % ninhydrin in acetone.
Procedure: The paper is dipped through the solution and either allowed to dry at room temperature or heated for 1–2 min. at 80 °C.
Results: Free amino sugars give reddish-purple colors while aminouronic acids give light brown colors turning purple on standing.

125. Nitraniline-Periodic Acid

Preparation:
Solution a. Add 2 parts of water to 1 part by volume of a saturated aqueous sodium metaperiodate solution.
Solution b. Add 1 part by volume of conc. HCl to 4 parts by volume of a 1 % ethanolic *p*-nitraniline solution.
Procedure: Spray with *a*, wait for 10 minutes, then spray with *b*.
Results: Deoxy sugars and glycols show yellow spots with intense fluorescence under U.V. light. Further spraying with a 5 % methanolic sodium hydroxide solution turns the spots green.

126. Nitrophenylhydrazine

Preparation:
Solution a. 0.25 g *p*-nitrophenylhydrazine in 100 ml ethanol.
Solution b. 0.5*N* alcoholic NaOH.
Procedure: Spray with *a*, heat 20 min. at 100 °C, wash out excess reagent with ethanol, spray again with *b*, and wash out excess alkali with ethanol.
Results: 2-Deoxy sugars detected as yellow or yellow-brown spots.

127. Orcinol-Trichloroacetic Acid

Preparation: Mix 0.5 g recrystallized orcinol and 1.5 g trichloroacetic acid in 100 ml water-saturated *n*-butanol.
Procedure: Spray dried chromatogram and heat at 105 °C for 15–20 min.
Results: Ketohexose sugars detected as yellow spots.

128. Periodate-Anisidine

Preparation:
Solution a. 1 g *p*-anisidine in 100 ml 70 % ethanol.
Solution b. 10 ml of 0.1*M* sodium periodate in 100 ml acetone.
Procedure: Spray with *a*, heat 5–10 min. at 105 °C, dip in *b*.
Results: Spots detected on a brownish background, sensitivity 1–20 μg; polyols—white; sugar acids (uronic acids—red to brown, aldonic acids—white); 2-deoxy sugars—yellow; amino sugars—brown or yellow; pentoses and hexoses—red fluorescence in U.V. light.

129. Periodic Acid-Benzidine

Preparation:
Solution a. 2.28 g periodic acid in 100 ml water (stable in cold). Mix 1 : 19 with acetone (stable for few hours).
Solution b. Dissolve 184 mg benzidine in 95 ml acetone, add 4.4 ml water and 0.6 ml acetic acid (turns yellow but is stable indefinitely).
Procedure: Dip in *a*, allow to stand 3–4 min., dip in *b*.
Results: White spots on blue background. Practically all sugars and sugar alcohols react; sucrose, trehalose and glycosamines are negative.
Comments: *o*-Tolidine or *o*-dianisidine may be substituted for benzidine. *Caution*! All three chemicals are carcinogenic. Periodic acid-Schiff's Reagent is also used for the detection of nonreducing and reducing sugars.

130. Phenol-Sulfuric Acid

Preparation: 3 g phenol plus 5 ml conc. H_2SO_4 in 95 ml ethanol.
Procedure: Spray and heat 10–15 min. at 110 °C. Additional heating may intensify spots.
Results: Carbohydrates detected as brown spots.

131. Phenylenediamine

Preparation: Dissolve 3.6 g of *m*-phenylenediammonium dichloride in 100 ml of 70 % ethanol.
Procedure: Spray and heat briefly to 105 °C.
Results: Reducing sugars detected as intensely fluorescent colors under U.V. light.

132. Phloroglucinol Reagent

Preparation:
Solution a. 0.7% phloroglucinol in acetone.
Solution b. 40% trichloroacetic acid in water.
Color reagent. Mix *a* and *b* (9 : 1).
Procedure: Dip paper and heat to 105 °C for several minutes.
Results: The paper is dipped in freshly mixed reagent and then heated to 105–110 °C for a few minutes. Ketopentoses yield strong green colors whereas other ketoses yield pale yellow-browns with an intense green fluorescence in U.V. light; the background is colorless. The reagent will not detect uronic acids or aldoses and is less sensitive than naphthoresorcinol.

133. Pyridinium Barbiturate

Preparation: 1% aqueous solution of pyridinium barbiturate.
Procedure: Treat chromatogram with the reagent and heat.
Results: Reducing sugars detected as brown spots. Also detects carbonyls as pink spots and glyoxal as a deep red spot.

134. 1-(2-Pyridylazo)-2-naphthol

Preparation:
Solution a. 0.4% 1-(2-pyridylazo)-2-naphthol in ethanol.
Solution b. 0.8 g cobalt nitrate in 100 ml water.
Solution c. 2*M* Sodium acetate buffer pH 4.6 (iron free).
Solution d. A mixture of 4 ml of *b* and 2 ml of *c* diluted to 50 ml.
Procedure: Spray with *a* followed by *d* with drying between sprays.
Results: Detects glucosiduronates as violet spots on yellow background.

135. Seliwanoff's Reagent

Preparation:
Solution a. 5% alcoholic resorcinol solution.
Solution b. 10 ml conc. H_2SO_4 in 375 ml 95% ethanol.
Color reagent. Mix 0.4 ml *a* and 10 ml *b*.
Results: Detects oligosaccharides.

136. Sodium Nitroprusside-Sodium Hydroxide (Legal Test)

Preparation: 1% sodium nitroprusside solution in 50% ethanol, also 1*N* in NaOH.
Results: α,β-unsaturated lactone compounds detected as red to red-violet spots.

137. Sodium Nitroprusside-Sodium Periodate

Preparation:
Solution a. Mixture of 1 part by volume of saturated aqueous sodium periodate solution and 2 parts by volume of water.
Solution b. Mixture of 1 part by volume of saturated aqueous sodium nitroprusside solution, 3 parts by volume of water and 20 parts by volume of a saturated solution of piperazine in 96% by volume ethanol.
Procedure: Spray with *a*, dry for 10 min. at room temperature, then spray with *b*.
Results: Maximal blue color of deoxy sugars after 5–10 min. Sensitivity of detection may not be as high as with nitraniline-periodic acid.

138. Starch-Iodine-Potassium Iodide

Preparation:
Solution a. 2% aqueous starch.
Solution b. Dissolve 50 mg iodine in 100 ml 1% aqueous potassium iodide solution.
Procedure: Spray with *a*, then place chromatogram into a moist chamber at 40–50 °C for one hour. Dry chromatogram at room temperature, spray with *b*.
Results: Amylases detected as white spots on violet or brown background.

139. Thiobarbituric Acid

Preparation:
Solution a. 10.6 g sodium periodate in 0.05*N* H_2SO_4.
Solution b. Ethylene glycol-acetone-conc. H_2SO_4 (50 : 50 : 0.3).
Solution c. 6% aqueous sodium-2-thiobarbiturate.
Procedure: The dried paper is sprayed with *a* and left for 15 min. before spraying with *b*. After a further 10 min. the paper is sprayed with *c* and heated at 100 °C for 10 min.
Results: Amino sugars detected as red spots, sensitivity about 3 μg.

140. Urea-Acid

Preparation: Dissolve 5 g of urea in 20 ml of 2*N* HCl. All 100 ml of ethanol to the solution.
Results: Ketoses and oligosaccharides containing ketoses turn blue.
Alternate preparation: Mix 1 g urea, 4.5 ml 85% H_3PO_4, 48 ml *n*-butanol saturated with water.
Procedure: Spray, heat 5 min. at 90 °C.
Results: Heptoses turn blue-green.

141. Vanillin-Perchloric Acid

Preparation:
Solution a. 1% vanillin in ethanol.
Solution b. 3% aqueous perchloric acid.
Color reagent. Mix *a* and *b* (1 : 1).
Procedure: Spray and heat 10 min. at 85 °C.
Results: Deoxy sugars detected as spots of various colors.

Carboxylic Acids
(lower and higher fatty acids, aliphatic hydroxy acids, keto acids, phenolic acids)

See Tests: 16, 47, 48, 64, 142–171, 187, 250, 253, 263, 268, 291, 328, 365, 367, 372, 374, 376, 377, 378.

142. Acridine

Preparation: 0.1 g acridine in 100 ml of 99.5% ethanol.
Procedure: Dip paper, drain, and lay on another sheet of paper.
Results: Acidic compounds appear as pale yellow spots on the white background. Viewing the chromatogram under U.V. light greatly increases location of the spots. when most of these appear to have an intense green-yellowish fluorescence, although some of them appear darker (brown-yellow) and phenylpyruvic acid is located as a black spot.

143. Ammonium Vanadate

Preparation: Saturated solution of ammonium vanadate in water.
Procedure: The chromatogram is rapidly drawn through the reagent and the spots which appear are marked rapidly, while still wet.
Results: This reagent gives a yellow color with most acids, but is relatively insensitive. It is, however, useful for the location of tartaric acid, which yields a red color, and ascorbic acid which appears as a blue-grey spot.

144. Aniline-Xylose

Preparation:
Solution a. Add 1 g xylose to 3 ml water.
Color reagent. Add 1 ml aniline to *a*, and dilute to 100 ml with methanol.
Procedure: Dip paper, hang in air 5–10 min., and heat damp paper at 105–110 °C for 5–10 min.
Results: General spray for acidic compounds; brown spots on pale yellow background, sensitivity 10 μg.
Comments: Spots are permanent. Other location reagents cannot usually be subsequently applied. The reagent slowly darkens in color and yields a darker background color.

145. Benzidine-Metaperiodate

Preparation:
Solution a. 0.1% aqueous sodium metaperiodate.
Solution b. Add 70 ml of water, 30 ml of acetone and 1.5 ml of 1*N* HCl to a solution of 2.8 g of benzidine in 80 ml of 96% ethanol.
Procedure: Spray with *a*; partially dry and spray moist chromatogram with *b*.
Results: Detects organic acids; also detects sugars and sugar alcohols.
Comments: *Caution*! when using benzidine.

146. Bromcresol Green

Preparation:
Solution a. 0.1% bromcresol green in 99.5% ethanol. Add 1*N* NaOH until color becomes blue-green.
Color reagent. Mix *a* and acetone (1 : 4).
Procedure: Dry papers thoroughly and draw rapidly through the reagent. Lay paper flat on another sheet of paper.
Results: A general location reagent for organic acids. Acids give yellow spots on green background, basic components give blue spots.
Comments: This reagent does not affect most other specific location reagents which may be applied later. Can be added directly to the chromatographic solvent.

147. Bromcresol Purple

Preparation: 0.04 g Bromcresol purple in 100 ml of 50% ethanol. Adjust to pH 10 with 0.1*N* NaOH.
Results: Lower fatty acids detected as yellow spots on purple-blue background. Also detects halogen anions except fluoride.
Alternate preparation: 0.04% bromcresol purple in formaldehyde-ethanol (1 : 5).
Procedure: Spray and expose to NH_3.
Results: Organochlorine herbicides detected as yellow spots on purple backgrounds. Colors fade but are regenerated by exposure to NH_3.

148. Bromphenol (or Bromophenol) Blue

Preparation: Dissolve 0.05 g of bromphenol blue in 100 ml water; 0.2 g citric acid may be added.
Procedure: Remove acidic or basic residues of solvent. For acids, adjust to pH 7–8 with buffer. For bases or salts of acids when basic solvents are used, do not adjust pH.
Results: Acids yield yellow spots on blue-green background; for bases, colors are reversed. NH_4^+ and ethylamine salts give blue colors.

149. Chlorine-Starch-Iodide

Preparation:
Solution a. 2% potassium iodide in water.
Solution b. 2% soluble starch in water.
Color reagent. Mix *a* and *b* (1 : 1); prepare fresh.
Procedure: Place chromatogram in atmosphere of gaseous chlorine for 10 min. Hang in current of air until no background is obtained with the color reagent when a trial portion of chromatogram is tested. Dip chromatogram and lay flat on clean filter paper.
Results: Compounds with an active hydrogen on the nitrogen atom are located as blue spots, turning brown and fading in a few hours. Pyrrolidine carboxylic acid and phenylacetylglutamine react.
Comments: Iodoacids detected as yellow spots by exposure to chlorine gas alone.

150. Chlorophenol Red

Preparation: Dissolve 0.04 g chlorophenol red in 100 ml water. Adjust to pH 7 with 0.1*N* NaOH.
Results: Detects organic acids.

151. Copper Acetate-Dithiooxamide (Rubeanic Acid)

Preparation:
Solution a. 5% aqueous copper acetate, 4 ml, diluted to 100 ml with distilled water.
Solution b. 0.03% Dithiooxamide in 95% ethanol.
Procedure: The paper is immersed in *a* for 20 min. Excess copper acetate is then removed by washing in running tap water for 20 min. After drying, the copper salts are detected by dipping in *b* for 30 sec. Excess dithiooxamide is removed by washing in ethanol for 1 min.
Results: Fatty acids appear as green spots against a light green background.

152. Copper Acetate-Potassium Ferrocyanide

Preparation:
Solution a. Dilute 4 ml of 5% aqueous copper acetate to 100 ml with distilled water.
Solution b. 0.1% aqueous potassium ferrocyanide.
Procedure: Immerse paper in *a* for 20 min., wash under running tap water for 20 min., dry, and dip in *b* for 30–45 sec. Remove excess ferrocyanide by washing in water.
Results: Fatty acids yield red-brown spots on lighter background.

153. α-Dextrin-Iodine

Preparation:
Solution a. 1% α-dextrin in 30% ethanol.
Procedure: Spray, air-dry, and then leave for 1 hr. in a high humidity chamber at room temperature. Expose to iodine vapors.
Results: Monoglycerides give white spots on a violet background. Unsaturated compounds give white spots turning brown or yellow. Reexposure to iodine develops faded spots. Sensitivity is about 20 μg.

154. 2,6-Dichlorophenolindophenol (Tillman's Reagent)

Preparation: 0.1% 2,6-dichlorophenolindophenol in 95–99.5% ethanol.
Procedure: Dip or spray chromatogram, blot, and lay flat on a sheet of filter paper. A short heating period may help bring out color.
Results: Most acids present in high concentration give pink spots. Ascorbic acid bleaches the dye and is readily detected.

155. Dimethylglyoxime-Nickel Biuret Reagent

Preparation:

Solution a. 1% dimethylglyoxime in 95% ethanol.

Solution b. Mix 1 g $NiSO_4 \cdot 7H_2O$ plus 1 g biuret in 50 ml water; add 1 volume of $1N$ NaOH to 5 volumes of this solution, allow to stand 30 min., filter off nickel hydroxide, and use the clear, amber filtrate. Prepare fresh.

Solution c. Conc. NH_3-water-ethanol (5 : 500 : 500).

Procedure: If acidic solvent is used, dry paper and then steam to remove all traces of acid. Partly dry again and dip in *a*. Partly dry and spray with *b*.

Results: Acidic compounds give pink spots on colorless background. After 1–2 min., wash chromatogram twice in *c* for 1–2 min. each time; dry in current of air and store in dark. Colors stable for several months.

156. Diphenylcarbazone

Preparation: 0.1–0.2% s-diphenylcarbazone in 95% ethanol.

Results: Addition compounds of unsaturated acids (e.g., with mercury) are dyed purple. Spray with $0.05N$ nitric acid in ethanol to intensify color. Produces purple spots with acetoxymercuric-methoxy derivatives of unsaturated esters and barbiturates. A 0.01% solution of diphenylcarbazone in chloroform gives red-violet spots for dialkyltin salts; trialkyl do not react.

Comments: Alternate procedure for barbituric acids: spray with 1% silver nitrate followed by the reagent.

A saturated solution in 96% ethanol followed by 25% NH_4OH solution detects Ag, Zn and Cd ions.

157. Ferric Chloride

Preparation: 2 g ferric chloride anhydrous in 100 ml water and 1 ml $2N$ HCl.

Procedure: The reagent is diluted five times with water for use. The paper is dipped, drained, blotted and laid flat. The colored spots are marked immediately as they tend to fade.

Results: Many acids, especially hydroxy acids, when present in high concentration, react with the ferric chloride reagent, yielding yellow or brown spots. The sensitivity of the reagent is very poor, so that it cannot be advised as a general location technique, but it is useful for the location of phenylpyruvic acid, which gives a distinctive green color. 3 : 4 Dihydroxyphenolic acids give green spots, other acids red, brown and purple spots, and some weak yellow spots. Sensitivity of phenols is about 50 μg. Thiocyanate appears red and ferricyanide blue. Phenothiazines (red to violet) are differentiated from phenothiazine sulfoxides (no reaction). Hydroxamate derivatives of bile acids are also detected.

158. Glucose-Aniline (Schweppe Reagent)

Preparation:

Solution a. Dissolve 2 g glucose in 20 ml water.

Solution b. Dissolve 2 ml aniline in 20 ml ethanol.

Color reagent. Mix *a* and *b* together in a 100 ml volumetric flask and dilute to volume with *n*-butanol.

Procedure: Spray with the reagent solution and heat chromatogram 5–10 min. at 125 °C.

Results: Organic acids detected as dark brown spots on white background.

159. Methyl Red

Preparation: Dissolve 0.3 g methyl red in 250 ml pH 8.5 borate buffer solution and dilute to one liter with water.

Alternate preparation:

Solution a. 0.1% methyl red solution in ethanol.

Solution b. pH 7 phosphate buffer solution.

Color reagent. Mix 1 part solution *a* and 10 parts solution *b* by volume.

Procedure: Spray and place chromatogram into NH_3 vapor.

Results: Detects organic acids.

160. Methyl Red-Bromthymol Blue

Preparation: Dissolve 0.2 g methyl red and 0.2 g bromthymol blue in a mixture of 100 ml of formaldehyde and 400 ml of 96% ethanol. Adjust solution to pH 5.2 with $0.1N$ NaOH.

Procedure: Spray chromatogram and place in NH_3 vapor.

Results: Organic acids detected as yellow spots on pink background changing to red-orange spots on green background after exposure to NH_3.

161. Nile Blue

Preparation: Add about 15 ml triethanolamine to 50 ml of a 0.2% solution of nile blue sulfate in ethanol until its blue color turns to bright red. Dilute the resulting solution with 50 ml ethanol.

Results: Acids give blue spots on a red background.

162. Phenol Red-Chloramine

Preparation:

Solution a. Dissolve 0.024 g phenol red in 2.4 ml 0.1*N* NaOH and dilute to 100 ml with acetone.

Solution b. Dissolve 6.8 g sodium acetate in 3 ml glacial acetic acid and some water. Dilute to 100 ml with water.

Color reagent 1. Mix 3 parts by volume of solution *a* with 1 part by volume of *b*.

Color reagent 2. Dissolve 0.025 g of chloramine in 100 ml of a mixture (1 : 1) of acetone and water. This solution is stable only one day.

Procedure: Spray with reagent 1 followed by reagent 2.

Results: Detects organic acids.

163. *o*-Phenylenediamine-Trichloroacetic Acid

Preparation: Dissolve 50 mg of *o*-phenylenediamine in 100 ml of 10% aqueous trichloroacetic acid solution.

Procedure: After spraying, heat the chromatogram for not more than 2 min. to 100 °C in the drying oven, then inspect the fluorescent spots under U.V. light.

Results: Detects α-keto acids.

164. Potassium Ferrocyanide-Ferric Ammonium Sulfate

Preparation:

Solution a. 10% potassium ferrocyanide in water.

Solution b. 0.5% ferric ammonium sulfate in 70% ethanol.

Procedure: The chromatogram is dipped through *a* and allowed to dry. It is then dipped through *b* and allowed to dry again.

Results: This reagent is most useful for the detection of oxalic acid, which yields a bright blue color; sensitivity, 10 μg. Many other organic acids are located as colored spots (which are much less intense than the oxalic acid one), when the chromatogram is heated at 100 °C for 5–10 min. and the blue-green background is bleached with 10% ammonia.

165. Potassium Permanganate

Preparation: Dissolve 0.16 g potassium permanganate in 1 liter water (0.001*M*).

Procedure: Dip paper and then rinse in water to remove excess reagent.

Results: Unsaturated fatty acids give brown spots on white background.

166. Quinidine

Preparation: 0.3% solution of quinidine in chloroform.

Procedure: Heat chromatogram for about 30 min. in a hood at 60–80 °C to remove volatile acids from the solvent. Spray vigorously (paper chromatograms are sprayed on both sides), heat chromatogram for 10 min. at 110 °C and inspect under U.V. light.

Results: Detects organic acids.

167. Silver Nitrate-Eriochromecyanine

Preparation:

Solution a. 5% aqueous silver nitrate solution.

Solutions b and c. 0.5% aqueous eriochromecyanine solution.

Procedure: Dip the chromatogram for one minute into solution *a*, allow the solution to drip off, then dip successively into solutions *b* and *c*. Subsequently rinse with distilled water. Dry chromatogram at 150 °C for 10 min.

Results: Halogen acids turn yellow, saturated acids dark brown.

168. Silver Nitrate-Phenol

Preparation:

Solution a. Dissolve 1.7 g silver nitrate in 100 ml water.

Solution b. Mix phenol with aqueous 0.05*N* NaOH (1 : 1) in a separatory funnel and shake to saturate the phenol with the base. Use the heavier phase.

Procedure: Spray with *a* and heat at 105 °C. Then spray with *b* and heat.

Results: Reducing acids form brown spots and nonreducing acids white spots on a light ochre background with solution *a*. Solution *b* gives white spots on a dark brown background.

169. Silver Nitrate-Pyrogallol

Preparation:

Solution a. Dissolve 0.17 g silver nitrate in 1 ml of water. Add 5 ml conc. NH_4OH and dilute to 200 ml with ethanol.

Solution b. Dissolve 6.5 mg pyrogallol in 100 ml of ethanol.

Procedure: Spray with *a* and then *b*. For greater stability of color, spray then with 40% sodium thiosulfate solution and rinse with water.

Results: Detects organic acids.

170. Sodium Hydroxide-Ethanol

Preparation: 2% NaOH in 90% ethanol; dissolve alkali in water, cool, and dilute to volume with ethanol.
Procedure: Dip papers.
Results: Colors appear immediately, and the shade and intensity is dependent on the chromatographic solvent used; the colors slowly fade, some returning to the original yellow and others to weak browns. 1–2 μg can be detected after chromatography.

171. Ultraviolet Light

Results: Visible color and ultraviolet light are primary methods for detecting ketoacids. All hydrazones are yellow and 5–10 μg can be detected. DNP-hydrazones absorb 360 nm U.V. light and appear as dark spots; sensitivity less than 1 μg.

Drugs (Barbiturates)

See Tests: 16, 20, 156, 157, 172–183, 297, 304.
See also Table 2 at the end of this section.

172. Cobalt Nitrate-Ammonia (Zwikker Reagent)

Preparation: 1% Cobaltous nitrate in acetone for paper *or* 5% in ethanol for TLC.
Procedure: After drying, the paper is dipped through the reagent, dried again and then exposed to ammonia vapor; a convenient method of doing this is to place a little strong ammonia solution at the bottom of the glass tank and hang the papers inside.
Results: The barbiturates give bluish-violet spots, best seen by transmitted light. The color persists for about 20 min. but returns on reexposure to ammonia vapor, even after the lapse of several years. When the initial violet color has faded a further identification may be made; thiobarbiturates give a permanent light green, hexobarbitone gives a permanent light brown, and cyclobarbitone gives a faint yellowish spot.
Comments: It is essential to dry the paper thoroughly before exposing to ammonia, failure to do so gives a confusing blue-green background in place of the normal white or faint pink one.

The best way to dry paper chromatograms is to leave them exposed to the atmosphere for 10 min. The use of an oven or hot air fan may produce a pink background which makes it difficult to observe the violet barbiturate spots.

The reagent may be used for reverse phase chromatograms though tributyrin prepared papers have an adverse effect on its sensitivity. The 5% solution of cobalt nitrate in alcohol is more effective on TLC plates and will detect about 5 μg of barbiturate.

This reagent is far more diagnostic for barbiturates than the more frequently used mercury spray reagents. It is stable for several months.

173. Fluorescein-Peroxide

Preparation:
Solution a. 2N NaOH.
Solution b. Half saturated fluorescein in glacial acetic acid.
Solution c. H_2O_2.
Solution d. 0.5% copper acetate.
Procedure: The chromatogram is sprayed with *a*, heated at 100 °C for 3 min. and sprayed with a mixture of equal volumes of *b* and *c* containing a drop of *d* and reheated as before.
Results: Brominated compounds (e.g., carbromal) appear as pink spots on a yellow background. When viewed in 360 nm U.V. light, spots appear brown on a brilliant yellow fluorescent background.

174. FPN Reagent

Preparation:
Solution a. 5% ferric chloride solution.
Solution b. 20% perchloric acid.
Solution c. 50% nitric acid.
Color reagent. Mix *a*, *b*, and *c* (5 : 45 : 50).
Procedure: Spray on the dry chromatograms.
Results: Drugs with a phenothiazine type structure are located as orange, red or blue spots.
Comments: To differentiate phenothiazines (red-violet) from phenothiazine sulfoxides (no color), use 2% aqueous ferric chloride. Pyrazolones are detected with 5% ferric chloride-2N acetic acid (1 : 1).

175. Furfural-Hydrochloric Acid

Preparation:
Solution a. 10% furfural in ethanol.
Solution b. Conc. HCl.
Procedure: Chromatograms are sprayed lightly with *a*, followed by *b*. Alternatively the plate or paper may be exposed to HCl vapor.
Results: Carbamates with free NH_2 groups produce a purple to black spot. N-substituted carbamates do not react. Ethinamate, meprobamate, and styramate are among compounds detected.

176. Mandelin's Reagent

Preparation: Add 1.0 g ammonium vanadate to 100 ml conc. H_2SO_4. Shake thoroughly before use.
Results: Detects antihistamine drugs.

177. Marquis Reagent

Preparation: Mix 1 volume formalin (formaldehyde solution) and 20 volumes conc. H_2SO_4.
Procedure: This reagent is made up when required and poured onto the plates in a fume hood. It may be used on paper chromatograms (which must be thoroughly dry).
Results: Phenothiazine drugs give red or purple colors, some of the stimulant drugs give orange colors and many of the classic and synthetic drugs also give orange-red or purple colors. It is a good reagent to use if morphine or morphine derivatives are suspected.

178. Mercuric Sulfate-Diphenylcarbazone

Preparation:
Solution a. Mercuric sulfate: 5 g mercuric oxide dissolved in 100 ml water + 20 ml conc. sulfuric acid (stock solution).
Solution b. Water.
Solution c. 0.1% diphenylcarbazone in ethanol.
Procedure: *Paper Chromatograms.* Immediately before use 1 volume of *a* is mixed with 1 volume of *b* and the dried chromatogram is dipped through the solution. Paper chromatograms must be washed in running water for 15 min. and then placed on a pad of blotting paper to dry. They are then sprayed with solution *c*.
Results: Barbiturates give a bluish-violet spot which is fairly permanent if stored away from sunlight.
Procedure: *TLC plates.* The reagent is mixed as above and sprayed on the TLC plate. No washing with water is necessary. White spots are visible on the wet plate if a mercury reacting compound is present. Other compounds may give this reaction apart from barbiturates. When the white spots have been marked, the plate is sprayed with solution *c*.
Results: Barbiturates give a bluish-violet color whereas many of the other mercury-reacting compounds give only a pink color. Barbiturates containing an allyl group give a more bluish shade than the other barbiturates.

179. NQS Reagent (Sodium 1,2-naphthaquinone-4-sulfonate)

Preparation:
Solution a. 0.1*N* NaOH (4.0 g per liter of water).
Solution b. Saturated solution of sodium 1,2-naphthaquinone-4-sulfonate in ethanol-water (1 : 1).
Procedure: Dried chromatogram is sprayed with *a* and then *b*.
Results: Thiazide diuretic drugs appear as stable orange spots within 15 min. Barbiturates do not react. Useful for basic compounds with primary amine groups or reactive methylene groups.

180. Potassium Permanganate

Preparation: 0.1% potassium permanganate in water.
Procedure: Chromatograms are dipped or sprayed. Reverse-phase tributyrin treated papers and TLC plates require more reagent.
Results: Unsaturated barbiturates give yellow spots on pale pink background. Mark as soon as visible. Also reacts with some alkaloids in same way.
Comments: Can be applied after cobalt reagent if NH_3 is removed from chromatogram. Positive test given by aminopyrene, apronal, ethinamate, methylpentynol carbamate, pentylene tetrazole, persedon, piperidione, and thalidomide.

181. Quinidine-Copper Sulfate

Preparation: Dissolve 200 mg cupric sulfate, 2 ml pyridine and 20 mg quinidine in 100 ml of water.
Procedure: Spray the chromatogram, dry and place into HCl vapors.
Results: Barbituric and thiobarbituric acids detected as dark spots under U.V. light.

182. Silver Nitrate-Diphenylcarbazone

Preparation:
Solution a. 1% silver nitrate.
Solution b. 1% diphenylcarbazone in 95% ethanol.
Procedure: Spray with *a* and then *b*.
Results: Barbiturates detected as purple-blue spots.

183. Ultraviolet Light

Procedure: Dry chromatogram and view under 254 nm and 360 nm light.
Results: Barbiturate spots appear dark on fluorescent background if papers have been exposed to a saturated ammonia atmosphere (or fluorescein solution, below) and viewed in 254 nm light. Sensitivity is 10–25 μg. With 360 nm light, only thiobarbiturates are observed. For TLC, layers with fluorescent material incorporated can be used.

Or, regular layers are used and dried chromatograms examined with U.V. light for fluorescent spots, then sprayed with dilute fluorescein solution (4 mg sodium fluorescein, 4 g NaOH, 100 ml water) and reexamined.

A few alkaloids fluoresce in 360 nm U.V. light, and some give dark spots in 254 nm light.

Dyes and Pigments

See Tests: 184.

184. Ultraviolet Light

Procedure: Inspect chromatogram under U.V. light after marking colors observed in daylight.
Results: Most compounds are naturally colored and visible in daylight. Chlorophylls detected as red-violet fluorescent zones. Porphyrins, coporphyrin isomers, porphyrin esters and metal complexes are detected by 354 nm U.V. light. Wetting the paper chromatogram with isooctane prior to illumination is sometimes helpful. Pteridines may decompose if exposed for long periods to U.V. light.

Inks should be examined under U.V. light because some noncolored components may show strong fluorescence.

General Reagents

See Tests: 2, 4, 80, 149, 185–191, 216, 236, 253, 256.

185. Antimony Chloride

Preparation: 10–20% antimony pentachloride in carbon tetrachloride or saturated antimony trichloride in alcohol-free chloroform.
Procedure: Spray and heat to 100–120 °C. Observe in daylight and U.V. light.
Results: These are general reagents giving varied colors with many compounds.

186. Fluorescein (sodium)

Preparation: Dissolve 50 mg sodium fluorescein in 100 ml of 50% methanol.
Procedure: Spray chromatogram and view under U.V. light.
Results: A general detection reagent for aromatic and heterocyclic compounds.

187. Iodine Vapor

Procedure: Dried chromatogram is placed in a dry tank containing crystals of iodine, which rapidly volatilize to a purple iodine vapor.
Results: Many compounds absorb iodine reversibly to produce brown to yellow spots on a faint yellow background. Compounds for which test is especially useful include unsaturated fatty acids. Phospholipids detected with sensitivity of about 1 μg.
Comments: When thin layer plate is removed from the tank the colors fade, and this can be hastened by a stream of air. The colors can be preserved if the plate is covered with a second plate and the two sealed together with tape.

188. Perchloric Acid (60–62% or 70–72%)

Procedure: Spray with 25% acid solution and heat to 150 °C.
Alternate procedure: Allow 70% acid to diffuse into the layer at right angles to the development direction.

189. Potassium Permanganate-Sulfuric Acid

Preparation: 500 mg potassium permanganate in 15 ml conc. H_2SO_4. *Caution*!—mix only small quantities as manganous heptoxide is explosive.
Results: A general reagent giving white spots on pink background.

190. Sulfuric Acid

Preparation:

Solution a. Conc. H_2SO_4.
Solution b. $3N$ H_2SO_4.
Solution c. 1-3N ammonium sulfate.

Procedure: Spray with *a*, *b* or *c* and heat at 110–130 °C for a few minutes. Inspect in daylight and under U.V. light.
Results: Brown to black spots for most organic compounds; frequently the charred products fluoresce.
Comments: Heating at lower temperature often has value in that different compounds may undergo a series of color changes before charring. For example, cholesterol esters and free cholesterol yield red to purple spots while other lipids do not react. Can be applied to iodine-treated chromatograms after removing the iodine.
Alternate preparation: A 1 : 3 mixture of sulfuric acid-acetic anhydride is another general spray reagent, as is a 1 : 1 mixture of sulfuric acid-nitric acid.

Corrosive reagents can be used only on inorganic thin layers or glass-fiber papers.

191. Water

Procedure: Spray silica gel thin layers thoroughly with water and view in reflected light.
Results: Alkaloids, steroids, sugar acetates, etc. show up as opaque areas on a semi-transparent background.

Hydrocarbons
(aliphatic and aromatic hydrocarbons, unsaturated hydrocarbons, halogenated derivatives)

See Tests: 11, 66, 70, 192–197.

192. Dicobaltoctacarbonyl

Preparation:
Solution a. 0.5% solution of dicobaltoctacarbonyl in petroleum ether (120–135 °C).
Solution b. 0.5% α-nitroso-β-naphthol in acetic acid-water (1 : 1).
Procedure: Spray dried plate with reagent *a*. After 10 min. spray with 1*N* HCl and dry again. Spray with Neatan and after thoroughly hardening soak off the chromatogram and wash thoroughly for approximately 2 hr. Then press between filter paper to remove excess moisture and expose to bromine vapor for 1 min. Dip in reagent *b* and wash off excess reagent with 0.5% ammonia.
Results: Polyacetylene compounds give brown-red spots on yellow background.

193. Fluorescein-Bromine Test (for unsaturated compounds)

Procedure (according to Stahl): The plates are prepared with a 0.04% aqueous solution of sodium fluorescein instead of with water. After development of the substances, blow bromine vapors over the dried plate.
Results: Formation of eosine kills fluorescence under U.V. light, however, not at sites containing vapors over the bromine addition compounds.
Alternate procedure (according to Kirchner): Spray with 0.05% sodium fluorescein solution, then blow bromine surface.
Results: Yellow spots on pink background.

194. Osmium Tetroxide

Procedure: Expose chromatogram to vapors of osmium tetroxide in a sealed chamber, 5–10 min. for isolated double bonds, 1 hr. or more for conjugated double bonds.
Results: Brown to black spots; detects hydrocarbons with double bonds; also used for lipids and steroids.

195. Ozone-Indigo

Preparation: Dissolve 130 mg of indigo in 1 ml conc. sulfuric acid by heating on a water bath for 1 hr. Dilute mixture to 500 ml.
Procedure: Expose chromatogram in chamber containing 10–15% ozone for 15–20 min. Air plate to remove excess ozone, then spray with reagent.
Results: Unsaturated compounds detected as white, yellow, or brown spots on blue background.

196. Tetrachlorophthalic Anhydride

Preparation: 2% tetrachlorophthalic anhydride in acetone-chlorobenzene (10 : 1).
Procedure: Aromatic hydrocarbons are detected by viewing under U.V. light; nonfluorescent zones are first sprayed with the reagent.

197. Tetracyanoethylene

Preparation: Saturated solution of tetracyanoethylene in benzene.
Results: Detects hydrocarbons, phenols and heterocyclics.

Inorganic Compounds
(cations, anions)

See Tests: 70, 147, 156, 157, 198–234, 391.

198. Alizarin

Preparation:
Solution a. Saturated solution of alizarin in alcohol or 2% alizarin in chloroform.
Solution b. 1*N* NaOH or 25% NH_4OH.
Solution c. Glacial acetic acid.
Procedure: Spray with *a*, dry briefly, then spray with *b* and finally *c* to eliminate background color.
Results: Detects Ba, Ca, Mg, Al, Ti, Fe, Zn, Li, Th, Zr, NH_4^+, Se, Ag, Hg, Pb, Cu, Cd, Bi, Cr, Mn, Co, Ni, Ga, In, Be, Zr, rare earths, Ce, Sc, Pd, Pt, and U as violet to red spots.

199. Ammonium Molybdate-Sodium Sulfite

Preparation:
Solution a. 5% ammonium molybdate in 2*N* H_2SO_4.
Solution b. 5% aqueous sodium sulfite solution.
Procedure: Spray with *a* and then *b*.
Results:

	Color before b	*Color after b*
Sulfide	violet-blue	deep-blue
Thiosulfate	violet-blue	deep blue
Phosphate	yellow	green turning to blue-grey on warming.

200. Ammonium Molybdate-Stannous Chloride

Preparation:
Solution a. 1% ammonium molybdate in water.
Solution b. 1% stannous chloride in 10% HCl.
Procedure: Treat with *a*, dry, treat with *b*.
Results: Phosphate and phosphite ions give blue spots.

201. Ammonium Sulfide

Preparation: Saturated aqueous H_2S made alkaline with NH_3.
Procedure: Dip or spray chromatogram.
Results: Detects cations as follows: Black—Ag, Hg(I), Hg(II), Co, Ni; brown—Au, Pd, Pt, Pb, Bi, Cu, V, Tl; yellow—Cd, As, Sn; yellow-orange—Sb.

202. Benzidine

Preparation: Dissolve 0.05 g benzidine base or hydrochloride in 10 ml acetic acid, dilute to 100 ml with water, filter. *Caution*! Benzidine is hazardous.
Procedure: Spray and heat to 85 °C for 30 min.
Results: Detects Au(III), Tl(III), chromate, Mn(IV) (spray with alkali first and heat), Ce(III).

Colors of Spots with Benzidine Reagent

Compound	Color
Cerium ammonium sulfate	brown
Cobalt acetate	red
Cobalt nitrate	grey
Ferric chloride	brown
Nitric acid	brown
Potassium dichromate	brown, grey
Potassium ferricyanide	blue
Potassium periodate	brown
Potassium permanganate	brown
Phosphoric acid	brown
Silver nitrate	brown, purple
Sulfuric acid	brown
Uranium acetate	brown

203. Brucine

Preparation:
Solution a. 0.02% brucine in 2*N* H_2SO_4.
Solution b. 2*N* NaOH.
Procedure: Spray with *a*, warm gently and note colors, spray with *b*.
Results:

	Acid spray	*Base spray*
BrO_3^-	deep red	blood red
NO_3^-	red, then yellow	orange-yellow
$C10_3^-$	red-brown	blood red

204. Cinchonine-Potassium Iodide

Preparation: Dissolve 1 g cinchonine in 100 ml hot water containing a few drops of HNO_3. Cool and add 2 g potassium iodide. The solution should always be prepared fresh.
Results after spraying: Bi, orange; Ag, Hg(II), Pb, Sb, V, Tl, yellow; Cu, brown; Pt, pink.

205. Cobalt Nitrate-Lead Nitrite

Preparation:

Solution a. Dissolve 5 g of cobaltous nitrate and 5 g of lead nitrate in 100 ml of water. Then add 1–2 drops of nitric acid.

Solution b. Saturated sodium nitrite solution in 2*N* acetic acid.

Procedure: Spray with *a*. After drying, spray with *b*, then rinse paper chromatogram with water and dry.

Results: Detects NH_4^+ and K ions.

206. Copper Sulfate-Mercury Ammonium Sulfate

Preparation:

Solution a. 0.1% cupric sulfate-2*N* H_2SO_4 (9 : 1).

Solution b. Dissolve 2.7 g mercuric chloride and 3.0 g ammonium thiocyanate in 100 ml water.

Procedure: Spray with *a* and then *b*.

Results: Zn, red to violet; Cu, yellow; Fe(III), red; Au, orange-pink, and Co, blue.

Comments: If cupric sulfate is replaced by zinc sulfate, Cu, Ni and Co are detected.

207. Dimethylglyoxime

Preparation: 10% dimethylglyoxime in ammoniacal ethanol.

Procedure: Spray or dip chromatogram.

Results: Detects Ni ions as red spot.

208. Diphenylcarbazide

Preparation:

Solution a. 0.1% s-diphenylcarbazide in 96% ethanol.

Solution b. 25% NH_4OH.

Procedure: Spray with *a* followed by *b*.

Results: Detects heavy metal ions including Ni (blue), Co (orange-brown), Ag, Pb, Cu, Sn, Mn (brown), Zn (purple) and Ca.

209. Dithiooxamide (Rubeanic Acid)

Preparation: 1% dithiooxamide in ethanol-water (6 : 4).

Procedure: Expose to NH_3 and then dip or spray.

Results: Ag, Fe, dark-brown; Pd, Hg(II), yellow; Hg(I), black; Bi, yellow-brown; Cu, green; Co, orange; Ni, blue-purple. General detection reagent for heavy metals.

Comments: Pentacyanoaminoferrate-rubeanic acid complex reagent is prepared by dissolving 0.70 g trisodium pentacyanoaminoferrate in 20 ml water and pouring the resultant solution into a solution of 0.25 g rubeanic acid in 10 ml ethanol. The mixture is shaken for 15 min., filtered and used as a spray reagent followed by washing paper with 0.2*N* acetic acid. Must be prepared fresh daily. Detects Cu, Ag, Au, Zn, Cd, Hg, Tl, rare earths, Sn, Pb, Ti, Zr, Hf, Th, Bi, Mo, U, Mn, Fe, Co, Ni, Pd.

210. Dithizone (Diphenylthiocarbazone)

Preparation: 0.05–0.10% dithizone in chloroform or carbon tetrachloride.

Procedure: Spray chromatogram (do not dip). Note colors. Overspray with 25% NH_4OH and note colors.

Results: Detects cations as follows: Co, Ni, Ag, Pb, Bi, Cd, Sn, red-violet; Hg(II), pink-yellow; Cu, brown; Zn, pink-red. Also detects organotin salts.

211. Ferrous Sulfate

Preparation: 2% ferrous sulfate in 5% H_2SO_4.

Procedure: Spray or dip chromatogram.

Results: Ferricyanide anions detected as blue spot.

212. 5-Hydroxy-2-(hydroxymethyl)-4H-pyran-4-one

Preparation:

Solution a. 2.5 g 8-hydroxyquinoline and 0.5 g 5-hydroxy-2-(hydroxymethyl)-4H-pyran-4-one in 500 ml 90% ethanol.

Solution b. 25% NH_4OH solution.

Procedure: Spray with *a* and then *b*. View under U.V. light.

Results: Detects Al and Mg ions.

213. 8-Hydroxyquinoline (Oxine)

Preparation:

Solution a. Dissolve 0.5 g of 8-hydroxyquinoline in 60 ml ethanol and 40 ml water.

Solution b. 25% NH_4OH solution.

Solution c. 10% 8-hydroxyquinoline in ammoniacal ethanol.

Procedure: Spray with *a* and then *b*, or spray with *c*; inspect under U.V. light.

Results: Detects Al, Be, Ca, Sr, Ge, Mg, Zn, Sn, as bright spots; many other cations show up as dark spots.

214. 8-Hydroxyquinoline-Kojic Acid

Preparation:

Solution a. Dissolve 2.5 g 8-hydroxyquinoline and 0.5 g kojic acid in 500 ml of 90% ethanol.

Solution b. 25% NH_4OH.

Procedure: Spray with *a* and then *b*, inspect under U.V. light.

Results:

	Color	
	Daylight	U.V.
Ag	light brown	yellow
Hg(I)	yellow-green	black
Pb	pale yellow	dark grey
Cu	green	black
Bi	pale yellow	dark brown
Cd	pale yellow	bright yellow
Hg(II)	bright yellow	dark brown
As	colorless	—
Sb	colorless	—
Sn(II)	pale yellow	dirty yellow
Sn(IV)	colorless	blue
Co	yellow-brown	black
Ni	yellow-green	black
Fe(III)	black	black
Al	pale yellow	whitish-yellow
Cr	yellow-green	violet
Mn	yellow-brown	black
Zn	pale yellow	bright yellow
Ba	colorless	whitish-blue
Sr	colorless	whitish-blue
Ca	colorless	whitish-blue
Mg	colorless	white
Na	colorless	violet
K	colorless	violet

Comments: Spraying with *a* followed by ammoniacal hydrogen sulfide water detects metals with characteristic yellow, brown, orange, green and black colors.

215. Kojic Acid

Preparation: Dissolve 0.1 g of kojic acid in 100 ml of 60% ethanol.
Procedure: After spraying, inspect fluorescence under U.V. light.
Results: General detection reagent for metal ions.

216. Morin (2′,3,4′,5,7-pentahydroxyflavone)

Preparation: 1% solution of morin in glacial acetic acid.
Procedure: Spray, dry briefly at 100 °C and inspect under U.V. light.
Results: Detects Al ions as light green fluorescent spot.
Comments: 0.005–0.05% morin in methanol is a general reagent for organic compounds, yielding yellow-green fluorescent or dark spots on fluorescent background.

217. 2-Nitroso-1-naphthol-4-sulfonic Acid

Preparation:

Solution a. 0.05% solution of 2-nitroso-1-naphthol-4-sulfonic acid in 70% by volume ethanol.

Solution b. 25% NH_4OH.

Procedure: Spray with *a* and then *b*.
Results: Fe ions detected as green spot.

218. Phenylfluorone

Preparation: 0.05% phenylfluorone in 96% ethanol-conc. HCl (3 : 1).
Results: Detects Ge ions.

219. Potassium Ferrocyanide

Preparation: 1–2% aqueous potassium ferrocyanide.
Procedure: Dip or spray chromatogram.
Results: Detects cations as follows: Cu, red-brown; Fe, blue; Mo, U, dark brown; V, green-yellow; W, yellow.

220. Potassium Iodide

Preparation: 1% aqueous potassium iodide.
Procedure: Spray or dip chromatogram.
Results: Detects cations as follows: V, Hg(II), Bi, orange; Pb, Tl, Ag, yellow; Hg(I), yellow-green; Cu, Fe, brown-red.
Alternate preparation: 5% potassium iodide in water plus 10% conc. HCl.
Results: Brown spots given by NO_3^-, ClO_3^-, BrO_3^-, IO_3^-, F^-, NO_2^-.

221. Potassium Thiocyanate

Preparation: 1% aqueous potassium thiocyanate.
Procedure: Spray or dip chromatogram.
Results: Detects cations as follows: Au, orange; Pt, Mo, orange-red; Hg(I), black; Bi, U, yellow; V, Co, blue; Ni, green; Fe, deep-red; Cr, purple; Cu, green-black.
Comments: Mo and Fe are differentiated by further treatment with $SnCl_2$ in dilute HCl. The red Fe(III) complex is decolorized leaving orange Mo unaffected.

222. 1-(2-Pyridylazo)-2-Naphthol

Preparation: 0.25% 1-(2-pyridylazo)-2-naphthol in ethanol.
Results: Detects U(VI) ions; sensitivity 1 μg.

223. Quercetin

Preparation:
Solution a. 0.2% solution of quercetin in 96% by volume ethanol.
Solution b. 25% NH_4OH solution.
Procedure: Spray with *a* and then *b*. Inspect under U.V. light.
Results: Detects Cr (green, sensitivity 0.06 μg), U (brown), V(yellow-brown), Cu, Ni, Fe, Mn, K, Li, Be ions.

224. Quinalizarin

Preparation: 0.05% solution of quinalizarin in 70% by volume ethanol.
Procedure: Spray and place chromatogram into a moist chamber saturated with ammonia.
Results: Detects many cations; Be gives blue spot, sensitivity 0.7 μg.

225. Silver Nitrate

Preparation: 5% aqueous silver nitrate.
Procedure: Spray or dip chromatograms.
Results: The metals (Ba, Ca, Sr, Mg, Li, Na, K) are separated chromatographically as chlorides. On treatment with the reagent and removal of excess Ag by washing, the residual bands of insoluble AgCl are reduced to metallic silver, either by exposure to U.V. light or by immersion in photographic developer, when black stains are formed.

226. Silver Nitrate

Preparation:
Solution a. 0.1–0.5*N* silver nitrate with added NH_4OH until precipitate dissolves. *Caution*—prepare fresh prior to use and do not store—explosive compounds may form—do not expose to direct sunlight.
Solution b. Mixture 50 ml ammoniacal silver nitrate, 50 mg fluorescein and 50 ml saturated, aqueous Laurent's acid (1-naphthylamine-5-sulfonic acid).
Procedure 1. Spray with *a* and heat at 110–120 °C for 10 min. Exposure to U.V. light for 10 min. may be necessary.
Results: Detects many anions including halogens (except fluoride), sulfur-containing anions, arsenate, arsenite, phosphate, phosphite.
Comments: Also detects terpenic phenols and α-glycol groupings. Detects some vitamins (α-tocopherol, black; vitamin C, brown).
Procedure 2: Spray with *b*, air-dry 2 hours and examine in visible and U.V. light.
Results:

	Daylight	U.V. light
Fluoride	pale grey	dark spot
Ferrocyanide	bright yellow	bright spot
Arsenate	green-yellow	dark spot
Chromate	brown	dark spot
Dichromate	brown	dark spot
Sulfide	dirty green	dark spot
Phosphate	yellow-green	bright spot
Cyanide	bright green-yellow	bright spot
Sulfate	bright yellow	bright spot
Ferricyanide	pink	dark spot
Borate	pale grey	dark spot
Thiosulfate	brown	dark spot

Results:

	Daylight	U.V. light
Carbonate	pale yellow-green	bright spot
Iodate	yellow	bright spot
Arsenite	dirty yellow	dark spot
Sulfite	pale brown	dark spot
Bromate	yellow	bright spot
Nitrite	pale yellow	bright spot
Chloride	grey	bright spot
Bromide	dark grey	dark spot
Nitrate	yellow	bright spot
Chlorate	pale yellow	bright spot
Iodide	red	dark spot
Thiocyanate	pink	bright spot

227. Sodium Dithionite

Preparation: 0.1–0.2% aqueous solution of sodium dithionite.
Results: As(III), orange-brown spot; As(V), yellow; Bi, dark brown; Sb(III) and Sb(V), orange-brown.

228. Sodium Rhodizonate

Preparation:
Solution a. 0.1% aqueous sodium rhodizonate.
Solution b. 2*N* HCl-2*N* acetic acid.
Solution c. 25% NH_4OH.
Results: Sr, red-orange spot, decolorized by spraying with *b*; Ba, red-orange spot, not decolorized by *b*; Pb, violet spot which is colorless on a pink background after spraying with *c*.

229. Sodium Tetraphenylboron

Preparation:
Solution a. 2% aqueous sodium tetraphenylboron.
Solution b. 0.1% bromphenol blue and 2.5% mercuric chloride in 80% ethanol, adjusted to highest acidity that will still produce a blue spot on dry paper.
Procedure: Dip paper chromatogram into *a*, wash with 50 ml water to remove excess reagent, dry with low heat, spray lightly with *b*.
Results: K, yellow spot on blue background, sensitivity 0.025 μmoles. Cs, Rb, Tl, Ag, NH_4^+ ions also react.

230. Stannous Chloride-Potassium Iodide

Preparation: Dissolve 5.6 g of stannous chloride in 10 ml of conc. HCl. After dilution with water to 100 ml, add 0.2 g of potassium iodide to the solution.
Results: Te and Au ions detected as grey to black spot, sensitivity 0.1 μg. Rh, brown; Se, Pt, orange.

231. Universal Indicator

Preparation: Dilute universal indicator 1 : 10 with freshly boiled water.
Procedure: Dip or spray chromatogram.
Results: CO_3^{-2}, blue-green; acetate anion, yellow.

232. Violuric Acid (Acid Violet)

Preparation: 1.5% aqueous solution of violuric acid; keep below 60 °C when preparing solution.
Procedure: Spray and heat to 100 °C for 20 min.
Results: Detects alkali and alkaline earth metals: Li, red-violet; Na, violet-red; K, violet; Be, yellow-green; Mg, yellow-pink; Ca, orange; Sr, red-violet; Ba, light red; Co, green-yellow; Cu, yellow-brown.

233. Zinc Uranyl Acetate

Preparation: Saturated solution of zinc uranyl acetate in 2*N* acetic acid. Filter before use.
Procedure: Spray and inspect under U.V. light.
Results: Li and Na ions, blue-green fluorescence.

234. Zirconium Alizarin Lake

Preparation: Dissolve 0.05 g zirconium dichloride octahydrate and 0.5 g sodium alizarin sulfonate in 100 ml 2*N* HCl.
Results: Detects fluoride ions.

Lipids
(phospholipids, sphingolipids)

See Tests: 3, 16, 52, 119, 187, 190, 194, 235–256, 268, 338, 415.

235. Ammonium Molybdate-Perchloric Acid

Preparation:
Solution a. 3 g ammonium molybdate in 25 ml of water.
Solution b. $1N$ HCl.
Solution c. 60% $HClO_4$.
Color reagent. Mix *a* with 30 ml *b* and 15 ml *c*.
Procedure: Treat chromatogram and heat at 105 °C for 20 min.
Results: General reagent for lipids—blue-black spots.

236. Ammonium Sulfate

Procedure: In preparing TLC plates, use slurry of 30 g Silica gel G (14% gypsum), 60 ml water and 1–10% $(NH_4)_2SO_4$. After spreading, dry plates 10 min. at room temperature and then heat 30 min. at 110 °C.
Results: After development, lipids are revealed as charred spots by heating at 200 °C for 20 min.
Comments: A general detection method.

237. Bromthymol Blue

Preparation: 0.1% bromthymol blue in 10% aqueous ethanol, made just alkaline with conc. NH_4OH.
Alternate preparation: 40 mg bromthymol blue in 100 ml $0.01N$ NaOH.
Procedure: Spray chromatogram.
Results: Detects lipids and phospholipids with 0.1–1.0 μg sensitivity as blue-green spots.

238. Cresyl Violet

Preparation: Dissolve 20 mg cresyl violet in 1 liter of 1% acetic acid.
Procedure: The chromatogram is immersed in this solution for 10 min. at 60 °C and then washed 10 min. in water.
Results: Cerebrosides show up as violet or brown spots on a light violet background.

239. Cyclodextrin

Preparation: 1% cyclodextrin in 30% ethanol.
Procedure: Spray with reagent and dry. Place in humidity cabinet for 1 hr. at room temperature, then expose to iodine vapor.
Results: Saturated alcohols, fatty acids, esters and monoglycerides remain white. Corresponding unsaturated compounds turn yellow or brown.

240. Diphenylamine

Preparation: Dilute 20 ml of a 10% solution of diphenylamine in alcohol with 100 ml conc. HCl and 80 ml glacial acetic acid.
Procedure: Spray lightly. Heat at 110 °C after covering with another glass plate until spots appear (30–40 min.).
Results: Glycolipids detected as blue spots.

241. Dragendorff's Reagent

Preparation:
Solution a. 17 g basic bismuth nitrate in 100 ml 20% aqueous acetic acid.
Solution b. 40 g potassium iodide dissolved in 100 ml distilled water.
Color reagent. Store *a* and *b* at 4 °C and mix immediately before use 4 : 1, with 14 parts water.
Procedure: Spray plates.
Results: Choline-containing phospholipids give orange or red-orange spots, sensitivity 0.6 μmoles.

242. Ferric Chloride-Sulfosalicylic Acid

Preparation: Dissolve 0.1 g $FeCl_3 \cdot 6H_2O$ and 7.0 g sulfosalicylic acid in 25 ml water and dilute to 100 ml with 95% ethanol.
Procedure: Spray and observe under U.V. light.
Results: Detects phosphate groups in lipids and other compounds as white fluorescent spots on purple background.

243. Fluorescein

Preparation: 0.1% 2 : 7 dichloro- or dibromofluorescein in ethanol.
Procedure: Spray chromatogram and inspect under U.V. light.
Results: Many lipids show up as bright yellow fluorescent spots on a dark background.

244. Fluorescein-Bromine

Preparation: 0.05% fluorescein in water.
Procedure: Spray plates with reagent and then expose briefly to bromine vapor (avoid excess bromine).
Results: Fluorescein reacts with the bromine to form the red dye eosin. Bromine is added rapidly onto the double bonds of unsaturated lipids and this maintains the yellow fluorescein color over their locations. The red color formation is enhanced in the presence of alkali and inhibited by acid. It is advisable therefore to include a few drops of ammonia into the spray if the plates have been developed with solvents containing acid.
Comments: Many other indicators can be used instead of fluorescein including methyl orange, phenol red and rhodamine B.

245. Gentian Violet-Bromine

Preparation: 0.1% gentian violet in methanol.
Procedure: Spray and expose to bromine vapor.
Results: Detects lipids as blue spots on yellow background.

246. Hypochlorite-Benzidine

Preparation:
Solution a. 5.25% hypochlorous acid: 5 ml commercial bleach solution (5%) (e.g., Clorox®) is shaken with 45 ml benzene and 5 ml glacial acetic acid. The upper phase is used immediately since it becomes cloudy on storage. The bleach solution should contain no free NaOH or preservative, and must have a low pH and a high oxidation potential.
Solution b. 1% benzidine in aqueous 50% ethanol in which is dissolved one small crystal of potassium iodide. The solution should be protected from light. Exercise caution when using benzidine.
Procedure: Plates are sprayed with the sodium hypochlorite solution, dried in a fume hood until only traces of unbound chlorine remain (as detected by smell). They are then lightly sprayed with benzidine solution.
Results: Sphingolipids (amide-containing lipids) give blue spots.
Comments: Detects acid polysaccharides if replace benzene above with water.

247. Liebermann-Burchard Reagent

Preparation: 20% conc. H_2SO_4 in acetic anhydride. Add the acid to ice-cold anhydride. *Caution*—use in hood—highly lachrymatory.
Procedure: Treat chromatogram and inspect under U.V. light.
Results: Detects cholesterol and its esters as green to blue spots. Triterpenoid glycosides detected as red spots showing fluorescence for several minutes under U.V. light.
Comments: Reagent can be used on starch-bound thin layers.

248. Molybdenum Blue Reagent

Preparation:
Solution a. To a liter of 25*N* H_2SO_4 (70% v/v) is added 40.11 g MoO_3 and the mixture boiled until the MoO_3 is dissolved.
Solution b. To 500 ml of solution *a* is added 1.78 g of powdered molybdenum and the mixture boiled gently for 15 min. The solution is cooled and decanted from any residue that may be present.
Color reagent. Equal volumes of solutions *a* and *b* are mixed and the combined solution mixed with 2 vols. of water. The final solution is greenish-yellow in color. If too little water is used it will be blue, if too much, yellow. The spray stores well.
Procedure: Plates are sprayed lightly.
Results: Phospholipids immediately show up as blue spots that increase gradually in intensity and then fade within one day (sensitivity 0.005 μmole phospholipid). If the plates are sprayed previously with ninhydrin reagent and heated, it is preferable to spray the phosphate reagent only after plates are cooled to room temperature, otherwise a dark background may develop. The sulfuric acid in the reagent can be used to char all lipids nonspecifically if the plates (after phospholipid detection) are heated at 110–120 °C.

249. Orcinol-Ferric Chloride (Bials Reagent)

Preparation: 40.7 conc. HCl, 0.1 g orcinol, 1 ml of 1% ferric chloride solution diluted to 50 ml with water.
Procedure: Place chromatogram in HCl atmosphere for 1.5 hr. at 80 °C, then spray with the reagent and heat again at 80 °C until the color develops.
Results: Glycolipids appear as violet spots on white background.

250. Periodic Acid-Schiff Reagent

Preparation:
Solution a. 0.5 g periodic acid in 100 ml 90% acetic acid.
Solution b. Mix equal volumes of cold (0 °C) 30% sodium metabisulfite and 3*N* hydrochloric acid.
Solution c. 200 mg fuchsin and 5 ml of 10% sodium metabisulfite in 85 ml of water. (Keep for 12 hr., then treat with carbon and filter).
Procedure: Spray lightly with *a*, followed by *b* and *c*, consecutively. Heat for 15 min. at 90 °C.
Results: Unsaturated monoglycerides detected as violet spots; polyeneacids, grey-green spots.

251. Phosphotungstate

Preparation: 10% phosphotungstic acid in ethanol.
Procedure: Spray and heat at 90–100 °C for 1–15 min.
Results: Cholesterol and its esters give red to pink spots, sensitivity 2–4γ for TLC.

252. Reinecke Salt

Preparation: 0.05*M* Reinecke salt.
Procedure: Immerse chromatogram for 2 hr. or more at room temperature.
Results: Red spots at sites of choline lipids.
Comments: Rinsing with water removes excess reagent; intensify spots by spraying with Na_2O_2 in 30% acetic acid containing 1% benzidine—blue spots.

253. Rhodamine B

Preparation:
Solution a. 0.05–0.1% rhodamine B in ethanol.
Solution b. 3% hydrogen peroxide.
Solution c. 10*N* potassium hydroxide.
Solution d. 0.2% rhodamine B in water.
Procedure: Spray with *a* and observe in daylight and under U.V. light. Spraying with *b* may enhance colors.
Results: Detects higher fatty acids. Many lipids give a bright red fluorescence. For glycerides, spray with *a* and then *c*; sensitivity may be increased by repeating spray with *c* after a few minutes. Lipids yield purple spots on a pink background, glycerides bright spots on a pink-red to blood-red background.
Comments: Food preservatives give purple spots intensified by spraying with *b*. Solution *d* is an alternative for *a* in all applications.
Rhodamine B is a general reagent which detects many classes of compounds.

254. Schiff's Reagent

Preparation:
Solution a. Dissolve 1 g of parafuchsin in 700 ml of water and 50 ml of 1*N* HCl. After solution is complete, add 4.57 g of sodium pyrosulfite and make up with water to 1 liter. The reagent is discolored within 24 hrs. after being stirred frequently.
Solution b. 1% aqueous sodium pyrosulfite solution.
Color reagent. Add 1% mercuric chloride to *a*.
Procedure: Dip the dry chromatogram for 10 min. and remove the excess dye by rinsing with *b* for several hours. Change the receiver 2–3 times and finally rinse the chromatogram under running water.
Results: Acetalphosphatides and plasmalogens appear as red-violet spots on blue background.

255. Sodium Periodate-Schiff Reagent

Preparation:
Solution a. 0.5% sodium periodate.
Solution b. 0.5% *p*-rosaniline decolorized with sulfur dioxide.
Solution c. 1% perchloric acid.
Procedure: Spray with *a* and after 5 min. (while still damp) expose to sulfur dioxide and spray with *b*. After 1 hr. lighten background by spraying with *c*.
Results: Phospho- and glycolipids detected as blue spots on yellow background.

256. Sulfuric Acid-Potassium Dichromate

Preparation: 10–50% aqueous sulfuric acid to which is added 0.6 g potassium dichromate.
Procedure: Spray plate and heat at 120–180 °C.
Results: Detects 0.1–1.0 μg phospholipids; unsaturated compounds char more intensely.
Comments: A solution of 3 g sodium dichromate in 20 ml water diluted with 10 ml conc. H_2SO_4 is a general reagent, when followed by heating, for organic compounds.

Nitro- and Nitroso Compounds

See Tests: 257–261, 330.

257. *p*-Diethylaminobenzaldehyde

Preparation: Dissolve 0.25 g diethylaminobenzaldehyde in 0.25*N* HCl in absolute ethanol.
Procedure: For use when a zinc reducer has been incorporated in the thin layer (3 g zinc dust plus 30 g silica gel).
Results: Sensitivity 1–4 μg for nitroso diphenylamines and nitro derivatives.

258. Dimethylaminobenzaldehyde-Tin Chloride-Hydrochloric Acid

Preparation:
Solution a. Mix 3 ml of a 15% stannous chloride solution with 15 ml of conc. HCl. Add 180 ml of water to the solution. (To be always freshly prepared!).

Solution b. Dissolve 1 g of 4-dimethylaminobenzaldehyde in a mixture of 30 ml of ethanol, 3 ml of conc. HCl and 180 ml of *n*-butanol.
Procedure: Spray with *a*, dry in the air, then spray with *b*.
Results: After drying in the air, yellow spots will appear on the chromatogram to detect nitro compounds. 3,5-Dinitrobenzoyl derivatives of aliphatic amines are detected.
Alternate procedure: Spray dry chromatogram with 0.2% aqueous $SnCl_2$ in conc. HCl, dry, spray with 0.3% ethanolic DMAB in conc. HCl.
Results: Alcohol 3,5-dinitrobenzoates detected as yellow spots.

259. Diphenylamine

Preparation: 1% diphenylamine in 95% ethanol.
Procedure: Spray and expose to U.V. light (254 nm).
Results: Nitrate esters give yellow-green spots on colorless background. Explosives give varied colors when 5% reagent solution used.

260. Malonic Acid Diethylester

Preparation:
Solution a. 10% ethanolic malonic acid diethylester.
Solution b. 10% aqueous sodium hydroxide.
Procedure: Spray with *a* and then *b*. Heat for 5 min. at 95 °C.
Results: Red-violet spots; 3,5-dinitrobenzoic acid esters are already visible under short-wave U.V. light as dark-violet quenched spots. The spots are also visible under white light.

261. α-Naphthylamine

Preparation:
Solution a. 1% α-naphthylamine in ethanol.
Solution b. 10% methanolic potassium hydroxide.
Procedure 1. Spray with *a* and then *b*.
Results: 3,5-Dinitrobenzoates detected as red-brown spots.
Procedure 2. Spray with *a* alone.
Results: 3,5-Dinitrobenzoates detected as yellow to orange spots. Also detects 3,5-dinitrobenzamides.
Comments: Spots visible under white light with Procedure 1.

Nitrogen Heterocyclic Compounds
(pyrroles, pyrazole derivatives, imidazoles, indoles, pyridine derivatives, phenoxazines, quinoline derivatives)

See Tests: 39, 46, 48, 55, 66, 197, 262–292, 374, 376.

262. Anisidine Reagent

Preparation:
Solution a. 1% *p*-anisidine in ethanol containing 1% conc. HCl.
Solution b. 2% amyl nitrite in ethanol.
Solution c. 0.4 or 2% sodium hydroxide in water.
Results: Imidazoles give immediate stable brown or red spots. Many phenols, especially polyphenols, yield red or brown colors. Sensitivity is low for simple phenols (tyrosine). Hydroxy indoles react strongly.
Comments: The more concentrated alkali is used when applied after Ehrlich reagent in multiple reagent sequences. Phenol solvents must be washed off with ether or dry ethanol before this reagent will be successful.

263. Benzidine-Copper Sulfate

Preparation:
Solution a. Dissolve 0.3 g of copper sulfate in 100 ml of a mixture of 5 parts by volume of water and 4 parts by volume of ethanol.
Solution b. 0.1% solution of benzidine in 50% ethanol.
Procedure: Spray with *a*, dry chromatogram at 60 °C and rinse with *b*.
Results: Pyridinemonocarboxylic acids detected as blue spots.

264. Boric Acid-Citric Acid

Preparation: Dissolve 0.5 g of boric acid and 0.5 g of citric acid in 20 ml of methanol.
Procedure: Heat for 10 min. at 100 °C. Inspect under U.V. light.
Results: Detects quinolines; 8-hydroxyquinoline shows yellowish-green fluorescence.

265. Cinnamaldehyde

Preparation: 5 ml cinnamaldehyde in ethanol-conc. HCl (95 : 5). Prepare fresh before use.
Results: Detects indole derivatives, hydroxyskatoles. Colors range from brown to pink to yellow.

266. *p*-Dimethylaminocinnamaldehyde

Preparation: 1% dimethylaminocinnamaldehyde in conc. HCl, diluted 1 : 4 with acetone just before use.
Procedure: Use as dip reagent.
Results: More sensitive but less selective than Ehrlich reagent; background colors are troublesome. Valuable for detecting low concentrations of serotonin (bright blue), for certain indoles which do not react with Ehrlich reagent (e.g., β,β-dimethyltryptamine, blue-purple), and for differentiating amides (urea gives slow pink, citrulline no reaction). Indole gives green spot, skatole purple.

267. Dimethyldihydroresorcinol-Ferric Chloride

Preparation:
Solution a. 10% ethanolic dimethyldihydroresorcinol.
Solution b. 5% ferric chloride solution.
Procedure: Spray with *a*, dry, and spray with *b*.
Results: Detects aldehydes and ketones of pyridine bases as violet or red-brown spots. Sensitivity about 1 $\mu g/cm^2$.

268. 2,4-Dinitrophenylhydrazine

Preparation: Saturated solution 2,4-dinitrophenylhydrazine in 2*N* HCl.
Procedure: Dip chromatogram, lay flat and blot.
Results: Indole-3-aldehyde, which reacts poorly with general indole reagents, gives an immediate reddish-brown color. Other carbonyl-containing indoles react more slowly to give brown or yellow products. Ketoacids give yellow spots on pale yellow background. Detects ketoses.
Alternate preparation: 0.4 g 2,4-dinitrophenylhydrazine in 100 ml 2*N* HCl.
Procedure: Spray chromatograms, heat at 105 °C, view in visible and U.V. light.
Results: Tests for α,β-unsaturated ether lipids (plasmalogens). Compounds containing a free ketone group can be viewed in the visible or U.V. range of the spectrum. Plasmalogens are detected after heating the plate at 105 °C for 10 min. and thus allowing the HCl in the reagent to hydrolyze the vinyl ether bond and produce an aldehyde. The plate can then be viewed in the visible or U.V. range for aldehyde hydrazones. Brown, red or orange-red spots can be seen against a yellow background.

269. Ehrlich Reagent

Preparation:
Solution a. 10% *p*-dimethylaminobenzaldehyde in conc. HCl.
Color reagent. Mix *a* and acetone, 1 : 4, just before use.
Procedure: Dip paper as soon as reagent is prepared. Then hold flat, blow off acetone, and place on white paper and observe colors.
Results: Colors begin to develop at once in air, all appearing within 20 min. Indoles, purple; hydroxyindoles, blue; aromatic amines and ureides, yellow; tyrosine, purple-red. Many original colors change over a few hours, some fading completely, and others forming stable blue, grey or purple color. Sensitivity of indoles is about 1 μg.
Comments: Some batches of acetone contain an unknown impurity which produces a red color with the reagent; this does not affect the colors obtained.

Chromatograms should be inspected at intervals over the first hour and again the next day. The rate of appearance, initial colors, changes in color and permanence can help to identify a compound. Spots can fade and then reappear with an enhanced or different color.

Ehrlich reagent is not specific for the indole nucleus. Some pyrroles give red to cerise colors and some phenols react on long standing or heating. Aromatic amines and carbamoyl compounds produce yellow or orange colors with varying speeds of development: urea, immediate bright yellow; citrulline, slow yellow; kynurenine, orange; anthranilic acid, immediate yellow; sulfonamide drugs and metabolites, yellow.

270. Ferric Chloride-Perchloric Acid

Preparation:
Solution a. 0.05*M* ferric chloride.
Solution b. 5% $HClO_4$.
Color reagent. Mix 2 ml *a* and 100 ml *b*.
Results: Indoles detected as red spots, blue-yellow after 24 hr.

271. Flavylium Perchlorate

Preparation: 0.25% flavylium perchlorate solution.
Procedure: Spray and heat for 5 min. at 105 °C.
Results: Fluorescence exhibited by indole, indolylacetic acid, malonic acid, pyrogallol and *m*-toluylenediamine.
Comments: The reagent may be prepared from salicylaldehyde and acetophenone.

272. Fluorindal Reaction

Preparation: Saturated sodium acetate.
Procedure: Papers treated with acidic Ehrlich reagent are dipped through the reagent.
Results: The orange-brown product from the reaction of indoxyl sulfate with Ehrlich reagent turns bright red with an intense orange U.V. fluorescence, sensitivity 0.1 μg indoxyl sulfate. Indoxyl glucuronide reacts with Ehrlich reagent to give an immediate blue color fading to grey, and then reddish-orange by the fluorindal reaction.

273. Formaldehyde-Hydrochloric Acid (Procházka Reagent)

Preparation: 35% formaldehyde-25% HCl-95% ethanol (1 : 1 : 2) (freshly prepared).
Procedure: Spray and heat for 5 min. at 100 °C.
Results: Indole derivatives, varied colors in daylight, fluorescent in U.V. 6-Hydroxyskatole, blue; other skatoles, brown.
Comments: May be intensified by spraying with *aqua regia* (3 vol. conc. HCl + 1 vol. conc. HNO_3).

274. Formaldehyde-Schiff's Reagent

Preparation:
Solution a. 1% formaldehyde solution.
Solution b. Schiff's reagent: 1 g fuchsin, 110 ml of $1N$ HCl and 5 g sodium bisulfite are mixed and diluted to one liter with water.
Procedure: Spray with *a*, evaporate excess at 110 °C, and spray with *b*.
Results: Triazines detected as red spots.

275. Gold Chloride

Preparation: 0.5% aqueous gold chloride.
Results: 7-Hydroxyskatole, violet spot; 4-, 5-, 6-isomers, grey-green spots.

276. Iodine

Preparation: 1% iodine in carbon tetrachloride.
Procedure: Neutral papers are dipped and suspended in a hood. Inspect under U.V. light.
Results: Imidazoles detected as transient brown spots which reappear on redipping, and as dark spots under U.V. light. Quite unspecific.
Comments: The following multiple sequence can yield considerable information: U.V., iodine, U.V., ninhydrin or TCQ, anisidine or sulfanilic acid.

277. Malonic Acid-Salicylaldehyde

Preparation: Dissolve 0.2 g of malonic acid and 0.1 g of salicylaldehyde in 100 ml of absolute ethanol.
Procedure: Heat the chromatogram for about 15 min. to 120 °C and inspect under U.V. light.
Results: Yellow fluorescent spots produced by heterocyclic compounds containing nitrogen. Also detects amines.

278. Ninhydrin-Acetic Acid

Preparation:
Solution a. 0.2% ninhydrin in acetone.
Solution b. Glacial acetic acid.
Color reagent. Mix *a* and *b* (9 : 1). Prepare fresh.
Procedure: Dip chromatogram, evaporate acetone, heat paper at 110 °C for 2 min.
Results: Tryptamines, blue-green fluorescence in U.V. (360 nm) light, sensitivity, 0.01 $\mu g/cm^2$. At higher concentrations, brownish-pink spot in visible light.
Comments: If Ehrlich reagent is applied after this reagent, tryptamines giving fluorescence will not give Ehrlich reaction—other indoles will. Sulfanilic acid will detect phenolic indoles when used after this reagent.

279. Nitraniline

Preparation:
Solution a. Dissolve 0.6 mg nitraniline in 1 ml $1.2M$ HCl.
Solution b. Dissolve 1.2 g sodium nitrite in 100 ml water.
Solution c. $0.15M$ phosphate buffer, pH 7.
Solution d. $1N$ NaOH.
Color reagent. Mix *a* plus 1 drop *b*, plus 5 ml *c* plus *d* to give pH 6.5, then dilute to 10 ml with water.
Results: Detects 5-hydroxyindoles as red spots.

280. Nitrite-Nitric Acid

Preparation:
Solution a. Conc. HNO_3.
Solution b. Acetone.
Solution c. 5% sodium nitrite in water.
Color reagent. Mix in order *a*, *b* and *c* (5 : 45 : 1).
Procedure: Use reagent within 2 min.; dip paper and allow to stand.
Results: Indolyl-acetonitrile gives greyish-blue or olive-green color with intense green U.V. fluorescence. Other indoles give faint brown or yellow colors.

281. Nitrosonaphthol-Nitrous Acid

Preparation:

Solution a. 1% α-nitroso-β-naphthol in 95% ethanol.
Solution b. 5% sodium nitrite solution, freshly prepared.
Solution c. 2*N* HCl-solution *b* (98 : 2).

Procedure: Dip paper in *a* and dry; then dip in *c*.
Results: 5-Hydroxyindoles revealed as violet spots on faint yellow background, sensitivity 20 μg or greater.

282. Nitrous Acid

Preparation: Freshly prepared solution of 1 g of sodium nitrite in 100 ml of 1*M* HCl.
Procedure: Spray and heat to 100 °C.
Results: Indoles detected as red spots.
Comments: Also detects thiazole derivatives as light green spots.

283. Potassium Nitrite-Nitric Acid

Preparation: 1 g potassium nitrite in 20 ml conc. HNO_3 and 80 ml 95% ethanol.
Results: Indoles detected as red, yellow, orange and brown spots.

284. Potassium Persulfate

Preparation:

Solution a. Saturated solution of potassium persulfate, freshly prepared.
Solution b. Conc. HCl.
Solution c. Acetone.
Color reagent. Mix as needed 1 drop *a*, 10 ml *b* and 40 ml *c*.

Procedure: Dip chromatogram and evaporate acetone; inspect after 10 min. and 1 hr.
Results: Indolylacetic acid gives a pink color after a few min., intensifying rapidly. Sensitivity is at least as sensitive as Ehrlich reagent. Compounds giving indolylacetic acid or hydrolysis (amides, esters) give a pink color, but more slowly. Indolylacetyl derivatives of amino acids give violet colors, developing slowly. The colors of other acids vary. Indoxyl sulfate gives a rapid indigo color. Other indoles, including tryptophan and tryptamines, give slow yellow colors.
Comments: This persulfate dip reagent is less toxic than some similar reagents (e.g., ferric chloride—$HClO_4$ mixtures) and gives identical results.

285. Proline

Preparation: 0.1% proline solution.
Procedure: Treat chromatogram and heat.
Results: Isatin, which does not react with Ehrlich reagent, is specifically identified by blue color.
Comments: This is the reverse of the isatin test for proline.

286. Sodium Nitroprusside-Sodium Carbonate (Thormählen's Reagent)

Preparation:

Solution a. 2% sodium nitroprusside.
Solution b. 5% sodium carbonate.
Solution c. 50% aqueous acetic acid.

Procedure: Spray chromatogram with *a* and then *b*, partially dry, and spray with *c*.
Results: Indoles unsubstituted in positions 1, 2 or 3 are detected as blue spots.

287. Sulfanilic Acid

Preparation:

Solution a. 9 g sulfanilic acid dissolved in 90 ml conc. HCl and 900 ml water.
Solution b. 5% sodium nitrite in water.
Color reagent. Mix *a* and *b* (10 : 1), stand in ice 5 min., destroy remaining HNO_2 with solid ammonium sulfamate.

Procedure: Dip the paper.
Results: Specific test for 6-hydroxyindoles or 6-alkoxy-substituents—red color, perhaps turning purple later.

288. Terephthaldehyde

Preparation: 0.2 g terephthaldehyde in 90 ml acetone plus 10 ml acetic acid.
Procedure: Spray chromatogram.
Results: 6-Hydroxyskatole detected as blue spot.

289. *N*-2,6-Trichloro-*p*-benzoquinone Imine

Preparation: 0.1–0.2% TCQ in ethanol.
Procedure: The neutral (well-dried) chromatogram is dipped through the reagent.
Results: As the solvent evaporates, thiol-imidazoles appear as red spots. Cysteine give a yellow color, disubstituted disulfides (glutathione, etc.) are negative but a number of other compounds give grey spots which slowly appear. When applied over the iodine reagent the colors are reddish-brown and somewhat reduced in intensity. Vitamin B_6 gives a blue color, phenolic terpenes varied colors.

290. Ultraviolet Light

Inspection under ultraviolet light reveals some imidazoles as bright spots. Imidazoles treated with iodine are detected as dark spots.

291. Xanthydrol

Preparation: 0.2 g xanthydrol in 90 ml ethanol and 10 ml conc. HCl. Prepare just before use.
Procedure: Use as dip reagent.
Results: Stable colors appear as paper dries. Almost all compounds containing an indole structure of the tryptophan-indolylacetic acid type give pinkish-purple colors, or blue colors if bearing a 5-OH substituent. 2-Substituted indoles react.
Comments: Some phenolic acids, steroids and pyrolles react.

292. Zinc Acetate (Schlesinger Reagent)

Preparation: Suspend 5 g of zinc acetate in 100 ml of 90% ethanol.
Procedure: Shake the suspension before spraying. Inspect the air-dried chromatogram under U.V. light.
Results: Detects urobilin and stercobilin as fluorescent spots.
Comments: Bile pigments are easily detected by their colors in daylight. Other useful reagents are Ehrlich's reagent for urobilinogen and stercobilinogen, and diazo-coupling reagents for bilirubin.

Organometallic Compounds

See Tests: 156, 210, 293.

293. Pyrocatechol Violet

Preparation: 100 mg pyrocatechol violet in 100 ml ethanol.
Procedure: Expose to U.V. for 20 min., then spray with reagent.
Results: Detects organotin compounds as deep blue to violet spots on grey-brown background.

Organic Phosphorus Compounds (phosphate esters)

See Tests: 242, 294, 305, 383, 411.

294. Enzymatic Hydrolysis

Preparation:
Solution a. 1% intestinal phosphatase solution in 0.1*N* ammonium acetate buffer, pH 8.9.
Solution b. Dissolve 5 g ammonium molybdate in 100 ml water and 30 ml conc. HNO_3.
Solution c. Dissolve 100 g benzidine in 10 ml glacial acetic acid and dilute with water to 100 ml.
Solution d. Saturated aqueous ammonium acetate.
Procedure: Spray with *a* and put in humid chamber for about 1.5 hr. Liberated inorganic phosphate is revealed by spraying with *b*, drying at 50–55 °C, then spraying with *c* and drying at 37 °C and finally spraying with *d*.
Results: Phosphates revealed as blue spots.

Organic Sulfur Compounds (sulfonic acids, thiophosphates, thiols, sulfones, thiourea derivatives, thiocarbamates, sulfonamides, phenothiazines, isothiocyanates)

See Tests: 20, 63, 66, 92, 108, 295–311, 377, 393, 411.

295. Copper Acetate-Rhodamine B

Preparation:
Solution a. 0.5% aqueous cupric acetate solution.
Solution b. 0.1% rhodamine B solution.
Procedure: The chromatogram is immersed for 1 min. in *a*, the excess of which is washed out with water; after drying at 105 °C, the chromatogram is immersed in *b*, washed with water and again dried.
Results: Lipophilic alkyl sulfates are detected in U.V. light.

296. Copper Sulfate

Preparation: 10% cupric sulfate.
Procedure: Spray and heat for 20 min. at 120 °C.
Results: Sulfur-containing glycosides detected as brown spots on a green background.

297. Diethylamine-Copper Sulfate

Preparation: Dissolve 0.5 g of copper sulfate in 100 ml of methanol. Add 3 ml of diethylamine to the solution. Shake prior to use; stable for only a few days.
Results: Thiobarbituric acids detected as green spots.

298. *p*-Dimethylaminobenzaldehyde-Ferric Chloride (Van Urk's Reagent)

Preparation: 0.125 g *p*-dimethylaminobenzaldehyde and 0.1 ml 5% ferric chloride in 100 ml 65% H_2SO_4.
Results: Detects phenothiazine compounds and hydroxyskatoles.

299. 5,5′-Dithiobis(2-Nitrobenzoic Acid) (Ellman Reagent)

Preparation:
Solution a. 0.1% solution of 5,5′-dithiobis(2-nitrobenzoic acid) (Caliochem, Los Angeles, Calif., U.S.A.) in a 1 : 1 mixture of ethanol and 0.45*M* tris(hydroxymethyl)aminomethane hydrochloride buffer at pH 8.2.
Solution b. Freshly prepared 0.4% solution of sodium borohydride in 95% ethanol.
Solution c. Mixture of glacial acetic acid, 6*N* HCl and acetone (8 : 2 : 90).
Solution d. 0.2*N* NaOH solution in 50% aqueous ethanol.
Solution e. 0.1 g phenol red (phenolsulfonephthalein) in 28.2 ml 0.01*N* NaOH, diluted with water to 250 ml.
Procedure: *For Thiols.* Apply *a*.
For Disulfides. Solution *b* (one volume) is applied to the chromatogram. 15–20 min. later the borohydride is destroyed by spraying with *c* (three volumes). The chromatogram is air-dried for 1 hr. Solution *e* is spotted in several positions along the edges of the chromatogram which is then exposed to an ammonia atmosphere in a glass cylinder containing a dish with conc. ammonia until the indicator spots turn red. After air-drying for 4–5 min., *a* is applied.
For Thioesters. The chromatogram is sprayed with *d* followed 2–3 min. later by *a*. A yellow background gradually develops on standing.

300. Iodine-Azide

Preparation:
Solution a. 1.27 g iodine in 100 ml ethanol.
Solution b. 3.25 g sodium azide in 25 ml water plus 75 ml ethanol.
Color reagent. Mix equal volumes *a* and *b*.
Procedure: Dip paper and lay flat.
Results: White spots on brown iodine background; background fades slowly, but spots remain visible in U.V. light even after background disappears. Thiols (R-SH) and disulfides (R-S-S-R) react but thio-ethers (R-S-R e.g., methionine) do not. Detects penicillins, thioureas.

301. Isatin

Preparation: 0.4% isatin in conc. H_2SO_4.
Procedure: Spray, observe, then heat at 120 °C several minutes and observe again.
Results: Detects thiophene derivatives as spots with various colors.

302. 2-Naphthol-Sodium Nitrite

Preparation:
Solution a. 1 g of sodium nitrite in 100 ml of 1*N* HCl; prepare fresh.
Solution b. 0.2% solution of 2-naphthol in 1*N* KOH.
Procedure: Spray with *a*; after 1 min. spray with *b*. Dry the chromatogram at 60 °C.
Results: Detects sulfonamides and aromatic amines by diazotization and coupling reactions.

303. *N*-(1-Naphthyl)ethylenediamine (Bratton-Marshall Reagent)

Preparation:
Solution a. 1*N* HCl.
Solution b. 5% sodium nitrite.
Solution c. 100 mg *N*-(1-naphthyl)ethylenediamine dihydrochloride in 100 ml water.
Procedure: Spray *a*, then *b*, and mark any yellow spots. Dry at 100 °C to remove excess nitrous acid. Spray with *c*.
Results: Sulfonamides detected as reddish-purple spots.

304. Palladium Chloride

Preparation: 0.5% palladium chloride in dilute HCl.
Results: Thiophosphoric acid esters detected as yellow spots on pale brown background, sensitivity $< 5\gamma$. Phenothiazines give varied colors.

305. Periodic Acid-Perchloric Acid

Preparation: 10 g periodic acid and a few mg vanadium pentoxide in 100 ml 70% $HClO_4$.
Procedure: Dry plate thoroughly and spray with well-mixed reagent.
Results: Detects thiophosphoric acid esters.

306. Potassium Ferricyanide-Ferric Chloride

Preparation:
Solution a. 1% aqueous potassium ferricyanide.
Solution b. 1% aqueous ferric chloride.
Procedure: Spray with *a* and then *b*, inspect under U.V. light.
Results: Detects thiosulfates.

307. Resorcinol-Ammonia

Preparation: 10% resorcinol solution.
Procedure: Spray and expose to NH_3 vapor.
Results: Detects sulfonic acids.

308. Silver Nitrate-Ammonia-Sodium Chloride

Preparation:
Solution a. 0.1*N* silver nitrate solution.
Solution b. 10% ammonia solution.
Solution c. Mix 50 ml *a* and 50 ml *b*. Do not store!
Solution d. 10% aqueous sodium chloride solution.
Procedure: Spray with *c*, then dry and spray with *d*. Expose the chromatogram to daylight for some time until maximal visualization of the spots.
Results: Detects thioacids.

309. Sodium Nitroprusside-Hydroxylamine (Grote's Reagent)

Preparation: Dissolve 0.5 g of sodium nitroprusside in 10 ml of water. Add to the solution 0.5 g of hydroxylammonium chloride and 1 g of sodium hydrogen carbonate. After gas generation is complete, add 2 drops of bromine. Then dilute to 25 ml. The reagent is stable for about two weeks.
Results: Detects xanthates, thiodantoins.

310. Sodium Nitroprusside-Potassium Permanganate (Roux Reagent)

Preparation:
Solution a. Dissolve 10 g of sodium nitroprusside in 100 ml water.
Solution b. 33% aqueous NaOH.
Solution c. 0.1*N* potassium permanganate.
Color reagent. Mix *a*, 2 ml *b*, 5 ml *c*, and filter.
Procedure: Spray with reagent and inspect under U.V. light.
Results: Detects sulfonamides.

311. Sodium Periodate-Benzidine

Preparation:
Solution a. 0.1% sodium metaperiodate.
Solution b. 0.5% benzidine in butanol-acetic acid (4 : 1).
Procedure: Spray with *a* and then after 4 min. with *b*.
Results: Bivalent sulfur compounds detected as white spots on dark blue background. Sensitivity: DL-Methionine 5–10γ. Aromatic sulfur compounds 2–30γ.
Comments: Use benzidine with caution!

Oxo Compounds
(aldehydes, ketones, quinones)

See Tests: 3, 8, 108, 133, 312–323, 330, 424, 446.

312. Chlorosulfonic Acid-Acetic Acid

Preparation: Chlorosulfonic acid-acetic acid (1 : 2).
Procedure: Spray and heat to 130 °C for 1 min.
Results: Detects sapogenins and olefins.

313. *o*-Dianisidine

Preparation: Saturated solution of *o*-dianisidine in glacial acetic acid.
Results: Detects aldehydes and ketones with yellow to orange to brown to violet to grey colors. Sensitivity 5–50 μg.

314. 3,5-Dinitrobenzoic Acid

Preparation: 1 g 3,5-dinitrobenzoic acid dissolved in 20 ml methanol; add 10 ml 15% NaOH.
Procedure: Spray wet chromatogram.
Results: Ketones detected as blue-purple zones on yellow background.

315. 2,4-Dinitrophenylhydrazine

Preparation: 0.4 g 2,4-dinitrophenylhydrazine in 100 ml 2*N* HCl.
Alternate preparation: Add 10 ml conc. HCl to 1 g 2,4-dinitrophenylhydrazine in 1000 ml ethanol.
Results: Aldehydes and ketones detected as yellow to red spots.
Comments: Sodium ethoxide solution (0.3 g Na in 100 ml ethanol) intensifies colors of 2,4-dinitrophenylhydrazones.

316. Fuchsin-Sulfurous Acid (Schiff's Reagent)

Preparation:
Solution a. Pass SO_2 through 0.1% fuchsin solution until colorless.
Solution b. 0.05*M* mercuric chloride.
Solution c. 0.05*M* H_2SO_4.
Color reagent. Mix 1 ml *a*, 1 ml *b*, 10 ml *c* and dilute with water to 100 ml.
Results: Detects compounds with aldehyde groups as violet spots on pale violet background.

317. Hydrazine Sulfate

Preparation: 1% hydrazine sulfate in 1*N* HCl.
Alternate preparation: Saturated hydrazine sulfate—4*N* HCl (9 : 1).
Procedure: Spray and observe moist chromatogram in daylight and U.V. light. Heat to 100 °C and again observe in U.V. light.
Alternate procedure: Spray and observe moist chromatogram before and after steaming with NH_3 under U.V. light.
Results: Detects aldehydes.

318. Hydrochloric Acid Vapors

Procedure: Expose in chamber to HCl vapors.
Results: Chalcones detected as red spots. Also detects 4-dimethylaminobenzene and metabolites.

319. Magnesium Acetate

Preparation: 0.5% magnesium acetate solution in methanol.
Procedure: After spraying, dry for 5 min. at 90 °C.
Results: Hydroxyanthraquinone detected as orange to violet spot. Also detects aldehydes and ketones.

320. Methylene Blue (reduced)

Preparation: Filter through glass wool a mixture of 20 ml 0.001*M* methylene blue, 2 ml conc. H_2SO_4, and 1 g zinc dust.
Results: Quinones detected as blue spots; naphthoquinones do not react.

321. Nile Blue A (reduced)

Preparation: Mix 20 ml of 0.001*M* Nile Blue A, 1 g zinc dust and 2 ml conc. H_2SO_4. Filter through glass wool.
Results: Detects quinones and naphthoquinones.

322. Potassium Ferricyanide-Ferric Chloride

Preparation: 0.2% potassium ferricyanide plus 0.01% ferric chloride hexahydrate in 2*N* HCl.
Results: Detects 2,4-dinitrophenylhydrazones. Rate of color formation and color changes depends upon compounds.

323. Rhodanine

Preparation: Alcoholic solution of rhodanine.
Procedure: Spray with reagent solution followed by conc. NH_4OH.
Results: Detects polyene aldehydes; sensitivity 0.03 μg.

Oxygen Heterocyclic Compounds
(coumarins, anthocyanins, anthocyanadins, catechins, tannins)

See Tests: 108, 197, 324–334, 368, 369, 378.
See also Table 3 at the end of this section.

324. Aluminum Chloride

Preparation: 1–5% ethanolic solution of aluminum chloride.
Procedure: Spray chromatogram and inspect under filtered U.V. light and in daylight.
Results: Detects flavonoids.

325. Benedict Reagent

Preparation:
Solution a. Dissolve by heating 173 g of sodium citrate and 117 g of sodium carbonate in 700 ml of water. If necessary, filter the solution.
Solution b. Dissolve 17.3 g of cupric sulfate in 100 ml of water.
Color reagent. Add *b* to *a*, stirring slowly. After cooling, dilute to 1000 ml with water.
Results: Detects flavonoids.

326. Diphenylboric Acid-β-Aminoethyl Ester

Preparation: 1% diphenylboric acid-β-aminoethyl ester in methanol.
Procedure: Observe fluorescence under 366 nm U.V.
Results: Detects flavonols, coumarins, and derivatives.

327. Ferric Ammonium Sulfate

Preparation: 0.2% aqueous solution of ferric ammonium sulfate.
Procedure: Spray and inspect under filtered U.V. light.
Results: Detects flavonoids.

328. Hydrogen Peroxide-Ferric Chloride

Preparation:
Solution a. 0.5% hydrogen peroxide, freshly prepared.
Solution b. 2% aqueous ferric chloride.
Procedure: Spray with *a*, dry at 105 °C, then spray with *b*. Heat in drying oven at 105 °C until spots appear.
Results: Detects coumarins. Also detects benzoic acids as follows: *p*-hydroxybenzoic acid, grey-black; esters of *p*-hydroxybenzoic acid, grey; benzoic acid, brown-violet; *p*-chlorobenzoic acid, brown-red; salicylic acid, red-violet.

329. Lead Acetate

Preparation: Spray solution. 25% aqueous basic lead acetate solution.
Dip solution. Filter a saturated aqueous basic lead acetate solution.
Procedure: Spray or dip; after dipping, blot the chromatogram and expose for several minutes to steam.
Results: Detects flavonoids; also detects uronic acids.

330. Potassium Hydroxide

Preparation:
Solution a. 1% potassium hydroxide in ethanol.
Solution b. Mixture of 2 volumes of 5% aqueous potassium hydroxide and 1 volume of acetone.
Solution c. 11.2 g potassium hydroxide dissolved in 100 ml ethanol.
Procedure: Spray with *a* and dry chromatogram and inspect under U.V. light.
Results: Detects coumarins.
Alternate procedure 1: Spray with *b* or *c*, heat to 80–100 °C and inspect under U.V. light.
Results: Detects aromatic nitro compounds, amines, and acetylated citrate esters (plasticizers).
Alternate procedure 2: Spray first with acetic anhydride-conc. phosphoric acid-dioxane (5 : 0.5 : 5) and heat for 30 min. at 100 °C. Cool and proceed with alternate procedure 1.
Results: Detects nonacetylated citrate esters as yellow fluorescent spots.
Comments: Potassium hydroxide also detects 4-nitrophenylhydrazones of aromatic carbonyls as various colored spots.

331. Sodium Boron Hydride-Hydrochloric Acid

Preparation: 2% methanolic sodium boron hydride.
Procedure: Spray, partially air-dry and expose to HCl fumes in a closed chamber.
Results: Specific for flavanones, blue-red to violet colors.

332. Sulfuryl Chloride

Preparation:
Solution a. Distilled sulfuryl chloride, which may be diluted with carbon tetrachloride.
Solution b. 10% aqueous potassium hydroxide.
Procedure: Spray dry chromatogram with *a* followed by *b*.
Comments: Detects oxygen heterocyclics.

333. Trichloroacetic Acid

Preparation: Dissolve 25 g of trichloroacetic acid in 100 ml of chloroform.
Procedure: After spraying, dry the chromatogram for 2 min. at 100 °C and inspect under U.V. light.
Results: Stropanthus glycosides give yellow fluorescence, sensitivity 0.4 μg. Menthofuran gives pink spots with 4% reagent in $CHCl_3$ after 10–30 min. standing. Reagent detects flavonoids, steroids and glycosides.

334. Ultraviolet Light

Procedure: Inspect chromatogram in daylight and U.V. light.
Results: Some flavonoids and most anthocyanins can be seen as colored spots in daylight. Examination under U.V. light with and without NH_3 vapor detects most of these compounds as fluorescent spots with characteristic coloration.

Peroxides

See Tests: 335–338.

335. Ammonium Thiocyanate-Ferrous Sulfate

Preparation:
Solution a. 0.2 g ammonium thiocyanate in 15 ml acetone.
Solution b. 4% aqueous ferrous sulfate.
Color reagent: Add 10 ml *b* to *a* just before spraying.
Results: Peroxides detected as brownish-red spots.

336. Dimethylaminoaniline

Preparation: Dissolve 1.5 g *p*-dimethylaminoaniline in a mixture of 25 ml methanol, 25 ml water, and 1 ml acetic acid.
Procedure: Spray chromatogram.
Results: Organic peroxides give various colors.

337. Dimethyl-*p*-phenylenediamine Dihydrochloride

Preparation:
Solution a. Dissolve 1.5 g *N,N*-dimethyl-*p*-phenylenediamine dihydrochloride in 128 ml methanol, 25 ml water and 1 ml acetic acid.
Solution b. 0.5 g of the diamine in 100 ml ethanol containing 1 g sodium (freshly prepared).
Procedure: Spray with reagent.
Results: With solution *a*, organic peroxides give purple-red spots. Spraying with *b* followed by spraying with water and then exposure to U.V. light for 1 min. detects chlorinated pesticides as dirty violet to green spots.

338. Potassium Iodide-Starch

Preparation:
Solution a. Mix 10 ml of a 4% solution of potassium iodide with 40 ml glacial acetic acid and add a small spatula pointful of zinc powder.
Solution b. 1% aqueous solution starch, freshly prepared.
Procedure: Immediately before use, solution *a* is filtered free from zinc powder and the plate sprayed. After 5 min., it is sprayed copiously with solution *b* until the thin layer looks transparent.
Results: Peroxides appear as blue spots due to free iodine. Detects peroxides in lipids.

Pesticides (insecticides, herbicides, fungicides)

See Tests: 147, 337, 339–361.

339. Bioautography

Procedure: Dry chromatogram thoroughly at room temperature for at least 12 hr. Spray with a suspension of *Stemphylium consortiale* (Thüm) in nutrient solution (50 g sucrose, 5 g $NaNO_3$, 1.25 g KH_2PO_4, 1.25 g $MgSO_4 \cdot 7H_2O$, 500 ml water, pH adjusted to 4.6). Lay chromatogram on glass plate and incubate in moist atmosphere for 72 hr. at 27 °C.
Results: Fungicides detected as distinct areas on light grey background, 0.1–5 μg sensitivity.

340. Brilliant Green

Preparation: 0.5% brilliant green in acetone.
Procedure: Spray dry chromatogram and expose immediately to bromine vapor.
Results: Triazine herbicides detected as deep green spots on off-white background. Some organophosphorous compounds also react.

341. Bromine-Congo Red

Preparation:
Solution a. 0.4% congo red in 50% aqueous ethanol.
Solution b. 10% bromine in carbon tetrachloride.
Procedure: Expose dry chromatogram to bromine vapors generated from solution *b* for 20 sec. Aerate to remove bromine vapors and spray with *a*.
Results: Thiophosphate pesticides detected as red spots on blue background, sensitivity 0.5 μg.
Comments: Metanil yellow, yellow RFS and methyl orange can be substituted for congo red to yield purple, red and pink spots, respectively, on a yellow background.

342. Bromine-Ferric Chloride-Sulfosalicylic Acid

Preparation:
Solution a. 0.1% ferric chloride in 80% ethanol.
Solution b. 1% sulfosalicylic acid in 80% ethanol.
Procedure: Expose to bromine vapor for 10 min., then spray with *a*, let dry 15 min., spray with *b*.
Results: Organophosphorus pesticides detected as white spots on mauve background, sensitivity 5 μg.

343. Copper Chloride

Preparation: 2 g cupric chloride in 11 ml ethanol, acidified with 2.5 ml conc. HCl.
Procedure: Spray.
Results: Detects Systox and Meta-Systox.

344. 2,6-Dibromoquinonechlorimide (DCQ Reagent)

Preparation: 0.5% 2,6-dibromoquinonechlorimide in cyclohexane.
Procedure: Spray, heat at 110 °C for 7 min.
Results: Thiophosphate pesticides detected as yellow to orange to red to brown spots with a sensitivity of 1–20 μg.

345. Diphenylamine-Zinc Chloride

Preparation: 0.5 g each of diphenylamine and zinc chloride in 100 ml of acetone.
Procedure: Spray the dried plate and then heat for 5 min. at 200 °C.
Results: Chlorinated pesticides detected with varied colors.

346. Ferric Chloride-Sulfosalicylic Acid

Preparation:
Solution a. 1% 5-sulfosalicylic acid in 80% ethanol.
Solution b. 0.1% ferric chloride in 80% ethanol.
Procedure: Expose chromatogram to bromine vapor for 10 min. Spray with *b*, dry 15 min., spray with *a*.
Results: Thiophosphate pesticides detected as white spots on mauve background, sensitivity 5 μg.

347. H-Acid-Nitrous Acid

Preparation:
Solution a. 1% $NaNO_2$ solution in 80% aqueous acetone.
Solution b. 20% HCl solution in acetone (should be always fresh).
Solution c. 0.25% disodium salt of H-acid in 50% aqueous acetone.
Procedure: The chromatogram is first sprayed with *a*, then with *b* and finally, after 10 min., with *c*.
Results: 3-Amino-1,2,4-triazole is revealed immediately as a violet-red spot, with sensitivity of about 1–2 μg.

348. Malachite Green

Preparation:
Solution a. 1 g KOH in 10 ml water diluted to 100 ml with 95% ethanol.
Solution b. 1 ml saturated acetone solution of malachite green oxalate in 51 ml water, 45 ml acetone, and 4 ml of pH-7 buffer (Beckman #3581).
Procedure: Spray chromatogram with *a* and heat 5 min. at 150 °C. Wash cooled chromatogram with acetone to remove organic residues. Spray with *b* to detect potassium sulfite.
Results: Organic sulfite pesticides detected as white spots on blue background.

349. Methylumbelliferone

Preparation:
Solution a. 0.5% iodine in ethanol.
Solution b. A solution of 0.075 g of 4-methylumbelliferone in 100 ml of 50–50 ethanol-water. The solution is made alkaline with 10 ml of 0.1*N* ammonium hydroxide.
Procedure: Spray first with *a* and record spots, then spray with *b* and observe under U.V. .
Results: Organic phosphorus pesticides detected.

350. Nitrobenzenediazonium Fluoroborate

Preparation:
Solution a. 15% aqueous KOH.
Solution b. 1*N* methanolic acetic acid.
Solution c. 0.1% methanolic *p*-nitrobenzenediazonium fluoroborate.
Procedure: Spray chromatogram with *a*, expose for 1 min. to wet steam, spray with *b*, dry under infrared lamp, spray with *c*.
Results: Aromatic carbamates detected as orange to red spots, intensified by spraying with 15% aqueous HCl.
Comments: Carbaryl (Sevin) detected as blue spot when *p*-nitrobenzenediazonium fluoroborate in diethyleneglycol-ethyl alcohol (1 : 9) is used, sensitivity 0.1 μg.

351. Nitrobenzylpyridine-Tetraethylenepentamine

Preparation:
Solution a. 2% *p*-nitrobenzylpyridine in acetone.
Solution b. 10% tetraethylenepentamine in acetone.
Procedure: Spray with *a*, heat to 110 °C for 10 min., overspray with *b*.
Results: Phosphate insecticides detected as purple-blue spots on white background, sensitivity 50 ng.

352. Potassium Iodide-Phosphoric Acid

Preparation: 5*N* potassium iodide-85% H_3PO_4 (1 : 15), mix just before use.
Procedure: Dry and spray with reagent. Colors appear in some cases within 30 min., in some cases only after 6 hrs.
Results: Detects rotenone (blue) and related pesticides.

353. Potassium Permanganate-Formaldoxime or Benzidine

Preparation:
Solution a. 0.1% potassium permanganate solution (freshly prepared).
Solution b. 7 g hydroxylamine hydrochloride and 3 g paraformaldehyde are boiled with 10 ml water until a clear solution is obtained; dilute with ethoxyethanol and 40% aqueous NaOH (1 : 10 : 1).
Procedure: Immerse chromatogram in *a* for 5 sec., wash for 10 min. in running water, dry at 110 °C, spray with *b*.
Results: After about 2 min., pyrethroids appear as red-brown spots on orange background.
Alternate procedure: After $KMnO_4$ treatment, washing and drying, draw through 0.5% benzidine solution in acetone containing 5% acetic acid.
Results: Pyrethroids detected as deep blue spots, sensitivity < 1 μg.
Comments: Caution when handling benzidine.

354. Silver Nitrate-Bromophenol Blue

Preparation:
Solution a. 0.5% silver nitrate in ethanol.
Solution b. 0.2% bromophenol blue plus 0.15% silver nitrate in ethanol-ethyl acetate (1 : 1).
Procedure: Spray *a* and dry at 100 °C for 5 min., then spray *b* and dry at 100 °C for 10 min.
Results: Chlorinated pesticides detected as yellow spots on blue background.

355. Silver Nitrate-Formaldehyde

Preparation:
Solution a. 0.05*N* silver nitrate solution.
Solution b. 35% formaldehyde solution.
Solution c. Methanolic 1*N* potassium hydroxide solution.
Solution d. Mixture of equal parts by volume of 30% H_2O_2 and conc. nitric acid (freshly prepared).
Procedure: Spray with *a*, dry in the air for 30 min., spray with *b* and dry again in the air for 30 min. After spraying with *c*, dry in the drying oven at 130–133 °C for 30 min. Finally spray with *d*, keep the chromatogram in the dark for 12 hrs. and then expose to sunlight or U.V. light.
Results: Dark brown spots for chlorinated insecticides.
Comments: For herbicides, spray with 0.1% $AgNO_3$ in 3*N* HNO_3, dry at 80 °C for 5 min. and expose to daylight 10–15 hrs.

356. Silver Nitrate-Phenoxyethanol

Preparation: 0.1 g silver nitrate (0.425–1.7 g has also been used) in 1 ml of water with 10 ml 2-phenoxyethanol added and the mixture diluted to 200 ml with acetone.
Procedure: Spray, dry for 5 min. in hood and then at 75 °C for 15 min. Expose to U.V. for a minimum period of time using standards as controls (not over 15 min. for silica gel and up to 50 min. for Al_2O_3). (Layers should be pre-washed to remove interfering chlorides).
Results: Chlorinated pesticides, black spots; sensitivity, 0.01–0.1 μg.
Comments: This reagent detects nonionic chlorinated pesticides as well as free or methylated chlorophenoxy acid herbicides. Some compounds give spots of other colors, e.g., carbophenothion (fuzzy yellow) and chlorbenside (fuzzy grey) on Al_2O_3 plates developed with heptane.

357. Silver Nitrate-Phenoxyphenol

Preparation: Mix 0.1 g silver nitrate in 1 ml water with 10 ml 2-phenoxyphenol and dilute to 200 ml with acetone.
Procedure: Spray, dry in hood for 5 min., then at 75 °C for 15 min., and expose to U.V. light.
Results: Detects chlorinated pesticides, 0.01–0.1 μg sensitivity.

358. Succinimide-Fluorescein

Preparation:
Solution a. Dissolve 0.035 g of *N*-bromosuccinimide in 100 ml of methyl chloroform.
Solution b. Dissolve 0.33 g of fluorescein in 100 ml of 0.1*N* NaOH and dilute 3 ml of this solution to 100 ml with ethanol.
Procedure: Spray with *a*, dry at room temperature, then spray with *b*.
Results: Sulfurous insecticides are visualized as fluorescent spots under U.V. light.

359. Tetrabromophthalein-Silver Nitrate-Citric Acid

Preparation:
Solution a. 10 ml of 1% tetrabromophthalein ethyl ester in acetone diluted to 50 ml with acetone.
Solution b. Dissolve 0.5 g silver nitrate in 25 ml water and dilute to 100 ml with acetone.
Solution c. Dissolve 5 g citric acid in 50 ml water and dilute to 100 ml with acetone.
Procedure: Spray with *a*, after which chromatogram will be vivid blue. Spray with *b* to give blue-purple chromatogram with discernible spots. After 2 min., spray with *c*.
Results: Thiophosphate pesticides detected as blue or purple spots on yellow background. Maximum color intensity after 5–10 min. After 10 min., background changes from yellow to greenish-blue; respray with *c* to bring out spots again.
Comments: This reagent is used with Al_2O_3 plates or paper containing dimethylformamide as stationary phase and developed with methylcyclohexane.

360. *o*-Toluidine

Preparation: 0.5% *o*-toluidine in ethanol.
Procedure: Spray, dry, expose to 254 nm U.V. light.
Results: Chlorinated pesticides detected as green spots on white background, sensitivity 0.5–1 μg.
Comments: *o*-Dianisidine may be used instead of toluidine.

361. 1,3,5-Trinitrobenzene

Preparation:
Solution a. 1 g KOH in 10 ml water and diluted to 100 ml with 95% alcohol.
Solution b. Saturated solution of 1,3,5-dinitrobenzene in acetone.
Procedure: Spray chromatogram with *a* and heat 5 min. at 150 °C. Then wash cooled plate with acetone to remove organic residues. Spray with *b* to detect potassium sulfite.
Results: Organic sulfite pesticides detected as pink to red spots.

Phenols
(plant phenols)

See Tests: 40, 48, 157, 197, 226, 262, 291, 362–379, 400, 438.

362. Ammonium Vanadate-Anisidine

Preparation:
Solution a. Saturated, aqueous ammonium vanadate.
Solution b. Dissolve 0.5 g *p*-anisidine in 2 ml H_3PO_4, dilute to 100 ml with ethanol and filter.
Procedure: Spray with *a* and while still wet with *b*; dry at 80 °C.
Results: Phenols detected as spots with various colors on a pink background.

363. Benzidine, Tetrazotized

Preparation:

Solution a. 0.5% benzidine in dilute HCl.

Solution b. 10% sodium nitrite in water.

Color reagent. Equal volumes *a* and *b* are mixed as required to form a clear, bright-yellow solution. The benzidine is prepared as follows: 5 g benzidine is triturated with 12*N*, 15 ml, HCl and the resulting suspension is dissolved in 980 ml water, the resulting solution being stable for one week.

Results: Phenols of the phloroglucinol-resorcinol type afford red azo-dyes with tetrazotized benzidine, whereas those of the catechol-pyrogallol type give products of ill-defined color; the latter type are therefore better located with ferric chloride-ferricyanide reagent. Tetrazotized benzidine is used as a specific reagent for the red-staining phloroglucinol-resorcinol type of phenols. Sensitivity, 2–3 μg.

364. Boute Reaction

Preparation: Nitrogen dioxide, prepared from conc. HNO_3 and copper.

Procedure: Expose chromatogram to NH_3 vapor and then nitrogen dioxide.

Results: Compounds with phenolic hydroxide detected as yellow spots, stable for several days.

365. Brentamine Fast Red GG

Preparation:

Solution a. Saturated solution of sodium carbonate in water.

Solution b. Brentamine fast red GG salt, 1% aqueous solution. This is a stabilized *p*-nitrobenzenediazonium salt and is best freshly made and may need filtering.

Procedure: The oven-dried chromatogram, after examination under U.V. light, is sprayed both sides of the paper with *a*, and then air-dried. The chromatogram is again viewed under U.V. light and then sprayed with *b*.

Results: Most phenols give stable intense colors although catechol derivatives are weak. Red mottling may indicate presence of phenolic atmospheric contaminants, presence of buffers on chromatograms or an insufficient period of drying to remove acidic solvents from the chromatogram. Phenolic acids are detected, as are catacholamines.

366. 2-Chloro-4-nitrobenzenediazonium naphthalene-2-sulfonate

Preparation: 0.1% solution of 2-chloro-4-nitrobenzenediazonium naphthalene-2-sulfonate in dilute acetic acid (pH 2).

Procedure: Prepare diazo reagents right before use. Developed chromatograms are washed in dilute HCl and examined on a sheet of polyethylene film.

Results: Detects phloroglucinol compounds such as phloretin, phlorin and phlorrhizin.

367. *p*-Dimethylaminobenzaldehyde-Acetic Anhydride (Altman Reagent)

Preparation:

Solution a. 5% *p*-dimethylaminobenzaldehyde in acetic anhydride.

Solution b. Dry acetone.

Color reagent. Mix *a* and *b* (1 : 4). (Highly lachrymatory—caution!).

Procedure: Dip paper and hang immediately in hood. Colors may begin to appear within 20 min., but the chromatogram should be left overnight as the rate of color formation is dependent on the concentration of the conjugate; heating for 2–3 min. at 130 °C will bring up the colors. All aroyl-glycines react to yield orange or orange-red colors which appear to be stable indefinitely and which fluorescence yellow in U.V. light. Either Ehrlich or sulfanilic acid reagents, or both in sequence, can be applied over this, and the usual colors are obtained in practically all cases.

The reagent is highly specific for substituted benzoyl-glycines and compounds as chemically similar as substituted acetyl-glycines are negative.

Comments: This reagent is also useful for the location of many of the citric acid cycle acids. Aconitic acid appears even before heating the chromatogram as a violet spot (sensitivity: less than 5 μg), whereas citric, α-keto-glutaric and oxalacetic acids give pink spots. Fumaric acid gives a yellowish spot, which appears dark under U.V. light.

Among the acids chemically related to the citric acid cycle acids, glutaconic acid gives an intense pink color. The same color, but far less intense, is given by itaconic acid, whereas tricarballylic and citraconic acids yield only pale yellow colors. When present in relatively high concentrations (about 50 μg), malonic and tartaric acids appear as green spots, lactic and phenyllactic as yellow ones. Hydrochloric acid is also located as a yellow spot.

The same reagent gives an orange color with hippuric acid, due to the reaction of *p*-dimethylaminobenzaldehyde with that acid giving an azlactone. Colors close to that found with hippuric acid are also given by the other aroyl-glycines, so that the use of *p*-dimethylaminobenzaldehyde in acetic anhydride has the great advantage of locating at the same time many acids of the citric acid cycle and (with a quite different color) aroyl-glycines, two types of important compounds which occur simultaneously on most chromatograms of biological fluids.

368. Ethylenediamine

Preparation: *Solution a.* 13.3 g ethylenediamine hydrochloride in 100 ml water.

Color reagent. Add free ethylenediamine to solution *a* to pH 10. Add equal volume water to the resulting solution.

Results: Ethylenediamine reagent gives an intense-blue fluorescence under U.V. light with gallates, gallic acid and gallotannins, and sodium nitrite with ellagitannins gives a sequence of color changes:

red→violet→blue→green (Griessmayer reaction).

369. Ferric Chloride-Ferricyanide

Preparation:

Solution a. 3% $FeCl_3$ in water.

Solution b. 3% $K_3Fe(CN)_6$ in water.

Color reagent. The reagents are prepared and stored in dark bottles. When required, each solution is diluted ten times and equal volumes of the two are mixed.

Procedure: The chromatograms are dipped through the clear, bright brown solution, washed successively with dilute HCl and water and air-dried. The reagent detects less than 1 μg of many phenols and tannins. Where the chromatogram has previously been exposed to ammonia, care must be taken to remove residual traces prior to dipping. For spraying, use 0.1*M* ferric chloride-0.1*M* $K_3[Fe(CN)_6]$ (1 : 1), freshly prepared.

Results: With few exceptions, phenols and tannins can be located by ferric chloride-ferricyanide reagent with the formation of Prussian blue spots. The catechol-pyrogallol type of phenols and tannins form intense spots, and a greater concentration of the phloroglucinol-resorcinol type is necessary to give spots of the same size and intensity as those afforded by more dilute solutions of the catechol-pyrogallol type. Measurement of the total color of the Prussian blue spots can therefore be used for the estimation of several phenols. The low redox potential of ellagic acid explains the poor response which this substance gives with ferric chloride-ferricyanide. A few exceptions to this general reaction have been noticed. Thus, *p*-hydroxybenzoic acid does not form Prussian blue, and such phenols as phloracetophenone and salicylic acid chelate preferentially with Fe^{3+} ion to give violet-colored spots.

Also used as reagent for aromatic amines (blue spots), tryptamine, and phenolic steroids.

370. Folin-Ciocalteau Reagent

Preparation:

Solution a. Mix 10 g sodium tungstate, 2.5 g sodium molybdate and 70 ml H_2O. Add, consecutively, 5 ml 85% H_3PO_4 and 10 ml conc. HCl. Reflux for 10 hr., then add 15 g Li_2SO_4, 5 ml H_2O and 1 drop Br_2, boil again 15 min. Cool and dilute to 100 ml. Reagent should not be green.

Solution b. 20% aqueous Na_2CO_3.

Procedure: Spray with *b*, dry for a short period, dilute *a* with 3 vols. of water and spray.

Results: Blue spots. Detects phenols, phenolic carboxylic acids and derivatives and estrogens. Also detects uric acid.

Comments: More sensitive and easier to use than the Folin-Denis reagent.

371. Mercury-Nitric Acid (Millon's Reagent)

Procedure: Digest 1 part mercury with 2 parts fuming HNO_3, dilute solution with two parts water.

Procedure: Lightly spray and dry at 35 °C; repeat spraying if required. Heat.

Results: Phenols and aromatic methoxy compounds react, as do phenol and phenol ether glycosides.

372. Nitraniline

Preparation:

Solution a. 1.5 g *p*-nitraniline in 45 ml conc. HCl and 95 ml water.

Solution b. 5% sodium nitrite in water.

Solution c. 10% anhydrous sodium carbonate in water.

Color reagent. Add 0.2 volume *b* to 10 volumes *a* and then add 10 volumes *c*.

Procedure: Oven-dried paper is dipped and laid flat or hung to dry.

Results: Yields stronger colors with many phenols than sulfanilic reagent; cannot be used over Ehrlich's reagent.

Comments: For detection of plant phenols, *a* is 0.3% *p*-nitraniline in 8% HCl; *a* and *b* are cooled and mixed (5 : 30), and 50 parts cold *c* is added. If the diazonium acetate is required, then 2*M* sodium acetate is used for *c*. This latter reagent gives rose-pink spots for sinapic and ferulic acids, distinguishing them from umbelliferone and scopoletin, which are yellow.

Alternate preparation:

Solution a. 0.1% *p*-nitraniline in 0.1% 1*N* HCl; heat to dissolve.

Solution b. 0.2% aqueous sodium nitrite.

Solution c. 10% aqueous sodium carbonate.

Procedure: 1 volume *a*, 1 volume *b*, and 2.5 volumes *c* are separately cooled to 5 °C in an ice bath, reagent *a* being cooled in the spray bottle. Reagent *b* is added to *a* and kept cool for a further 5 min. Reagent *c* is then added and the papers sprayed at once.

The spray reagent must be prepared fresh and used at once. A total volume of 10 ml is sufficient for one 10 in. paper and not more than 40 ml should be prepared at one time due to deterioration of the reagent. No background should be evident on the chromatogram which can be stored in a filing cabinet with little deterioration over a period of months.

373. Nitrosodimethylaniline

Preparation: 1% *p*-nitrosodimethylaniline in 50% ethanol.

Results: Phenols detected as spots with various colors.

374. Silver Nitrate, Alkaline

Preparation:

Solution a. Saturated aqueous silver nitrate.

Solution b. 0.5% NaOH in 80% ethanol.

Procedure: Dip in freshly prepared *a*, evaporate acetone, dip in *b*.

Results: Black or dark brown spots given by aminophenols (e.g., 3- and 5-hydroxyanthranilic acids), indoles with a free phenolic group (e.g., serotonin, bufotenin) and ketoacids in the enolic form (e.g., freshly prepared indole-pyruvic acid). The other indoles react slowly. Organic acids give a variety of colors.

Comments: Test cannot be used on chromatograms run in chloride solvents.

Alternate preparation:

Solution a. Saturated aqueous silver nitrate-acetone (0.1 : 20, 0.1 : 100, or 1 : 20).

Solution b. 0.5% NaOH in 80–90% ethanol.

Results: When used as above, sugars, and sugar alcohols give dark brown to black spots on a yellow to brown background in less than 10 min. Immersing in 2*N* ammonia may remove background color. Very sensitive but nonselective reaction. Amino sugars also react.

Dihydroxy- and many polyhydroxy-compounds yield grey or grey-brown spots; simple monohydroxy phenols usually react more slowly. Many dihydroxyphenols react before alkali is applied.

375. Starch-Iodate

Preparation:

Solution a. 11% aqueous starch solution.

Solution b. 1% aqueous potassium iodate.

Procedure: Spray dried chromatogram with *a* and then *b*; while still wet, expose to U.V. light for 3–4 min.

Results: Iodophenolic compounds and iodoamino acids (sensitivity 0.05 μg) detected as blue spots which fade quickly.

376. Sulfanilic Acid (Pauly's Reagent)

Preparation:

Solution a. Dissolve 9.55 g sulfanilic acid in 2.5*N* HCl. Store at 2 °C.

Solution b. 4.5% sodium nitrite. Store at 2 °C.

Solution c. 10% aqueous potassium carbonate.

Color reagent. Mix equal volumes of *a* and *b*.

Procedure: Spray with the reagent, dry completely without heat, spray with *c*.

Results: Range of colors is from reddish-purple (tetraiodophenols) to orange (iodophenols). 10–20 μg thyroxine detected. Histidine and iodohistidines react.

Comments: *N,N*-diethylsulfanilamide reagent is prepared in exactly the same way as above. It is somewhat more sensitive than diazotized sulfanilic acid, with colors in the purple range.

Alternate preparation:

Solution a. Add 9 g sulfanilic acid to 90 ml conc. HCl in 500 ml water and warm until dissolved. Cool and dilute to 900 ml with water.

Solution b. 5% sodium nitrate in water.

Solution c. 10% anhydrous sodium carbonate in water.

Color reagent. Mix 1 volume *a* and 1 volume *b* and let stand 5 min. at room temperature (cool in ice if room temperature is above 20 °C). Add 2 volumes *c* carefully as vigorous effervescence will occur.

Procedure: Dip oven-dried (4–5 min.) chromatogram rapidly through the reagent and lay flat on clean, white paper.

Results: Phenolic compounds, including 4-, 5-, and 6-hydroxyindole compounds react to give red to brown to violet colors—detectable below 1 μg. Some indolic acids give weak orange colors, nonphenolic indoles do not react.

Many phenolic acids yield intense, characteristic blue, purple, red and yellow colors; a number of dihydroxy compounds give weak colors.

Imidazoles are most commonly detected by Pauly's Reagent, giving red-brown colors. *N*-substituted compounds do not react. Imidazoles with —CHO or —COOH groups directly attached to the ring may give faint colors. Ammonium salts give yellow colors.

377. *N*-2,6-Trichloro-*p*-Benzoquinone Imine (TCQ) (Gibb's Reagent)

Preparation:

Solution a. 0.05% TCQ in absolute ethanol; stable 2 weeks in the dark.

Solution b. Borate buffer, pH 9.3, 4.75% $Na_2B_4O_7 \cdot 10H_2O$.

Procedure: Dip papers, relatively free from acid, in *a* and allow to air-dry. Spray lightly with *b*, on both sides of paper.

Results: Blue, purple and red spots. Phenolic compounds with unsubstituted para position react well (ortho- and meta-tyrosines and tryamine). Parasubstituted phenols do not generally react (*p*-tyrosine and tryamine) but there are exceptions (octopamine, *m*-nephrine, *p*-hydroxyphenylserine). Phenolic compounds and thiols react. Antioxidants are detected.

Comments: Overspraying with 10% acetic acid changes colors of phenolic compounds from blue to magenta; 4-hydroxy-3-methoxyphenyl compounds become orange to yellow.

378. Ultraviolet Light

Procedure: Examine chromatogram under 360 nm U.V. light.

Results: Some phenolic acids fluoresce blue, purple, yellow or green. Since many types of compounds fluoresce, compounds should also react with sulfanilic acid, ferric chloride-ferricyanide or nitraniline before being considered as phenols. Exposure to NH_3 may cause a change in color of fluorescence.

Maximum amounts of information for plant phenols and tannins is obtained by using U.V. light followed by ferric chloride-ferricyanide reagent or tetrazotized benzidine reagent or by ferric chloride and vanillin reagents.

379. Vanillin

Preparation:
Solution a. 10% vanillin in ethanol.
Solution b. 12*N* HCl.
Color reagent. Mix *a* and *b* (2 : 1).
Procedure: The reagent is freshly mixed, chromatograms are dipped, held vertically, blown free of solvent and placed on polyethylene film. The spots are outlined in pencil and their rate of appearance recorded.
Results: 5 μg of the phloroglucinol-resorcinol type of phenol is locatable. More selective reagent than tretrazotized benzidine. Catechols detected as red spots.

Plastics
(plasticizers, resins)

See Tests: 330, 380–382, 427.

380. Nitraniline

Preparation:
Solution a. 0.5*N* KOH in ethanol.
Solution b. 1 g *p*-nitraniline in 200 ml 2*N* HCl.
Solution c. 5% sodium nitrite solution.
Solution d. Add *c* to 10 ml of *b*, with stirring, until mixture is colorless.
Procedure: Spray with *a* and heat 15 min. at 60 °C. Then spray with *d*.
Results: Detects plasticizers.

381. Resorcinol-Sulfuric Acid

Preparation:
Solution a. 20% resorcinol in ethanol (containing a little $ZnCl_2$).
Solution b. 4*N* sulfuric acid.
Procedure: Spray with *a*, heat 10 min. at 150 °C, then spray with *b* and heat 20 min. at 120 °C. Finally spray with 40% potassium hydroxide.
Alternate procedure: Spray with 50–50 mixture of *a* and *b* and heat to 120 °C for 10 min. Cool and expose to ammonia vapors.
Results: Plasticizers (phthalate esters) detected with sensitivity of 20γ.

382. Thymol-Sulfuric Acid

Preparation:
Solution a. 20% thymol in ethanol.
Solution b. 4*N* sulfuric acid.
Procedure: Spray with *a* and heat 10 min. at 90 °C, then spray with *b* and heat 10–15 min. at 120 °C.
Results: Plasticizers detected with varied colors.

Purines, Pyrimidines, Constituents of Nucleic Acids
(nucleotides)

See Tests: 15, 370, 383–394.

383. Ammonium Molybdate-Perchloric Acid (Phosphate Reagent) (Hanes and Isherwood Reagent)

Preparation:
Solution a. 1 g finely powdered ammonium molybdate in 8 ml water.
Solution b. Conc. HCl.
Solution c. 12*N* $HClO_4$.
Solution d. Acetone.
Color reagent. Mix *a*, *b*, *c* and *d* (8 : 3 : 3 : 86); prepare fresh.
Procedure: Dip paper, dry, and expose to U.V. light for at least 30 min.
Results: Nucleoside mono-, di-, and triphosphates appear as blue spots. Enhanced sensitivity can be obtained by leaving the paper overnight; by the following morning the entire paper is colored blue. If, however, it is then exposed to ammonia fumes this color disappears leaving only blue spots indicating the presence of the nucleoside phosphates. Alternatively, the paper after being dipped in the reagent and allowed to dry is heated to 85 °C for 7 min. It is then steamed for a few minutes by holding it over a vigorously boiling water bath, placed in a tall cylinder or beaker and H_2S led into the bottom of the apparatus. Nucleoside mono-, di-, and triphosphates again appear as blue spots. This second method is less convenient than the first, but it has the advantage of greater sensitivity.
Alternate preparation: 2% ammonium molybdate in 5% HNO_3.
Procedure: Spray or dip chromatogram.
Results: $PO_4^{\equiv}$ appears yellow.

384. Chloramine-T-Ammonia

Preparation:
Solution a. 10% chloramine-T in water.
Solution b. 1*N* HCl.
Procedure: Spray with *a* and then with *b*. Heat at 97 °C to remove chlorine, then expose to NH_3.
Results: Detects caffein as rose-red colored spot.

385. Chlorine-Ammonia

Preparation: Use gases in saturated chamber.
Procedure: The chromatogram with a 50–100% content of water is introduced into an atmosphere of chlorine and, after drying at 80–90 °C, it is exposed for several min. to ammonia vapor.
Results: Xanthine derivatives show up as violet spots while all other purine derivatives exhibit a green fluorescence. The sensitivity of the reaction is about 0.2 μg.
Alternate procedure: Purines are also detected by spraying a chlorinated chromatogram, after heating at 105 °C, with a solution composed of 2 ml 10% KI in 100 ml 0.5% benzidine in ethanol.

386. Cysteine-Sulfuric Acid (Modified Dische Reagent)

Preparation:
Solution a. 0.5% cysteine hydrochloride in 3*N* H_2SO_4.
Solution b. Acetone.
Color reagent. Mix *a* and *b* (1 : 9).
Procedure: Dip chromatogram, dry, and then heat 5–10 min. at 85 °C.
Results: Deoxyribonucleosides and their mono-, di-, and triphosphates appear as pink or grey spots, purine derivatives tending to react more rapidly than pyrimidine derivatives. This is a fairly sensitive method. A deoxynucleoside spot which is clearly visible in U.V. light will generally give a positive reaction.

387. Eosine-Mercury Chloride

Preparation: Dissolve 0.2 g of eosine and 32.5 g of mercuric chloride in 100 ml of 96% by volume ethanol.
Procedure: After brief drying, wash out the excess reagent with 50% ethanol in a trough.
Results: Purines detected as red-violet spots which are visible as fluorescent spots especially under filtered U.V. light.

388. Mercuric Acetate-Diphenylcarbazone

Preparation:
Solution a. Dissolve 0.25 g of mercuric acetate in 100 ml of 96% by volume ethanol adding a few drops of glacial acetic acid.
Solution b. Dissolve 0.05 g of diphenylcarbazone in 100 ml of 96% by volume ethanol.
Procedure: Spray first with *a*, then with *b*. The chromatogram becomes uniformly violet, but shows shadows at the sites where the purines are present. Heating to 120 °C over a hot plate or in the drying oven gradually discolors the background.
Results: Detects purines.
Comments: The various mercury spots are of different stability and disappear gradually during heating, requiring constant observation during heating. The spots are preferably circled in pencil immediately after their appearance.

389. Mercuric Nitrate-Ammonium Sulfide

Preparation:
Solution a. Dissolve 8.1 g of mercuric nitrate in 100 ml of 0.5*N* nitric acid.
Solution b. Dilute 1 part by volume of ammonium sulfide solution with 2 parts of water.
Procedure: Spray with *a*, then with 0.5*N* nitric acid and subsequently rinse with water. After drying, spray with *b*.
Results: Purines and pyrimidine bases detected as black spots.

390. Potassium Cyanide

Preparation: 1*M* KCN (*Caution*!—cyanide is poisonous).
Procedure: Treat chromatogram with 1*M* aqueous KCN, inspect under U.V. light.
Results: Oxidized pyridine nucleotides detected as fluorescent zones; adenine-containing compounds detected as quenching zones.

391. Silver Nitrate-Bromophenol Blue (Wood Reagent)

Preparation:
Solution a. 0.4% bromophenol blue in acetone.
Solution b. 2% silver nitrate in water.
Color reagent. Mix equal volumes of *a* and *b*.
Procedure: The chromatogram is dipped in the mixture and hung up in air for 10 min. It is then, while still damp, transferred to a shallow tray of distilled water for 5 min. The wash water is then poured off and replaced by fresh distilled water. After about 5 min. in this second wash most of the blue dye should have been removed from the paper, except for the areas containing purine and pyrimidine derivatives, which will still retain the dye. Any trace of unwanted dye remaining can be removed by a third wash in fresh distilled water. The paper may then be hung up to dry.

Results: Adenine, guanine, hypoxanthine, xanthine, and their derivatives give blue spots of a purine-silver-dye complex. Cytosine and its derivatives give similar spots, royal blue in color and easily distinguishable from those given by the purines. Chloride, bromide and iodide give violet spots and inorganic phosphate a grey-brown spot. Histidine gives a blue spot the color of which is quite distinct from that given by purine or cytosine derivatives.

Comments: Mark all spots as soon as they become visible as they may fade during washing. Keep the number of changes of distilled water to a minimum. Sensitivity = 0.05 μmoles purines and 0.2 μmoles cytosines, or greater.

392. Silver Nitrate-Sodium Dichromate

Preparation:

Solution a. 2% aqueous silver nitrate.

Solution b. 0.5% aqueous sodium dichromate.

Solution c. 0.5*N* nitric acid.

Procedure: Dip briefly into *a*, then dry the chromatogram in the air for 10 min. and dip into *b*. Dip the red-dyed chromatogram into *c*, thus discoloring the background.

Results: Purines detected as red spots.

393. Thiocarbamide Reaction

Preparation:

Solution a. Dissolve 25 g trichloroacetic acid in 50 ml water.

Solution b. Dissolve 40 mg dried ruthenium trihydroxide in 1 ml water.

Color reagent. Mix *a* and *b* and let stand 24 hr. in dark until it develops a red-brown color. Stable 3–4 weeks.

Procedure: Spray and heat 5–10 min. at 80 °C.

Results: Sulfur derivatives of purines and pyrimidines detected as green or blue spots.

394. Ultraviolet Light

Procedure: View paper under 250–280 nm U.V. light with visible light filtered out.

Results: Purine and pyrimidine derivatives generally appear as dark spots against the rather faint light blue fluorescence of the paper. A notable exception to this rule is that, after chromatography in an acid solvent or exposure to the fumes of HCl, guanine and xanthine and their compounds fluoresce quite strongly. They are therefore easy to distinguish from other naturally-occurring purine and pyrimidine derivatives. The minimum amount of material which can be detected in U.V. light depends on the nature of the lamp and the size of the spot. As a rough guide it may be said that 0.01 μmole in a spot 1.5 cm in diameter should be quite clearly visible, except in the case of uric acid, which is not readily detectable by this method. Spots detected in U.V. light may subsequently be cut out and eluted.

A permanent record of any chromatogram can easily be obtained by pinning it over a sheet of photographic paper on a board, and exposing to the U.V. lamp for a few seconds. The photographic paper can then be developed like an ordinary document copy. Spots of U.V.-absorbing material appear white against the dark background of the rest of the paper.

Steroids
(sterols, bile acids)

See Tests: 16, 122, 157, 194, 291, 333, 369, 370, 395–429, 438.
See also Tables 4–7 at the end of this section.

395. Allen Test

Preparation: Conc. H_2SO_4-ethanol-water (40 : 9 : 1).

Results: Detects 16-dehydrosteroids and their acetates as mauve, rose, yellow or purple spots.

396. Anisaldehyde (Modified Kagi-Miescher Reagent)

Preparation: Mix 1 ml conc. H_2SO_4 and 100 ml acetic acid and add 0.1 ml anisaldehyde immediately before use.

Procedure: Dip, blot and heat at 110 °C for 5 min. Detects steroids and bile acids. Results are summarized below.

Necessary structure	Not abolished by	Exceptions
Blue or green color produced		
3β-ol-5-ene	A or P series, spirostane, 17, 20-ones; 16, 20-ol,	A-17-ols
17 : 21 and 16 : 17 diols of P series	5α, 5β; 3, 11-ols	
Red or orange color produced		
-4-ene-3-ones	A or P; 20-ones; 11α; 11β, 17α, 17β, 20α, 20β, and 21-ols; 16-Me, 9α-F;	A-17-ones
8 other miscellaneous steroids		
Yellow or nondescript color		
93 other steroids		10 steroids gave no color

Sensitivity in TLC about 1 μg.

397. Anisaldehyde-Antimony Trichloride (AACS Reagent)

Preparation: Mix 1 ml *p*-anisaldehyde with 100 ml saturated antimony trichloride in chloroform, and then add 2 ml conc. H_2SO_4. Keep solution in dark for 1.5 hr. at room temperature.
Procedure: Dip chromatogram into the upper layer, dry in darkened hood, then heat at 90 °C for 3 min. Inspect in daylight, heat again 3 min., and inspect under U.V. light.
Alternate procedure: Spray with upper layer, dry 5 min. in dark, heat 3 min. at 90 °C. Observe by daylight and U.V. light.
Results: Steroids detected as various colored spots.

398. Antimony Chloride (Carr-Price Reagent)

Preparation: Dissolve 25 g of antimony trichloride in 75 g of chloroform freed from ethanol. Chloroform is freed from ethanol by passing through a column of activated aluminum oxide.
Alternate preparation: Saturated reagent solution in chloroform.
Procedure: Heat the sprayed chromatogram for 10 min. at 100 °C. Inspect chromatogram in daylight and under U.V. light.
Results: Detects steroid glycosides, vitamin A, and bile acids. For steroids with Δ^4 double bands, use saturated solution in ethanol containing 10% thionyl chloride.

399. Arsenomolybdic Acid

Preparation: Dissolve 25 mg ammonium molybdate in 450 ml water and mix with 21 ml conc. H_2SO_4. Add 3 g $Na_2HAsO_4 \cdot 7H_2O$ in 25 ml water, leave mixture 48 hr. at 37 °C and filter. Store in brown bottle.
Procedure: Place paper on a glass plate heated to 65 °C and lightly wet with the solution. Cover with another plate and leave for 30 min. at 65 °C.
Results: Blue spots formed by steroids with a ketol group and 3-keto-Δ^4 conjugation. The yellow-green background is eliminated by brief immersion in 5% ammonium citrate.

400. Brentamine B Reagent

Preparation:
Solution a. 0.5% brentamine fast blue B salt in water. Store in cold—stable few weeks.
Solution b. 1% sodium hydrogen carbonate adjusted to pH 9 with NaOH.
Color reagent. Mix *a* and *b* (1 : 1).
Procedure: Dip paper and blot.
Results: Phenols, including estrogens, are located as orange-red spots, sensitivity 5–10 $\mu g/cm^2$.

401. *tert*-Butyl Chromate

Preparation: Mix 10 ml *tert*-butanol and 10 ml CCl_4, add 5 g CrO_3 and shake for 10 min. Add 65 ml CCl_4 and pass through 10 g Na_2SO_4 (anhydrous) on a glass sintered filter. Keeps 2 months and more at 4°C over Na_2SO_4.
Color reagent. Dilute 1 ml solution with 80 ml xylene and 20 ml pyridine. Shake well and use immediately.
Procedure: Spray evenly (dipping dissolves out steroid), heat at 100 ± 5°C for 5 min., dip through 1*N* NaOH and dry at 100 °C.
Results: Yellow colors (5 $\mu g/cm^2$) and yellow fluorescence (1 $\mu g/cm^2$) are given by 3β-hydroxy-5-enes and 3-keto-4-enes. The latter are distinguished by U.V. absorption.

If Zimmermann Reagent is now used, 17-ketones themselves and as formed from 17-hydroxy-pregnane derivative give the purple color, 2 $\mu g/cm^2$. A black color indicates the 3 : 6-diketone possibly formed from the unsaturated 6-ol or 6-one.

402. Chlorine-Antimony Chloride

Preparation: Saturated solution of $SbCl_3$ in chloroform-acetic anhydride (8 : 2).
Procedure: Expose for 20 min. to chlorine gas, spray lightly and heat 2–4 min. at 90 °C; inspect in U.V. light.
Results: Steroids give colored spots fluorescent in U.V. light.

403. 2,4-Dinitrophenylhydrazine

Preparation: Saturated solution 2,4-dinitrophenylhydrazine in 0.3% conc. HCl in methanol.
Procedure: Dip, blot and heat at 90 °C for 5 min. Cool and wash with (1) 2*N* NaOH in water, (2) water and (3) 2*N* HCl in water.
Results: Δ^4-3-ketones appear as orange spots, sensitivity 1 $\mu g/cm^2$, and other ketones may appear as yellow spots, sensitivity, 2 $\mu g/cm^2$.

404. 2,5-Diphenyl-3-(4-styrylphenyl)-tetrazolium Chloride

Preparation:
Solution a. 1% methanolic solution of 2,5-diphenyl-3-(4-styrylphenyl)-tetrazolium chloride.
Solution b. 3% sodium hydroxide (aqueous).
Procedure: Mix 1 volume *a* with 10 volumes *b* and spray immediately for alumina plates. For silica gel layers, spray first with 2*N* NaOH to provide alkaline condition.
Results: Steroids detected as strong purple spots on yellow background with sensitivity of 0.1 μg or less.

405. Eriochromcyanine

Preparation:

Solution a. 0.05% aqueous eriochromcyanine solution.

Solution b. 1% acetic acid.

Solution c. 1% aqueous sodium carbonate solution.

Procedure: Dip chromatogram for 15 min. into *a*, then briefly into *b* and *c*, and subsequently wash with water.

Results: Cholestane and cholestene detected by blue color on light blue background.

406. Formaldehydogenic Reagent

Preparation:

Solution a. 15 g ammonium acetate in 85 ml of 80% methanol.

Color reagent. At time of use add to *a* 1 ml acetylacetone, 0.3 ml glacial acetic acid and 0.1 ml $HClO_4$ (50% aqueous solution). Prepare and use in dim light.

Procedure: Dip, blot and observe occasionally. The greenish-yellow fluorescent spots are most intense after an hour but are first visible after 10 min.

Results: 20-Hydroxy- or 20-ketonic- 21-ols are detected at 5 $\mu g/cm^2$.

407. Glycolic Acid

Preparation: 50% glycolic acid in water.

Procedure: Spray, heat 45 min. at 80 °C, inspect under U.V. light (257 nm).

Results: Detects ketals of α,β-unsaturated steroid ketones.

408. Hydroxylamine-Ferric Chloride

Preparation:

Solution a. 14 g hydroxylamine hydrochloride in 100 ml methanol.

Solution b. 3.5*N* KOH in methanol.

Solution c. 2 g $FeCl_3$ in 100 ml 10% HCl.

Solution d. Mix 5 volumes *a* and 4 volumes *b*, shake, and filter off KCl.

Procedure: Spray chromatogram with *d* (dipping elutes steroids), let stand 10 min., and spray with *c*. If brown $Fe(OH)_3$ appears, leave to dry and spray again with *c*.

Results: Esters of steroid alcohols (other than formates), methyl esters of steroid acids and steroid lactones give purple spots, visible at 2 $\mu g/cm^2$.

409. Iodoplatinate Reagent

Preparation:

Solution a. 5% $PtCl_4$ in 1*N* HCl.

Solution b. 10% potassium iodide.

Color reagent. Mix 5 ml *a*, 45 ml *b* and 100 ml water. Store in dark.

Procedure: Spray and wash out excess reagent.

Results: Detects Girard's T hydrazones as red to orange spots. Monoketo steroids detected with 1 μg sensitivity, steroids with more keto groups with higher sensitivity.

410. Lead Tetraacetate-Acetic Anhydride

Preparation: 2.5% lead tetraacetate in glacial acetic acid containing 10% acetic anhydride (fresh).

Procedure: The paper is crisply dried with a hairdryer (oven drying destroys these steroids), dipped, blotted between filter papers and hung up for 15 min. The acetic acid is then blown off with a hairdryer and the Zimmermann reagent is applied. Purple spots are obtained from all steroids which possess the side chains —COH · CHOH · CH_3 and —COH · CHOH · CH_2OH as these are oxidized to 17-ketosteroids by the lead tetraacetate; sensitivity 5 $\mu g/cm^2$. Those steroids which normally react with the Zimmermann reagent will also react.

411. Methylene Blue

Preparation: Dissolve 20 mg methylene blue histological stain and 5 g Na_2SO_4 in 100 ml water and add 1 ml conc. H_2SO_4 just before use.

Procedure: Dip, blot, lay in a dish of $CHCl_3$ and agitate gently for 1–2 min.

Results: White zones appearing on the blue background indicate sulfates at more than 1 $\mu g/cm^2$. Large quantities of sulfate appear as pink zones before the $CHCl_3$ wash. This reaction is given by steroid sulfates but the phosphates would probably also react as do the aromatic phosphates.

Comments: Counterstaining by 0.01% rhodamine-6G in $CHCl_3$ produces reddish spots on the blue background which give a yellow fluorescence under 360 nm U.V. light. The sensitivity is increased tenfold.

412. Naphthoquinone-Perchloric Acid

Preparation: 0.1% solution of 1,2-naphthoquinone-2-sulfonic acid in a mixture of ethanol-60% perchloric acid-40% formaldehyde-water (2 : 1 : 0.1 : 0.9).

Procedure: Spray uniformly and then dry at 70–80 °C observing the color formation. Too long a heating period converts all the spots to a brown-black color.

Results: Detects sterols with 0.03 μg sensitivity.

413. Perchloric Acid

Preparation: 2% aqueous perchloric acid.
Procedure: Spray, heat 10 min. at 150 °C.
Results: Steroids detected as brown spots.

414. Phenylenediamine-Phthalic Acid

Preparation: 0.9% phenylenediamine and 1.6% phthalic acid in *n*-butanol (water saturated). Prepare fresh each day.
Procedure: Spray and heat at 100–110 °C.
Results: Steroids detected as yellow or brown spots.

415. Phosphomolybdate Reagent

Preparation: 5% dodeca-molybdophosphoric acid in *n*-propanol; filter if cloudy.
Procedure: The chromatogram is dipped, blotted between filter papers and on heating to 105 °C blue spots are obtained.
Results: Strongly reducing steroids (positive to the tetrazolium reagent) react rapidly, but most other poly-oxygenated steroids need 2–5 min. heating. Steroids as unreactive as pregnanediol will react with this reagent, but care must be taken as the paper itself may produce a blue background color; sensitivity, 2–20 $\mu g/cm^2$. Bile acids are detected.
Alternate preparation:
Solution a. 2–20% phosphomolybdic acid in ethanol or methyl cellosolve.
Solution b. 4 ml conc. HCl plus 100 ml of 10% phosphomolybdic acid in 95% ethanol.
Procedure: For gypsum-bound thin layers: spray with *a*, heat to 100 °C for 20 min. For saturated triglycerides, expose to iodine vapor for 5 min. prior to spraying.
For starch-bound thin layers: spray with *a* (10%), evaporate solvent with hot air blower, then heat at 100 °C until solvent front appears (10 min. or less).
Results: Detects antioxidants, lipids, steroids.

416. Phosphoric Acid

Preparation: 70% phosphoric acid in methanol.
Procedure: Dip, spread the paper on a glass sheet and heat at 90 °C for 5 and 30 min. Observe the colors in daylight and the fluorescence emission under 360 nm U.V. light.
Results: Typical results are listed below.

Steroid	5 minutes heating		30 minutes heating	
	Color	Fluorescence	Color	Fluorescence
androsterone	yellow	blue	yellow	blue
etiocholanolone			brown	orange
epi-androsterone			blue	salmon-pink
dehydro-*epi*-androsterone	blue	yellow	blue	yellow
5α- and 5β-androstan-3:17-dione			blue	salmon-pink
testosterone				yellow
cis-testosterone	blue	orange	blue	orange
methyl-testosterone		blue		blue
pregnanetriol	purple	pink	purple	pink

Alternate preparation: For spray reagent, dilute 1 part conc. H_3PO_4 with 1 part water.
Procedure: Spray plates until transparently moist, heat to 120 °C for 20 min., inspect under U.V. light. Bile acids are detected.

417. Porter-Silber Reagent (Phenylhydrazine · HCl)

Preparation: Dissolve 43 mg phenylhydrazine hydrochloride in a mixture of 34 ml ethanol, 41 ml H_2SO_4 and 25 ml H_2O.
Results: Steroid-21-aldehydes react at once with the spray, but compounds of the dihydroxyacetone type require 30–120 min.

418. Resorcyaldehyde

Preparation:
Solution a. 0.5% resorcyaldehyde in glacial acetic acid.
Solution b. Conc. H_2SO_4 in glacial acetic acid.
Color reagent. Mix *a* and *b* (1 : 1).
Results: Detects 16-dehydrosteroids and their acetates as mauve, blue, orange or red spots.

419. Sodium Hydroxide

Preparation: 10% aqueous sodium hydroxide solution.
Procedure: After spraying, dry the chromatogram for 10 min. at 80 °C.
Results: Δ^4-3-keto steroids show a yellow fluorescence under filtered U.V. light.

420. Sulfuric Acid

Preparation: 1% H_2SO_4 in ethanol.
Procedure: Dip, blot and heat at 100–120 °C. Watch carefully and remove from the oven at the first sign of charring.
Results: Summarized below.

Necessary structure	Not abolished by	Abolished by
Red color produced		
A^4-3-one with 17-ol	6β-ol; 19-nor; 17α-alkyl	2α-ol; 11β-ol; 1-ene
P^4-3-one with 20-ol or 20-one	6β, 11β, 21-ols; 11-one 16-ene	11α-ol; 16α-Me; 9α-F; 1-ene; 17-acetoxy
P^5-3β-ol with 17α-ol-20-one		21-ol
Fluorescence produced, of any color		
3, 11, 17 or 20-ones	2α, 6β, 7α, 11β, 17α, 17β, ols; 19-nor; 17α-alkyl; 5α, 5β, 5-ene, 4-ene, 1:4-diene	6-methyl

421. 2,4,2′,4′-Tetranitrodiphenyl

Preparation:
Solution a. Saturated solution of 2,4,2′,4′-tetranitrodiphenyl in benzene.
Solution b. 10% KOH in 50% methanol.
Procedure: Treat with cold solution *a*, dry 10 min. at room temperature, spray with *b*.
Results: Compounds with butanolide ring detected as blue spots.

422. Tetrazolium Reagent

Preparation:
Solution a. 0.2% blue tetrazolium in water.
Solution b. 2*N* NaOH in water.
Solution c. Methanol.
Color reagent. Freshly mix *a*, *b*, *c* (6 : 20 : 10).
Procedure: The paper is dipped, blotted between filter papers and warmed gently (if necessary).
Results: Reducing steroids yield blue spots; sensitivity 1 μg/cm². Reducing steroids are mainly those with a —CO · CH_2OH side chain although the 16-hydroxy-17-ketosteroids and 2-hydroxy-3-ketosteroids are also positive.
Comments: If papers are warmed gently and examined periodically under U.V. light (360 nm), Δ^4-3-ketone steroids give bright yellow fluorescent spots.

423. Trichloroacetic Acid-U.V. Light

Preparation: 10 g trichloroacetic acid in 20 ml ethanol.
Procedure: Dip paper, blot, heat to 70 °C for 10 min.
Results: The preganetriols [3α:17α:20(α or β)-trihydroxy-pregnane] give blue spots (10 μg/cm²) and a blue fluorescence under 360 nm U.V. light (1μg/cm²). Only etiocholane-3α:17β-diol has been found to give a similar reaction. Certain steroids, though giving no color or fluorescence at 70 °C, give other fluorescence colors on heating at 110 °C for 10 min.
Alternate preparation: 25 g trichloroacetic acid in 100 ml chloroform.
Procedure: Spray, dry at 100 °C, inspect under U.V. light.
Results: Strophanthus glycosides, yellow fluorescence, 0.4 μg sensitivity; menthofuran, pink spot after standing.

424. 2,3,5-Triphenyltetrazolium Chloride

Preparation: Mix equal volumes of methanolic solutions of 4% TTC and 1*N* NaOH.
Procedure: Spray and then heat for 5–10 min. at 110 °C.
Results: Red spots. Detects glycosides, steroids, reducing sugars and thio acids.

425. Ultraviolet Light

Procedure: Paper chromatogram is examined under 254 nm light.
Results: Δ^4-3-ketone steroids give dark spots on fluorescent background. Sensitivity 1 μg/cm² on paper. Sensitivity is increased by ten if the absorption is recorded by a document copying process.

Comments: The following multiple reagent sequences after inspection under U.V. light can be used.
(1) Zimmermann reagent followed by dinitrophenylhydrazine for 17-ketosteroids.
(2) Phosphomolybdate followed by Zimmermann reagent for dioxy alcohols and ketones.
(3) Tetrazolium reagent followed by inspection under U.V. light for fluorescence followed by lead tetraacetate test followed by dinitrophenylhydrazine for adrenocortical steroids.
(4) Tetrazolium reagent followed by trichloroacetic acid-U.V. for pregnanetriol among corticosteroids.

426. Uvitex

Preparation:
Solution a. 0.05% Uvitex CF conc. (Ciba) in acetone-water (85 : 15).
Solution b. 0.05% Uvitex SWN conc. (Ciba) in acetone-water (90 : 10).
Procedure: Spray *a* or *b*.
Results: After *a*, estrogens and α,β-unsaturated ketosteroids are detected as quenching spots in short-wave U.V. light; estrogens fluoresce in long-wave U.V. light. After *b*, estrogens form quenching spots in long-wave U.V. light, α,β-unsaturated ketones fluoresce in short-wave light.

427. Vanillin-Sulfuric Acid

Preparation: 0.5% vanillin in H_2SO_4-ethanol (4 : 1); prepare fresh daily.
Procedure: Spray, heat for 5 min. at 100 °C. Extended heating turns all spots brown.
Results: Detects bile acids, steroids (5 μg/cm^2), terpenes, plasticizers as various colored spots.

428. Zimmermann Reagent

For Paper Chromatography:
Preparation:
Solution a. Shake an excess of solid KOH pellets, a few mg ascorbic acid, and ethanol until a syrupy, saturated solution is obtained. Filter through Whatman No. 54 paper and store under nitrogen in refrigerator.
Solution b. 2% *m*-dinitrobenzene in ethanol.
Procedure: The paper is dipped in *a* and blotted between two sheets of filter paper. It is then dipped in *b*, blotted again and warmed with a hairdryer when purple, blue, or brown spots appear. If the KOH is too weak it may be necessary to warm more strongly but care should be taken not to overheat the paper as the background then intensifies to yellow or even brown.
Results: 17-Ketosteroids yield stable purple spots; sensitivity 2 μg/cm^2; 3-ketones yield blue spots lasting for 5–10 min., sensitivity 10 μg/cm^2 and 20-ketones give brown spots lasting for 5–10 min., sensitivity 20 μg/cm^2. 17-Hydroxy-20-ketones give red spots, sensitivity 5 μg/cm^2.

This reagent is suitable for all keto-methylene compounds including nonsteroid compounds; α-substituted ketosteroids, such as 16-hydroxy-17-ketosteroids, do not react.
Comments: As reagent *a* is difficult to prepare and has poor keeping properties (depending mainly on the quality of the ethanol) a modified reagent may be prepared, immediately before use, by diluting 1 volume of 15*N* aqueous KOH (8 g KOH + 5 ml H_2O) with 5 volumes of absolute ethanol; stir until homogenous. Dip in modified *a*, blot, dip in *b* and roughly dry in a cold airstream before warming. This procedure is not so sensitive for 3 or 20 ketones, but is equally sensitive for 17-ketones, when compared with the unmodified reagent.
For Thin Layer Chromatography:
Preparation: 3 g *m*-dinitrobenzene in 190 ml methanol plus 10 ml propylene glycol plus 2.5 g KOH in 20 ml methanol plus 5 ml water.
Procedure: Spray and inspect at room temperature and heat to elevated temperature.
Results: Detects 3- and 17-oxo steroids.

429. Zinc Chloride

Preparation: 30% zinc chloride in methanol, filtered.
Procedure: Spray, heat for 1 hr. at 105 °C, cover with glass plate on removing from oven to prevent moisture pickup, examine under 360 nm U.V. light.
Results: Detects steroids as fluorescent spots with sensitivity of 0.1 μg or less.

Steroid Glycosides
(saponins, sapogenins, cardiac glycosides)

See Tests: 312, 333, 398, 424, 430–433.

430. *p*-Anisaldehyde

Preparation: Freshly prepared solution of 0.5 ml *p*-anisaldehyde in 5 ml 70% $HClO_4$, 10 ml acetone and 40 ml water.
Procedure: Spray, heat at 75–80 °C for 4–5 min. and observe in visible and U.V. light over period of 1 hr.
Results: Detects digitalis glycosides with 0.1 μg sensitivity in visible, 0.02 μg in U.V. light.

431. 1,3-Dinitrobenzene (Raymond Reagent)

Preparation:
Solution a. 10% 1,3-dinitrobenzene solution in benzene.
Solution b. Dissolve 6 g of sodium hydroxide in 25 ml of water. Add 45 ml of methanol to the solution.
Procedure: Spray with *a* and dry at 60 °C. Then spray with *b*.
Results: Cardiac glycosides detected as purple spots, changing to blue. Spots fade rapidly.
Comments: Formamide-impregnated chromatograms are dried at 60 °C before spraying.

432. 3,5-Dinitrobenzoic Acid (Kedde Reaction)

Preparation: Dissolve 1 g of 3,5-dinitrobenzoic acid in a mixture of 50 ml of methanol and 50 ml of aqueous 2*N* potassium hydroxide.
Results: Detects digitaloid five-membered ring lactones; steroid glycosides react.

433. Trichloroacetic Acid-Chloramine T

Preparation: Mix 10 ml of a freshly prepared 3% aqueous chloramine-T solution with 40 ml of a 25% solution of trichloroacetic acid in 96% by volume ethanol. (Trichloroacetic acid is stable for several days).
Procedure: Preheat papers impregnated with formamide for 10 min. at 110 °C before spraying. Spray and heat for 7 min. at 110°C in the drying oven.
Results: Digitalis glycosides detected as blue spots under U.V. light; glycosides of the A-series show yellow spots.

Terpene Derivatives (azulenes, terpene acids)

See Tests: 3, 108, 226, 247, 289, 427, 434–439.

434. *p*-Dimethylaminobenzaldehyde-Phosphoric Acid (Modified Ehrlich Reagent)

Preparation: Add 1 g *p*-dimethylaminobenzaldehyde to 5 g conc. phosphoric acid and 50 g glacial acetic acid. Dilute to 100 ml with water. Store in brown bottle.
Procedure: Spray chromatogram and heat to 100 °C for several minutes.
Results: Azulenes turn deep blue.

435. Ferric Chloride, Anhydrous

Preparation: Saturated solution of anhydrous ferric chloride in methanol.
Results: Detects terpene alcohols.

436. Phenol-Bromine

Preparation: 50% phenol in carbon tetrachloride.
Procedure: Spray with reagent and then expose to bromine vapor.
Results: Detects terpenes.

437. Phosphotungstic Acid

Preparation: 25% alcoholic phosphotungstic acid.
Procedure: Spray and dry at 115–118 °C for 2 min.
Results: Triterpenoids detected as colored spots on white background, sensitivity 3–5 μg.

438. Stannic Chloride

Preparation: 30% $SnCl_4$ in chloroform.
Procedure: Dip chromatogram and heat 5–20 min. at 90 °C. Inspect in daylight and under long-wave U.V. light.
Results: Detects triterpenes, sterols and steroids, phenols and polyphenols.

439. Vanillin-Sulfuric Acid

Preparation: 1% vanillin in conc. H_2SO_4 or 1% vanillin in 50% H_3PO_4.
Procedure: Spray, heat, and observe in daylight and U.V. light.
Results: Detects terpenes.

Vitamins
(water soluble and fat soluble vitamins, growth factors)

See Tests: 11, 21, 55, 154, 226, 289, 398, 440–453.

440. *p*-Aminobenzoic Acid-Cyanogen Chloride

Preparation: 5% *p*-aminobenzoic acid in methanol.
Procedure: Spray chromatogram and place in an atmosphere of cyanogen chloride (toxic!).
Results: Detects nicotinic acid as red spot, sensitivity 0.1 μg; nicotinic acid amide, orange-red spot.
Comments: Cyanogen chloride is freshly prepared from 20 ml 28% chloramine suspension in water, 20 ml 1*N* HCl, and 10 ml 10% potassium cyanide solution. *Caution*: Poison!

441. Cacotheline (Tegelhoff Reagent)

Preparation: 2% aqueous cacotheline solution.
Procedure: Spray and heat to 100 °C.
Results: Detects Vitamin C as purple spots.

442. 4-Chloro-1,3-dinitrobenzene

Preparation:
Solution a. 1% solution of 1,3-dinitro-4-chlorobenzene in methanol.
Solution b. 3*N* Sodium hydroxide.
Procedure: Spray with *a*, then spray with *b*.
Results: Detects nicotinic acid, nicotinamide, pyridoxol.

443. *o*-Dianisidine, Diazotized

Preparation:
Solution a. 5% sodium carbonate solution.
Solution b. Dissolve 0.5 g pure *o*-dianisidine · 2HCl in 60 ml water.
Solution c. 5% aqueous $NaNO_2$.
Solution d. 5% aqueous urea solution.
Color reagent. Add 6 ml conc. HCl, 12 ml *c*, and 12 ml *d* (after 5 min.) to *b*. The reagent is used after 24 hrs. and may be kept for 10 days.
Procedure: The chromatogram is first heavily sprayed with *a* and then lightly with the reagent.
Results: γ-Tocopherol and δ-tocopherol show up as purple and red spots respectively; α,β,ϵ and ζ-tocopherols do not react.

444. 2,6-Dibromoquinonechlorimide

Preparation: 0.4% 2,6-dibromoquinonechlorimide in methanol.
Results: Detects Vitamin B_6.

445. Dipicrylamine

Preparation:
Solution a. Add 1 g of dipicrylamine to 0.12 g of magnesium carbonate and 15 ml of water. Heat the mixture for 15 min. on a boiling water bath and then filter.
Color reagent. Add to 0.2 ml of *a*, 50 ml of methanol, 49 ml of redistilled water and 1 ml of ammonia solution.
Results: Detects Vitamin B_1.

446. Emmerie-Engel Reagent

Preparation:
Solution a. 2% solution of α,α'-dipyridyl in chloroform.
Solution b. 0.5% aqueous ferric chloride solution.
Procedure: Spray with *a*, then spray with *b*.
Results: Ferric salt is reduced by tocopherol to ferrous salt, which forms a red complex with α,α'-dipyridyl.
Alternate preparation: 0.5% reagent in 95% ethanol-0.2% $FeCl_3$ in 95% ethanol (1 : 1).
Results: Detects hydroquinones.

447. Iodine-Potassium Iodide-Starch

Preparation: 0.001–0.005% iodine, with a small amount of potassium iodide, in a 0.4% starch solution.
Procedure: Spray chromatogram.
Results: Ascorbic acid detected as white spot on blue background.

448. Leucomethylene Blue

Preparation: Shake 0.1 g methylene blue in 100 ml ethanol and 1 ml acetic acid with 1 g zinc powder until colorless.
Procedure: Immerse chromatogram.
Results: Ubiquinones turn blue and are marked before 5 min. when the background also turns blue.

449. Methoxynitraniline-Sodium Nitrite

Preparation:
Solution a. Dissolve 0.5 g of 4-methoxy-2-nitroaniline in 125 ml glacial acetic acid. Dilute the solution to 250 ml with 10% sulfuric acid.
Solution b. 0.2% aqueous sodium nitrite solution.
Solution c. Mix 1 part by volume of *a* with 1 part by volume of *b*.
Solution d. 2*N* sodium hydroxide.
Procedure: Spray with *c* and then *d*.
Results: Vitamin C detected as blue spots on orange background.

450. Phenylhydrazine

Preparation: Dissolve 0.3 g phenylhydrazine and 0.45 g sodium acetate in 10 ml water.
Results: Detects dehydroascorbic acid.

451. Potassium Ferricyanide (Thiochrome Reaction)

Preparation:
Solution a. 1% aqueous potassium ferricyanide solution.
Solution b. 20% NaOH solution.
Color reagent. Mix 3 ml *a*, 45 ml water, and 15 ml *c*.
Procedure: Spray, dry, inspect under U.V. light.
Results: Detects Vitamin B_1.

452. Potassium Iodobismuthate

Preparation: 5 g Potassium iodobismuthate is boiled with 0.5 ml conc. HCl in 100 ml water. After cooling, the solution is filtered.
Procedure: The chromatogram is sprayed several times with this reagent and the background may then be washed with water-saturated ether; the spots of some compounds, however, are liable to fade.
Results: The more basic the character of the nitrogenous compound, the more intense the blue color of the spot (betaine, acetylcholine). Other nitrogenous compounds are revealed as orange (thiamine triphosphate), red or purple (thiamine) spots.

453. Titanium Chloride-Sodium Nitrite-1-Naphthylamine

Procedure: Folic acid can be converted on the chromatogram to *p*-aminobenzoic acid by reductive splitting. For this reduction, Komenda has recommended spraying with a mixture of 10% $TiCl_3$ in conc. HCl and 15% aqueous trisodium citrate (1 : 1) which is allowed to act for 24 hr. in the air. This is followed by spraying with a 0.2% $NaNO_2$ solution in 0.1*N* HCl, partial drying of the chromatogram and final spraying with an 0.2% ethanolic 1-naphthylamine solution or 0.1% aqueous *N*-(1-naphthyl)-ethylenediamine · 2HCl.
Results: Folic acid is revealed as red spots.

Section II.I

REFERENCES

These detection reagents and the procedures for their use have been compiled from books, scientific articles and manufacturer's literature, including:

a. "Dyeing Reagents for Thin Layer and Paper Chromatography", E. Merck AG, Darmstadt, Germany; distributed by Brinkmann Instruments Co., Westbury, N.Y.

b. "Thin Layer Chromatography", Stahl, E., editor, Academic Press, N.Y., 1965, pp. 485–502.

c. "Guide to TLC Visualization Reagents", J. T. Baker Chemical Co., Phillipsburg, N.J.

d. "TLC Visualization Reagents and Chromatographic Solvents", Publication JJ-5, Eastman Kodak Co., Rochester, N.Y.

e. "Thin Layer Chromatography", Randerath, K., Academic Press, N.Y., 1963.

f. "Thin Layer Chromatography", Bobbitt, J. M., Reinhold Publishing Co., N.Y., 1963.

g. "Thin Layer Chromatography", Kirchner, J. G., Vol. XII, Technique of Organic Chemistry, Interscience Publishing Co., N.Y., 1967, pp. 147–191.

h. "Paper Chromatography and Paper Electrophoresis", Block, R. J., Durrum, E. L., and G. Zweig, Academic Press, N.Y., 1958, 2nd ed.

i. "Paper Chromatography", Sherma, J. and G, Zweig, Volume II of Paper Chromatography and Electrophoresis", Zweig, G. and Whittaker, J. R., Academic Press, N.Y., 1970.

j. "Paper Chromatography", Hais, I. M. and Macek, K., eds., Academic Press, N.Y., 1963.

k. "Chromatographic and Electrophoretic Techniques", I. Smith, ed., Vol. I, Chromat., Interscience Publishers, N.Y., 1969.

Section II.I

Detection Reagents for Paper and/or Thin-Layer Chromatography

The following tables represent summary information on a number of classes of compounds, various color reagents, colors produced, and in some cases sensitivity of detection. Detailed procedures for preparation of detection reagents are found at the end of each table or in the earlier parts of this section.

Table 1: Sugars

2: Drugs

3: Flavonoids

4: Steroids

5: Sterols

6: Estrogens

7: Sterols

TABLE 1
REACTION OF SUGARS WITH VARIOUS REAGENTS

Reagent	Aldo-hexoses	Aldo-pentoses	Keto-hexoses	Keto-pentoses	Uronic acids	Methyl pentoses	Sugar alcohols	Deoxy sugars	Glycosides	Amino sugars	Comments
1. **Ammoniacal $AgNO_3$**	+	+	+	+	+	+	+	−	+	+	Unspecific; sensitivity: 1 μM glucose
2. **Alkaline permanganate**	+	+	+	+	+	+	− +	+	− +	+	Sensitivity: 10 μM glucose; unspecific; not permanent
3. **Alkaline 3,5-dinitrosalicylate**	+	+	+	+	+	+	−	+	−	+	Sensitivity: 10 μM glucose
4. **Alkaline 3,4-dinitrobenzoic acid**	+	+	+	+	+	+	−	+	−	+	Ketoses react more quickly
5. **Triphenyltetrazolium chloride**	+	+	+	+	+	+	−	−	−	+	Sensitivity: 5 μM
6. **Aniline phthalate**	brown	red			brown	brown					
7. ***p*-Anisidine**	light brown	brown	yellow		red-pink	green		light brown			
8. **Benzidine**					+	+	+				*N*-acetylglucosamine amine + alloxan +
9. ***m*-Phenylenediamine**	yellow fl.[a]	orange-yellow fl.[a]	yellow fl.[a]	yellow fl.[a]	+ —					+ −	
10. ***p*-Aminohippuric acid**	orange fl.[a]	orange fl.[a]			purple						
11. **2-Aminobiphenyl**	green-brown	red									
12. **Naphthoresorcinol**		blue violet	red		blue	blue violet					
13. **Resorcinol**	pink	blue green	red								
14. **Anthrone**			yellow	purple							Heptulose-orange

[a] fl. = fluorescence.

1. 0.1*N* $AgNO_3$–5*N* NH_4OH (1 : 1).
2. 1% aq. $KMnO_4$ containing 2% Na_2CO_3.
3. 0.5% 3,5-dinitrosalicylate and 4% NaOH in water.
4. 1% 3,4-dinitrobenzoic acid in 2*N* Na_2CO_3.
5. 2% aq.triphenyltetrazolium chloride–1*N* NaOH (1 : 1).
6. 930 mg aniline and 1.6 g phthalic acid in 100 ml *n*-butanol, water saturated.
7. 3% *p*-anisidine · HCl solution in *n*-butanol.
8. 500 mg benzidine, 200 ml glacial acetic acid, 80 ml absolute ethanol.
9. 0.2*M* phenylenediamine in 76% ethanol.
10. 0.3% *p*-aminohippuric acid in alcohol.
11. 1.69 g 2-aminobiphenyl, 0.9 g oxalic acid, 5 ml glycerol, 10 ml water, 84 ml acetone.
12. 0.2% naphthoresorcinol in ethanol–2% trichloroacetic acid in water (1 : 1).
13. 0.2 g phloroglucinol plus 80 ml 90% ethanol plus 20 ml trichloroacetic acid.
14. 300 mg anthrone in 10 ml glacial acetic acid, 20 ml ethanol, 3 ml conc. H_3PO_4, 1 ml water.

Reference: Isherwood, F. A. *Brit. Med. Bull.*, **10**, 202, 1954. Reprinted from "Paper Chromatography and Electrophoresis", Block, R. J., Durrum, E. L., and G. Zweig, 1958, p. 179, with permission of Academic Press, Inc., New York, N.Y.

TABLE 2

DETECTION OF DRUGS

Drugs Reacting with Ninhydrin-Acetone and with p-Nitroaniline (PNA)

Drug	Ninhydrin-acetone spray		PNA spray		$R_F \times 100$		
	Min. amt. detected, μg	Color	Min. amt. detected, μg	Color	*S1*	*S2*	*S3*
1. **Amphetamine**	3	purple	1	orange	26	10	45
2. **Betazole**	50		—	orange	5	0	36
3. **Chlorphentermine**	50		—	orange	44	—	50
4. **Metaraminol**	20	pink[a]	1	orange	8	2	51
5. **Methoxamine**	2	purple[b]	1	orange	14	7	48
6. **Naphazoline**[c]	10	blue	5	orange	10	0	10
7. **Phenylpropanolamine**	2	pink[b]	1	yellow	15	9	55
8. **Tranylcypromine**	5	purple[b]	2	orange	76	25	73
9. **Tuaminoheptane**	3	purple	1	orange	14	9	29

[a] Becomes pink after next spray. [b] Not observed after ninhydrin and iodoplatinate spray. [c] Fluorescence.

Drugs Reacting with Dithiocarbamate Reagents and with Ninhydrin-Acid

Drug	Dithiocarbamate reagent		Ninhydrin-acid		$R_F \times 100$		
	Min. amt. detected, μg	Color	Min. amt. detected, μg	Color	*S1*	*S2*	*S3*
10. **Butethamine**[a]	1	brown	10(uv)[b]	purple	49	23	70
11. **Cyclopentamine**	10	brown	10(uv)	purple	20	5	21
12. **Desipramine**	1	brown	3(uv)	purple	28	6	33
13. **Ephedrine**	1	brown	3	pink	10	7	30
14. **Isocarboxazid**[c]	1	brown	6(uv)	pink	91	88	77
15. **Isonicotinylhydrazine**	5	yellow	4(uv)	purple	22	9	65
16. **Mephentermine**	10	brown	15	purple	21	15	28
17. **Methamphetamine**	1	brown	5	purple	21	7	37
18. **Methoxyphenylamine**	1	brown	3	pink	15	7	33
19. **Methylphenidate**	10	brown	6(uv)	purple	79	19	76
20. **Nialamid**[c]	5	yellow	6(uv)	purple	30	14	75
21. **Nortriptyline**	5	brown	2	purple	48	13	38
22. **Phenothiazine**	1	green	3(uv)	purple	97	94	81
23. **Phenylephrine**	10	brown	10	purple	5	6	38
24. **Phenylpropylmethylamine**	1	brown	1	purple	23	5	34
25. **Pipradol**[c]	20	brown	5	purple	69	26	75
26. **Propitocaine**	10	brown	10(uv)	purple	20	60	79
27. **Propylhexedrine**	5	brown	6	purple	14	5	23

[a] Also detected in the primary aromatic amine group. [b] uv denotes uv absorption after application of ninhydrin–acid and heat. [c] Fluorescence.

TABLE 2—(Continued)
DETECTION OF DRUGS
Drugs Reacting with Iodoplatinate[a]

Drug	Min. amt. detected, μg	$R_F \times 100$ S1	S2	S3	Drug	Min. amt. detected, μg	$R_F \times 100$ S1	S2	S3
28. **Adiphenine**	1	90	55	70	66. **Methaqualone**	5	96	86	75
29. **Aminophenylline**	5	95	41	67	67. **Methixene**	1	55	9	52
30. **Aminopyrine**	5	87	42	79	68. **Methysergid**	1	51	24	79
31. **Amitryptyline**	1	55	14	56	69. **Morphine**	3	21	1	46
32. **Atropine**	5	18	0	24	70. **Nicotine**	1	68	9	60
33. **Benactyzine**	5	87	52	75	71. **Nikethamine**	5	86	49	67
34. **Benzonatate**	10	94	—	74	72. **Nylidrin[c]**	10	25	55	69
35. **Benzphetamine**	1	98	63	81	73. **Orphenadrine**	1	63	12	60
36. **Brompheniramine**	1	30	7	—	74. **Papaverine**	2	91	58	80
37. **Bupivacaine**	5	95	46	80	75. **Pentazocine**	2	43	60	75
38. **Caffeine**	1	89	24	73	76. **Pentylenetetrazol**	1	91	50	75
39. **Carbetapentane**	20	44	8	49	77. **Phenocaine**	1	61	76	80
40. **Chlordiazepoxide**	1	85	91	78	78. **Phendimetrazine**	10	92	21	66
41. **Chlorpheniramine**	1	37	7	42	79. **Pheniramine**	1	42	6	43
42. **Cinchonine[b]**	1	31	9	55	80. **Phenmetrazine[c]**	1	61	11	64
43. **Cinchocaine**	1	78	11	78	81. **Phenyramidol**	5	92	75	85
44. **Cocaine**	10	80	14	74	82. **Physostigmine**	—	56	12	68
45. **Codeine**	1	40	2	46	83. **Piperidolate**	5	93	30	76
46. **Cyclomethycaine**	1	67	16	68	84. **Piperilate**	5	90	28	71
47. **Dextromethorphan**	1	42	6	37	85. **Piperocaine**	1	68	13	67
48. **Diazepam**	1	95	84	73	86. **Pramoxine**	1	90	45	66
49. **Diethylpropion**	10	89	42	85	87. **Procyclidene**	1	49	15	51
50. **Dimethoxanate**	1	43	27	48	88. **Propoxyphene**	1	95	60	74
51. **Diphenidol**	1	68	16	71	89. **Pyrilamine**	1	51	10	60
52. **Diphenhydramine**	1	76	11	77	90. **Quinacrine[b]**	1	25	5	50
53. **Diclomine**	1	80	14	63	91. **Quinidine[b]**	1	39	14	65
54. **Ethoheptazine**	1	36	9	40	92. **Quinine[b]**	1	33	15	67
55. **Halocaine**	1	65	35	83	93. **Scopolamine**	1	52	100	27
56. **Heroin**	1	58	8	54	94. **Strychnine**	1	44	3	29
57. **Hydromorphone**	5	30	2	45	95. **Tetracaine**	1	77	14	67
58. **Isopentylhydrocupreine**	5	40	24	66	96. **Theobromine**	20	60	30	—
59. **Isopropamide**	5	14	0	15	97. **Theophylline**	10	52	41	64
60. **Levallorphan**	1	41	32	76	98. **Thiothixene**	1	56	7	51
61. **Lidocaine**	10	95	71	73	99. **Trimethobenzamide**	1	46	6	58
62. **Meperidine**	2	71	16	64	100. **Triprolidine**	1	33	9	52
63. **Mepivacaine**	10	87	49	74	101. **Yohimbine[b]**	10	84	27	79
64. **Methadone**	1	32	11	53	102. **Zoxazolamine**	10	78	87	84
65. **Methapyrillene**	2	71	9	65					

[a] All compounds yield a blue to purple product. [b] Fluorescence. [c] Not tertiary amines but cannot be detected in amounts of 20 μg with the previous reagents.

TABLE 2—(Continued)

DETECTION OF DRUGS

Drugs Reacting with *p*-Dimethylaminobenzaldehyde (DMB), Used after Iodoplatinate

Drug	Iodoplatinate spray, min. amt. detected, μg	DMB spray		$R_F \times 100$		
		Min. amt. detected, μg	Color	*S1*	*S2*	*S3*
103. **Aminoglutethimide**	10	1	yellow	87	93	78
104. **Benzocaine**	20	1	yellow	94	92	18
105. **Butacaine**	5	1	yellow	70	82	80
106. **Carphenazine**	1	1	lavender	51	12	72
107. **Chlorpromazine**	1	1	purple	53	13	61
108. **Chlorprocaine**	1	1	yellow	46	15	76
109. **Ethopromazine**	1	5	purple	84	94	75
110. **Fluphenazine**	1	1	pink	85	19	72
111. **Hydroxyzine**	1	1	violet	90	44	79
112. **Imipramine**	1	1	green	62	22	58
113. **Lysergic acid diethylamide**	1	1	bluish-gray	65	32	75
114. **Mepazine**	1	1	purple	63	7	59
115. **Metabutoxicaine**	1	1	yellow	89	15	78
116. **Methopromazine**	1	1	purple	50	8	48
117. **Methotrimepazine**	1	5	green	90	19	54
118. **Perphenazine**	1	1	pink	77	7	68
119. **Pipamazine**	1	1	purple	49	11	70
120. **Procaine**	1	1	yellow	46	7	75
121. **Procainamide**	20	1	yellow	10	1	55
122. **Prochloroperazine**	1	1	pink	74	3	53
123. **Promazine**	1	1	purple	48	10	54
124. **Promethazine**	1	1	pink	74	17	64
125. **Propiomazine**	1	1	purple	93	87	78
126. **Prothipendyl**	1	1	brown	70	9	47
127. **Sulfisoxazole**	20	1	yellow	19	71	77
128. **Sulfanilamide**	20	1	yellow	9	76	72
129. **Sulfathiazole**	5	1	yellow	34	45	71
130. **Thiopropazate**	1	1	lavender	100	23	72
131. **Thioridazine**	1	5	purple	91	21	55
132. **Trifluoperazine**	1	5	lavender	97	16	59
133. **Trimeprazine**	1	1	purple	90	21	61

TABLE 2—(Continued)

DETECTION OF DRUGS

Developing solvents (proportions by volume). *S1*: chloroform–methanol (90:10). *S2*: isopropyl ether–ethanol (80 : 20). *S3*: methanol–ammonia (100 : 1.5) [Ammonia is "aqua ammonia" (28% NH_3 in water)].

Spray reagents. Ninhydrin in acetone. Dissolve 0.4 g of ninhydrin in acetone and dilute to 100 ml. This reagent must be freshly prepared.

Ninhydrin–acid. Dissolve 0.3 g of ninhydrin in 100 ml of isopropyl alcohol and 1 ml of glacial acetic acid.

Dithiocarbamate reagent. Pour 10 ml of carbon disulfide into a 150 ml beaker containing 10 ml of concentrated ammonium hydroxide. The size of the beaker is critical. The two chemicals must not stratify. Each must be exposed to air. The beaker is placed inside a glass developing chamber. In 10 to 15 min. the chamber fills with dense white vapors and is ready to use. It can only be reused throughout one day, unless the contents of the beaker become orange colored, in which case a fresh mixture must be prepared.

Copper chloride. Dissolve 5 g in 100 ml of water.

Potassium iodoplatinate. Platinum chloride, 1 g, is dissolved in 100 ml of water containing 10 g of potassium iodide. This mixture is diluted to 500 ml with water.

p-Dimethylaminobenzaldehyde (DMB). Dissolve (with gentle warming) 1 g of DMB in 100 ml of 1*N* hydrochloric acid.

p-Nitroaniline (*PNA*) *reagent.* Dissolve 2.5 g of PNA in 250 ml of 1*N* hydrochloric acid and dilute to 500 ml with ethanol. Just before use, add 2 ml of a solution of sodium nitrite (5 g/100 ml) to 10 ml of PNA. Cool this mixture to 5° to 10 °C (refrigerator) for 10 min. and use only when cold.

Sodium hydroxide reagent. Dissolve 50 g of sodium hydroxide in 100 ml of water. Ten milliliters of this solution is diluted to 100 ml with 95% ethanol just before use.

Procedures: Every colored spot that forms should be recorded after each spray operation.

Expose the chromatogram developed in solvent *S1* to 350-nm and 254-nm radiation and observe any absorption or fluorescence. Then spray this chromatogram with ninhydrin–acetone and expose it to 350-nm radiation for 10 min., or until the background becomes slightly pink. Place the plate inside a chamber containing the dithiocarbamate reagent for 10 min., withdraw it from the chamber. Then spray it lightly with the copper chloride solution. Excessive spraying with copper chloride is undesirable because this increases background color and so makes spots harder to see when the iodoplatinate spray is applied. Heat the plate at 90 °C for 15 min. Observe,[1] then follow the copper chloride spray with iodoplatinate. Air-dry the chromatogram and again apply the iodoplatinate. Observation of the color intensity of the reference standards serves as a guide to the amount of spray required. Air-dry the chromatogram and overspray with concentrated hydrochloric acid. Again air-dry and spray the plate with DMB. The sprayed plate is observed immediately after this spray is applied and 2 to 14 hr. later, when the background has faded.

Spray the chromatogram developed in *S3* with acid ninhydrin and again place in an oven at 90 °C for 5 min. After the plate has cooled to room temperature use the iodoplatinate spray. Overspray with concentrated hydrochloric acid, air-dry the plate, then spray with PNA reagent. The freshly prepared PNA is sprayed lightly. A black background should appear promptly. If it does not, this indicates the PNA reagent was not diazotized. Allow the mixture of PNA and sodium nitrite to react for 5 to 10 min. more, then respray the plate. The background should now become black. Avoid wetting the plate. Should this happen, the plate must be air-dried until the background turns grey. Then spray the chromatogram with the sodium hydroxide reagent. This reagent should be sprayed until the black background disappears or until the amphetamine reference spot becomes red.

Those spots with R_F values of 0.80 or greater when developed in the chloroform–methanol solvent can be better identified in a third system which uses *S2* as the developing solvent. Thus, the tubes containing aliquots of those samples with high R_F values should be separated from those previously saved, and aliquots of each of these should be applied on another plate coated with silica gel G and developed in the isopropyl ether–ethanol system. When developed and dried, this plate should be sprayed as in the *S1* system.

Spraying of the chromatograms should be inter-digitated if one person is doing these operations; with two people, each could confine his activity to one spray sequence.

[1] Morphine forms a brown spot; this is an adaptation of Deniges reaction for morphine. In the presence of copper ion, ninhydrin oxidizes the morphine to form a brown compound.

Reference: Bastos, M. L., Kananen, G. E., Young, R. M., Monforte, T. R., and I. Sunshine, *Clin. Chem.*, **16**, 931 (1970). Permission of Hoeber Medical Division, Harper & Row, Inc., Scranton, Pa.

TABLE 3
THE COLORS AND COLOR REACTIONS OF FLAVONOIDS ON PAPER

		Color reactions[a] in the following flavonoid classes										
Reagent	Light source	Flavone	Flavonol	Isoflavone	Flavanone	Aurone	Chalcone	Pelargonidin glycosides	Cyanidin glycosides	Peonidin glycosides	Delphinidin and petunidin glycosides	Malvidin glycosides
None	Visible	pY	pY	C	C	bY	Y	O or OR or OY	M	P	Pu	Ma
None	Ultraviolet	dB	bY	fPu	C	bY	dB	dR or FY	dM or bR	dP or FR	dPu	dMa or FCe
NH_3 vapor	Ultraviolet	bG	bY	fPu	C or pY	bR	dR					
$AlCl_3$[a]	Visible	pY	Y	C	C	pY	Y	–	+	–	+	–
$AlCl_3$[a]	Ultraviolet	FG	FY	FY	FG	FG	FO					
Na_2CO_3[b]	Visible	bY	Y	pG	G	O	R					
$NaBH_4$[c]	Visible	C	C	C	M	C	C					
$FeCl_3-K_3Fe(CN)_6$[d]	Visible	Bl	Bl	Bl	Bl	Bl	Bl					
Sulfanilic acid[e]	Visible	BO	BO	RB or BO or Pu	O or B or P							

[a] Key: B = brown; b = bright; Bl = blue; C = colorless; Ce = cerise; d = dull; F = fluorescent; f = faint; G = green; M = magenta; Ma = mauve; O = orange; P = pink; p = pale; Pu= purple; R = red; Y = yellow; + = positive color change; – = no color change.

[a] 5% ethanolic aluminum chloride.
[b] 5% aqueous sodium carbonate.
[c] 1% sodium borohydride in isopropanol.
[d] 1% aqueous ferric chloride–1% aqueous potassium ferricyanide (1 : 1).
[e] diazotized sulfanilic acid.

Reference: Reprinted from "Paper Chromatography", Sherma, J. and G. Zweig, Academic Press, 1971, p. 349. Permission of Academic Press, Inc., New York, N.Y.

TABLE 4
A COMPARATIVE STUDY OF THE REACTIONS OF STEROIDS WITH FOUR GENERAL STEROIDS TESTS[a]

Steroid	Ethanolic phosphoric acid		Carr-Price		Kagi-Miescher		AACS	
	Visible	UV (366 nm)	Visible	UV (366 nm)	Visible	UV (366 nm)	Visible	UV (366 nm)
Androsterone	—	Violet white 1	Purple 2	Red orange 4	Violet 1	Blue 2	Blue 4	Purple 4
Epiandrosterone	Violet 0	—	Purple 2	—	—	—	Blue 2	Purple 2
Dehydroepiandrosterone	Brown violet 1	Gray white 2	Orange brown 4	Wine 4	Blue 1	Blue gray 2	Blue 4	Blue black 2
4-Androstene-3,17-dione	Violet 0	Orange pink 1	Tan ±	White yellow 2	Wine purple 2	Rust 4	Orange 3	Gold 4
5β-Androstane-3,11,17-one	—	—	—	White yellow 1	Yellow 0	Brown 2	—	—
Androsterone benzoate	—	Blue white 2	Purple gray 2	Wine 2	—	—	Blue 3	Purple 2
17β-Hydroxy-5β-androstane-3-one	Violet 1	—	Pink 1	Pink orange 4	Blue 4	Brown 1	Wine 2	—
Testosterone	Violet 0	Gray white 2	Red violet 2	Orange 4	Purple 2	Pink 3	Purple 2	Wine 3
Testosterone propionate	—	White 0	Tan 1	Pink orange 1	Violet 1	Brown 3	Pink 2	Orange 2
Testosterone benzoate	—	White 0	Purple 1	Yellow white 0	Blue black 2	Brown 3	Wine 3	Wine 3
17α-Ethyl-19-nortestosterone	Orange 0	Pink 1	Orange pink 4	Gold 4	Blue 1	Blue gray 2	Purple 4	Wine 4
19-Norandrost-4-ene-17α-ethyl-17β-ol 3β-propionate	Blue 0	Light blue 1	Gray 2	Violet 1	Blue 1	Blue gray 1	Blue 2	Violet 4
Pregnenelone	—	Pink 1	Red brown 4	Wine 4	Yellow 1	Blue gray 2	Blue 3	Blue violet 4
5α-Pregnane-3β,20α-diol	—	—	Brown 2	Dark orange 4	—	—	Blue 4	Violet 4
5α-Pregnane-3β,20β-diol	—	White 0	Brown 2	Dark orange 4	—	—	Blue 3	Violet 4
3β-Hydroxy-5α-pregnane-20-one	—	Blue white 2	Red gray 2	Yellow 0	Yellow 0	Rust 0	Blue brown 3	Brown 3
5β-Pregnane-3,20-dione	Violet 0	Blue white 2	Gray 1	Yellow 2	Yellow 1	Brown 4	Brown 3	Red brown 4
Progesterone	—	White 1	Tan 0	Yellow white 2	Purple 2	Pink 4	Orange 3	Gold 4
11α-Hydroxyprogesterone	Orange 0	Violet white 0	—	Orange yellow 2	Violet 2	Brown 3	Orange 3	Gold 4

TABLE 4—(Continued)
A COMPARATIVE STUDY OF THE REACTIONS OF STEROIDS WITH FOUR GENERAL STEROIDS TESTS[a]

Steroid	Ethanolic phosphoric acid		Carr-Price		Kagi-Miescher		AACS	
	Visible	UV (366 nm)	Visible	UV (366 nm)	Visible	UV (366 nm)	Visible	UV (366 nm)
3β,21-Dihydroxy-5α-pregnane-20-one	Violet 0	Blue 2	Brown orange 4	Orange 4	Blue 0	Blue 1	Blue gray 2	Tan 0
Deoxycorticosterone	Violet 0	Gray white 2	Tan 1	Pink orange 1	Blue black 4	Dark brown 4	Brown 4	Olive 3
Corticosterone	Yellow 0	Yellow white 4	Tan yellow 1	Blue white 4	Brown 2	Brown 1	Gold 3	Olive 3
21-Hydroxy-4-pregnane-3,11,20-trione	—	White 1	Purple 1	Pink orange 1	Brown 3	Orange brown 3	Amber 3	Orange 3
3β,17α,21-Trihydroxy-5-pregnene-20-one	Violet 1	Orange white 2	Brown orange 4	Orange 4	Yellow 2	Blue 2	Blue 2	Blue black 4
17α,21-Dihydroxy-5β-pregnane-3,11,20-trione	Yellow 0	Blue 3	Brown 1	Purple 3	Brown 3	Brown 3	Wine 3	Wine 3
17α,21-Dihydroxy-5α-pregnane-3,11,20-trione	Yellow 0	—	Brown 1	Purple 3	Brown 3	Yellow 4	Yellow 4	Orange 3
11β,17α,21-Trihydroxy-5β-pregnane-3,20-dione	Yellow orange 2	Yellow white 3	Yellow 0	Blue white 3	Yellow 1	Brown 2	Brown 2	Orange 4
Reichstein S	Violet 3	Brown orange 4	Purple 1	Orange 1	Orange brown 3	Orange 4	Wine 3	Brown 3
Cortisol	Yellow 3	Chartreuse 4	Brown 1	Yellow 1	Yellow black 3	Brown 3	Purple 4	Purple 3
Cortisone	Yellow 0	Light blue 4	Tan 1	Violet 1	Brown 2	Brown orange 3	Light wine 3	Orange 2
Δ^1-Cortisone	Yellow 1	White 3	Tan 0	Violet 0	Yellow 3	Tan 1	Tan 2	Purple 3
Δ^1-Cortisol	Brown orange 1	Orange white 2	Tan 2	Blue violet 1	Yellow 1	Tan ±	Blue brown 3	Blue violet 4
3α,17α-Dihydroxy-21-acetoxy-5β-pregnane-11,20-dione	—	—	—	White yellow 1	—	—	Tan 1	—

[a] These data are based on 10 μg/cm² steroid spotted on chromatographic paper. Dash = no color response. The numbers following the colors indicate their relative intensity rating: 4 = approximately 2 μg of steroid/cm² is readily distinguishable; 3 = 4 μg/cm²; 2 = 7 μg/cm²; 1 = 10μg/cm²; 0 = 15–25 μg/cm².

Reference: Katz, S. *Arch. Biochem. Biophys.*, **91**, 54 (1960). Reprinted from "Paper Chromatography", Sherma, J. and G. Zweig, Academic Press 1971, pp. 204–205. Permission of Academic Press, Inc., New York, N.Y.

TABLE 5
COLOR REACTIONS SHOWN BY SOME STEROLS

		Color reaction in the following reagents										
		a	b	c	d	e	f	g	h	i	j	k
Compound	Ultraviolet light 365 mμ	$SbCl_3$	Sb_2Cl_5	$BiCl_3$	$CaCl_2$ in ultraviolet light	Trichloro-acetic acid	Phospho-tungstic acid	Silico-tungstic acid	Dimethyl-*p*-phenyl-enediamine	Millon's reagent	Urea in ultraviolet light 365mμ	$NaIO_4$–$KMnO_4$
Cholesterol	–	Violet	Yellow-brown	Violet	–	—	Pink-violet	Pink-orange	—	Very faint yellow	–	—
β-Sitosterol	–	Violet	Very faint yellow	Violet	–	—	Pink-violet	Pink-orange	—	—	–	—
Stigmasterol	–	Faint violet	Gray-purple	Rose-violet	–	—	Violet-brown	Faint purple brown	—	—	–	—
Lanosterol	–	Orange	Yellow	Orange	–	—	Orange-yellow	Orange-yellow	—	—	–(365 mμ) +(256 mμ)	Yellow
Ergosterol	+	Very faint purple	Pink	—	++	Faint purple	Faint purple	Faint purple-brown	Very faint blue	Yellow	++	—
Zymosterol	–	Pink-brown	Orange-yellow	Faint yellow	Faint	—	Yellow-brown	Yellow	Blue	Yellow	Faint (365 mμ) +(256 mμ)	Yellow
7-Dehydrocholesterol	+	Purple-brown	Brown-blue	Faint purple-brown	+	Green-purple	Purple-brown	Purple-brown	—	Yellow	+	Yellow
Vitamin D_2	+	Brown	Brown-blue	Gray-brown	+	—	Brown	Brown	Blue	Faint yellow	–	Yellow
Lumisterol	+	Faint brown	Purple	–	+	Purple	Purple-brown	Purple-brown	Blue	Yellow	+	Yellow

a.—50% $SbCl_3$ in ethanol; heat 5–10 min. at 70 °C, inspect in daylight and UV light.
b.—20% Sb_2Cl_5 in $CHCl_3$.
c.—33% $BiCl_3$ in ethanol, heat a few seconds at 60 °C, inspect in daylight and UV light.
d.—50% $CaCl_2$ in 50% aqueous ethanol, heat 15 min. at 85 °C, inspect in 365 nm UV light.
e.—Moisten chromatogram with trichloroacetic acid dissolved in 2 drops water.
f.—15% phosphotungstic acid in ethanol, heat 3–4 min. at 60 °C.
g.—25% silicotungstic acid in ethanol, heat 3–4 min. at 60 °C.
h.—A 1% mixture of dimethyl-*p*-phenylenediamine and *m*-tolylenediamine (1 : 1) in water.
i.—One part mercury dissolved in two parts conc. HNO_3, heat 2–4 min. at 40–50 °C, respray and reheat.
j.—50% urea in water, heat 10–15 min. at 80 °C.
k.—Spray with 1% $NaIO_4$ in water, and after 5 min. with 1% $KMnO_4$.

Reference: Copius Peerboom, J. W., Roos, J. B., and H. W. Bukes, *J. Chromatogr.*, **5**, 500 (1961); reprinted from "Paper Chromatography", Sherma, J. and G. Zweig, Academic Press 1971, pp. 206–207. Permission of Academic Press, Inc., New York, N.Y.

TABLE 6
DETECTION OF ESTROGENS ON FILTER PAPER[a]

Compound	Test *a* Color	Test *b*		Test *c* Color	Test *d*		Test *e*		Test *f*	
		Color	Fluor-escence		Color	Fluor-escence	Color	Fluor-escence	Color 1st dip	Color 2nd dip
Estradiol-17α	or	y	gr y	oc br	r or	or pi	or → br	or y	cor → or	or r
Estradiol-17β	or t	gr y	gr	ol → br	y oc	or pi	or pi → or br	gr y → pi	y or	or br
Estrone	t or	pi	pe	oc br	y → y br	gr y	gr y	or y → pi or	y	t or
Equilin	y t	gr y	gr y	pu r → ro						
Equilenin	or r → ver	pi	pe	sal r	br or	gr y	oc → or br	pu	y → or y	or
6-Dehydroestrone	—	pi	pi	pi → ro	ol gr	or r	br	r cor	or	or
17α-Ethinylestradiol	oc y → or br	pi cor	r or	ol r br	ol br	pi	br	or pi	or	or br
7-Ketoestrone	or br	pi	or cor	y	wi	cor	wi	cor pi	or → wi	wi br
1α-Hydroxyestrone	y	or pi	gr bl	y → y or	ol br	pi	y br	pi cor	y oc	br
6-Ketoestradiol	r or → r br	t	or pi	y	or y	bl	y	gr bl	or pi	pi br
Estriol-3,16α,17β	or → or br	pi	pe pi	oc → or br	y	gr y	y	gr y	—	—
Estriol-3,6β,17β	or r → r br	ol y	bl	r br	y → r	or pi	ol → pi t	pi	pi	or
Diethylstilbestrol	pi br → vi	—	—	gr → ol gr	ol gr br	gr	ol → br	pi	gr	oc
Methoxydoisynolic acid	—	—	bl	lav	or	—	—	—	y or → or	br
2-Hydroxyestradiol-17β	br	pi	pi	br	ol	gr y	y	pi	gr y	pi or
2-Methoxyestrone	or br → br	or t	pe	br r	br	gr y	br	gr bl	or pi	or → br
2-Methoxyestriol	br or	—	gr y	br y	t	r or	t	or pi	or br → r br	r br
10-Hydroxy-$\Delta^{1,4}$-estradiene-3,17-dione	or br	y	g y	or	y or	pi or gr y	y y	y gr bl	or → y br or	br or

[a] Key: r = red, or = orange, oc = ochre, y = yellow, br = brown, ol = olive, gr = green, wi = wine, t = tan, pi = pink, bl = blue, pe = peach, pu = purple, ro = rose, sal = salmon, lav = lavender, vi = violet, ver = vermillion, cor = coral. Tests are described below.

TABLE 6—(Continued)

DETECTION OF ESTROGENS ON FILTER PAPER

a.—(A) 0.5% solution of sulfanilic acid in 2% HCl. (B) 0.5% solution of $NaNO_2$. (C) 10% solution of $NaCO_3$. All reagents are stable separately. A mixture of equal volumes of reagents A and B is freshly prepared. The test strip is dipped into the reagent and then held in the air for 3 seconds. It is then passed through the carbonate solution (reagent C). The color develops immediately and continues to intensify or change color for 15 minutes. Sensitivity of the test for the estrogens is 1–3 μg per square centimeter of filter paper.

b.—Solution of 4.0 g urea and 0.3 g stannous chloride in 10 ml of 40% H_2SO_4 (gentle heating is necessary). This reagent should be prepared fresh each day. The test strip is dipped into the freshly prepared reagent, placed on a glass plate, and heated until maximum color is produced (surface temperature of hot plate is about 80 °C). This strip is then viewed under ultraviolet light. Sensitivity of the test for estrogens is 2–5 μg per square centimeter of paper.

c.—2% solution of *p*-nitrobenzenediazonium chloride in 50% acetic acid. The reagent is stable for at least 1 month. The test is carried out by dipping the strip into the reagent and heating it on a glass plate at about 100 °C until maximum color intensity develops. The *p*-nitrobenzenediazonium chloride solution is stable for at least 2 months if kept in a brown bottle. The test varies in sensitivity from 2 to 5 μg per square centimeter of paper for the estrogens.

d.—(A) 50 : 1 mixture (v/v) of concentrated H_2SO_4 and formalin. This reagent is stable for about 2 weeks. (B) Mixture of equal volumes of chloroform and acetic anhydride. The strip is passed through reagent (A) and placed into a puddle of reagent (B) which has been pipetted onto a glass plate. The strip is then immersed completely by means of a glass rod. After observing the developed color, the strip is viewed under the ultraviolet lamp for fluorescences. If reagent (B) evaporates too rapidly, a little may be pipetted directly onto the strip. Sensitivity of the test varies for the estrogens from 1 to 4 μg per square centimeter and for the sterols from 4 to 8 μg per square centimeter of paper.

e.—(A) 2 : 1 mixture (v/v) of concentrated H_2SO_4 and formalin. The mixing is done in cracked-ice bath to prevent overheating of the solution. This reagent is stable for about 1 week. (B) Mixture of equal volumes of chloroform and acetic anhydride. This procedure is exactly the same as that in d. Sensitivity of the test varies from 2 to 5 μg per square centimeter for the estrogens and from 4 to 10 μg per square centimeter for the sterols.

f.—Four grams of $ZnCl_2$ is mixed with 0.5 ml of water and 25 ml acetyl chloride is slowly added with continuous stirring. This reagent is usable for about 1 hour from time of preparation. The strip is passed through the boiling reagent and placed on a preheated glass plate. Heating (90–100 °C) is continued until maximum color intensity develops. Redipping and reheating of the strip will further change the color in most cases. This test should be done in a hood because of the noxious effects of the acetyl chloride vapors. Sensitivity of the test is from 2 to 5 μg per square centimeter for the estrogens and from 4 to 8 μg per square centimeter for the sterols.

Reference: Axelrod, L. R. and J. E. Pulliam, *Arch. Biochem. Biophys.*, **89**, 105 (1960). Reprinted from "Paper Chromatography", Sherma, J. and G. Zweig, Academic Press 1971, pp. 208–209. Permission of Academic Press, Inc., New York, N.Y.

TABLE 7

THE DETECTION OF STEROLS ON FILTER PAPER[a]

Compound	Test d Color	Test d Fluorescence	Test e Color	Test e Fluorescence	Test f Color 1st dip	Test f Color 2nd dip
Cholesterol	Brown → brown purple	Orange pink	Blue → purple	Pink	Salmon pink	Salmon orange
Cholestanol	Yellow ochre	Blue yellow	—	Blue	—	—
Ergosterol	Orange → red brown	Orange pink	Pink → wine	Pink orange → brown orange	Red	Red → brown
7-Ketocholesterol	Yellow	Green yellow	Yellow	Blue	Orange	Orange
Cholestan-3-one	—	Blue	—	Blue	—	—
Δ^4-Cholesten-3-one	—	Blue green	—	Blue yellow	—	—
Lanosterol	Tan → ochre	Green yellow	Yellow	Yellow blue	Orange	Orange
Zymosterol	Yellow brown	Blue → yellow	Yellow ochre	Yellow blue	Ochre	Ochre
Calciferol (Vitamin D_2)	Orange brown	Orange	Orange → brown	Blue yellow → orange	Orange → red brown → brown	Brown
Vitamin D_3	Orange brown	Salmon orange	Yellow brown	Blue pink → orange pink	Yellow → ochre brown	Brown
Coprostanol	Yellow	Yellow → pink yellow	—	Blue	Violet	Yellow → orange
7-Dehydrocholesterol	Red → brown red → purple brown	Salmon	Orange → pink purple	Peach	Orange red → brown red	Red brown
Squalene	Ochre	Blue	—	Blue	Olive pink	Pink purple

TABLE 7—(Continued)

THE DETECTION OF STEROLS ON FILTER PAPER[a]—(Continued)

Steroid	Test b (10 $\mu g/cm^2$) Color	Fluorescence
Dehydroepiandrosterone	Red → purple	Light blue
Reichstein's Substance A	Orange → red	Rose-coral
Δ^4-Pregnene-2α,17α,21-triol-20-one	Red → brown	Coral
3α,11β,20α,21-Tetrahydroxypregnane	Red	Yellow-white
Cortisol	Red	Coral
Corticosterone	Tan → green	Yellow-green
Tetrahydrocortisol	Red	Coral
$\Delta^{1,4}$-Androstadien-10-ol-3,17-dione	Yellow	Yellow
Cholic acid	Pink → pink-orange	Brilliant blue

Steroid	Test f (10 $\mu g/cm^2$) Color 1st dip	Color 2nd dip
Dehydroepiandrosterone	Red purple → brown	Brown → purple → gray
Δ^4-Androstene-3,17-dione	Pink → purple	Pink → purple
Prednisolone	Yellow	Brown
Δ^9-Etiocholanolone	Brown	Brown
Progesterone	Purple → red	Wine
Pregnanolone	Ochre	Purple → brown
$\Delta^{1,4}$-Androstadien-10-ol-3,17-dione	Yellow → orange	Pink → orange
Δ^4-Androsten-1α-ol-3,17-dione	Purple	Brown → purple
3β,11β,17α,20β,21-Pentahydroxyallopregnane	Yellow → brown	Yellow → brown

[a] Tests are described in Table 6.

Reference: See Table 6, but pp. 186–187. Permission of Academic Press, Inc., New York, N.Y.

Volume Two

SECTION II

II.II Selected Methods of Sample Preparation Including Derivatizations

Section II.II

ALPHABETICAL INDEX SELECTED METHODS OF SAMPLE PREPARATION INCLUDING DERIVATIZATIONS

Section II.II

SELECTED METHODS OF SAMPLE PREPARATION INCLUDING DERIVATIZATIONS

The procedures in this Section for extraction, hydrolysis, cleanup and derivatization of samples prior to chromatography were selected by the Editors, in many cases on the advice of members of the Advisory Board, from research journals and expert treatises on chromatography. Some procedures were contributed directly by members of the Board. The Editors have attempted to select procedures which appear to be reliable and most suitable for laboratory work with a large variety of compound types.

Various formats have been used in preparing this section. In many instances exact descriptions in detail are provided, while in others only references to recommended procedures or review-like compilations of procedures are given. It is hoped that the methods can, in many cases, be used directly by researchers for the preparation of samples for chromatography. The methods should at least serve as a guide, illustrative of the kinds of steps which are required, for those workers designing their own procedures for compounds or sample types not included.

It is planned that this Section will be revised, updated and expanded in future editions of the Handbook with the help of the Board and other experts who wish to offer suggestions or contribute procedures.

At the end of each procedure a specific reference is cited, or where a number is given, the literature citation will be found at the end of this section.

The following sections are arranged according to chemical classes of compounds. Numbers refer to specific methods or procedures.

ALCOHOLS

See Numbers 1–5, 58

1. Preparation of Alcohol Xanthates

Dissolve 0.10 mg KOH in 0.10 ml of the sample and add 0.15 ml of CS_2. Dissolve the precipitate in 5 drops of acetone and use the solution for chromatography.

Reference: Ruzicka, B., *Chem. Anal.* (*Warsaw*), **10,** 1165 (1965).

2. Preparation of Alkyl 2,4-Dinitrobenzyl Ethers

Introduce into a micro test tube 0.1 g of 2,4-dinitrobenzyl bromide and 0.1 ml of lower alcohol. With alcohols above C_5, also add a few drops of benzene. Seal the tube and heat on a water bath for two hours (up to C_4) or 4 hours (C_4 to C_8). For alcohols above C_8, heat for 4 hours in an oil bath at 160 °C. After cooling, the tubes are opened and the reaction mixture diluted with benzene and applied directly to the chromatogram.

Reference: Churacek, J., Komarek, K., Vanasek, V., and M. Jurecek, *Collect. Czech. Chem. Commun.*, **33,** 3876 (1968).

3. Preparation of 3,5-Dinitrobenzoates (*Gasparič and Borecký*)

(a) Pyridine method: The alcohol (50–100 mg) is dissolved in benzene (1 ml) and 3,5-dinitrobenzoyl chloride (0.5 g) dissolved in benzene (3 ml), and pyridine (1 ml) is added to the solution which is then heated for 30 min on a boiling water bath. After cooling, the mixture is extracted twice with 50% KOH (5 ml); water (50 ml) is added after each extraction to facilitate the separation of phases. The benzene solution is extracted twice with water (5 ml), twice with HCl (1 : 1; 5 ml) and finally with water or saturated sodium sulfate solution until a neutral reaction is obtained. The benzene layer is dried with anhydrous sodium sulfate and applied to paper.

(b) Preparation of dinitrobenzoates and dinitrobenzamides in aqueous solution: 3,5-dinitrobenzoyl chloride (0.5 g) in benzene (30 ml) is added to the aqueous solution (approximately 10 ml) containing about 1.5 mmole of the alcohol or amine hydrochloride. K_2CO_3 (10 g) is then added to the solution which is cooled and agitated. The mixture is allowed to stand for 20 min (secondary alcohols and amines overnight) at laboratory temperature and the separated benzene layer is extracted with KOH, HCl and water as above. After drying with anhydrous sodium sulfate, the solvent is distilled off, the residue dissolved in the required quantity of benzene and applied for chromatography.

Reference 5, pp. 832–833.

4. Preparation of Allyl-Urethanes and their Mercuric Adducts (*Kaufmann and Kessen*)

The alcohol (2 g) is converted to the corresponding urethane by refluxing for 2 hr with a twofold molar quantity of allyl isocyanate as a 10% solution in benzene. The solvent and excess reagent are then evaporated under reduced pressure on a water bath and the residue is dissolved in benzene or toluene to give a 1% solution which is applied to paper.

Mercuric adducts are prepared by refluxing 0.1 g of the allyl urethane with saturated methanolic mercuric acetate solution (10 ml) for 10 min. The solvent is then evaporated under reduced pressure and the residue dissolved in dry benzene (10 ml) with mild heating, the excess mercuric acetate remaining undissolved. An approximate 1% solution of the allyl urethane mercuric adduct is obtained after filtering the mixture.

Reference 5, pp. 832–833.

5. Derivatives of Alcohols Suitable for GC

(*a*) *TMS ethers—see* section on General Methods.

(*b*) *Acetate derivatives.* Reflux alcohols with acetic anhydride, hydrolyze excess reagent, isolate acetylated products from water. [Esposito, G. G. and M. H. Swann, *Anal. Chem.*, **33**, 1854 (1964); Link, W. E., Hickman, H. M., and R. A. Morrissette, *J. Amer. Oil Chem. Soc.*, **37**, 447 (1960).]

(*c*) *Nitrate esters and olefins.* Nitrate esters were prepared from a mixture of sodium nitrite and tartaric acid, and olefins were formed after an alcohol solution had been dehydrated over a support containing H_3PO_4. In both cases, the reactions occurred in a reaction tube that was part of the injection part of the GC instrument. [von Drawert, F., Felgenhauer, R., and G. Kupfer, *Angew. Chem.*, **72**, 555 (1960).]

(*d*) *Hydrocarbons.* C_{12}–C_{33} monohydric alcohols and glycols are heated with iodine and red phosphorus to form iodides. The latter are reduced to the corresponding hydrocarbons with $LiAlH_4$ in ether. [Downing, D. T., Kranz, Z. H., and K. E. Murray, *Aust. J. Chem.*, **13**, 80 (1960).]

(*e*) 3,5-*Dinitrobenzoates.* Aqueous alcohol solutions are shaken with 3,5-dinitrobenzoyl chloride in benzene and the benzene phase is injected for GC. [Galetto, W. G., Kepner, R. E., and A. D. Webb, *Anal. Chem.*, **38**, 34 (1966).]

Reference: The above material is abstracted from Reference 9, pp. 89–92.

ALKALOIDS

See Numbers 6–8, plus Section on drugs

6. Extraction of Alkaloids

Alkaloids are extracted from vegetable matter with aqueous acids; the extract is made alkaline, and the alkaloids are reextracted with ether or chloroform. Alternatively, dried and ground material is made alkaline and extracted directly with chloroform. Extractions of stable alkaloids can be made with hot ethanol in a Soxhlet extractor. Heat labile alkaloids (e.g., pyrrolizidine alkaloids) are extracted in an apparatus which enables continuous flow of room temperature solvent through the plant-material, absorption of dissolved alkaloids from the solvent onto a cation-exchange resin bed, and washing and recirculation of used solvent. The bases are eluted from the column with 0.8*N* NH_3 [*see* Mattocks, A. R., *J. Chem. Soc.*, C, p. 329 (1967).]

For extraction from animal material, the procedure is similar. For example, *Datura* alkaloids are extracted for forensic toxicological examination by saturating a slurry of 50 g tissue and 100 ml 5% acetic acid with solid $(NH_4)_2SO_4$. The mixture is kept at 100 °C for 30 minutes and then filtered. The residue is washed three times with 50 ml 5% acetic acid, and the combined filtrates are extracted with diethyl ether. The ether phase is extracted with HCl, and this solution is adjusted to pH 7.5 with NH_3, saturated with $(NH_4)_2SO_4$, and extracted with ether–chloroform (3 : 1 v/v). This extract is evaporated to dryness, dissolved in chloroform, and spotted for chromatography.

Extraction of alkaloids from edible oils is achieved by adding 25 ml hexane, 20 ml ethanol, and 5 ml HCl to about 50 ml oil and warming for 10 minutes. The ethanol layer is separated, washed with three 10 ml portions of hexane, made alkaline with 10% aqueous NH_3, and extracted three times with chloroform. The combined chloroform extracts are washed with water, and the alkaloids are extracted three times with 20 ml 33% acetic acid. This extract is made alkaline, the alkaloids are reextracted into chloroform, and the chloroform is removed by evaporation. The residue is dissolved in 2 ml chloroform, and a portion containing 50–100 μg alkaloids is applied to the paper for chromatography.

Reference 1, pp. 460–461.

7. Isolation of Alkaloids from Urine

Ten ml of urine is adjusted to pH 9–10 with dilute Na_2CO_3. The alkaloids are extracted with 10 ml of isoamyl- or amyl acetate, and the sample is centrifuged. Several drops of 15% formic acid are added to the organic phase and the sample is again centrifuged. The alkaloids are thereby converted to the formate derivatives, which are water soluble. Aliquots of the water phase are applied on paper.

Reference 4, pp. 356–357.

8. Extraction of Quinidine and Quinidine Metabolites from Biological Fluids and Tissues

The sample is mixed with 0.1*M* NaOH and extracted with benzene-amyl alcohol (2:1). The organic layer is separated by centrifuging and treated with 0.05*M* H_2SO_4. The aqueous layer, made alkaline with 1*M* NaOH, is extracted with benzene-amyl alcohol (2:1). The organic layer is concentrated under nitrogen prior to TLC.

Reference: Härtel, G. and A. Korhonen, *J. Chromatogr.*, **37**, 70 (1968), with permission of copyright owners, Elsevier Publishing Company, Amsterdam, The Netherlands.

AMINES

See Numbers 9–12, 58

9. Formation of Amine, Amino Acid and Phenol Dansyl Derivatives on the Nanogram Scale for PC and TLC

To one volume of amine solution (in water or 0.2N $HClO_4$) containing 10–0.01 nmoles amine, 3 volumes of a solution of DANS Cl (DANS Cl = dansyl chloride = 1-dimethylamino-naphthalene-5-sulfonyl chloride) in acetone is added. The amount of DANS-Cl should be present in a several-fold excess and its concentration should not be below 5 mM in the final reaction mixture. Which amount of DANS-Cl is achieved depends therefore on the concentration of the substances that can react with dansyl chloride and the volume of their solution. Solutions of 5–45 mg DANS-Cl per ml acetone have been used in practical labeling experiments. If amines or amino acids are to be dansylated, the reaction mixture is saturated with sodium bicarbonate; if phenols or similar compounds are to be reacted, the reaction mixture is saturated with sodium carbonate to increase the pH. Solid sodium bicarbonate and sodium carbonate may be substituted by 0.5–1M solutions of $KHCO_3$ or Na_2CO_3, or even by other strong bases—triethylamine, for example. Most easily handled are solutions with 1–5 nmoles amine in 0.1–0.5 ml. In this case the reaction is carried out in 10-ml centrifuge tubes with ground glass stoppers. Though in principle the reaction volume is not limited, it is more convenient to work with amine solution volumes not exceeding 1 ml. Salts or buffer components without reacting groups do not disturb the reaction. Oxidizing or strong reducing agents have to be excluded from the reaction mixture. In most cases larger volumes of the amine solutions can easily be brought to a small volume without losses by evaporation in a desiccator or in a stream of air or nitrogen.

The reactions are complete within a few minutes under favorable conditions. To ensure quantitative dansylation even of substances with low reaction velocities, the reaction mixtures are stored at room temperature for 3 to 4 hours or overnight in a dark place. After this time the excess of dansyl chloride is hydrolyzed to DANS-OH. In special cases of quantitative analysis, the dansyl chloride excess is chosen very high, so that even after a 16-hour storing of the reaction mixture a DANS-Cl excess may be present. In this case a solution of proline (or glutamic acid) in water is added to the reaction mixture to eliminate the DANS-Cl. Dansyl chloride would cause blue-green fluorescing streaks on the chromatograms, since it is easily hydrolyzed on the silica gel layers.

Most of the DANS-derivatives of amines are soluble in benzene or ethyl acetate, and can be extracted from the alkaline reaction mixtures by shaking with these or similar solvents and separating the solvent phases by centrifugation. The extraction of the DANS-amides with 5 ml benzene is practically quantitative from a reaction mixture composed of 0.5 ml amine solution, 1.5 ml dansyl chloride solution in acetone and saturated with sodium carbonate. Normally 20-μl aliquots of the benzene or ethyl acetate extract are applied to the chromatograms for identification of the DANS-amides, if the amounts of amines in the reaction mixture were in the range 1–5 nmoles. If smaller amounts of amine have to be detected, the organic phase can be evaporated to dryness, redissolved in a small solvent volume and quantitatively spotted to the thin-layer plates. But in this case it is preferable to dansylate as many concentrated amine solutions as possible, since with the increased reaction volumes more reagents are applied, so that the absolute amount of impurities increases in the reaction mixture. As small as 50-μl amine solution samples can very easily be processed in small tubes (4 × 50 mm). Working with small sample volumes is essential for DANS-derivatives, which cannot be extracted by nonpolar organic solvents, for example, in the case of DANS-choline, amino sugars, and similar compounds. After completion of the dansylation reaction in these cases, a five to tenfold volume of acetone is added to the samples. The salt-saturated water phase is separated by centrifugation and aliquots or the total acetone phase is applied to the thin-layer plates. Though the DANS-OH which is formed during the reaction by hydrolysis of DANS-Cl should be enriched in the water phase, a considerable amount is extracted by acetone and has to be separated later on by chromatography; this can cause a serious problem. With small reaction volumes, the DANS-OH formation is reduced.

Though some DANS-amino acid derivatives are extracted together with the amine derivatives from the alkaline reaction mixture, even with benzene, and considerably higher amounts with ethyl acetate, the DANS-amino acid derivatives normally do not disturb the chromatographic separation of the DANS-amides. If it is desired to extract the DANS-amino acid derivatives together with the amine derivatives, the reaction mixture should be brought to pH 3 with NaH_2PO_4 and extracted with ethyl acetate. DANS-Glutamic acid, DANS-aspartic acid, DANS-cysteic acid, DANS-taurine and the monoDANS-derivatives of the basic amino acids are not extracted under these conditions. They can be isolated by acetone extraction.

Reference 10, pp. 105–106.

10. Derivative Formation for Determination of Basic (Amine) Drugs in Blood

The formation of suitable derivatives for the electron capture GC analysis of basic drugs in blood has been studied by many workers. Derivatives studied include *trichloroacetamide* [Noonan, J. S., Murdick, P. W., and R. S. Ray, *J. Pharmacol. Exptl. Therap.*, **168**, 205 (1969)], *trifluoroacetamide* [Kawai, S. and Z. Tamura, *Chem. Pharm. Bull.*, **16**, 1091 (1968)], *pentafluoropropionamide* [Anggard, E. and G. Sedvall, *Anal. Chem.*, **41**, 1250 (1969)], *heptafluorobutyramide* [Vessman, J., Moss, A. M., Horning, M. G., and E. C. Horning, *Anal. Letters*, **2**, 81 (1969)], and *2,4-dinitrophenyl* [Walle, T., *Acta Pharm. Suecica*, **5**, 367 (1968)]. The most promising, however, appears to be formation of *pentafluorobenzoyl derivatives* using pentafluorobenzoyl chloride [Wilkinson, G. R., *Anal. Letters*, **3**, 289 (1970)] or *pentafluorobenzoylimidazole* [Pierce Previews, Pierce Chemical Co., Sept. 1971, p. 2] as the reagent.

The procedure of Wilkinson is as follows:

Preparation of Derivatives

Macro-procedure. Molar excess of the appropriate anhydride[1] is added dropwise with stirring to 1 g of β-phenylethylamine.[2] After the reaction has ceased, 20 ml distilled water is added, the solution neutralized with 10% NaOH

[1] Trifluoroacetic anhydride, pentafluoropropionic anhydride, heptafluorobutyric anhydride, perfluorooctanoic anhydride or pentafluorobenzoyl chloride were used.

[2] Used as model compound since the β-phenylamine skeleton is a common feature of a number of biologically interesting amines.

solution and refrigerated overnight. The precipitated product is recrystallized from ethanol-water. For chromatography, the appropriate molar solutions and dilutions are prepared with 95% ethanol.

Micro-procedure. Exactly 10^{-3} moles of base and triethylamine are weighed into a 100 ml volumetric flask and dissolved in 20 ml ethyl acetate. Approximately 1.5×10^{-3} moles of pentafluorobenzoyl chloride per theoretically replaceable hydrogen is then added dropwise with shaking. The mixture is allowed to stand for 2 hr and then evaporated to dryness under vacuum at 50 °C. The dry residue is dissolved in 95% ethanol and the solution made to volume. Appropriate dilutions are made with 95% ethanol through the concentration range 10^{-9} to 10^{-13} mole/μl before GC. A 5 ft column of 3% OV-17 at 125 °C (190 °C for pentafluorobenzamides) is used.

Reference: Guilbault, *Anal. Letters*, Volume 3, No. 6, "The GLC Separation of Amphetamine and Ephedrines as Pentafluorobenzamide Derivatives and their Determination by Electron Capture Detection," by Wilkinson, pp. 289–298. Permission of Marcel Dekker, Inc., New York, N.Y.

11. Preparation of Dinitrophenylamine Derivatives

About 1.0 g amine (C_1–C_4 primary or secondary) is dissolved in 50 ml borate buffer solution (2.5% aqueous $Na_2B_4O_7 \cdot 10\ H_2O$). Dinitrofluorobenzene (2 ml in 25 ml *p*-dioxane) is added and heated on a steam bath for 1 hour. Add 50 ml of 2*N* NaOH and heat another hour to hydrolyze excess reagent. Cool, filter the solid, wash with 0.1*N* Na_2CO_3 and recrystallize from ethanol-water. Lower melting derivatives do not solidify in the reaction mixture. These mixtures are extracted with hexane, which was washed with 0.1*N* Na_2CO_3, dried with anhydrous Na_2SO_4, and evaporated to dryness on a rotary vacuum evaporator. The residue is recrystallized from petroleum ether–cyclohexane. DNP-amines are gas chromatographed on a 6 ft 2% DEGS column at 190 °C.

Reference: Day, E. W., Jr., Golab, T., and J. R. Koons, *Anal. Chem.*, **38**, 1053 (1966).

12. Acetyl, Propionyl and Pentafluoropropionyl Derivatives of Tryptamine-Related Amines and Catecholamines for GC

(*a*) *Acetyl derivatives.* Place a 10 mg quantity of amine or amine hydrochloride in 0.3 ml acetonitrile, add 0.1 ml acetic anhydride and 0.1 ml pyridine and heat to reflux temperature. Evaporate excess reagents in a vacuum desiccator.

(*b*) *Propionyl derivatives.* Prepare as for acetyl derivatives by reacting the amine or amine hydrochloride with propionic anhydride in the presence of pyridine with acetonitrile as the solvent. Mixtures are allowed to stand overnight before GC.

(*c*) *Pentafluoropropionyl derivatives.* Prepare by the general procedure above. In this case direct injection gives erratic results and the derivatives must be isolated by adding $NaHCO_3$ solution to the reaction mixture, extracting the aqueous solution with ethyl acetate, and washing the ethyl acetate solution with $NaHCO_3$ solution and water. The organic solution is dried over anhydrous $MgSO_4$, evaporated and injected for GC.

References: Horning, E. C., Horning, M. G., Van den Heuvel, W. J. A., Knox, K. L., Holmstedt, B., and C. J. W. Brooks, *Anal. Chem.*, **36**, 1546 (1964); Brooks, C. J. W. and E. C. Horning, *Anal. Chem.*, **36**, 1540 (1964).

AMINO ACIDS, PEPTIDES, PROTEINS

See Numbers 9, 13–21, 27

13. Extraction of Phenolic Iodoamino Acids

The following procedure recovers iodothyroxines and iodotyrosines from plasma: Serum plus methanol (pH <6) are boiled and centrifuged. The precipitate is reextracted with methanol and the combined extracts are evaporated to dryness. The dry residue is redissolved in water. Lipids are eliminated through a chloroform shaking, pH is adjusted below 6, and the iodoamino acids are quantitatively transferred to a small amount of butanol. The butanol extract is washed to remove salts, concentrated, and used for PC or TLC.

Reference: Zappi, E., in "Progress in Thin Layer Chromatography and Related Methods", Volume I, Ann Arbor—Humphrey Science Publishers, Inc., 1970, pp. 163–164.

14. Preparation of Urine Samples for TLC

The amino acids of native urine can be obtained as a pure fraction by treating the sample on a small cation-exchange column, using a slight variation of a method by Harris *et al.* A 5-ml aliquot of urine is centrifuged for 10 minutes at 2000 rpm. Then 2.0 ml of the supernatant is acidified to a pH of 3–4 with about 2 drops of glacial acetic acid and allowed to stand for 10 minutes to decompose any carbonates present. Meanwhile, a filter paper disc (Whatman No. 1) cut out with a paper hole-punch to measure 6 mm in diameter is inserted across the bottom of a miniature chromatography column (0.6×15 cm). It is then filled with 300 mg of moist cation-exchange resin (Dowex 50×8, 100–200 mesh) in the H^+ form. The acidified urine is gently poured over the column. The amino acids (with the exception of taurine) are retained by the resin along with the other cations whereas the anions, proteins, and neutral substances pass through the column. The sample becomes more acidic as the cations are exchanged against the H^+ ion of the resin. Care must be taken against overacidification of the sample since this leads to ionization and adsorption of urea. If, on the other hand, the effluent has not reached a pH of at least 2, it should be further acidified and recirculated over the column. The resin is then washed, first with 2 ml of 0.5*N* acetic acid and then with 2 ml of water. The effluent plus washings are discarded. Next the column is eluted with 2 ml of 2*N* triethylamine in 20% acetone, which removes all the amino acids and the ammonia while it liberates only traces of metallic cations. The recovery of the amino acids is essentially quantitative.

The eluate, which is collected on a watch glass, is evaporated overnight *in vacuo* over H_2SO_4. It is redissolved next day with exactly 0.2 ml of distilled water, yielding a tenfold concentration of the amino acids (minus taurine) originally present in the urine specimen. After removal of 5 μl of the redissolved eluate for determining the α-amino nitrogen, cysteine and methionine are oxidized according to Hirs by adding a few drops of performic acid to the sample and evaporating it over NAOH *in vacuo*. The following day the oxidized sample is redissolved in enough 0.1*N* HCl to yield a concentration of 50 μmole of amino acid per ml, based on α-amino nitrogen determination. The solvent may contain taurine as internal standard, 5 μmole taurine per ml. From this solution, 13 μl are spotted for TLC.

References: Reference 10, Vol. 2, chapter by Detterbeck, F. J. and H. A. Lillevik, pp. 237–238; Harris, C. K., Tigane, E., and G. S. Hanes, *Can. J. Biochem. Physiol.*, **39**, 439 (1968); Hirs, C. H. W., *Methods of Enzymology*, **11**, 197 (1967).

15. Amino Acids in Blood and Urine—Preparation of Dinitrophenyl Derivatives

Many workers claim satisfactory results in TLC by applying urine directly, as long as not more than 10 μl samples are applied. If larger quantities are to be studied the urine may require desalting. Electrolytic desalting leads to large losses of amino acids. Ion-exchange resins have been used, in particular, Amberlite IR 120 (H^+). The urine is first deproteinized using an ultrafilter; the amino acids are taken up by the resin and are eluted with concentrated (1*M* or more) ammonium hydroxide. The eluate is evaporated, the amino acids are redissolved, and the solution is spotted for chromatography.

Another approach consists of evaporating the urine, then extracting the amino acids in 1–2 ml 0.5% HCl in 95% alcohol. This extract is evaporated and the residue is dissolved in a small volume of 0.5% HCl for spotting.

To study serum, the sample must first be deproteinized. This is generally accomplished by adding either ethanol or acetone: 0.5 ml serum plus 1.5 ml ethanol, 0.4 ml serum plus 1.6 ml ethanol, 1 ml serum plus 9 ml ethanol/acetone (7 : 3), or 1 volume acetone. The now insoluble protein is centrifuged down, and the supernate is spotted for chromatography.

It is possible to avoid the desalting problem entirely in either blood or urine by converting the amino acids to dinitrophenyl derivatives before extraction. In acid solutions the derivatives are sufficiently nonpolar to extract into nonpolar solvents. With urine the procedure is as follows:

The urine (25 ml) is adjusted to phenolphthalein pink with 5*N* NaOH, is allowed to stand 5 minutes, and is centrifuged. To 20 ml of supernate (use brown bottle) and 5 ml buffer (8.4 g $NaHCO_3$ + 2.5 ml 1*N* NaOH to 100 ml with water) add 2 ml fresh 20% dinitrofluorobenzene (DNFB) in ethanol. The mixture is shaken one hour at 40 °C, cooled to 5 °C for 15 minutes, and extracted with 3 × 10 ml diethyl ether. The ether, which contains the unreacted DNFB, is discarded. The aqueous phase is acidified to congo blue with 6*N* HCl and is evaporated to dryness. The DNP derivatives are redissolved in a small amount of ethyl acetate for chromatography.

To convert serum amino acids to DNP derivatives, the serum is deproteinized, adjusted to phenolphthalein pink with 5*N* NaOH, and the procedure above is followed exactly as written.

Reference 6, pp. 80–81.

16. Hydrolysis of Peptides for Amino Acid Analysis by TLC

(a) Acid Hydrolysis

Before the HCl hydrolysis of a protein or peptide, it is necessary to remove salts and carbohydrates since serine, threonine, cystine, and tyrosine are otherwise decomposed for the most part. On the one hand, methionine is converted into methionine sulfoxide and other ninhydrin-positive compounds, and on the other hand methionine, homocysteic acid, and homocystine form from methionine sulfoxide. Tyrosine is chlorinated and even brominated; however, these changes can be reduced if fresh distilled hydrochloric acid is used and small quantities of easily oxidized substances (e.g., thioglycolic acid) are added to the reaction mixture. Tryptophan is completely decomposed under the conditions of acid hydrolysis and, consequently, is chromatographed after alkaline hydrolysis. Tryptophan can also be determined in the bound form.

The hydrolysis is conducted in carefully cleaned vacuum tubes in the absence of air. The substance is treated with a 200–500-fold excess of 6 *N* HCl (distilled two or three times) and is frozen in the vacuum tube. After displacement of the supernatant air by pure nitrogen, the tube is evacuated to about 1 torr and the ampule is fused (lower part cooled with dry ice). Hydrolysis takes place at 110 ± 1 °C for 18–72 hr. in a thermostat.

The removal of hydrochloric acid by allowing the product to stand over NaOH in an evacuated desiccator results in losses of serine and threonine and, therefore, cannot be recommended. It is preferable to remove the HCl in a rotary evaporator.

Even under these improved working conditions, some serine and threonine losses are unavoidable. The original content of hydroxyamino acids can be determined approximately in quantitative determinations by comparing 24- and 72-hr. hydrolysates. Leucine, isoleucine and valine require about 72 hr. of hydrolysis if they are combined in peptide linkage. Cystine is decomposed more or less and should, therefore, be determined after performic acid oxidation in the form of cysteic acid. In this reaction, methionine is converted into methionine sulfone, while histidine and threonine are partially decomposed. Finally, it should be mentioned that pyrrolidone carboxylic acid is formed from glutamic acid in an equilibrium reaction (ratio of 98 : 2).

Milder conditions must be used for the oxidative cleavage of disulfide bridges. The method of Hirs is suited for this purpose. Tryptophan is partially decomposed, cystine converts into cysteic acid, and methionine converts into methionine sulfone. Compounds containing tryptophan after performic acid oxidation can, therefore, be used only to a limited extent for further sequential analysis.

(b) Alkaline Hydrolysis

As mentioned above, tryptophan decomposes during the HCl hydrolysis. If this compound is to be detected in chromatography, the cleavage must be carried out with bases. If α-aminobutyric acid is to be reliably detected, an alkaline hydrolysis should also be used, since α-aminobutyric acid is formed from threonine in the course of an acid hydrolysis according to Heyns and Walter and according to Brieskorn and Glasz. During hydrolysis with $Ba(OH)_2$, cystine, cysteine, serine, and threonine are decomposed for the most part.

Five to ten mg of sample with 1 ml water + 65 mg $Ba(OH)_2 \cdot 8H_2O$ in a fused tube are heated to 125–130 °C for 24 hr. The cooled reaction mixture is adjusted to pH = 6 with $2N$ H_2SO_4 and is boiled and centrifuged. The barium sulfate is washed with a small amount of distilled water. The solution and wash water are combined, evaporated to dryness, and the residue is dissolved in 0.5–1 ml water and $0.1N$ HCl respectively.

(c) Hydrolysis with Ion Exchangers

It has been known for some time that the peptide bond can be quantitatively cleaved by means of strong acid cationic exchangers. Hydrolysis experiments with Dowex 50(H) have shown that aspartic acid, serine, and threonine are liberated very rapidly and valine and isoleucine, on the other hand, only slowly compared to HCl hydrolysis. Indoles are decomposed for the most part and glutamic acid is partly converted into pyrollidone carboxylic acid. The cleavage of cystine and cysteic acid peptides is incomplete. Most disadvantages are extensively alleviated if the reaction is carried out in 70–90% ethanol in the absence of air; under these conditions, the formation of humine is also completely prevented.

According to Pöhm, 0.05–2 g peptide with 1 g Amberlite IR-112 (H) per milliequivalent amide nitrogen in 3–10 ml 80% ethanol are fused into an ampule under nitrogen and heated to 90–95 °C for 6–10 hr. After cooling, the amino acids are eluted from the resin with a 10% ammonia solution. The method was found useful for the cleavage of ergot alkaloids with a peptide structure and for the hydrolysis of di- and tripeptides. The expected amino acids, such as tryptophan and phenylalanine, could be found quantitatively even in the presence of carbohydrates and fats.

Reference 12, pp. 114–116; Hirs, C. H. W., *J. Biol. Chem.*, **219**, 611 (1956); Heyns, K. and W. Walter, *Naturwissenschaften*, **39**, 507 (1952); Brieskorn, C. H. and J. Glasz, *Naturwissenschaften*, **51**, 216 (1964); Pohm, M., *Naturwissenschaften*, **48**, 551 (1961).

17. Dinitrophenylation of Amino Acids

1. Amino Acids

(*a*) *Preparation of dinitrophenyl-amino acids.* According to Levy and Chung, the reaction is carried out in aqueous solution. Amino acid (10 mmoles) and Na_2CO_3 (2 g anhydrous) are dissolved in 40 ml water at 40 °C. This solution is treated with 10 mmoles DNFB (2,4-dinitrofluorobenzene) in the form of a 10% acetone solution. Amino acids with two reactive groups require the double quantity of DNFB, and histidine requires the 2½-fold amount. The suspension is shaken vigorously for 30–90 min. at 40 °C in the absence of light, while the DNFB-droplets slowly disappear. After the reaction has been completed, the product is extracted with ether in order to remove any remaining DNFB. The solution is carefully acidified with about 3 ml concentrated hydrochloric acid; the precipitated DNP-amino acids are filtered or may be extracted with ether.

According to Rao and Sober, the conversion takes place in ethanol solution. Amino acid and DNFB (see above) are shaken in 50% ethanol in the presence of excess sodium bicarbonate for 2–5 hr. (for reaction conditions, (see above) After the ethanol has been removed at room temperature, the product is extracted 3 times with ether. The aqueous solution is acidified with $6N$ HCl, and the precipitated DNP-amino acid is washed repeatedly with small quantities of ice-cooled water.

For the purification (both methods), the precipitated DNP-amino acids are dissolved in ether; usually they already crystallize during concentration of the ether solution. Recrystallization is successful by solution in benzene to which a small amount of ethanol is added and by adding petroleum ether to the hot solution. Highly polar DNP-amino acids are recrystallized from aqueous methanol; ether-insoluble derivatives are reprecipitated by solution in dilute hydrochloric acid and neutralizing (e.g. pyridine).

(*b*) *Dinitrophenylation of an amino acid mixture.* The conversion of an amino acid mixture (e.g. protein hydrolysate) with DNFB can be carried out in aqueous or in ethanol solution.

Dinitrophenylation in aqueous medium: According to Wallenfels, the dry hydrolysis residue of 2–5 mg of air-dried protein, oxidized with performic acid is dissolved in 2 ml CO_2-free water at room temperature with vigorous stirring. An aliquot (1.2 ml) is pipetted into a small reaction vessel with a magnetic stirrer, it is diluted with 1.8 ml CO_2-free water, 0.1 ml $3.1N$ KCl is added, and the solution is heated to 40 ± 0.1 °C. The pH is now adjusted to 8.9 by the addition of $0.2N$ NaOH with vigorous stirring. Approximately 0.1 ml DNFB is added in a small excess in the absence of light, and the pH is held at 8.9 for 100 min. by means of an autotitrator. The reaction kinetics can be followed by automatic recording of the alkali uptake. After the reaction is terminated, the excess DNFB is removed by extracting twice with 5 ml each of peroxide-free ether. If ether with a peroxide content is used, DNP-methionine sulfone forms from DNP-methionine. The reaction mixture is acidified (0.5 ml of a solution of 1 part HCl, $D_4^{20} = 1.19$ + 1 part water) and the ether-soluble DNP-amino acids are extracted by treating five times with 4 ml peroxide-free ether. The extracts are combined and brought to 25 ml with ether. For the quantitative chromatography, 1 ml is removed, is concentrated somewhat, and is quantitatively applied on the layer. During the reaction, 2,4-dinitrophenol (DNP-OH) forms from DNFB. If this compound is present in larger quantities, it may mask a few of the DNP-amino acids under certain conditions. In such cases, it is advisable to remove the dinitrophenol. The aqueous phase contains α-mono-DNP arginine, α-mono-DNP-histine, DNP-cysteic acid, and a part of di-DNP-histidine. After removal of dissolved ether, the aqueous phase is filled to 10 ml with CO_2-free water. For the chromatography, 0.5 ml is removed, is evaporated to dryness in vacuum, is taken up in a minimum amount of acetone (possibly acetone-$6N$ HCl 2 : 25), and is quantitatively applied on the layer. Biserte *et al.* prefer the following procedure. The sodium of the water-soluble DNP-amino acids is extracted repeatedly with *sec*-butanol-ethyl acetate (1 : 1), the extracts are combined, evaporated to dryness, and taken up in acetone as described above. The acetone solution contains the mentioned water-soluble DNP-amino acids.

Dinitrophenylation in alcohol solution: According to Lucas *et al.*, the dry hydrolysis residue of 2–5 mg protein that had been dried over P_2O_5 and possibly oxidized with performic acid is dissolved in 5 ml water. This solution is treated with 100 mg $NaHCO_3$ and a solution of 100 mg DNFB in 8 ml ethanol. The single-phase mixture obtained is allowed to stand for 3 hr. at room temperature in darkness. After termination of the reaction, the ethanol is evaporated in vacuum; the temperature should not exceed 40 °C. Now 50 mg $NaHCO_3$ are added and the product is extracted three times with ether. The aqueous phase is acidified with concentrated HCl to such an extent that the HCL-concentration amounts to about 1–2 *M*. Subsequently, it is extracted five times with ether; the extracts are combined, are evaporated to dryness in vacuum, and are dissolved in acetone or ethyl acetate. Under these conditions, di-DNP-histidine, DNP-arginine, and DNP-cysteic acid remain in the aqueous phase. These compounds are chromatographed directly or are extracted with *sec*-butanol-ethyl acetate (1 : 1).

Although histidine in alcohol solution is reported to furnish only di-DNP-histidine, it was found by Lucas *et al.* that a reaction of 16 hr. is necessary for a complete conversion. The authors recommend that two reactions be conducted simultaneously; one for the determination of all amino acids without histidine, and the other for the determination of histidine.

2. Peptides

(*a*) *Conversion with dinitrofluorobenzene.* Dinitrophenylation according to Sanger and Thompson; A solution of 0.2 μmole peptide in 0.1 % trimethylamine is treated with 10 μl DNFB dissolved in 0.2 ml ethanol. After 2 hr. in darkness, a few drops of water and trimethylamine solution are added, followed by extracting three times with fresh ether. The solution is evaporated in vacuum to dryness.

Dinitrophenylation according to Lockhart and Abraham: 50–150 μg peptide are dissolved in 0.1 ml 1.5 % (g/v) trimethylammonium carbonate solution (pH ~ 9.3), 0.2 ml of a 5 % alcohol solution of DNFB is added, and the mixture is allowed to stand in darkness for 2½ hr.; the ethanol is then evaporated in vacuum, the product is treated with 0.24 ml trimethylammonium carbonate solution and 1 ml ether, followed by mixing with a vibromixer, centrifuging in order to separate the phases, separation of the ether (discard) and evaporation of the aqueous solution in vacuum to dryness.

(*b*) *Total hydrolysis of a dinitrophenyl peptide.* The DNP-peptide is taken up in 0.1 ml 6*N* HCl and is heated for 9 hr. under nitrogen to 105 °C in a bomb tube (concerning the losses during hydrolysis, see below). The hydrolysate is diluted with 2 vols. water and extracted with ether (ether-soluble DNP-amino acids). The water-soluble DNP-amino acids are applied directly or are first extracted with *sec*-butanol-ethyl acetate, are taken up in acetone and chromatographed.

3. Polypeptides and Proteins

(*a*) *Conversion with dinitrofluorobenzene.* According to Levy and Li, 0.2 μmole substance is dissolved in 30 ml 0.05*N* aqueous KCl at 40 °C, the pH is adjusted to 8 (addition of 0.05*N* KOH by an autotitrater), about 0.1 ml DNFB is added, and the mixture is stirred vigorously in darkness, while the pH and temperature are maintained constant. The reaction is terminated when no further base is consumed. The solution is extracted three times with ether and then is acidified. The precipitated DNP-compounds are centrifuged, are washed with water, acetone and ether, and dried over P_2O_5.

(*b*) *Total hydrolysis of a dinitrophenyl protein.* For a qualitative end-group determination, the DNP-protein is hydrolyzed with the 100-fold quantity of double-distilled 5.7*N* hydrochloric acid at 105 °C for 16 hr. (in a bomb tube under nitrogen). Under these conditions, some DNP-amino acids, such as the DNP-derivatives of glycine, proline, tyrosine and cystine (the latter is best converted to cysteic acid), are decomposed for the most part. According to Fittkau *et al.*, DNP-glycine and DNP-proline are not significantly modified in control experiments. DNP-glycine, DNP-proline, and other acid-sensitive DNP-derivatives are decomposed to a considerably smaller degree if the hydrolysis is carried out with Dowex-50 (H) (Steven). If the end-groups are to be determined quantitatively, several hydrolyses should be carried out side by side (variation of the time, HCl concentration and reagent). The hydrolysate is diluted to such an extent that the HCl-concentration amounts to about 1 *N*. Extraction proceeds three times with peroxide-free ether and five times with ethyl acetate for the isolation of di-DNP-histidine. The extracts are washed with 0.1*N* HCl. The ether and ethyl acetate extracts are combined and the aqueous phase is combined with the wash water. *Ether-soluble DNP-amino acids:* Larger quantities of dinitrophenol may be unfavorable for the separation under certain conditions. DNP-OH can be removed by sublimation (where methionine, as well as cysteine, are partially lost) or by adsorption on aluminum oxide or on silica gel.

Silica gel (5 g, 100 mesh Mallinkrodt) is carefully mixed with 2.5 ml 0.067*M* Na_2HPO_4, suspended in chloroform, and filled into a 30 × 1 cm column. The ether-soluble DNP-compounds are most suitably charged on the column in chloroform. Elution is carried out first with chloroform, saturated with 0.067*M* Na_2HPO_4; dinitrophenol and dinitranaline are only partly ionized in this alkaline medium and are therefore eluted. On the other hand, the ionized DNP-amino acids are retained on the column. They are eluted with chloroform containing 1 % glacial acetic acid. The eluate is finally concentrated and taken up in acetone or ethyl acetate.

Water-soluble DNP acids: The following compounds can be present in this fraction: DNP-arginine, DNP-cysteic acid, mono-DNP-derivatives of cysteine, cystine, histidine, lysine, ornithine, and tyrosine, as well as a small amount of di-DNP-histidine. These compounds can be directly identified by chromatography in spite of the presence of free amino acids (care is necessary in the ninhydrin reaction). The aqueous solution is evaporated several times to dryness with a repeated addition of water and is taken up in 0.5*N* HCl, in glacial acetic acid or in acetone-glacial acetic acid (about 1 ml per 10 μ mole protein; load about 1 μl; care should be taken that the acid solvent is completely evaporated before chromatography). Otherwise, the water-soluble DNP amino acids can be extracted with *sec*-butanol-ethyl acetate (1 : 1). Another possibility is offered by a selective adsorption of the DNP-amino acids (except DNP-cysteic acid) on Hyflo-Super-Cel-Talc.

(*c*) *Partial hyrolysis of a dinitrophenyl protein.* The acid or enzymatic partial hydrolysis of a DNP-protein is of considerable practical importance in sequential analysis. In chromatograms or "fingerprints," the *N*-terminal fractions are recognized by their yellow color, while other than *N*-terminal fractions are colorless (exception: non-*N*-terminal lysine peptides contain ϵ-DNP groups and, consequently, are also yellow).

Peptides containing ϵ-DNP-lysine can easily be separated from the free peptides and amino acids. Fractionation of the α- and ϵ-DNP-peptides is often difficult, at least when extraction is used. For other data, see Keil.

Reference 12, pp. 127–131; Levy, A. L. and D. Chung, *J. Amer. Chem. Soc.*, **77**, 2899 (1955); Rao, K. A. and H. R. Sober, *J. Amer. Chem. Soc.*, **76**, 1328 (1954); Wallenfels, K. and A. Arens, *Biochem. Z.*, **332**, 217 (1960); Biserte, G., Hollemann, J. W., Holleman-Dehove, J., and P. Sautiere, *Chromatogr. Rev.*, **2**, 59 (1960); Lucas, F. J., Shaw, T. B., and S. G. Smith, *Anal. Biochem.*, **6**, 335 (1963); Sanger, F. and E. O. P. Thompson, *Biochem. J.*, **53**, 353 (1953); Lockhart, I. M. and E. P. Abraham, *Biochem. J.*, **58**, 633 (1954); Levy, A. L. and C. H. Li, *J. Biol. Chem.*, **213**, 487 (1955); Fittkau, S., Hansen, H., Marquardt, I., Diessner, H., and U. Kettmann, *Z. Physiol. Chem.*, **338**, 180 (1964); Steven, F. S., *Anal. Biochem.*, **4**, 316 (1962); Keil, B., *Collect. Czech. Chem. Commun.*, **23**, 740 (1958).

18. Preparation of *N*-(2,4-Dinitro-5-aminophenyl)-Amino Acids

Phenylalanine (0.8 g), $NaHCO_3$ (0.9 g), DNFA (2,4-dinitrofluoroaniline) (1.5 g), and ethanol (30 ml) are heated until a clear solution is obtained. The mixture is allowed to stand for 30 min. at room temperature, is filtered, and 20 ml water is added. The solution is concentrated in vacuum and acidified with dilute hydrochloric acid. DNAP-phenylalanine can be recrystallized from methanol.

19. Quantitative Conversion of an Amino Acid Mixture into PTH-Derivatives (*3-Phenyl-2-Thiohydantoins*)

Peptide or protein (0.5–1 mg) is fused into a quartz tube with 0.3 ml double-distilled hydrochloric acid of constant boiling point (5.7*N*) under nitrogen and is heated for 22 hr. at 110 °C for the purpose of hydrolysis; the cooled hydrolysate is repeatedly evaporated in vacuum to dryness with repeated water additions; the residue is treated with 250 μl buffer (2 ml 2*N* acetic acid + 1.2 ml triethylamine + distilled water to 25 ml + 25 ml acetone; pH = 10.1) and with 250 μl PITC (phenyl isothiocyanate) acetone solution (corresponding to 6 μl PITC); the carefully mixed sample is allowed to react in a well-closed tube for 2½ hr. in a water bath of 25 °C; the reaction mixture is freed from solvent for 15 min. with a water-jet pump and subsequently over P_2O_5 in a high vacuum. The residue (phenylthiocarbamyl-amino acids) is dissolved in 100 μl distilled water and 200 μl glacial acetic acid saturated with HCl, and the solution is held at 25 °C for 6 hr. The solvent and acid are removed in the manner described above. The residue contains the PTH-amino acids. A parallel experiment without amino acid addition is carried out for a chromatographic comparison. Cysteine and cystine must be oxidized with performic acid before the hydrolysis. For chromatography, the phenylthiohydantoins are dissolved in 90% acetic acid.

Reference 12, p. 151.

20. Methods for Identification of *N*-Terminal Amino Acids in Peptides and Proteins for Analysis of Protein Structure

An article by Rosmus and Deyl [*Chromatogr. Rev.* **13**, 163–302 (1971)] gives detailed instructions for cleavage and derivative formation, arranged according to the nature of the chemical reaction involved in the first step of the *N*-terminal amino acid determination. Although space does not permit inclusion of all these methods, the procedures available in the original reference are listed below, both to show what procedures can be found and to indicate the types of reactions used for this purpose.

1. Methods that specifically cleave the *N*-terminal amino acid without its modification
   - Enzymatic methods
     - Cleavage of the *N*-terminal amino acid with leucine aminopeptidase
   - Non-enzymatic methods
     - Hydrolysis of the *N*-terminal peptide bond with β-hydroxyaquotriethylenetetramine cobalt(III) ion
2. Methods transforming the *N*-terminal amino group to another functional group
   - Methods requiring total hydrolysis for releasing the modified *N*-terminal amino acid
     - Deamination of the *N*-terminal amino acid and its destruction
   - Methods that specifically release the *N*-terminal amino acid in a subsequent reaction
     - Removal of *N*-terminal amino acid after transamination
3. Alkylation and arylation methods
   - Methods requiring total hydrolysis for releasing the *N*-terminal amino acid derivative
     - Reaction with formaldehyde
     - Reaction with magnesium bromoacetate
     - Reaction with 2,4-dinitrofluorobenzene (deferred to a later paper)
     - Reaction with 2,4,6-trinitrobenzene sulfonic acid
     - Reaction with 2,4-dinitro-5-fluoroaniline and 2,4-dinitro-5-fluoroacetanilide
     - Reaction with nitro-2-methanesulfonyl-4-fluorobenzene
     - Reaction with 3,5-dinitro-2-chloropyridine and with 2-chloro-5-nitropyrimidine
     - Reaction with 2-fluoro-3-nitropyridine and 2-fluoro-5-nitropyridine
     - Reaction with 3-fluoro-4-nitropyridine *N*-oxide
     - Reaction with 3-(2-chloroethyl)-7-nitro-1,2,4-benzothiodiazine-1,1-dioxide
     - Reaction with 7-chloro-4-nitrobenzo-2-oxo-1,3-diazole

Methods that specifically release the *N*-terminal amino acid derivative in a subsequent reaction
Reaction with 4-methoxycarbonyl-2-nitrofluorobenzene and following cyclization to 7-methoxycarbonyl-3,4-dihydro-2-quinoxalone
Reaction with 2,4-dinitrofluorobenzene, reduction to diaminophenyl derivative and cyclization to 7-amino-2-hydroxyquinoxaline
Reaction with nitro-2-methanesulfonyl-4-fluorobenzene and cyclization to methanosulfonylalkylquinoxalones
Reaction with 3,5-dinitro-2-fluoroaniline or *tert*-butyl-3,5-dinitro-2-fluorocarbanilate and subsequent cyclization to alkyl dihydroquinoxalones
Reaction with 2-fluoropyridine *N*-oxide
Reaction with 3,5-dinitro-2-chloropyridine

4. Acylation methods
Methods requiring total hydrolysis for releasing the *N*-terminal amino acid derivative
Reaction with methyl chloroformate
Reaction with iodobenzene-*p*-sulfonyl chloride (pipsyl chloride)
Reaction with *p*-azobenzene sulfochloride
Reaction with 5-(dimethylamino)-1-naphthalenesulfonyl chloride (dansyl chloride)
Reaction with *N*-methyl-2-anilino-6-naphthalenesulfonyl chloride (mansyl chloride)
Reaction with 2-*p*-chlorosulfophenyl-3-phenylindone (sulfoindonyl chloride)
Methods that specifically release the *N*-terminal amino acid derivative in a subsequent reaction
Reaction with ethyl chloroformate and cyclization to alkyl-(dihydroxyimidazolyl)propionic acid
Reaction with methyl ethyl xanthate followed by cyclization to thiazolid-2,5-dione
Reaction with *N*-acetyldithiocarbamate methyl ester and the subsequent cyclization to 2-thiohydantoins
Reaction with cyanomethyl dithiobenzoate

5. Addition methods
Methods requiring total hydrolysis for releasing the *N*-terminal amino acid derivative
Reaction with acrylonitrile
Reaction with α-acetyl-β-ethoxy-*N*-ethoxycarbamyl acrylamide
Methods that specifically release the *N*-terminal amino acid derivative in a subsequent reaction
Reaction with carbon disulfide followed by cyclization to 2-thiothiazolid-5-one
Reaction with potassium cyanate and subsequent cyclization to hydantoins
Reaction with methyl isothiocyanate and cyclization to methylthiohydantoins
Reaction with phenyl isothiocyanate and cyclization to phenylthiohydantoin (deferred to a later paper)
Reaction with 1-naphthyl isothiocyanate, 2-nitrophenyl isothiocyanate and (4-phenylazo)phenyl isothiocyanate and cyclization to the respective thiohydantoins
Reaction with 4-dimethylamino-3,5-dinitrophenyl isothiocyanate and cyclization to 4-dimethylamino-3,5-dinitrophenylthiohydantoins
Reaction with fluorescein isothiocyanate and cyclization to fluoresceinthiohydantoin
Reaction with 4-dimethylamino-3,5-dinitrophenyl isocyanate and cyclization to the 4-dimethylamino-3,5-dinitrophenylhydantoin
Solid phase degradations of the *N*-terminal amino acid

21. Derivatives for the GC Analysis of Amino Acids and Peptides

The following derivatives have been employed.

(*a*) *Oxidation to aldehydes.* Amino acids have been converted into aldehydes by use of a special microreactor connected as part of a continuous flow system to the GC column. [Zlatkis, A, Oro, J. F., and A. P. Kimball, *Anal. Chem.*, **32**, 162 (1960).]

(*b*) *Decarboxylation.* Amino acids have been decarboxylated to amines prior to GC analysis using *p*-dimethylaminobenzaldehyde and diphenylmethane as solvents. [Bier, M. and P. Teitlebaum, *Ann. N.Y. Acad. Sci.*, **72**, 641 (1959).]

(*c*) *Oxidation to acids.* After oxidation to the corresponding aldehydes, oxidation with alkaline permanganate forms acids which are extracted into ether and injected for GC following destruction of excess $KMnO_4$ and acidification. [Baraud, M. J., *Bull. Soc. Chim. France*, 1960, 785.]

(*c*l) *α-Chloromethyl esters.* Amino acids are reacted with concentrated HCl plus concentrated HNO_3. The α-chloro acids are extracted into ether and esterified with diazomethane. [Melamed, N. and M. Renard, *J. Chromatogr.*, **4**, 339 (1960).]

(*c*2) *α-Hydroxymethyl esters.* Amino acids are treated with H_2SO_4 and $NaNO_2$ to convert them to α-hydroxy acids. The deaminated acids are extracted with ether, dried, and the solvent removed. [Wagner, J. and G. Rausch, *Z. Anal. Chem.*, **194**, 350 (1963).]

(*d*) *Free base and methyl ester salts.* L-Leucine and L-methionine are esterified with methanol and thionyl chloride. The ester hydrochloride is isolated after driving off SO_2 and HCl. [von Brenner, M. and W. Huber, *Helv. Chim. Acta.*, **36**, 1109 (1953).] Methyl ester hydrochlorides in anhydrous methanol are converted to the free base on dehydrated Dowex-1 ion-exchange resin in the hydroxide form; acetates are prepared similarly using anhydrous Dowex-1 resin in the acetate form. [Nicholls, C. H., Makisumi, S., and H. A. Saroff, *J. Chromatogr.*, **11**, 327 (1963).]

(*e*) *Methyl N-formyl esters.* Amino acids are converted to *N*-formyl esters by reaction with formic acid plus acetic anhydride. The mixture is esterified with diazomethane in methanol-ether. [Losse, G., Losse, A., and J. Stoeck, *Z. Naturforsch.* **17b**, 785 (1962).]

(*f*) *N-Acetyl n-propyl esters.* Amino acids are esterified with *n*-propanol and an acidic catalyst. Benzene is used to remove water azeotropically. The esters are acetylated with acetic anhydride and the derivatives extracted and diluted prior to GC. [Graff, J., Wein, J. P., and M. Winitz, *Fed. Proc.* **22**, 244 (1963).]

(*g*) *N-Acetyl n-butyl esters.* Amino acids are heated with *n*-butanol and HCl so that the butanol-water azeotrope distills. Excess solvent is evaporated and the mixture acetylated with acetic anhydride at room temperature. [Youngs, C. G., *Anal. Chem.*, **31**, 1019 (1959).]

(*h*) *N-Acetyl n-amyl esters.* Amino acids suspended in *n*-amyl alcohol are esterified by passage of anhydrous hydrogen bromide. Excess solvent is removed under vacuum, and the residual hydrobromide mixture is mixed with acetic anhydride and allowed to stand. The solution is evaporated under vacuum to a syrup, which is dissolved in *n*-amyl alcohol for injection. [Johnson, D. E., Scott, S. J., and A. Meister, *Anal. Chem.*, **33**, 669 (1961).]

(*i*) *N-Trifluoroacetyl methyl esters.* Two routes are available for forming *N*-TFA methyl esters: direct acetylation with trifluoroacetic anhydride in trifluoroacetic acid, followed by methylation with diazomethane in methanol, or esterification with dimethyl sulfite in methanol-HCl followed by trifluoroacetylation. [Cruickshank, P. A. and J. C. Sheehan, *Anal. Chem.*, **36**, 1191 (1964).] Alternatively, methylation can be carried out with methanol-HCl, followed by acetylation with trifluoroacetic acid alone or with ethyl acetate. [Makisumi, S. and H. A. Saroff, *J. Gas Chromatogr.*, **3**, 21 (1965).] *N*-TFA dipeptide methyl esters are prepared by reaction of an *N*-TFA amino acid thiophenyl ester with an amino acid to form a *N*-TFA dipeptide acid, which is then methylated with diazomethane. [Weygand, F., Kolb, B., and P. Kirchner, *Z. Anal. Chem.* **181**, 396 (1961).]

(*j*) *N-Trifluoroacetyl n-butyl esters.* The amino acid mixture (<60 mg) is placed in a 125 ml flat-bottomed flask, and 10 ml anhydrous methanol containing 1.20 ± 0.10 meq/ml anhydrous HCl is added. The flask is stoppered with a ground-glass stopper and the solution stirred for 30 min. at room temperature with a magnetic stirrer. The methanol is removed by vacuum distillation at 60 °C ± 1 °C. Ten ml of *n*-butanol containing 1.20 ± 0.10 meq/ml anhydrous HCl is added, the solution heated 3 hr. with magnetic stirring in an oil bath at 90° ± 3 °C, and the butanol removed by vacuum distillation at 60 °C. *n*-Butyl ester hydrochlorides are trifluoroacetylated by adding 5.00 ml methylene chloride and 0.50 ml trifluoroacetic anhydride and stirring 2 hr. at room temperature. The trifluoroacetic anhydride and solvent are removed by vacuum distillation at room temperature, and the derivatives dissolved in anhydrous $CHCl_3$ prior to GC. [Lamkin, W. M. and C. W. Gehrke, *Anal. Chem.*, **37**, 383 (1965); *see Biochem. Biophys. Res. Commum.* **19**, 328 (1965) and **22**, 329 (1966), and *Anal. Biochem.* **15**, 97 (1966) for further details on this method, and Mee, J. M. L. and C. C. Brooks, *J. Chromatogr.*, **62**, 138 (1971) for description of a simple apparatus for preparing these derivatives.]

(*k*) *N-Trifluoroacetyl n-amyl esters.* Amino acids (0.5–2.0 mg of each) are dissolved in 0.2 ml trifluoroacetic acid in a B 14 test tube. Two ml amyl alcohol is added and dry HCl gas bubbled through the mixture at 108° ± 2°C for 25 min. The alcohol is removed by rotary vacuum evaporation. The esters are taken up in minimum amounts of methyl alcohol and an aliquot transferred by means of a microliter syringe to a small Pyrex tube. The alcohol is removed by standing the tube in an oven at 70 °C. Trifluoroacetic anhydride (0.1 ml) is added, the tube sealed, and placed in an oven at 140 °C for 5 min. The tube is cracked open, the TFA anhydride removed on a rotary evaporator and the residue taken up in a known volume of dry methyl ethyl ketone prior to GC. [Darbre, A. and K. Blau, *J. Chromatogr.*, **29**, 49 (1967).]

(*l*) *2,4-Dinitrophenyl methyl esters.* Prepare amino acid dinitrophenyl derivatives and then esterify with diazomethane. [Pisano, J. J., Van den Heuvel, W. J. A., and E. C. Horning, *Biochem. Biophys. Res. Commum.*, **7**, 82 (1962).]

(*m*) *Phenylthiohydantoins.* Pisano *et al.* (*see* above) treat amino acids with phenylisothiocyanate in acetone, evaporate the mixture of thiocarbamates to dryness, treat with acetic and hydrochloric acids, and evaporate again to dryness. Cystine and cysteine are oxidized to cysteic acid before reaction with phenylisothiocyanate.

(*n*) *Nitriles.* Amino acids and powdered *N*-bromosuccinimide are mixed well, water is added, and reaction is allowed to proceed for 1 hr. Excess bromosuccinimide is destroyed with thiosulfate and the nitrile (with one less carbon atom than the acid) is extracted with *o*-xylene before injection. [Stevenson, G. W. and J. M. Luck, *J. Biol. Chem.*, **236**, 715 (1961).]

(*o*) *Reduction of peptides.* Ester groups in *N*-acetyl peptide ethyl esters are reduced to alcohols by overnight reaction with excess $LiAlD_4$ in tetrahydrofuran. The mixture is decomposed with water, the polyacetamido alcohols extracted with ether-methanol, dried, evaporated, and injected for GC. [Biemann, K. and W. Vetter, *Biochem. Biophys. Res. Commun.*, **3**, 578 (1960).]

Reference: The above material was compiled with the aid of Reference 9, pp. 78–79.

CARBOHYDRATES

See Numbers 22–32

22. Preparation of Sugar Samples from Plant Material (Scheffer *et al.*)

The freshly collected plant samples are minced using a blender. A few drops of 70% ethanol are added to prevent surface darkening, the samples are immediately frozen with dry ice and freeze-dried to a final humidity of 0.2%. The dried samples are stored in Erlenmeyer flasks or between two watch-glasses.

The preserved material (2–10 g, according to the sugar content) is introduced into extraction thimbles (25 × 100 mm) which are then inserted into a percolation tube; resistance wire is wound around the tube to allow the solution to be heated to 60–65 °C. A stream of nitrogen is supplied to the bottom of the thimble by means of a tube terminating in a sintered glass diffuser. After introducing 90% ethanol (about 25 ml), the supply of nitrogen is stopped and heating commenced; after 15 min, heating is stopped and the solution transferred to a flask; the whole extraction is repeated with 80%, 60%, 40%, and finally 20% ethanol (25 ml quantities). It is possible then to carry out an additional extraction with water and test qualitatively for the presence of the sugar in a portion of the extract: if this test is negative, the aqueous extract is not pooled with the other extracts.

The extracts are filtered through a quantitative filter paper with active charcoal, the filter thoroughly washed with water (qualitative test for the presence of sugars in the eluates) and the extract is concentrated under reduced pressure (to 2–3 ml) at 25–29 °C. The contents of the flask are transferred quantitatively to a 10 ml graduated flask and filled to the mark with 40% ethanol. This solution is then employed for chromatography.

Reference 5, pp. 834–835.

23. Preparation (Desalting) of Urine for Paper Chromatographic Analysis of Sugars

Vitek reports that the procedure below is useful with normal urine and for clinical urinary specimens if their quality is only slightly to moderately altered in respect to proteinuria and glucosuria. In working out the procedure, urine of a healthy 25-year-old female weighing 48 kg was collected over a period of four days without dietary restrictions. After each voiding, the urine was immediately frozen and at the end of the collection all portions were thawed and pooled. After filtration through a filter paper, the whole volume was divided into small aliquots that could be used within one working day. The frozen specimens were stored at −15 °C without preservatives.

Procedure. The frozen urine is thawed and warmed up to 30–40 °C until any eventual precipitate disappears. Deionization is carried out in portions corresponding to a 30- or 45-min. aliquot of daily diuresis, i.e., 31.5 or 47.2 ml. IR-120 (H^+) and IR-140 (acetate) resins (100 ml of each, 20–50 mesh wet) are placed in individual columns (28 mm d). The cation-exchange column is set up above the anion exchanger, and the two are joined with an air-tight joint so that the effluent from the upper tube enters directly into the lower. Add the urine carefully to the top bed (just submerged in water), allow to soak in, and add three or four 20–30 ml portions of water. These represent the initial portion of a total of 350 ml of water used for elution. The maximum flow rate is 2.0 ml/min. Discard the first 40 ml of effluent. The remaining part, including the water obtained by draining the columns after desalting, is evaporated on a rotary evaporator at 36–38 °C in a 1000 ml flask. The concentrate and flask washings are transferred through a small filter paper into a 50 ml centrifuge flask and lyophilized to dryness. Prior to chromatography, dissolve the residue in a suitable solvent.

Reference: Vitek, V. and K. Vitek, *J. Chromatogr.*, **60**, 381 (1971).

24. PC of Untreated Urine

Urinary sugars are separated as compact spots from 100 μl of untreated urine, spotted on Whatman 3MM paper. The necessary desalting is accomplished on the paper by a short ascending run in 90% pyridine. All common sugars have $R_F = 0.65$ and contaminants (urea, NaCl, amino acids) have R_F values below this. The section of paper containing the contaminants is cut off and the sugars separated by a run at right angles to the first using an appropriate solvent. A similar procedure has been described for urinary amino acids. For details, *see* Saini A. S., *J. Chromatogr.*, **61**, 378 (1971) and *Clin. Chim. Acta*, **31**, 482 (1971).

25. Preparation of Clinical Samples for Carbohydrate Analysis by TLC

Since carbohydrates are very polar molecules they are usually soluble only in very polar solvents such as water. In fact a common practice for precipitating carbohydrates from water solution is the addition of a miscible organic liquid such as ethanol or acetone. Unfortunately these solubility properties are shared by inorganic salts, which are quite often present in blood, urine, and other biological specimens of importance in clinical analysis. Removal of inorganic salts is usually necessary if one is to obtain clear, reproducible carbohydrate chromatograms.

Three procedures are generally used for deionization of samples: removal of ionic material from the sample by ion-exchange resins, electrolytic desalting, and preferential extraction of the carbohydrates with pyridine. For most purposes the latter procedure is convenient and satisfactory.

Ion-exchange resins are theoretically ideal for the removal of inorganic salts from carbohydrate solutions. Simple carbohydrates do not carry a charge and thus are not retained at all by the resin. In such a procedure both an anion and a cation exchanger are employed. Ion-exchange resins are not uniformly well suited to this procedure, however. For example, some degradation of carbohydrates was found to occur on IRA-400 (OH^-) resin and on Dowex 2 (OH^-) resin. Table I shows some resin combinations that have been applied.

Table I

Suggested Ion-Exchange Resins for Desalting Samples

Cation Exchanger	*Anion Exchanger*	*Treatment*	*S**
Dowex-50	Dowex-1	Batch process	B
Amberlite IR-120 (H^+)	Amberlite IRA-410 (acetate)	Batch process	U
Amberlite IR-120 (H^+)	Amberlite IRA-400 (OH^-)	Shake with each resin	U
Bio-Deminrolit	Permutite (CO_2 sat'd)	Batch process	U
Any combination of: Dowex-50 (H^+) Zeo-Karb 225 (H^+) *or* Amberlite IR-120 (H^+) *or* Amberlite MB-4 in HCO_3^- form	De-Acidite-G Amberlite-IR-45 (OH^- or acetate)	Batch process (1 ml resin/5 ml urine)	U
Amberlite IR-120 (H^+) (IR4b (OH^-))			U

* *S* = sample; B = blood; U = urine.

Electrolytic desalting is an excellent technique where only a few samples are involved and the volume is appropriate (a few milliliters is best). This procedure involves establishing an electrical potential across the solution so that the cations and anions migrate to opposite ends of the cell. At the anode dilute acid constantly circulates, separated from the solution by a permeable membrane. At the other end mercury is the cathode and is also kept moving through the chamber. The ions in the solution are thus washed away. The mercury is washed clean of ions with water and circulated back to the cell, while the dilute acid is simply discarded.

Pyridine extraction, as originally proposed, involves evaporating the sample to dryness on a water bath, then extracting the residue with dry redistilled pyridine for 10 minutes at 100 °C. Pyridine dissolves the carbohydrates, but not the inorganic material. The pyridine is then removed from the extract under reduced pressure, utilizing temperatures no greater than 40 °C. Care must be taken not to expose the carbohydrates too long to hot pyridine because of a side reaction destructive to the carbohydrates (i.e., epimerization).

A modification of the technique to minimize the heating of carbohydrates in pyridine has been reported. Two milliliters of pyridine are added to 0.5 ml sample to precipitate the salts. After standing 10 minutes the solid is centrifuged down. The supernate is spread across a large region of a sheet of paper as are two 0.5 ml pyridine washings of the precipitated salts. The dried sheet is then eluted with water in the manner of descending chromatography. Complete recovery of the sugars tested is reported.

Pyridine extraction also separates proteins from the carbohydrates, while some degree of deproteinization will occur using the ion-exchange resins. However, where proteins are the important contaminants or are not efficiently removed, there are reagents specific for this task. In one method 2 volumes 0.3*N* $Ba(OH)_2$ are added to the sample, then 2 volumes 5% $ZnSO_4 \cdot 7H_2O$ followed by vigorous shaking. The proteins and the precipitated zinc and barium salts are filtered off.

Proteins may be precipitated by adding ethanol to the sample, then centrifuging or filtering the proteins to remove them. One technique described the use of 2.0 ml 95% ethanol per 0.5 ml serum. In another 2.0 ml 95% ethanol is used per 0.1 ml serum. Care must be taken, since too high an ethanol concentration will result in removal of the carbohydrate.

Reference 6, pp. 54–56.

26. Selective Precipitation of Carbohydrates

Carbohydrates may be selectively precipitated from solution by converting them to osazones. The procedure for urine involves adding 0.4 g phenylhydrazine hydrochloride and 0.6 g sodium acetate to 10 ml urine. This is heated for 30 minutes in a boiling water bath, and the osazone crystals are removed by filtration. The crystals are washed in water and dissolved in dioxane-methanol (1 : 1) for chromatography.

Reference 6, p. 56.

27. Hydrolysis of Glycoproteins and Glycopeptides for Liberation of Neutral Sugars

Hydrolysis of the Glycoproteins

In order to liberate sugars from glycoproteins, acid hydrolysis is generally employed at present. Acid hydrolysis poses a major problem in the carbohydrate analysis of glycoproteins and other complex heteropolysaccharides associated with proteins. The stability of the free monosaccharides to hot acid varies considerably. Additional difficulties arise from the interaction of sugars with certain amino acids. The published data indicate that no generalized conditions exist for acid hydrolysis. Each glycoprotein presents a different problem and the optimum conditions for hydrolysis must be ascertained by preliminary experiments.

The hexoses are best released by 1*N* to 2.5*N* HCl at 100 °C for 1.5–6 hours. The sample was hydrolyzed in 0.3 ml 2*N* HCl in a vacuum-sealed tube for 2 hours (0.5–1 mg of glycoprotein or tissue extract containing 0.5–3% hexoses). The amino acids and the excess of mineral acid have to be removed by ion exchangers. In routine work 0.3 ml hydrolysate in 1.5–2*N* HCl is diluted with 0.4 ml of water in a hemolysis tube (12 × 70 mm) and is neutralized with 0.4 g of Amberlite IR-45 (OH^- form, 40–60 mesh). The pH of the solution is controlled and resin added, if necessary, to maintain pH 4–5. Using a capillary pipette, the liquid and the washings are transferred to the top of a column (5 × 120 mm) filled with Amberlite CG-120 (H^+ form, 200–400 mesh) to a height of 40 mm. The effluents are evaporated to dryness in a desiccator over KOH pellets *in vacuo* (<1 mm Hg).

Experiments carried out with the acetate and formate form of a strongly basic resin (Amberlite IR 400) to eliminate the Cl^- ions gave different retention rates for galactose, glucose and mannose. This could be avoided by a careful washing of the resin bed (30 ml water for 0.6 g resin). The use of Amberlite IR-45 (OH^- form) seems to be more advantageous because no selective retention was demonstrated for the three hexoses in the experimental conditions described above, when a washing liquid of 0.8–1 ml water was applied.

Hydrolysis of Glycopeptides

The glycopeptides isolated from the enzymatic hydrolysates may contain about 20–70% hexoses. In the cited experiments 0.05–0.2 mg glycopeptide were hydrolyzed in 0.1 ml 1.5*N* HCl for 2 hours at 100 °C. The hydrolysate, diluted with water to 0.3 ml, is lyophilized in 10 × 100 mm test tubes. The resynthesis of oligosaccharides during the evaporation of HCl-containing hydrolysates at room temperature presents difficulties in the quantitative analysis of sugars present in hydrolysates. Although formation of oligosaccharides can still be detected, no significant alteration of the proportion of hexoses was observed under this condition. To avoid the formation of oligosaccharides, as far as possible, the Cl^- ions have to be eliminated before the lyophilization. The latter purification process can be realized by ion exchangers as described in the section above, but the treatment with acid ion-exchanger resin may be omitted.

The outlined method of hydrolysis is applicable also to other types of carbohydrate-rich materials containing at least 15–20% hexoses.

Reference 10, Vol. I, pp. 170–171, chapter by Moczar, E. and M. Moczar.

28. Hydrolysis of Glycoproteins and Glycopeptides for Liberation of Hexosamines

A glyoprotein or glycopeptide sample containing 2–10 μg amino sugars is hydrolyzed under nitrogen in 0.1–0.2 ml 4*N* HCl in a sealed tube and in a boiling water bath for 4–8 hours. The hydrolysate is then evaporated to dryness *in vacuo* (<1 mm Hg) over KOH pellets. No appreciable decomposition of amino sugars occurs. The hydrolysates of the glycoproteins treated in analogous manner, *i.e.*, without purification of the acid hydrolysates, gave in the most cases satisfactory results.

Reference 10, Vol. I, chapter by Moczar, E., and M. Moczar, p. 175.

29. Partial Hydrolysis of Heteropolysaccharides

One to three mg of the sample are dissolved in 0.5–1 ml distilled water in 10 × 100-mm test tubes and 50–100 mg resin (Amberlite IR-120, 40–60 mesh in H^+ form) are added. The sealed tubes are shaken vigorously in a boiling water bath for one hour. The solution is drained off by a capillary pipette and dried over KOH pellets *in vacuo*. The residue is dissolved in 10 μl water, and 0.5–2 μl of this solution are applied on the plates for the two-dimensional TLC separation.

Reference 10, Vol. 1, chapter by Moczar, E. and M. Moczar, p. 183.

30. Acetolysis of Polysaccharides

The experimental procedure used for yeast mannans by Stewart and Ballou follows: 0.1 g substance is stirred at 40 °C in a mixture of acetic anhydride–acetic acid–concentrated H_2SO_4 (10 : 10 : 1 v/v). The reaction is stopped after 13–70 hours by the addition of pyridine in cooling ice water. The acetylated oligosaccharides were extracted from the water-diluted solution with chloroform. The organic layer was washed with water and evaporated to dryness.

Reference: Stewart, T. S. and C. E. Ballou, *Biochemistry*, **7**, 1855 (1968), permission from American Chemical Society.

31. Methylation and Hydrolysis of Polysaccharides

Use dimethylsulfoxide (DMSO) as solvent in the presence of dimethyl sulfinyl carbanions. Methyl iodide serves as the methylating agent. Extract the methylated polysaccharides from the reaction medium diluted with water [Hakomori, S., *J. Biochem.* (*Tokyo*), **55**, 205 (1964)]. If the polysaccharides and glycopeptides are not soluble in DMSO or DMF, carry out the experiment in suspension in DMF or DMSO according to Kuhn and Trischmann [*Chem. Ber.*, **96**, 284 (1963)]. Different mixtures of diluted acids are recommended for hydrolysis in order to avoid the slight demethylating action of the diluted HCl. A two-step procedure gives good results: the sample is treated in a sealed tube with 90% formic acid at 100 °C for one hour, and the cooled hydrolysate is diluted 1 : 4 with water or with 0.2*N* HCl. The hydrolysis is completed by heating the solution in the resealed tube in a boiling water bath for four hours. The samples are evaporated in a desiccator *in vacuo* (<1 mm Hg) over KOH pellets.

Reference 10, Vol. 1, Chapter by Moczar, E. and M. Moczar, p. 189.

32. Carbohydrate Derivatives for GC

The reader is referred to the two references below for detailed procedures for the preparation of acetal, ketal, alkyl, thioalkyl, dimethylsilyl ether, trimethylsilyl ether, alkylidene, acyl, aroyl, and sulfonyl derivatives of carbohydrates.

References: Bishop C. T. in *Methods of Biochemical Analysis*, Vol. 10, D. Glick, ed., Interscience Publishers, Division of John Wiley and Sons, Inc., N.Y., 1962, pp. 14–22. Wells, W. W., Sweeley, C. C., and R. Bentley, in *Biomedical Applications of Gas Chromatography*, H. A. Szymanski, ed., Plenum Press, N.Y., 1964, pp. 169–223.

CARBOXYLIC ACIDS

See Numbers 33–45, 58

33. Conversion of Volatile Aliphatic Acids to Hydroxamates

A solution containing 1 mg of the acid is made basic with NH_4OH, evaporated to dryness, and extracted twice with 1.0 ml portions of 0.4*N* HCl in ethanol. Ethereal diazomethane is added until the yellow color persists, and esterification is allowed to proceed for 10 minutes. Excess diazomethane is destroyed by adding several drops of 0.4*N* alcoholic HCl. Two milliliters of 2*N* NH_2OH sulfate–3.5*N* NaOH (1 : 1 v/v) is added, and the solution is allowed to stand at room temperature for 15 minutes. The hydroxamate solution is concentrated on a steam bath and spotted on the chromatographic paper. A modification of the procedure consists of a reflux period of 30 minutes at 90 °C in a water bath after the addition of a neutralized solution of the hydroxylamine reagent.

Reference: Bergmann, F. and R. Segal, *Biochem. J.*, **62**, 542 (1956); Ueno, Y., *J. Biochem.* (*Tokyo*), **48**, 161 (1960).

34. Preparation of Fatty Acid 2,4-Dinitrophenylhydrazones

Reflux fatty acids (10 mg) with thionyl chloride (0.3 ml) for 30 minutes and vacuum-distill the mixture. A dry pyridine solution (0.1 ml) of 5% 2,4-dinitrophenylhydrazine is added to the residue, the mixture is warmed and then cooled to room temperature and allowed to stand for 20 minutes. Benzene (2 ml) is added and the excess pyridine is extracted with 10–20 ml of warm water. The benzene layer is used for PC or TLC.

Reference: Inoue, Y. and M. Noda, *Bull. Agr. Chem. Soc. Japan*, **19**, 214 (1955).

35. Preparation of Keto Acid Nitroquinoxaline Derivatives

When a keto acid hydrazone produces several isomers on the finished chromatogram, such as *cis*- and *trans*-pyruvic acid, the nitroquinoxaline derivative of the acid may be preferred. With this technique, no isomerism has been reported. The preparation of this derivative is essentially the same as that for the hydrazones. Sufficient 1,2-diamino-4-nitrobenzene in 2*N* HCl is added to a deproteinized solution of α-keto acids; the mixture is warmed to 60 °C and allowed to stand for 16 hours at room temperature. The nitroquinoxalinol derivatives are extracted and purified in the same manner as described for the DNPH derivatives, except that a dilute solution of NaOH is substituted for the Na_2CO_3 solution.

Reference 1, p. 174.

36. Preparation of Samples of Higher Aliphatic Fatty Acids

(a) Hydroxamates

An ether solution of the acid is esterified by the addition of diazomethane solution. The ether is evaporated and the residue is dissolved in an alkaline solution of hydroxylamine in methanol (1 mole hydroxylamine hydrochloride–2 moles KOH–1 mole ester). The mixture is heated 2–3 minutes in a water bath; KCl is filtered off; excess KOH is neutralized with tetrahydrofuran–acetic acid (4 : 1); the solution is applied to the paper chromatogram for analysis.

(b) 2,4-Dinitrophenylhydrazones of Acetol Esters

An alcoholic solution of the fatty acids is acidified with 0.05*N* methanolic HCl. Bromoacetone is added and the mixture is refluxed 30 minutes at 80–90 °C. The mixture is cooled to 50 °C, and excess DNPH in 2*N* methanolic HCl is added and allowed to react for 30 minutes. Benzene layer is used for paper chromatography.

(c) Mercury Compounds

Unsaturated fatty acid methyl esters and 20% excess of mercuric acetate in absolute methanol (1–2 ml methanol; 1 g mercuric acetate) is heated 30 minutes at 80 °C. An excess of ether or benzene and water is added and the mixture is shaken vigorously. The organic layer is used for paper chromatography.

(d) Peracid Treatment

A 1-g mixture of fatty acids (saturated and unsaturated) is dissolved in 14 ml acetic acid followed by the addition of a 1 : 1 mixture of 88% formic acid and 30% hydrogen peroxide. The mixture is allowed to stand overnight; it is then diluted with 15 ml water and extracted with 2 ml chloroform; the extract is used for paper chromatography.

(e) Cholesteryl Esters of Long-Chain Fatty Acids

The esters of lauric, myristic, palmitic, stearic, oleic, linoleic, and linolenic acids are prepared by the method of Swell and Treadwell. A mixture of 0.182 mole thionyl chloride and 0.058 mole fatty acid is heated near the boiling point, with constant stirring, in a 250 ml Erlenmeyer flask. Excess thionyl chloride is removed by suction. The acid chloride is warmed and 0.040 mole cholesterol is added gradually. When reaction has subsided, 0.040 mole anhydrous pyridine is added and the mixture is heated at 80 °C for 20 minutes. Absolute alcohol is added to dissolve the ester; acetone is used if the fatty acid contains more than ten carbons. Labarrere *et al.* substituted oxalyl chloride for the thionyl chloride reagent because its use with unsaturated fatty acids was more efficient and because it was more easily removed from the reaction mixtures.

Reference 1, pp. 175, 176; Swell, L. and C. R. Treadwell, *J. Biol. Chem.*, **212**, 141 (1955); Labarrere, J. A., Chipault, J. R., and W. O. Lundberg, *Anal. Chem.*, **30**, 1466 (1958).

37. Preparation of α-Keto Acid 2,4-Dinitrophenylhydrazones

Two milliliters of 0.5% 2,4-dinitrophenylhydrazine (DNPH) in 6*N* HCl is added to 50 ml of deproteinized sample (diluted tenfold with water) of blood or urine, and the mixture is allowed to react at room temperature for 30 minutes. The aqueous solution is extracted three times with 15 ml portions of chloroform containing 20% ethanol or ethyl acetate. The combined solvent fraction is extracted with 15 ml of 1*N* Na_2CO_3. The retained Na_2CO_3 fraction is washed with 10 ml of the chloroform–ethyl solvent mixture; the carbonate solution is acidified in the cold (0–4 °C) with 5 ml 6*N* HCl. The hydrazones are extracted from the solution with three portions of chloroform–ethanol (or ethyl acetate); the combined extracts containing the keto acid and derivatives are concentrated by evaporation under a gentle air stream. It has been suggested that deproteinization of biological materials—for the preparation of DNPH derivatives—can be best accomplished by the addition of 0.05–0.1 volumes of ice-cold 60% $HClO_4$ to the homogenate which is kept in an ice bath. After 10 minutes, the mixture is filtered directly into an excess of freshly prepared DNPH solution (1 g DNPH in 1 liter of 2*N* HCl); the mixture is stored at room temperature for 2 hours and then overnight at 4 °C. Using these conditions, all keto acids investigated were quantitatively converted to the derivative form with the exception of β-mercaptopyruvate, which required several days of incubation. Some decomposition of acetoacetate in dilute $HClO_4$ was noted.

For clinical screening purposes, 2.5 ml urine is combined with 2.5 ml of 0.3% DNPH (in 1*N* HCl) in a stoppered tube and allowed to stand for 10 minutes. Ethyl acetate (10 ml) is added and the tube is shaken for 2 minutes. The ethyl acetate layer is removed and transferred to a beaker. The urine mixture is reextracted with 10 ml ethyl acetate, the ethyl acetate extracts are combined and concentrated at room temperature or under reduced pressure. The residue is dissolved in 0.25 ml of 1 : 1 ethanol–ethyl acetate and applied to the chromatographic paper for keto acid analysis.

Reference 1, p. 174.

38. Preparation of 2,4-Dinitrobenzyl Esters

A mixture of the sodium fatty acid salts (5×10^{-4} mole; e.g., calculated on the sodium salt of caprylic acid, mol. wt. 166) and 2,4-dinitrobenzyl bromide (4×10^{-4} mole) are dissolved in benzene-ethanol-water (9 : 16 : 2) mixture (2 ml) by warming. The mixture is then heated in a sealed reaction vessel for 1 hour on a boiling water bath. After cooling, the ampoule is opened and the resulting solution (2–6 μl) is applied to the chromatogram.

Reference 5, p. 839–840.

39. Isolations of Phenolic Acids from Urine

(a) *p*-Hydroxyphenylacetic Acid

The urine sample, 2% of a 24-hour specimen, is acidified to 15 volume percent with HCl. Two hundred milliliters of benzene is added and the system is refluxed for 30 minutes to hydrolyze complexes. The benzene layer is removed, the cooled urine is saturated with NaCl, and the urine is extracted with $4 \times \frac{1}{4}$ volumes diethyl ether. The benzene and ether extracts are combined, and are in turn extracted with $4 \times \frac{1}{4}$ volumes saturated $NaHCO_3$ to which 0.5% $Na_2S_2O_5$ is added (to prevent oxidation). The aqueous extracts are washed with $\frac{1}{20}$ volumes diethyl ether, adjusted to pH 3–4, and saturated with NaCl. The aqueous extracts are now extracted with $3 \times \frac{1}{4}$ volumes diethyl ether. This extract is washed with $2 \times \frac{1}{20}$ volumes saturated NaCl, and is evaporated to dryness. The residue is dissolved in 95% ethanol for chromatography.

(b) *o*-Hydroxyphenylacetic Acid

The urine sample can be spotted directly or solvent extracted in the case of a pathological urine (phenyl ketonuria). In normal patients an extraction and concentration procedure similar to (a) would be required.

Reference 6, p. 175, 177.

40. Isolation of Methyl Malonic Acid from Urine

The urine, 5–10 ml, is adjusted to pH 1 with 10*N* H_2SO_4, and is extracted with 5×1 volumes diethyl ether. This extract is concentrated by evaporation and is spotted for chromatography.

Reference: Dreyfus, P. M. and V. E. Dube, *Clin. Chim. Acta*, **15**, 525 (1967), permission from Elsevier Publishing Company, Amsterdam, The Netherlands.

41. Isolation of 3-Methoxy-4-Hydroxymandelic Acid from Urine

Adjust 5 ml of urine to pH 1–2 with HCl, and saturate with NaCl. Extract with 6 ml and then 5 ml of ethyl acetate, evaporate combined extracts, redissolve in methanol, and spot for chromatography. [Sarkoff, I. and T. L. Sourkes, *Can. J. Biochem.*, **41**, 1381 (1963).]

Some analysts spot a small (e.g. 2.5 μl) sample of urine directly on the thin layer plate. [Dittman, V. J. *Z. Klin. Chem.*, **4**, 265 (1966).]

42. 1,2-Diamino-4-Nitrobenzene Derivatives of α-Keto Acids in Blood and Urine

Mix 6–10 ml blood plus 40 ml 5% H_3PO_4 and centrifuge. Mix 10 ml urine plus sulfuric acid to make 0.1*N*. To either sample add 3 ml of 0.2% 1,2-diamino-4-nitrobenzene in 0.66*N* HCl. Extract with $\frac{1}{3}$ volume of ethyl acetate, then 3×10 ml ethyl acetate. Transfer sample into 5% Na_2CO_3 (4×8 ml). Wash the aqueous layer with ether to remove unused reagent. Adjust to pH 4 and extract (4×8 ml) with ethyl acetate. Evaporate and dissolve in a suitable solvent for chromatography. [Taylor, K. W. and M. J. H. Smith, *Analyst*, **80**, 607 (1955).]

43. Preparation of Methyl Esters of Fatty Acids for GC

In addition to the method using methanol-BF_3 described in the section on general procedures, fatty acid methyl esters were prepared in three other ways by Vorbeck, M. L., Mattick, L. R., Lee, F. A., and C. S. Pederson [*Anal. Chem.*, **33**, 1512 (1961).]

Diazomethane. Treat an ethereal solution of the acids with diazomethane, generated by adding a 50% KOH solution to an ethereal solution of *N*-nitrosomethylurea. Glassware with smooth surfaces should be used. [Roper, R. and T. S. Ma, *Microchem. J.*, **1**, 245 (1957).]

Methanol-HCl. Dissolve acids in benzene and add 5% HCl in dry methanol. Reflux, add water, and extract the ethers with petroleum ether. Neutralize and dry over a mixture of Na_2CO_3–$NaHCO_3$. Sublime the acids using micro methods. [Stoffel, W. and E. H. Ahrens, Jr., *Anal. Chem.*, **31**, 307 (1959).]

Methanol-HCl on ion-exchange resin. Absorb acids on the hydroxide form of Amberlite IRA-400 resin, and esterify directly on the resin with methanol-HCl according to Harnstein *et al.* [*Anal. Chem.*, **32**, 540 (1960)]. Extract esters with petroleum ether and dry over anhydrous Na_2SO_4. Remove excess solvent at room temperature in a rotary vacuum evaporator.

Gehrke and Goerlitz [*Anal. Chem.*, **35**, 76 (1963)] prepared fatty acid methyl esters by conversion of the acids to the potassium salts and then precipitation and drying of the corresponding silver salts. The esterification step, involving reaction of iodomethane with the silver salts, resulted in quantitative preparation with no side reactions or loss of volatile esters.

Nonvolatile acids such as pyruvic, lactic, glycolic and malonic were esterified with methanol-HCl and thionyl chloride by Gee [*Anal. Chem.*, **37**, 926 (1965)], who recommends an optimum esterification time of 10 min. under reflux. James and Webb [*Biochem. J.*, **66**, 515 (1957)] formed methyl esters of C_4–C_{11} dicarboxylic acids using diazomethane in ether, and McKeown and Read [*Anal. Chem.*, **37**, 1780 (1965)] esterified di- and tricarboxylic acids with both diazomethane and methanol-H_2SO_4. Mason and Waller [*Anal. Chem.*, **36**, 583 (1964)] transesterified glycerides containing C_6–C_{18} acids: a mixture of fat, benzene, methanol-HCl and dimethoxypropane was allowed to stand overnight, and after neutralization a sample was directly injected.

44. Preparation of Short-chain Fatty Acid 2-Chloroethanol Esters for GC

Weigh 10–25 mg acid into a 1 or 2 ml glass ampoule and add 1 ml 2-chloroethanol-HCl (CE-HCl) or 0.5 ml of 10% 2-chloroethanol-BF_3 (CE-BF_3). (Smaller samples down to 1 mg are esterified in sealed capillary tubes with 0.1 ml of either reagent.) The ampoule is sealed and heated in a boiling water bath, 1–2 hr. with CE-HCl, 10 min. with CE-BF_3. Cool and transfer quantitatively to a separatory funnel with 5 volumes of water. Extract the esters three times with ⅓ volume of petroleum ether (four to five extractions with pentane for formic and acetic acid esters), pool the extracts and wash twice with ¼ volume of water. Dry over Na_2SO_4 and evaporate solvent prior to GC. [Oette, K. and E. H. Ahrens, Jr., *Anal. Chem.*, **33**, 1847 (1961).]

45. Derivatives of Sulfonic Acids and Salts for GC

Preparation of Sulfonyl Chloride Derivatives

A 0.5 g sample of the sulfonic acid or salt is placed in a small round-bottomed flask fitted with a magnetic stirring bar and a hemispherical heating mantle. The flask is attached to a condenser and then 0.50 ml of dimethylformamide and 20 ml of thionyl chloride are added, respectively. The resulting solution is refluxed until no off-gas is detected with a bubbler tube attached to the condenser and containing chlorobenzene. The time required for complete reaction varies from several minutes to as long as 2 hours, depending on the sample. If the reactant is a salt of a sulfonic acid it is necessary to remove the insoluble chloride reaction product before preparing the solution for gas chromatographic analysis. This is accomplished by diluting the reaction with an equal volume of dichloromethane and carefully passing the yellow solution through a fine-porosity sintered-glass filter. Excess thionyl chloride and solvent are then removed by careful low-pressure distillation or by evaporation in a rotating vacuum evaporator. (If fairly volatile sulfonyl chlorides are present, elimination of these excess materials must be carried out carefully to prevent loss of the sample.) The final residue is dissolved in a suitable solvent such as carbon tetrachloride, transferred quantitatively to a 5-ml volumetric flask using solvent washes, and diluted to volume.

Sulfonic acids and salts may also be converted to sulfonyl chlorides with phosgene instead of thionyl chloride, using a similar procedure. The sample to be converted is refluxed with an inert solvent such as carbon tetrachloride containing dimethylformamide catalyst. Phosgene is passed into the solution until a yellow color develops. The reaction is continued for an additional 10 to 15 minutes to ensure completion, and the resulting solution worked up as described above.

Preparation of Methyl Sulfonates

A 0.5 g sample of free sulfonic acid is dissolved in a minimum quantity of diethyl ether. (A small amount of methanol may be added to put hydrates in solution.) Ethereal diazomethane solution is introduced slowly while agitating, until a yellow color persists. An additional 15–20% excess volume of diazomethane solution is added and the mixture is allowed to stand for about 10 minutes. The solvent is then carefully evaporated on a steam bath or with a stream of dry nitrogen, and the residue is transferred to a volumetric flask with a suitable solvent such as carbon tetrachloride or benzene.

Reference: Kirkland, J. J., *Anal. Chem.*, **32**, 1388 (1960), permission from American Chemical Society.

DRUGS

See Numbers 10, 46–53

46. Isolation of Barbiturates from Blood

To 6 ml of blood add 4 ml distilled water and 1 ml 10% sodium hydroxide. Shake 5 min. and add 6 ml 10% sodium tungstate, 6 ml 0.67*N* H_2SO_4 and shake again. Acidify with 18*N* H_2SO_4 and filter. Extract the filtrate with one volume of ethyl ether. The volume of the extract is reduced by distilling off the ether, and the remaining solution is spotted for chromatography.

Reference: Valov, P., *Ind. Eng. Chem. Anal. Ed.*, **18**, 456 (1946), permission from American Chemical Society.

A somewhat simpler technique eliminates the separate deproteinizing step.

To 3 ml serum add 15 ml chloroform, 0.1 ml concentrated HCl, and 2 g anhydrous Na_2SO_4, and shake the mixture. The chloroform layer is separated, evaporated to dryness on a water bath, and the residue redissolved in 0.2 ml ethanol. This is then spotted for chromatography.

Reference: Lehmann, J. and V. Karamustagaoglu, *Scand. J. Clin. Lab. Invest.*, **14**, 554 (1962). Permission from American Chemical Society.

47. Extraction of Drugs from Urine Prior to TLC and GC

(*a*) *Barbiturates.* 10 ml urine were made acid with 1 ml *N* HCl and extracted with 10 ml chloroform by shaking vigorously for 5 min. (Griffin Flask Shaker, Griffin & George, Alperton, Middlesex). After centrifuging, the aqueous layer was aspirated off and the organic layer washed with 10 ml of a 5% lead acetate solution. The aqueous layer was then removed and the chloroform dried by passing through a Whatman No. 90 filter paper into a 10 ml conical tube (BC24/C14T, Quickfit & Quartz, Stone, Staffordshire). The organic layer was quickly evaporated to dryness by placing this tube in a 250 ml beaker containing hot water and passing a stream of air through the solution. The dried residue is dissolved in 0.1 ml $CHCl_3$ prior to TLC.

(*b*) *Amphetamines.* 5 ml urine were pipetted into a 10 ml conical tube. Two drops of 2*N* NaOH were then added followed by 0.1 ml chloroform. The contents were mixed for 1 min. on a Whirlmix (Fisons, Loughborough) and then centrifuged hard for 5 min. to separate the chloroform layer. This layer is used for GC analysis.

(*c*) *Narcotics.* 10 ml urine were saturated with solid sodium bicarbonate and extracted with an equal volume of chloroform–isopropanol (9 : 1) by shaking vigorously for 5 min. After centrifuging, the aqueous layer was aspirated off and the organic phase dried and evaporated in the manner described previously for barbiturates. The dried extract is dissolved in 0.1 ml ethanol prior to TLC.

Reference: Berry, D. J., and J. Grove, *J. Chromatogr.*, **61**, 111 (1971), permission from Elsevier Publishing Company, Amsterdam, The Netherlands.

48. Methyl Derivatives of Barbiturates for GC

Pour an excess of diazomethane in ethereal solution on the solid barbituric acid or its sodium salt in a test tube and allow to stand overnight at room temperature in a fume hood. Wash the ethereal solution twice with an equal volume of saturated aqueous $NaHCO_3$, dry over anhydrous Na_2SO_4 and filter. Evaporate ether under reduced pressure. [Cook, J. G. H., Riley, C., Nunn, R. F., and D. E. Budgen, *J. Chromatogr.*, **6**, 182 (1961).]

49. Preparation of Plasma and Urine for Analyses of Hydroxyamylbarbitone by GC

(a) Plasma

To 2 ml plasma 10 ml tungstic acid reagent [mix 5 ml 10% sodium tungstate solution with 40 ml 0.083*N* H_2SO_4 just before use] was added and the mixture was allowed to stand for 10 min. After centrifuging at 3000 rev./min. for 5 min. the clear supernatant liquid was saturated with 15 g ammonium sulfate and extracted twice with 20 ml ether. The sample was centrifuged at 3000 rev./min. after each extraction and the ether layers were pooled. Then 1 ml of 0.2 mg/100 ml triphenylene in methanol was added as internal standard and the solution was evaporated to dryness, taken up in 0.1 ml of ether and 5 μl were injected on the gas–liquid chromatograph.

(b) Urine

To remove the interfering compounds from the urine a BTL chromatographic column, Type 2A, internal diameter 1 cm (Baird and Tatlock, Chadwell Heath, Essex) was first filled to a height of 8 cm with a Florisil slurry, then washed with 10 ml of distilled water and the excess was allowed to drain. 30 ml urine was passed through this column, the first 10 ml was rejected, and the remainder was collected. 2–5 ml of the eluate was made alkaline with 1 ml of 1*N* sodium hydroxide, saturated with 6 g of ammonium sulfate and extracted twice with 15 ml of ether. The pH was independent of the volume of the urine. Subsequent analysis was carried out by adding 1 ml of 0.2 mg/100 ml triphenylene in methanol and proceeding thereafter as described above for the plasma.

GC. Use a 5-ft column of 2% FFAP at 225 °C.

Reference: Grove, J. and P. A. Toseland, *Clin. Chim. Acta*, **29**, 253 (1970), permission from Elsevier Publishing Company, Amsterdam, The Netherlands.

50. Extraction of Methaqualone from Plasma for GC Analysis

A sample of 5.0 ml of plasma was made alkaline by the addition of 1.0 ml of 1*N* sodium hydroxide, and extracted with 15 ml of hexane by gentle shaking for 10 min. in a 30-ml centrifuge tube. After centrifugation at 3000 r.p.m., the organic layer was transferred to a second tube containing approximately 3 g of anhydrous sodium sulfate. On carrying out a second, 5 min. extraction with 10 ml of hexane, the organic fractions were bulked, thoroughly shaken with the anhydrous sodium sulfate, and left to stand for 10 min. The extract was then evaporated to dryness under a stream of nitrogen in a 10-ml conical centrifuge tube to which 1.0 ml of the butobarbitone standard solution had been added, the tube being immersed in a water-bath at 60 °C. The residue was taken up in 100 μl of absolute ethanol, and 3–5 μl of this were injected on to the gas chromatograph containing a 7 ft column of 3% CDMS at 200 °C.

Reference: Berry, D. J., *J. Chromatogr.*, **42**, 39 (1969). Permission from Elsevier Publishing Company, Amsterdam, The Netherlands.

51. Extraction of Paracetamol (*N*-Acetyl-*p*-aminophenol) from Plasma and Urine for GC Analysis

Extraction of Paracetamol from Plasma

1 ml of plasma, derived from venous blood, was saturated with 3 g of solid ammonium sulfate and extracted twice with 15 ml of ether. The sample was centrifuged after each extraction and the ether layers pooled. 1 ml of the internal standard solution (i) or (ii) was added to the organic layer. The extract was transferred in small portions to a 10 ml conical tube (BC/C14T Quickfit & Quartz, Stone, Staffordshire) and evaporated to dryness under a stream of air. The residue was then carefully reconstituted in 0.1 ml of ether and 5 μl injected into the gas chromatograph containing a 7 ft column of 2% FFAP at 240 °C.

Extraction of Paracetamol from Urine

Interfering compounds in the urine can be removed by the use of a Florisil column. A BTL chromatographic column, Type 2A, I.D. 1 cm (Baird & Tatlock, Chadwell Heath, Essex) was filled to a height of 8 cm with a slurry of Florisil which was then washed with 10 ml of distilled water and the excess allowed to drain. 30 ml of urine were then passed through this column, the first 10 ml were rejected and the remainder was collected. 1–5 ml of eluate was then saturated with solid ammonium sulfate and extracted twice with 15 ml of ether. Subsequent analysis was carried out by adding 1 ml of the internal standard solution and proceeding as described for plasma.

Reference: Grove, J., *J. Chromatogr.*, **59**, 289 (1971). Permission from Elsevier Publishing Company, Amsterdam, The Netherlands.

52. Extraction of Doxepin (Sinequan) from Urine and Chlordiazepoxide from Plasma for GC Analysis

(*a*) *Doxepin.* A 50 ml sample of urine, adjusted to pH 6–8 with dilute hydrochloric acid or ammonia solution, is extracted with 100 ml chloroform by shaking vigorously for 2 min in a 250 ml separating funnel. The extraction is repeated using 75 ml of chloroform and the organic phases combined. This is washed with 10 ml phosphate buffer (pH 7.4, 0.07*M*) followed by 10 ml of 0.5*N* sodium hydroxide and 10 ml of distilled water. The chloroform is dried by filtering through anhydrous sodium sulfate into a round bottom flask and taken to low volume on a rotary evaporator at 40° C under a vacuum of 300 mm of mercury. The contents are transferred to a 10 ml graduated centrifuge tube and gently evaporated just to dryness using a stream of dry nitrogen, the tube being immersed in a water bath at 45 °C. The residue is redissolved in 200 μl of diazepam internal standard solution and 5 μl of this injected into a FID gas chromatograph at a sensitivity setting of 1×10^{-9} A.

Reference: Dusci, L. J. and L. P. Hackett, *J. Chromatogr.*, **61**, 231 (1971). Permission from Elsevier Publishing Company, Amsterdam, The Netherlands.

(*b*) *Chlordiazepoxide.* 1 ml of plasma is mixed with 1 ml of distilled water; the mixture is made alkaline (pH 9–10) by addition of 0.1*N* sodium hydroxide and extracted with 5 ml of *n*-heptane–isoamyl alcohol (98.5 : 1.5) by mechanically shaking the flask for 15 min. After centrifugation, 4.5 ml of the organic phase is transferred to a 5-ml centrifuge tube; 2–9 μl of this extract is injected into the chromatograph (electron capture detector).

At low plasma levels, concentration of the drug in the extract is achieved by back-extraction in dilute acid: 1 ml of 0.1*N* hydrochloric acid is added to the heptane extract; the test tube is shaken by hand for 10 min. and centrifuged. The acidic aqueous solution is made alkaline (pH 9–10) by addition of 1*N* sodium hydroxide and reextracted with 0.3–0.5 ml of the *n*-heptane-isoamyl alcohol mixture. Following centrifugation, the aqueous layer is removed by aspiration and the heptane phase is collected in the tapered portion of the tube. Aliquots of this extract (3–9 μl) are analyzed by GC. 1-ml aliquots of the aqueous standard solutions containing 0.03–10 μg of chlordiazepoxide are added to 1 ml of water or drug-free plasma and extracted according to the procedure described above.

Extracts for TLC studies are prepared by pooling the heptane extracts from three 1-ml plasma samples at high concentration and by reextracting the drug in 3 ml of 0.1*N* hydrochloric acid. The acidic aqueous solution, made alkaline as described above, is reextracted with 0.3 ml of *n*-heptane-isoamyl alcohol. Synthetic plasma solutions containing comparable amounts of chlordiazepoxide, lactam and *N*-des-methyl metabolites are extracted according to the same procedure.

Reference: Zingales, I. A., *J. Chromatogr.*, **61**, 237 (1971). Permission from Elsevier Publishing Company, Amsterdam, The Netherlands.

53. Preparation of Plasma and Urine for GC Determination of Alclofenac (4-Allyloxy-3-chlorophenylacetic Acid) and Metabolites by GC

Plasma. 4 ml of plasma is taken and diluted with 6 ml of 1*N* HCl (final normality, 0.6). The 10-ml specimen is hydrolyzed at 100 °C for 20 min. and thereafter extracted twice with methyl isobutyl ketone (1:3) using an automatic shaker. The combined extract is dried with anhydrous Na_2SO_4 and evaporated under reduced pressure at 35 °C. The residue is dissolved in 100 μl of 1,4-dioxane. Silylation is performed by adding 100 μl of hexamethyldisilazane and 50 μl of trimethylchlorosilane. After standing overnight at room temperature, the mixture is centrifuged and 1 or 2 μl of the clear supernatant are injected into the gas chromatograph.

Urine. 1 ml of 12*N* HCl is added to 20 ml of clear urine. The sample is then hydrolyzed, extracted twice (1 : 3) and evaporated as described above. The residue is dissolved in 1 ml of 1,4-dioxane; 0.2 ml is silylated by adding 200 μl of HMDS and 100 μl of TMCS. 1 or 2 μl are injected into the gas chromatograph.

For *GC*, use a 2 meter column of 3% XE-60 at 140–190 °C, and flame ionization detection.

Reference: Roncucci, R., Simon, M.-J., and G. Lambelin, *J. Chromatogr.*, **62**, 135 (1971). Permission from Elsevier Publishing Company, Amsterdam, The Netherlands.

SYNTHETIC DYES AND NATURAL PIGMENTS

See Numbers 54–56

54. Extraction of Chloroplast Pigments from Plants

Many kinds of fresh plant material can be used as a source of the chloroplast pigments, e.g., cocklebur (Xanthium) leaves grown in a greenhouse and fresh spinach leaves obtained from a market as well as various species of algae. If spurious chromatographic observations are to be avoided, the pigments must be extracted quickly from fresh material under conditions that avoid their physical isomerization and chemical alteration. Two important extraction procedures are described; one employs a blender, the other employs scalding.

Blender Method

Two grams of tender, green leaves with large veins and petioles removed, are placed in a chilled blender with 60 ml of cold acetone or methanol and blended at high speed for 2 min. The mixture is then centrifuged, and the clear, green supernatant is put into a separatory funnel. Forty milliliters of cold petroleum ether (20–40 °C) and 100 ml of saturated aqueous NaCl is added. The mixture is shaken, and the layers allowed to separate. The lower layer is discarded, and the upper layer washed successively with two 100-ml portions of distilled water. The washed upper, green layer is poured out through the top of the funnel into a round-bottom flask and evaporated to dryness below 40 °C under vacuum. (A rotary evaporator is convenient, if available. If the extract is to be stored before use, it should be kept under vacuum in the dark and cold to avoid decomposition of the pigments.) The residue is dissolved in 1 ml of petroleum ether (60-110 °C) to prepare the sample solution. The xanthophylls and carotenes of plants are examined conveniently after removal of the chlorophylls by saponification with alkali. For this saponification, 10 ml of 30% KOH in methanol is added to the centrifuged acetone or methanol extract in the separatory funnel. After 30 min. with occasional swirling, 40 ml of cold 1 : 1 petroleum ether (20–40 °C)-diethyl ether plus 100 ml of 10% aqueous NaCl solution are added. The resultant upper golden-yellow layer is washed with water and taken to dryness as above. The sample solution is prepared by dissolving the residue in 1 ml of 1 : 1 petroleum ether (60–110 °C)-diethyl ether. This saponification procedure should not be employed with plant extracts containing xanthophylls that are decomposed by alkalies as are fucoxanthin, from diatoms and brown algae, and peridinin, from dinoflagellates.

Non-Blender Scalding Method

For extraction without a blender, 2 g of leaves are cut up and placed in 100 ml of boiling water in a flask or beaker. After 2 min., the vessel is placed in an ice bath and the water poured off when cool. The leaves are then extracted with 100 ml of 90% methanol-10% diethyl ether followed by 100 ml 70% methanol-30% diethyl ether. The extracts are combined in a separatory funnel, and 100 ml petroleum ether (20–40 °C) is added. The pigments are then transferred into the petroleum ether-diethyl ether mixture with aqueous salt solution, washed, and handled as described above. Saponification may also be carried out by adding KOH to the methanol-diethyl ether mixture in the separatory funnel. For a further discussion of the extraction of chloroplast pigments, see Strain, H. H. and W. A. Svec, in *The Chlorophylls* (Vernon L. P. and G. R. Seeley, eds), Academic Press, N.Y., 1966.

Reference: Strain, H. H. and J. Sherma, *J. Chem. Educ.*, **46**, 476 (1969). Permission of American Chemical Society.

55. Extraction of Porphyrins from Urine

To 10 ml urine in a centrifuge tube is added 2 ml 10% lead acetate. The precipitate is centrifuged and washed with 5 ml water. The pigments are extracted from the precipitate with 1 ml 15% HCl. The extract is dried *in vacuo* over pellets of NaOH, the residue is taken up in 0.2 ml 10*M* NH_4OH, and a portion of this solution is used for chromatography.

Reference 1, p. 335.

56. Preparation of Porphyrin Methyl Esters

Two milliliters blood, 10 ml urine, or 5 g feces are extracted with ethyl acetate-acetic acid (v/v). The extracts are concentrated *in vacuo* under nitrogen which is being passed through pyrogallol to remove any traces of oxygen. Twenty-five milliliters dry methanol and dry HCl gas are added to the residue, and esterification is allowed to proceed for 1 hr. with refluxing. Twenty-five milliliters chloroform is then added, and the excess methanol-HCl is washed out with small amounts of water to neutrality. The chloroform extract is taken to dryness, and the methyl esters are redissolved in 30 μl chloroform for chromatography.

Reference 1, p. 335.

GENERAL PROCEDURES

See Numbers 57–59

57. Preparation of Silyl Derivatives for GC

The following material is reprinted from "Handbook of Silylation", Handbook GPA-3, Pierce Chemical Co., Rockford, Ill., 1970, by permission of G. D. Brittain, vice president. Products for carrying out these procedures are available from Pierce Chemical Co.

(a) Introduction

Abbreviations used in silylation. The word silylation, itself, is usually employed as an abbreviation of trimethylsilylation. However, it may also be employed at times to designate the attachment of similar organo-silicon groups as dimethylsilyl [-$SiH(CH_3)_2$] or chloromethyldimethylsilyl [-$SiCH_2Cl(CH_3)_2$].

Some of the most common abbreviations follow:

TMS—Trimethylsilyl [-$Si(CH_3)_3$], as *N,O*-bis-(TMS)-acetamide. Sometimes used to designate a compound that has been completely trimethylsilylated, as "TMS-Sucrose" or "TMS-Leucine". This is, of course, incorrect nomenclature but is frequently used.

BSA—*N,O*-Bis-(trimethylsilyl)-acetamide, $CH_3C[OSi(CH_3)_3]{=}NSi(CH_3)_3$, a powerful silyl donor.

HMDS—Hexamethyldisilazane, $(CH_3)_3SiNHSi(CH_3)_3$, useful silylating reagent.

TMCS—Trimethylchlorosilane, $(CH_3)_3SiCl$, silylating reagent often used as a catalyst.

TSIM—Trimethylsilylimidazole, $CH_3Si\underline{NCH{=}NCH{=}C}H$, a highly useful and selective silylating reagent for silylating-OH groups only or for silylating sugars in the presence of moisture.

TMSDEA—Trimethylsilyldiethylamine, $(CH_3)_3SiN(C_2H_5)_2$, a potent silylating reagent.

Some of the less used abbreviations are:

BDSA—*N,O*-Bis(dimethylsilyl)-acetamide, $CH_3C[OSiH(CH_3)_2]{=}NSiH(CH_3)_2$, a *dimethyl* silylating reagent.

CMDMCS—Chloromethyldimethylchlorosilane, $(CH_2Cl)(CH_3)_2SiCl$, reagent for preparing chloromethyldimethylsilyl derivatives for electron capture.

DMCS—Used by some as abbreviation for dimethylchlorosilane, $H(CH_3)_2SiCl$, and by others for dimethyl*di*chlorosilane, $(CH_3)_2SiCl_2$; therefore its usage may lead to error.

TMDS—Tetramethyldisilazane, $H(CH_3)_2SiNHSi(CH_3)_2H$, a dimethylsilyl donor.

Effect of moisture. Since water decomposes both TMS reagents and derivatives, excessive moisture should be avoided. Since Pierce silylation reagents are packaged in **Hypo-vials** under nitrogen, dry box technique is not usually necessary, but work should not be carried out under highly humid conditions and sample to be treated should be reasonably dry. Use dry needle and syringe for handling reagents and samples.

Hydrolysis of TMS reagents or derivatives produces hexamethyldisiloxane [$(CH_3)_3SiOSi(CH_3)_3$]. The siloxane peak may be used to check moisture content. It should be borne in mind that a small amount of the siloxane may be present in the reagent. Hexamethyldisiloxane is quite inert and does not interfere with reagent activity in small amounts nor does it produce by-products with samples.

Reaction time. Although many compounds will silylate almost as soon as dissolved, and the majority of hydroxyl compounds will derivatize completely within 5 min., some compounds require longer reaction times. For determination of this time we suggest that you check your mixtures of silylating reagent and sample in your chromatograph at the following intervals after mixing; 5 min., 15 min., 30 min., 1 hr., 4 hr., and 8 hr. At any time in the intervals suggested above, when you have had no increase in product peak after three successive chromatograms, then you should feel safe in taking the lowest time at which this peak is reached as the derivatization time for the compound you have modified.

Hydrolytic stability. Although TMS derivatives are quite thermally stable, their sensitivity to moisture varies considerably. For instance, TMS sugars are quite stable to water at room temperatures while TMS amino acids hydrolyze most readily. The hydrolytic resistance of other derivatives lies between these two extremes. Regarding the amino acid derivatives, the *N*-TMS bond hydrolyzes preferentially sometimes resulting in a partially degraded product, causing extraneous peaks in the chromatograph. It is suggested that derivatives to be stored be kept in moisture proof containers with an excess of reagent.

Thermal stability. TMS derivatives have excellent thermal stability; no decomposition has been noted with injector or column temperatures to 300 °C. In a number of instances temperatures of 350° and over have been used successfully. Most of the TMS reagents are also quite thermally stable; however, the more powerful silyl donors such as BSA and BSTFA sometimes undergo slight decomposition at elevated temperatures. Therefore when using the gas chromatograph for checking the purity of these reagents it is suggested that an injector temperature of 125°–150° be used. Other factors may cause decomposition of derivatives and reagents and the effect of these factors may be in a direct ratio with temperature. We have noted that metal (even stainless steel) injector assemblies will sometimes catalyze decomposition. For a discussion of this subject see paragraph entitled "Glass Injector Ports."

Solvent suggestions. Since TMS reagents react with active hydrogen, it is obvious that water or alcohols cannot be used. Enolizable ketones should usually be avoided. Although nonpolar organics, such as hexane, ether and benzene are excellent solvents for the reagents and derivatives, they do not seem to sponsor rapid reactivity. We should emphasize that any solvent selected should be completely dry. Pyridine is one of the most broadly used solvents for TMS reactions. Not only is it an excellent solvent and reaction medium, but it is also an HCl acceptor in reactions involving organochlorosilanes. Dimethylformamide is also used extensively, particularly for steroids. Dimethylsulfoxide has been found useful in the preparation of TMS derivatives of some compounds with reluctant solubility and of tertiary alcohols. Tetrahydrofuran is of value with some difficultly soluble compounds. Acetonitrile has been shown to be of value, although its high degree of toxicity requires that extreme caution be exercised in the handling of the liquid and its vapor.

At times, it may be desirable to conduct a reaction in the pure silylating reagent without the use of a solvent.The reagents may perform as satisfactory solvents for many organic compounds. In some cases the silylated product may be quite soluble in the reagent even though the parent compound is not. This technique is most useful when working with minute samples and low concentrations.

Column conditioning. Columns used for TMS derivatives should be thoroughly conditioned before use. This may usually be accomplished by the injection of a TMS reagent, repeated until a stable base line is attained. HMDS may be used for this purpose but we particularly recommend SILYL-8 Column Conditioner. 10 to 15 μl should be injected directly into the chromatograph at few minute intervals until conditioning is completed. Thereafter, TMS samples will tend to keep the column perfectly conditioned. In the case of columns that have been used for non-TMS samples, it may be necessary to repeat this treatment to remove nonvolatile residues that can be silylated.

"Garbage" (by-products of reaction or degradation). Quite often it is desirable to identify the peaks representing these by-products. Trimethylsilylating reagents react with moisture and with samples to produce **hexamethyldisiloxane.** It is inert and does not interfere with reaction.

BSA not only produces hexamethyldisiloxane but also the partial degradation product **N-TMS-acetamide.**

Chloromethyldimethylsilyl reagents and derivatives may be expected to produce **1,3-bis-(chloromethyl)-tetramethyldisiloxane** and the bromo analogs produce **1,3-bis-(bromomethyl)-tetramethyldisiloxane.**

Glass injector ports should be used when chromatographing TMS reagents and derivatives (as well as many other sensitive or active compounds). Strange things can happen in chromatographs with stainless steel injector inlets. Erratic and irreproducible results begin to show up with silylated samples as well as other materials. This does not usually occur when the inlet is new, but after several weeks or months of use. The cause is corrosion of the s.s. insert and may be eliminated by installing a glass tube of proper size. Teflon film or tape can be wrapped on the tube to insure a snug fit. If you are chromatographing TMS derivatives or other compounds subject to breakdown by metal catalysis it is a good idea to make this modification before trouble begins.

It is not necessary, however, to use glass columns; stainless steel appears to be quite satisfactory. Observations of numerous chromatographers indicate that the transition from liquid to gas phase in the presence of metal is the most critical breakdown point. Once the gas phase has been attained TMS derivatives appear quite stable in the presence of stainless steel.

Handling precautions. Many TMS reagents are flammable and due care should be observed. The chlorosilanes are corrosive and release HCl upon exposure to moisture. Since some individuals may be sensitive to TMS reagents avoid contact with skin, particularly the eyes, and avoid inhalation of fumes.

(b) Methods of Silylation and Related Techniques

The following methods are quite adequate for a majority of silylatable compounds. There are numerous methods mentioned in the literature that are less effective or, at best, no more effective than the methods listed below. However, there are also a number of methods and special techniques for the silylation of some particular compounds that do not respond satisfactorily to the usual techniques. In such cases we suggest you refer to *Silylation of Organic Compounds* by Alan E. Pierce. This excellent volume may be obtained directly from Pierce Chemical Company or its authorized agents.

Method 1

TRI-SIL is a ready mixed formula based on the procedure of Sweeley, Bentley, Makita, and Wells, *J. Amer. Chem. Soc.*, **85**, 2495–2507 (1963). This is the most widely used silylation reagent of all. It is packaged in Hypo-vials or in ampules, providing a simple, convenient, and economical alternative to the handling of the sensitive and unpleasant components individually. It is used as follows:

Reagents required: **TRI-SIL.**

Introduce 5 to 10 mg of sample and 1.0 ml TRI-SIL into a small plastic stoppered vial. Shake vigorously 30 sec. to dissolve. (Difficultly soluble materials may be warmed to 75–85 °C). Allow to stand 5 min., or until derivatization is complete. Mixture is then ready for injection into chromatograph.

A majority of hydroxy and polyhydroxy compounds will be completely derivatized within less than 5 min.; e.g. sugars, phenols, organic acids, some amines, alcohols, etc. Highly hindered compounds such as some steroids may require 15 min. to 8 hr. Extremely intractable compounds may require refluxing for several hours.

Method 2

The method of Sweeley, Bentley, Makita, and Wells for the trimethylsilylation of sugars and related substances.

Reagents required: **Hexamethyldisilazane, Trimethylchlorosilane, Pyridine, silylation grade.**

A sample of 10 mg or less of carbohydrate is treated with 1.0 ml of anhydrous pyridine (dried over KOH pellets), 0.2 ml of hexamethyldisilazane and 0.1 ml trimethylchlorosilane (caution). The mixture is reacted in a 1 dram plastic stoppered glass vial. It is shaken vigorously for about 30 sec. and allowed to stand for 5 min. or longer at room temperature until derivatization is complete. (Upon addition of trimethylchlorosilane the solution may become cloudy due to a fine precipitate of ammonium chloride. It is not necessary to remove this precipitate since it interferes in no way with the ensuing gas chromatography.) In the case of carbohydrates which seem to be difficultly soluble in the mixture the vial may be warmed for 2 to 3 min. at 75 to 85 °C. In those cases where mutarotation is not a problem and rearrangements are not likely to occur, the carbohydrate may first be brought into solution with warm pyridine, then the hexamethyldisilazane and trimethylchlorosilane may be added. This method may be applied to proportionately smaller amounts of carbohydrates and reagents. From 0.1 to 0.5 μl of the reaction mixture obtained above is generally used for the chromatographic injection sample.

Method 3

TRI-SIL DMF is a two-solution formulation for uses where dimethylformamide is preferred as a solvent. It is particularly useful for 3-ketosteroids. Use as follows:

Reagents required: **TRI-SIL DMF.**

Mix equal parts of solutions 1 and 2 and thereafter follow the directions given for TRI-SIL (Method 1). The mixed stock solutions 1 and 2 form a working solution that is stable for at least 12 hr. under ordinary conditions. Therefore, it is suggested that working solution be discarded after 12 hr.

Method 4

TRI-SIL Concentrate contains no solvent. It is formulated to allow flexibility and your choice of solvent. Use as follows:

Reagents required: **TRI-SIL Poly solvent kit.**
(Contains TRI-SIL Concentrate and an assortment of solvents.)

To one part of TRI-SIL Concentrate add a suitable quantity of solvent (usually 3 to 5 parts); then proceed as directed under TRI-SIL (Method 1).

Dry solvents (see "Solvent Suggestions") should be used and the working solution is usually stable for several days, if protected from moisture, except when certain solvents that will react slowly with the mixture are used; e.g. dimethylformamide. Dimethylformamide solution should be discarded after 12 hr. Obviously, solvents such as water or alcohols cannot be used because they will react almost instantaneously with the reagent.

Method 5

TRI-SIL/BSA is a potentiated formulation of the powerful trimethylsilyl donor "BSA." It is available in two formulations: Formula P, in which pyridine is the solvent portion; and Formula D, in which dimethylformamide is the solvent portion. Procedure for use, which is the same for both formulas, is as follows:

Reagents required: **TRI-SIL/BSA, Formula P** or **TRI-SIL/BSA, Formula D.**

Introduce 5–10 mg of sample in 1 ml TRI-SIL/BSA into small plastic stoppered vial. Shake vigorously to dissolve (may be warmed to 65–70 °C if necessary). Many polar materials will silylate completely at room temperature within less than 5 min., some may require 15 min.–12 hr. Most difficult samples may require refluxing several hours or heating in tightly sealed tube or vial at temperatures up to 200 °C for up to 1 hr.

As with "BSA," TRI-SIL/BSA is not recommended for sugars where anomerization is a problem. Methods 1, 2, 8 and 9 are recommended for such cases. For some difficult silylations a drop or two of trimethylchlorosilane (caution) may be added to catalyze the reaction.

Method 6

"BSA," *N,O*-bis-(trimethylsilyl)-acetamide, CH_3-C[OSi$(CH_3)_3$]=N-Si$(CH_3)_3$, is a powerful trimethylsilyl donor that will silylate many usually intractable compounds. Because of its activity it is extremely sensitive to moisture and should therefore be handled under as dry conditions as is practicable. It may be used with or without a solvent depending upon conditions and preference. Use as follows:

Reagents required: **"BSA", Solvent (optional).** The following silylation grade solvents are suggested: **Acetonitrile, Pyridine, Dimethylformamide, Dimethylsulfoxide, Tetrahydrofuran.**

Introduce 5–10 ml of sample and 0.5 ml of "BSA" into a small plastic stoppered vial. Add necessary amount of appropriate solvent as needed or desired. Mixture may be warmed to facilitate solution. Usually samples are silylated when dissolved.

A number of amino acids may be silylated by conducting the above reaction in a sealed glass tube or tightly closed screw-capped container and heating to near the boiling point of the mixture until a clear solution is obtained. It is recommended that about 3 parts of an appropriate solvent be used to each part of "BSA" for silylating amino acids.

With some samples, such as some slowly reacting steroids, the reaction may be catalyzed by the addition of a drop or two of trimethychlorosilane (caution).

This method is not recommended for the silylation of sugars where anomerization may be a problem. In such cases use methods 1, 2, 8 and 9.

A variation of this method is the substitution of "BSTFA", *N,O*-bis-(TMS)-trifluoroacetamide, for "BSA." This reagent is simply the fluorinated analog of BSA and its greatest virtue is that two of its by-products—mono-TMS-trifluoroacetamide and trifluoroacetamide—are more volatile than the analogous by-products of BSA. Its use is indicated in some cases where GC peaks of BSA an its by-products interfere with the peaks of derivatives.

Method 7

"MSTFA", *N*-methyl-*N*-TMS-trifluoroacetamide, is a new reagent that shows great promise. Its unique properties offer unexplored avenues to those interested in new investigations and should make possible some determinations that are not presently feasible with other reagents. MSTFA is the most volatile TMS-amide yet available—more volatile than BSA or BSTFA and is described as having similar donor strength [Donike M., *J, Chromatogr.*, **42,** 103–104 (1969)]. Another important factor: its by-product, *N*-methyltrifluoroacetamide, has even lower retention time than the MSTFA itself. This will be of considerable value in gas phase determinations where the reagent or by-products obscure the derivative on the chromatogram. It will be of particular value in trace analysis where the interpretation of the small peak area on the chromatogram may be confused or lost in the tailing of other silylating reagents or by-products.

Reagents required: **"MSTFA" (*N*-Methyl-*N*-TMS-trifluoroacetamide). Solvents, optional (use Silylation Grade).**

Follow instructions for Method 6, substituting MSTFA for BSA.

Method 8

TRI-SIL "Z" is a prepared reagent with unique qualities. It will silylate in the presence of moderate amounts of water. It silylates sugars very rapidly and smoothly and with less anomerization than has been observed with any other method. It silylates hydroxy groups only and does not react with amines. It was developed primarily for use with syrups but has been found to be useful for all classes of hydroxyl compounds. It is formulated from "TSIM", *N*-TMS-imidazole in dry pyridine.

Reagents required: **TRI-SIL "Z".**

Introduce 10–15 mg of sample and 1 ml TRI-SIL "Z" into a stoppered vial. Shake occasionally until dissolved—may be heated to 60–70 °C if necessary. Sugars are usually completely silylated when dissolved. Inject reacted mixture directly into the gas chromatograph.

Method 9

This method is basically the same as Method 8 except the reagent and solvent are mixed before use and the solvent is one of choice.

Reagents required: **"TSIM", *N*-TMS-imidazole. Solvent** (your choice). The following Silylation Grade solvents are suggested: **Pyridine, Dimethylformamide, Acetonitrile, Dimethylsulfoxide, Tetrahydrofuran.**

Dissolve 2.1 g TSIM in sufficient silylation grade solvent to make 10 ml solution. Use this solution as TRI-SIL "Z" in Method 8. Solution may be stored in moisture proof container in refrigerator.

Method 10

The method of Brobst and Lott [*Cereal Chem.*, **43**, 35–43 (1966)]. This method was developed primarily for silylating syrups and concentrated aqueous solutions of sugars such as starch hydrolysates. The method works well when the procedure is closely followed. Use caution since considerable heat and ammonia gas pressure are evolved. The reagents cannot be pre-mixed.

Reagents required: **"HMDS", Hexamethyldisilazane, Trifluoroacetic Acid, Pyridine.**

1. Place 60–70 mg of 80% solids syrup in stoppered vial*.
2. Dissolve in 1 ml pyridine.
3. Add 0.9 ml HMDS.
4. Add 0.1 ml trifluoroacetic acid.
5. Shake vigorously for 30 seconds, let stand for 15 minutes with occasional shaking.
6. Inject portion into chromatograph.

*Hypo-vials are ideal containers for this reaction.

Method 11

This method depends on the reaction of an active hydrogen compound with trimethylsilyldiethylamine (TMSDEA) to produce a TMS derivative and diethylamine. Careful fractionation to remove the low boiling amine as produced has afforded excellent yields of amino acids and other compounds in our laboratories; e.g.

Reagents required: ***N*-Trimethylsilyldiethylamine.**

8 g DL-Threonine (0.067*M*) and 45 g trimethylsilyldiethylamine (0.31*M*) were placed in a small distillation apparatus and heated to 145 °C, when diethylamine began to distill; about 20 ml was removed in 4 hours. The reaction was cooled and then distilled under vacuum; after removal of excess TMSDEA (b. 26°/10 mm) an 86% yield (12 g) of pure tris-(TMS)-DL-threonine (b. 70–2 °/0.45 mm) was obtained.

Variations on this method include the use of (1) Trimethylsilyldimethylamine, to afford an even more volatile by-product; (2) The use of catalytic amounts (1% or less) of trimethylchlorosilane, to improve yields; and (3) Addition of 5 to 10% BSA, during the latter part of the reaction to give a final "kick" to components of the sample that are short of being completely silylated.

Method 12

This method was developed by Chambaz E. M. and E. C. Horning [*Anal. Letters*, **1**, 201–211 (1968)] for the silylation of hydroxyl groups in sterically unhindered positions in steroids. This includes such sites as 3, 7, 16, 17(sec),

20 and 21 positions in the steroid structure. This method may, of course, be used for silylating many hydroxy and polyhydroxy compounds other than steroids. (It is not recommended, however, for sugars. Methods 1, 2, 4, 8, 9 and 10 are better for sugars.) The method is based upon the use of BSA in an *uncatalyzed* reaction. It should be borne in mind that no trimethylchlorosilane should be used in this reaction and that hydrochlorides should be avoided since HCl will also act as a catalyst. The method follows:

Reagents required: **"BSA", *N,O*-Bis-(TMS)-acetamide, Pyridine, Silylation Grade,** or other silylation grade solvent.

Place 0.1 to 5 mg of sample into small septum capped vial—a 1 ml **Reacti-vial** is excellent for this reaction. Add 0.2 to 0.4 ml BSA. If material is not soluble in the BSA add 0.1 to 0.2 ml pyridine. (For example, cortical steroids will usually require addition to pyridine to dissolve.) Cap vial with screw cap and Teflon faced disc, shake well to dissolve—may be heated to 60 °C if necessary. Material is silylated at room temperature within times varying from a few minutes to a few hours. Heating will hasten reaction. Reaction mixture may be injected directly into chromatograph. If it is desirable to remove the pyridine or concentrate the mixture then the solvent may be removed by passing dry nitrogen through the mixture until the major portion of the pyridine has evaporated.

Workers interested in the analysis of steroids will also be interested in the next three methods, also relating to steroids.

Method 13

This is the method developed by Chambaz E. M. and E. C. Horning [*Anal. Letters*, **1**, 201–211 (1968)] for the silylation of moderately hindered hydroxyl groups in steroids (such as 11β-ols). Unhindered hydroxyl groups will also be silylated in this reaction. Highly hindered groups (such as the 17α-OH site in cortol) will not be silylated. The reagent TRI-SIL "BT" contains BSA with TMCS as a catalyst.

Reagents required: **TRI-SIL "BT", Pyridine, Silylation Grade,** or other silylation grade solvent. **Steroids Silylation Kit** contains above materials.

Follow same instructions given in Method 12, substituting TRI-SIL "BT" for BSA. Reaction times will generally be somewhat longer for derivatizing the moderately hindered sites than for the unhindered. Complete reaction will usually require 6 to 24 hr. at room temperature or 3 to 6 hr. at 60 °C.

Formation of ENOL TMS ethers. Milder methods of silylation do not usually complicate the analytical problem with the formation of enol-TMS ethers. This method, however, may do so when enolizable compounds are derivatized. In such cases the formation of the enol-TMS ethers is generally within the 5–15 % range. The problem may be prevented by first treating the sample to form methoximes at the keto sites, thus obviating enolization. Refer to Method 15 for preparing methoximes.

Method 14

This method is based upon an extremely powerful silylating formulation, TRI-SIL "TBT", composed of TSIM, BSA and TMCS. This combination resulted from the work of Chambaz E. M. and E. C. Horning [*Anal. Letters*, **1**, 201–211 (1968)]. It will silylate all hydroxyl groups in steroid structures, even the most sterically hindered (such as the 17α-hydroxy group in cortol). This method has also been used by Bacon G. E. and Sharon Kokenakes [*J. Lab. Clin. Med.*, **73**, 1030–1035 (1969)] to measure plasma prednisolone by GLC.

Reagents required: **TRI-SIL "TBT", Pyridine, Silylation Grade,** or other silylation grade solvents.

Follow same instructions given in Method 12, substituting TRI-SIL "TBT" for BSA. Complete reaction will usually require treating sample at 60–80°C for 6 to 24 hr.

Formation of ENOL-TMS ethers. This problem is discussed at the conclusion of Method 13 (which see) and the formation of enol-TMS ethers with TRI-SIL "TBT" is even greater than with TRI-SIL "BT", sometimes the major product may be the enol form. This problem may be alleviated by first treating the sample to convert the keto groups to methoximes. For this procedure refer to Method 15.

Method 15

This is a method for preparing methoxime derivatives of steroids (*1*, *3*, *4*) and keto-acids (*5*) prior to silylation and gas phase analysis to prevent the formation of troublesome enol ethers and to enhance the stability of the derivatives. While the production of enol TMS ethers from steroids is negligible with milder methods of silylation—such as HMDS-TMCS-Pyridine and uncatalyzed BSA—the more powerful formulations required to completely silylate sterically hindered hydroxyl sites will often result in the formation of considerable quantities of enol-TMS ethers. 4-ene-3-one groups readily form enol derivatives and 17 and 20-one groups are also susceptible (*1*).

The method of forming methoximes is based on the work of Fales and Luukkainen (*2*) and further applications by Horning and co-workers (*3*, *4*).

Reagents required: **"MOX".**

Two procedures have been used successfully by Horning, Moss and Horning (*4*). (1) A simplified procedure for stable ketones that are readily soluble in organic solvents and (2) A procedure for polar steroids, such as corticoids, which have several hydroxyl groups (*1*). An even simpler procedure (3) has been used by Gardiner and Horning (*3*) that is suitable for GLC. This method saves considerable work.

1. Dissolve approximately 2 mg of sample in 0.5 ml "MOX". Heat for 3 hr. at 60 °C in a screw capped vial with Teflon-lined seal. Dilute with 2 ml glass-distilled water and extract with three 5 ml portions of high purity benzene. Combine the benzene extracts, wash with 1*N* HCl, then with 1 % sodium bicarbonate

solution in glass-distilled water. Dry the organic solution with anhydrous magnesium sulfate. Finally, use a nitrogen stream to concentrate the solution to 0.5 ml. Aliquots of this may be used for TLC separations (use about 10–20 μl) and for GLC separations (use 0.5–2.0 μl).

2. Dissolve about 2 mg of sample in 0.5 ml "MOX". Allow to stand overnight at room temperature. Dilute with 2 ml saturated aqueous solution sodium chloride. Extract derivative with three 5 ml portions of high purity ethyl acetate. Combine the ethyl acetate extracts and wash first with salt saturated 0.1*N* HCl; next with saturated aqueous solution sodium chloride; third, with sodium chloride saturated 5% sodium bicarbonate solution; finally, with saturated sodium chloride solution. Dry the ethyl acetate solution with anhydrous magnesium sulfate. Concentrate the solution to 0.5 ml with a nitrogen stream. Aliquots of this may be used for TLC and GLC separations as suggested in procedure 1.

3. Some workers (*3*), after completing the methoxime reaction, have silylated the reacted mixture without further treatment. The resulting mixture was centrifuged to remove solids and aliquots of the liquid used for GLC. It should be borne in mind, however, that the liquid will contain some HCl, which will act as a catalyst in the silylation reaction. Therefore, moderately hindered groups as well as unhindered groups will also be silylated if a simple silylation reagent such as BSA is used alone.

The reagent "MOX" is formulated from 2% methoxyamine hydrochloride in pyridine. It is a near saturated solution and will precipitate upon refrigeration and redissolve upon warming to room temperature. It is quite stable when protected from exposure to moist atmosphere. "MOX" is packaged in Hypo-vials under nitrogen.

References:
1. Maume, B., Wilson, W. E., and E. C. Horning, *Anal. Letters*, **1**, 401 (1968).
2. Fales, H. M. and T. Luukkainen, *Anal. Chem.*, **37**, 955 (1965).
3. Gardiner, W. L. and E. C. Horning, *Biochim. Biophys. Acta*, **115**, 425 (1966).
4. Horning, M. G., Moss, A. M., and E. C. Horning, *Anal. Biochem.*, **22**, 284–294 (1968).
5. Horning, M. G., Boucher, E. A., Moss, A. M., and E. C. Horning, *Anal. Letters*, **1**, 713–723 (1968).

Method 16

Volasil is used for preparing *dimethylsilyl* ethers [R-O-SiH$(CH_3)_2$]. It is a single solution reagent, ready for use. Use as follows:

Reagents required: **Volasil.**

Use directions given for TRI-SIL (Method 1) substituting Volasil for TRI-SIL.

Dimethylsilyl ethers have greater volatility and shorter retention times than the trimethylsilyl derivatives. However, some resolution is sacrificed. It is particularly useful with higher-molecular-weight compounds.

Method 17

This is an alternate method for producing dimethylsilyl ethers. Prepare a mixture of tetramethyldisilazane and dimethylchlorosilane (caution) in dry pyridine. Use as follows:

Reagents required: **Tetramethyldisilazane, Dimethylchlorosilane, Pyridine, Silylation Grade.**

Follow Sweeley's method (Method 2), substituting tetramethyldisilazane for hexamethyldisilazane and dimethylchlorosilane for trimethylchlorosilane.

Method 18

This is a method for preparing chloromethyldimethylsilyl derivatives for use with electron capture detectors. Retention time of these derivatives is somewhat longer than that for the corresponding TMS derivatives due to the presence of the chlorine atom as might be expected. The carbon attached chlorine is quite stable and not highly reactive as is the case with silicon attached chlorines (e.g. trimethylchlorosilane, dimethyldichlorosilane). Chloromethyldimethylsilyl derivatives are slightly less sensitive to electron capture than monochloroacetates but retention times are lower.

Reagents required: **Chloromethyldimethylchlorosilane, 1,3-Bis-(Chloromethyl)-Tetramethyldisilazane, Pyridine Silylation Grade** or **Dimethylformamide, Silylation Grade.**

Follow the procedure given in Method 2, substituting chloromethyldimethylchlorosilane for TMCS and 1,3-bis-(chloromethyl)-tetramethyldisilazane for HMDS. Dimethylformamide may be substituted for pyridine, if desired.

Method 19

This is an alternate method for producing chloromethyldimethylsilyl ethers. This method replaces an earlier method using chloromethyldimethylsilyldiethylamine, which was found to be unstable. In this latter method chloromethyldimethylsilyldiethylamine is formed *in situ*.

Reagents required: **Chloromethyldimethylchlorosilane, Pyridine, Silylation Grade** or **Dimethylformamide, Silylation Grade, Diethylamine** (not supplied by Pierce).

Dissolve 5–10 mg sample in 1 ml pyridine or dimethylformamide. Add 0.5 ml chloromethyldimethylchlorosilane and 0.5 ml diethylamine. Reflux 2–3 hr. or until derivatization is complete. Use adequate ventilation or hood to dispose of unpleasant fumes.

Method 20

This method is used for the preparation of bromomethyldimethylsilyl ethers for use with electron capture technique. Their response to the electron capture detector is greater than that of monochloroacetates and approaches that of the heptafluorobutyryl derivatives. Retention times are about twice that of chloromethyldimethylsilyl derivatives and about five times that of corresponding TMS derivatives.

Reagents required: **Bromomethyldimethylchlorosilane, Pyridine, Silylation Grade** or **Dimethylformamide, Silylation Grade.**

Follow instructions given in Method 19, substituting bromomethyldimethylchlorosilane for chloromethyldimethylchlorosilane.

Method 21

This is a method for preparing heptafluorobutyryl or trifluoroacetyl derivatives of polar compounds using the reagents heptafluorobutyrylimidazole, "HFBI" or trifluoroacetylimidazole, "TFAI." These are excellent acylating reagents and have the advantage of not releasing acid into the reaction mixture, thus by-passing the danger of hydrolyzing delicate samples; inert imidazole is the reaction by-product. Both HFBI and TFAI derivatives are volatile and excellent for flame ionization detection. The heptafluorobutyryl derivatives are very sensitive to electron capture technique. These fluorinated acyl imidazoles will acylate hydroxyl groups and both primary and secondary amines. This procedure may also be used for nonfluorinated *N*-acyl imidazoles such as *N*-acetylimidazole.

Reagents required: **"HFBI", *N*-Heptafluorobutyrylimidazole, *N*-Trifluoroacetylimidazole, Hexane, Sequanal Grade.**

Place 0.1 to 2 mg of sample and 0.2 ml of the *N*-acylimidazole in a small screw capped vial equipped with Teflon faced liner. Heat 2–6 hr. at 60 °C. Mixture may be injected into chromatograph. If it is desired to concentrate the mixture it may be extracted three times with small volumes (0.4–0.8 ml) hexane, the hexane extracts combined and evaporated with a stream of nitrogen to 0.1 ml. This may be used for TLC and GLC separations.

Care should be taken in handling and storage of the fluorinated acyl imidazole reagents since they are extremely sensitive to moisture.

Method 22

This method utilizes heptafluorobutyric acid anhydride, "HFBA" or trifluoroacetic acid anhydride, "TFAA", to produce the corresponding fluorinated acyl derivatives.

Reagents required: **"HFBA", Heptafluorobutyric Acid Anhydride** or **"TFAA", Trifluoroacetic Acid Anhydride, Pyridine, Silylation Grade.**

Place 0.1 to 1 mg of sample in a screw capped vial equipped with Teflon faced liner, add 0.1 ml pyridine and 0.1 ml desired acid anhydride. Tightly close vial and heat for 2 hr. at 60 °C. Use reaction mixture for GLC determination.

Method 23

This method combines silylation of hydroxyl groups and acylation of amino groups. This ingenious method was first used by Horning, M. G., Moss, A. M., Boucher, E. A., and E. C. Horning [*Anal. Letters*, **1**, 311–321 (1968)] to prepare catecholamines for GLC and Mass Spec determinations. It takes advantage of the fact that TSIM will silylate hydroxyl groups only, effectively blocking those sites from acylation while leaving the amine sites open for acylation. The resulting *O*-TMS, *N*-fluoroacyl derivatives are volatile compounds, suitable for flame ionization detection and also (particularly the heptafluorobutyryl) for electron capture.

Reagents required: **"TSIM", *N*-TMS-Imidazole, "TFAI", *N*-Trifluoroacetylimidazole or "HFBI", *N*-Heptafluorobutyrylimidazole, Acetonitrile, Silylation Grade.**

Place about 1 mg of sample in small vial equipped with screw cap and Teflon faced liner. Dissolve sample in 0.1 ml acetonitrile and add 0.2 ml TSIM. Cap vial and heat for 3 hr. at 60 °C. Add 0.1 ml HFBI or TFAI (depending upon which acyl derivative is desired) and heat for 30 min. at 60 °C. This reaction mixture may be used directly for GLC.

If an unfluorinated acyl imidazole, such as *N*-acetylimidazole, is used in this procedure the final reaction should be heated for 3 hr. at 60 °C.

A word about the volatility of heptafluorobutyryl derivatives; due to the influence of the seven carbon-attached fluorines the volatility of these compounds is much higher than one might expect of a bulky butyryl group. In fact the HFB derivatives are even more volatile than the unfluorinated acetyl analogs.

(c) Silylation Reagents Available from Pierce Chemical Co. for Carrying Out the Above Procedures

1. TRI-SIL

TRI-SIL is a prepared solvent-reagent-catalyst formulation for rapidly producing TMS derivatives of polar compounds (e.g. sugars (*1*, *2*, *6*, *7*, *24*, *27*), phenols (*3*), steroids (*5*, *9*), sterols (*25*, *26*), bile acids (*8*) and other organic acids (*30*, *31*), some amines (*20*, *28*, *29*) and alcohols (*1*)) for gas chromatographic determinations and biochemical synthesis. The solvent portion is highly purified pyridine. For uses where pyridine may be undesirable; e.g. 3-ketosteroids (*9*), we offer TRI-SIL DMF, wherein the solvent portion is *N,N*-dimethylformamide.

What is it? TRI-SIL is a formulation for rapidly converting samples of polar materials (e.g., carbohydrates (*1, 2, 6, 7*), phenols (*3*), steroids (*5*), bile acids (*8*)) into volatile trimethylsilyl ethers for GLC separations and determinations.

How does it work? Utilizing a solvent-reagent-catalyst system, based on the procedure of Sweeley, Bentley, Makita and Wells (*1*) for the optimal conversion of organic hydroxy and polyhydroxy compounds into TMS ethers; the reaction proceeds as follows: $3\ ROH + Me_3SiNHSiMe_3 + Me_3SiCl \rightarrow 3\ ROSiMe_3 + NH_4Cl$.

Advantages:

1. *Simplicity*. TRI-SIL is a single solution formulation, ready for immediate use.
2. *Speed*. Within a few minutes the treated sample is usually ready for injection into the chromatograph.
3. *Broad applicability*. Carbohydrates such as sugars and related polyhydroxy compounds (*1, 2, 6, 7*), phenols (*3*), hydroxy- and keto-steroids* (*5, 9*), bile acids (*8*) and alcohols (*1*) are examples of the wide range of compounds to which this technique is most effective.
4. *Reliability*. The trimethylsilylation reaction of TRI-SIL proceeds smoothly, predictably, often quantitatively.
5. *Improved Resolution*. Formerly difficult or impossible separations are achieved by TRI-SIL treatment which promotes the separation of closely related compounds by emphasizing their structural differences in such a way as to facilitate resolution.
6. *Minimizes anomerization*. It has been shown (*1*) that the formation of anomers is reduced to a negligible minimum by the rapid action of reagent beginning coincidentally with solution.
7. *Prolongs column life*. Lower column temperatures may generally be used than have been required by former methods. Also, the reagents in TRI-SIL have a beneficial effect upon column supports (*4*). These side-benefits result in greatly enhanced column life and performance.

How is it used? Simply dissolve sample in TRI-SIL (10 mg or less to 1 ml), shake vigorously for 30 seconds, slight warming may be used to facilitate solution, allow to stand until derivatization is complete. This will usually be less than 5 min. with most hydroxy and polyhydroxy compounds (e.g. sugars). A few compounds such as some steroids may require 15 min. to 8 hr. for complete reaction. Mixture is then ready for injection into the chromatograph.

2. TRI-SIL DMF

Offered for applications where dimethylformamide is the preferred solvent or where pyridine (the solvent portion of TRI-SIL) might interfere with the reaction, such as with 3-keto-steroids (*9*).

3. TRI-SIL "Z"

A new reagent for quickly derivatizing hydroxy and polyhydroxy compounds either dry or in aqueous solution.

A preponderant majority of reported silylation procedures have been performed under anhydrous conditions. Quite often complete drying of the sample is an arduous and time consuming procedure. There have been numerous conjectures that, since silylating reagents will react with water to form hexamethyldisiloxane, an excess of reagent could be used to remove the water and derivatize the sample. A study of this theory was made (*38*) using the methods of Sweeley *et al.* (*39*), Brobst and Lott (*40*), and other methods with a broad range of silylation reagents in various proportions. In this study aqueous solutions of monosaccharides (50% w/v), disaccharides (50% w/v) and a trisaccharide (10% w/v) were used as samples. The results were compared against the same procedures with dry sugars. Sweeley's method was moderately successful with the monosaccharides but its effectiveness fell off sharply as the size of the sugar molecule increased. (Disaccharides showed an average of only 75% derivatization.) The method of Brobst and Lott gave good results but a premixed reagent cannot be used and there is generation of considerable heat and pressure. None of the other methods or mixtures worked as successfully as the foregoing two, with one exception. This reagent was a mixture of trimethylsilylimidazole in dry pyridine (1.5 meq/ml). This was designated TRI-SIL "Z".

In comparison with other methods the results obtained with TRI-SIL "Z" are most gratifying. All sugars studied thus far are apparently completely derivatized as soon as dissolved. As examples:

1. α-D-Glucose (50% w/v aqueous solution) completely derivatizes at room temperature within 1 min.
2. Raffinose, a trisaccharide (10% w/v aqueous solution) completely derivatizes at 60 °C for 15 min. (the time necessary to dissolve).

A further effect was noted in silylating dry monosaccharides; there was no detectable anomerization where TRI-SIL "Z" was used as the reagent.

A similar formulation was used by Horning, Moss and Horning (*41*) in the silylation of catecholamines. The authors remark that it silylates hydroxyl groups but not basic amino groups and suggest that this may be of value in other applications.

While our present studies have been confined to sugars it is apparent that this remarkable new reagent will be ideal for the silylation of many other types of compounds.

A recent survey shows that TRI-SIL "Z" is being used successfully for the silylation of alcohols and phenols, organic acids, hydroxyamines, amino acids, carbohydrates, flavonoids, glycols and polyglycols, nucleotides, steroids, hydroxy acids, barbiturates, narcotics, indoles and vitamins. A majority of the technicians reporting were preparing derivatives for GLC; some were using the derivatives in other techniques such as mass spectrometry, synthesis, infrared spectrometry and studies of analytical methods.

TRI-SIL "Z" is a convenient single solution reagent and is supplied in 25 ml Hypo-vials and in 1 ml ampules. It is quite easy to use and the following general directions may be adapted to individual use:

* It has been stated (*9*) that pyridine promotes the formation of secondary products from 3-keto-steroids by reaction, presumably with their -enol forms. For such applications we offer TRI-SIL, DMF, in which *N,N*-dimethylformamide replaces pyridine as the solvent portion.

Introduce 10–15 mg of sample and 1 ml TRI-SIL "Z" into a stoppered vial. Shake well and allow to stand a few minutes. May be heated to 60–70 °C if necessary to dissolve. Usually sugars are completely silylated within a few minutes after dissolving. Inject reacted mixture directly into the gas chromatograph.

4. TRI-SIL/BSA

Reacts with **alcohols, phenols,** some **enols** and other **hydroxy** and **polyhydroxy compounds** to form trimethylsilyl ethers; **organic acids** to form trimethylsilyl esters; **aromatic amides** to form *N*-trimethylsilyl derivatives; **amino acids** to form both *N*- and *O*-trimethylsilyl derivatives; **amines** to form *N*-trimethylsilyl derivatives.

A superior reagent for steroids. Derivatizes many steroids and sterols rapidly at room temperature, although heating may sometimes shorten reaction time significantly. May be catalyzed by the addition of 1–10% TMCS to derivatize moderately hindered steroids. (For silylating highly hindered steroids see "TRI-SIL TBT" in description of Steroids Silylation Kit.)

Not recommended for carbohydrates. This reagent seems to give erratic results with sugars. For such compounds we recommend regular TRI-SIL or TRI-SIL "Z", both described in this section.

Highly hindered phenols. Even highly hindered 2,6-di-*tert*-butylphenol is rapidly converted to the TMS ether by TRI-SIL/BSA (*34*).

Excellent for amino acids. Derivatized when dissolved. For instance, cysteine is completely trimethylsilylated in about 10 min. at room temperature—while an HMDS-TMCS mixture gives incomplete substitution after three days at 45 °C.

This is one of the handiest ready-prepared reagents in the GLC laboratory. Any time you need to chromatograph a difficult phenol, alcohol, organic acid, amine or amide try treating it with TRI-SIL/BSA and you will discover better quality control procedures for many formerly intractable or troublesome polar compounds.

Composition of TRI-SIL/BSA. TRI-SIL/BSA is offered in two convenient formulations differing only in the solvent used. Formula "P" is compounded from freshly distilled BSA (2.5 meq/ml)* and thoroughly dried silylation grade pyridine. Formula "D" is also compounded from freshly distilled BSA (2.5 meq/ml)* and thoroughly dried silylation grade dimethylformamide. Both formulations of TRI-SIL/BSA are packaged under nitrogen in 25 ml Hypo-vials and in 1 ml ampules. (*1.25 meq/ml for amides.)

Directions for use. Dissolve about 10 mg of sample in TRI-SIL/BSA and shake to dissolve. Many samples will be completely derivatized as soon as dissolved. Others may require heating to dissolve or react. Reaction times vary from 1–2 min. at room temperature to 8 hours or more at 60–80 °C. Reaction may be catalyzed to hasten reaction time or overcome moderate steric hindrance by the addition of a drop or two of TMCS to each ml of reagent.

5. TRI-SIL Concentrate

TRI-SIL concentrate. This is the TRI-SIL formulation prepared as a concentrated reagent-catalyst system containing no solvent. It is offered in the TRI-SIL Poly Solvent Kit, with specially purified anhydrous solvents individually packed, and in the Poly-Sil Kit, which offers a broad selection of the most useful silylation reagents and solvents. Thus, greater latitude is attained (e.g. pyridine may be used for sugars (*1*), dimethylformamide for 3-keto-steroids (*9*) and dimethylsulfoxide for tertiary alcohols (*32*).

TRI-SIL concentrate is used by mixing one part with an appropriate amount (usually 3 to 5 parts) of solvent. The sample is treated with this mixture, usually 5 min. at room temperature, and is then ready for injection into the chromatograph.

6. Steroids Silylation Kit for the Selective Silylation of Steroids*

This set of reagents provides a reliable and reproducible method for preparing volatile and stable TMS derivatives of steroids and related compounds for gas phase analysis knowing in advance just what active sites will be derivatized. This method will also be valuable for studies of derivative formation in synthetic work, structural determinations and separations other than gas phase.

Recent studies (*42, 43, 44, 45*) have shown that various hydroxyl sites on steroids may be selectively converted to trimethylsilyl derivatives depending upon their relative steric hindrance. The conclusions reached in these studies were supported by GLC data and confirmed by mass spectrometry. These sites fall into three distinct classes: unhindered, moderately hindered and highly hindered. Three reagents have been developed for the selective silylation of these sites: *TRI-SIL "TBT"* will silylate all three types of sites; *TRI-SIL "BT"* will silylate the moderately hindered and unhindered; BSA will silylate the unhindered groups. The structures of variously TMS-substituted Cortol (5β-pregnan-3α,11β,17α,20α,21-pentol) are an excellent illustration of this principle. Prednisolone has been determined quantitatively (*48*) by GLC using *TRI-SIL "TBT"*.

An additional reagent "*MOX*" may be used to form methoxime (MO) derivatives with ketones, eliminating the possibility of enol-TMS ether formation in keto-steroids.

Three useful solvents, especially prepared for silylation reactions, are included in the kit: acetonitrile, dimethylformamide and pyridine.

TRI-SIL "TBT" is a powerful silylating mixture composed of TMS-imidazole (TSIM):*N,O*-bis-(TMS)-acetamide (BSA) : Trimethylchlorosilane (TMCS): 3:3:2, by volume. It will convert all classes of hydroxyl groups to TMS ethers. Usual conditions are treatment of the sample with the reagent at 60–80 °C for several hours.

TRI-SIL "BT" is a catalyzed mixture containing 5 parts BSA to 1 part TMCS. It will convert moderately hindered groups such as 11β-ols and unhindered hydroxyl groups. Reaction is usually complete within a few hours at room temperature, but may be hastened by heating at 60 °C.

BSA is a single, uncatalyzed reagent that will silylate unhindered hydroxyl groups at room temperature in times ranging from a few minutes to a few hours and may be hastened by heating. This includes such sites as 3, sec-17α, 20, 21 and unhindered sites at the 12 and 16 positions.

* According to the method of Chambaz and Horning (*42*).

"*MOX*" is a reagent for the conversion of keto groups to methoxime derivatives (*46, 47*) thus preventing silylation of enols which would interfere with quantitation by producing additional derivatives and also causing extreme steric hindrance in some sites. 4-ene-3-one groups readily form enol TMS ethers and 17 and 20-one groups are also susceptible (*45*). "*MOX*" is a solution (2%) of methoxyamine HCl in pyridine.

Two procedures have been used successfully by Horning, Moss and Horning (*47*). (1) A simplified procedure for stable ketones that are readily soluble in organic solvents and (2) A procedure for polar steroids, such as corticoids, which have several hydroxyl groups. "*MOX*" has been formulated to adapt to these procedures as follows:

1. Dissolve approximately 2 mg of sample in 0.5 ml "*MOX*". Heat for 3 hr. at 60 °C in a screw capped vial with Teflon-lined seal. Dilute with 2 ml glass-distilled water and extract with three 5 ml portions of high purity benzene. Combine the benzene extracts, wash with 1*N* HCl, then with 1% sodium bicarbonate solution in glass-distilled water. Dry the organic solution with anhydrous magnesium sulfate. Finally, use a nitrogen stream to concentrate the solution to 0.5 ml. Aliquots of this may be used for TLC separations (use about 10–20 μl) and for GLC separations (use 0.5–2.0 μl).
2. Dissolve about 2 mg of sample in 0.5 ml "*MOX*". Allow to stand overnight at room temperature. Dilute with 2 ml saturated aqueous solution sodium chloride. Extract derivative with three 5 ml portions of high purity ethyl acetate. Combine the ethyl acetate extracts and wash first with salt saturated 0.1*N* HCl; next with saturated aqueous solution sodium chloride; third, with sodium chloride saturated 5% sodium bicarbonate solution; finally, with saturated sodium chloride solution. Dry the ethyl acetate solution with anhydrous magnesium sulfate. Concentrate the solution to 0.5 ml with a nitrogen stream. Aliquots of this may be used for TLC and GLC separations as suggested in procedure 1.

Some workers (*46*), after completing the methoxime reaction, have silylated the reacted mixture without further treatment. The resulting mixture was centrifuged to remove solids and aliquots of the liquid used for GLC. It should be borne in mind, however, that the liquid will act as a catalyst in the silylation reaction. Therefore, moderately hindered groups as well as unhindered groups will also be silylated if a simple silylation reagent such as BSA is used alone.

Solvents. Three useful silylation grade solvents are supplied in the kit: Pyridine, Acetonitrile and Dimethylformamide. While the silylation reagents themselves may sometimes serve as solvents, some steroids and related compounds may require one of the above solvents. For instance, pyridine is suggested (*43*) for cortols and cortolones (in this case it is recommended that the minimal amount required for solution of sample be used to enhance stability of derivatives).

7. *N,O*-Bis-(Trimethylsilyl)-Acetamide, "BSA"

$$CH_3C(OSi(CH_3)_3){=}N\text{-}Si(CH_3)_3$$

$Si(CH_3)_3$	M.W. 203.43	b.p. 71–73 °C/35 mm
O	n_D^{20} 1.4181	Purity 98% by GLC
$CH_3C{=}N\text{-}Si(CH_3)_3$		Colorless liquid

BSA is a highly reactive trimethylsilyl donor. Conversion of high-melting organic compounds to volatile and thermally stable TMS derivatives is often achieved quantitatively under relatively mild conditions. Consequently, GLC determinations of many usually intractable compounds are made possible and practical.

An impressive study of its silylating properties was made by Klebe, Finkbeiner and White (*34*). Their investigation showed the following reactions of BSA:

1. With amino acids to form both N and O bonded TMS derivatives.
2. With hydroxyl compounds to form TMS ethers.
3. As a rapid quenching agent for compounds with reactive protons.
4. With organic acids to form TMS esters and some enols to form TMS ethers.
5. With aromatic amides to form *N*-TMS derivatives.

8. *N,O*-Bis-(Dimethylsilyl)-Acetamide, "BSDA"

$CH_3[OSiH(CH_3)_2] = NSi(CH_3)_2$ Clear liquid, highly sensitive to moisture

For preparing *dimethylsilyl* derivatives. This is the dimethylsilyl analog of "BSA." DMS ethers are more volatile than TMS ethers, but do not resolve as well in GLC. It should also be borne in mind that this is a silicon hydride and can act as a reducing agent or add to double bonds under some conditions.

9. Bromomethyldimethylchlorosilane

$(CH_2Br)(CH_3)_2SiCl$ M.W. 187.53 b.p. 130 °C/740 mm

Has been used in silylating derivatives for electron capture technique.

Caution! Evolves toxic and corrosive fumes of HCl upon contact with moisture. Avoid contact with skin, eyes or clothing; do not breathe fumes.

10. Chloromethyldimethylchlorosilane, "CMDMCS"

$(CH_2Cl)(CH_3)_2SiCl$

Caution! Evolves toxic and corrosive fumes of HCl upon contact with moisture. Avoid contact with skin, eyes or clothing; do not breathe fumes.

11. 1,3-Bis-(Chloromethyl)-1,1,3,3-Tetramethyldisilazane

$[(CH_2Cl)(CH_3)_2Si]_2NH$

There has been some recent interest in these compounds for preparing silyl derivatives for use in electron capture technique. Generally, 1 volume of the chlorosilane is combined with 2 volumes of the disilazane in about 10 volumes of a suitable dry solvent (dry pyridine, for instance). Reaction with compounds such as sugars is fast and complete; usually less than 5 minutes. Steroids may require 3 hr. Derivatization is usually done at room temperature, although slight warming is sometimes necessary for completely dissolving the sample. Chloromethyldimethylchlorosilane has also been used as a catalyst with (chloromethyldimethylsilyl)diethylamine in preparing the same type derivatives (*35*).

12. Dimethylchlorosilane

$H(CH_3)_2SiCl$ M.W. 94.7 b.p. 36 °C

Caution! Evolves toxic and corrosive fumes of HCl upon contact with moisture. Avoid contact with skin, eyes or clothing; do not breathe fumes.

13. 1,1,3,3-Tetramethyldisilazane

$H(CH_3)_2SiNHSi(CH_3)_2H$ M.W. 133.4

The two reagents above are used for modifying samples to dimethylsilyl ethers (*35*) which have greater volatility than the trimethylsilyl derivatives. However, some resolution is sacrificed. It should also be borne in mind that these reagents are silicon hydrides and under some conditions can act as reducing agents and may add to double bonds.

14. Hexamethyldisilazane, "HMDS", Specially Purified Grade

$(CH_3)_3SiNHSi(CH_3)_3$ M.W. 161.41 b.p. 126 °C Purity > 99.7%

HMDS has been shown to have definite value in extending the practical range of VPC and in improving chromatographic results in the following ways:

Modification of samples. The trimethylsilyl ethers are readily formed by mixing equivalent amounts of HMDS and the hydroxy compound in pyridine or tetrahydrofuran solution with a small amount of trimethylchlorosilane, which serves to catalyze the reaction. The reaction may be expressed as follows:

$$2R\text{-}OH + (CH_3)_3SiNHSi(CH_3)_3 \rightarrow 2ROSi(CH_3)_3 + NH_3$$

A critical evaluation of the optimal proportions of HMDS and trimethylchlorosilane for production of maximum yield of trimethylsilyl derivatives was conducted by Sweeley, Bentley, Makita and Wells (*1*).

Treating column supports. The same reaction occurs if HMDS is brought in contact with the materials used as column packing supports. Thus the surface hydroxyl groups on any diatomaceous earth, firebrick, aluminum oxide, silica gel or similar supports are effectively blocked by treatment with HMDS (*16*, *17*, *18*). Once the polar groups are converted to trimethylsilyl ethers the following advantages accrue:

1. Tailing effects of polar compounds are sharply reduced.
2. Catalytic effects are minimized. This is particularly valuable where there is a possibility of reaction between the surface hydroxyl groups and sensitive components of the sample mixture.
3. Permits improved results with low liquid loadings, thereby reducing the harmful effects of carry-over of stationary phase into the detector cell.

A procedure has been reported by Bohemen, *et al.* (*4*) for treating column supports (it inhibits decomposition of sensitive materials by glass wool as well). It has been checked by our analytical research group and found to be quite adequate.

15. *N*-Methyl-*N*-Trimethylsilyltrifluoroacetamide "MSTFA"

$CF_3CONCH_3[Si(CH_3)_3]$ M.W. 199.25 b.p. 132 °C

Clear to light yellow liquid. Sensitive to moisture!

The most volatile TMS-amide yet available; more volatile than BSTFA or BSA and is described as having similar donor strength (*41*). Its by-product, *N*-methyltrifluoroacetamide, has even a lower retention time in GLC than the MSTFA. This is expected to be of considerable value in GLC determinations where the reagent or by-products obscure the derivative on the chromatogram. It will be of particular value in trace analysis of materials where the interpretation of the small peak area on the chromatogram may be confused or lost in the tailing of other silylating reagents and by-products.

16. Trimethylchlorosilane, "TMCS", Specially Purified Grade

$(CH_3)_3SiCl$ M.W. 108.7 Purity > 99% b.p. 57 °C

Free of dimethyldichlorosilane.

Trimethylchlorosilane is useful in biochemistry as an adjunct in the formation of trimethylsilyl ethers for gas chromatographic determinations (*1*, *2*, *8*) and recent work shows great promise in biochemical synthesis (*10*). TMCS may be used for preparing TMS derivatives of organic acids (*30*, *31*).

Caution! Evolves toxic and corrosive fumes of HCl upon contact with moisture. Avoid contact with skin, eyes or clothing; do not breathe fumes.

17. *N*-Trimethylsilylacetamide

$CH_3CONHSi(CH_3)_3$ M.W. 131.25 m.p. 52-54 °C

N-Trimethylsilylacetamide is covered by U.S.Patent 2,876,234, and its commercial manufacture must be licensed from Rohm and Haas Co. The use of this silylating reagent for producing TMS sugars is described by Birkofer, Ritter and Bentz (*12*).

18. *N*-Trimethylsilyldiethylamine, "TMSDEA"

$(CH_3)_3SiN(C_2H_5)_2$ M.W. 145.33 b.p. 127 °C/738 mm

N-Trimethylsilyldiethylamine has been found useful in preparing TMS derivatives of amino acids (*13, 36, 37*). Gas chromatography of TMS amino acids is reported (*14, 37*). Peptide synthesis with TMS amino acids has been reported by Birkofer, Konkol and Ritter (*15*). Recently TMSDEA has been used in the GLC of neomycin (*50*).

19. *N*-Trimethylsilyldimethylamine, "TMSDMA"

$(CH_3)_3SiN(CH_3)_2$ M.W. 117.3 b.p. 86–87 °C

N-TMS Dimethylamine shows promise in silylations where TMS diethylamine has been used. It seems to have a faster rate of reaction and has the advantage of generating a gaseous by-product (dimethylamine, b.p. 6–7 °C) which aids in driving the reaction to completion.

20. *N*-Trimethylsilylimidazole, "TSIM"

$(CH_3)_3Si\underline{NCH{=}NCH{=}C}H$ b.p. 99.5 °C/14 mm M.W. 140.26

A trimethylsilylating reagent of unique activity, reacting quickly and smoothly **with hydroxyl groups only** (*40, 49*) to produce volatile and thermally stable TMS ethers. Most useful in carbohydrate chemistry (*38*), TSIM is also finding applications with alcohols and phenols, amino acids, organic acids, hydroxyamines, steroids, flavonoids, glycols, nucleotides, hydroxy acids, barbiturates and narcotics. Birkofer and Ritter (*33*) have reviewed a number of unique synthetic possibilities of this interesting reagent; for instance, the reaction with thionyl chloride to form thionyl diimidazole and with PCl_3 to form triimidazolyl phosphine.

Horning, Moss, Boucher and Horning (*49*) have ingeniously demonstrated the sequential use of TSIM and *N*-heptafluorobutyrylimidazole, "HFBI", (described later in this section) in a single reaction mixture in preparing catecholamines for GLC and Mass Spec. First, all hydroxyl sites are silylated with TSIM, then the amino groups are acylated with HFBI, producing the excellent and distinctive *O*-TMS, *N*-HFB derivatives for either f.i.d. or e.c. detection.

21. *N,O*-Bis-(Trimethylsilyl)-Trifluoroacetamide, "BSTFA"

$CF_3C(-O-Si(CH_3)_3){=}N{-}Si(CH_3)_3$ M.W. 257.40 b.p. 40 °C/12 mm m.p. -10 °C

Description. BSTFA is a clear liquid, very sensitive to moisture. It hydrolyzes to form *N*-(trimethylsilyl)-trifluoroacetamide and trifluoroacetamide.

Action and uses. BSTFA is a powerful trimethylsilyl donor with approximately the same donor strength as the unfluorinated analog "BSA" [*N,O*-bis(trimethylsilyl)-acetamide]. It reacts to replace the labile hydrogen in polar compounds with a $Si(CH_3)_3$ group. Therefore, it has been found useful for preparing volatile and thermally stable derivatives of polar materials for gas chomatography and mass spectrometry.

The particular advantage of BSTFA over BSA is the greater volatility of its by-products, monotrimethylsilyltrifluoroacetamide and trifluoroacetamide, than that of the unfluorinated by-products of BSA. In the gas chromatography of some of the lower boiling TMS-amino acids and TMS Krebs cycle acids the by-products of BSA may have similar retention characteristics and thus obscure these derivatives on the chromatogram. The by-products of BSTFA will usually elute with the solvent front.

BSTFA may be used full strength or with a suitable solvent, such as pyridine, for silylating reactions. A two-fold or more excess of BSTFA is generally used. In some cases a small amount (1–2 %) of trimethylchlorosilane may serve to catalyze reactions with some highly hindered groups.

22. *N,O*-Bis-TMS-Trifluoroacetamide. Containing 1 % TMCS as Catalyst

New Acylating Reagents—*N*-ACYL Imidazoles

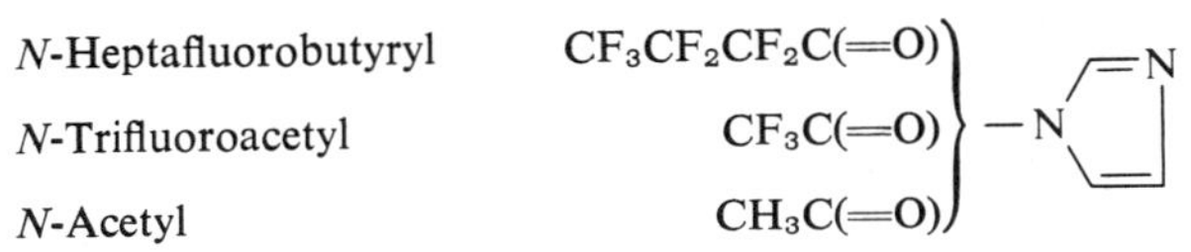

For acylation of samples to produce ideal derivatives for GLC, Mass Spec and for synthesis.

The *N*-acyl imidazoles offer considerable advantage in many instances, over the use of acid chlorides and anhydrides. Their reaction is smooth and positive and no acids are released in the system to hydrolyze valuable samples —relatively inert imidazole is the by-product, of course. The fluorinated acyl derivatives are ideal for flame detectors and the heptafluorobutyryl is especially sensitive to electron capture, in addition to being surprisingly volatile despite the bulk of the group. The closely bound fluorines are responsible for this effect, also contributing extreme stability to the group.

Ingenious use of HFBI for acylating catecholamines that have previously been silylated with TSIM to produce *O*-TMS, *N*-HFB derivatives for GLC and Mass Spec has been demonstrated (*40*, *49*).

References Cited in Section (c).

1. Sweeley, C. C., Bentley, R., Makita, M., and W. W. Wells, *J. Amer. Chem. Soc.*, **85**, 2495–2507 (1963).
2. Hedgley, E. V. and W. G. Overend, *Chem. Ind.* (*London*), 378 (1960).
3. Langer, M., Pantages, P., and I. Wendler, *ibid.*, 1664 (1958).
4. Bohemen, J., Langer, S. H., Perrett, R. H., and J. H. Purnell, *J. Chem. Soc.*, **1960**, 2444–2451.
5. Luukkainen, T., Van denHeuvel, W. J. A., Haahti, E. A. O., and E. C. Horning, *Biochim. Biophys. Acta*, **52**, 599–601 (1960).
6. Ferrier, R. J. and M. F. Singleton, *Tetrahedron*, **18**, 1143 (1962).
7. Ferrier, R. J. *ibid.*, **18**, 1149 (1962).
8. Makita, M., and W. W. Wells, *Anal. Biochem.*, **5**, 523 (1963).
9. Miettinen, Ahrens and Grundy, *J. Lipid Res.*, **6**, 411–424.
10. Iwai, I., Shimizu, B., and T. Nishimura, D22, 150th meeting A.C.S., Sept. 1965, Synthesis of Nucleosides from Trimethylsilyl Derivatives of Pyrimidines and Purines.
11. Wells, W. W., Sweeley, C. C., and R. Bentley, "*Biomedical Applications of Gas Chromatography*", H. A. Szymanski, Ed., 199, Plenum Press (1964).
12. Birkofer, L., Ritter, A., and F. Bentz, *Chem. Ber.*, **97**, 2196–2201 (1964).
13. Ruhlmann, K. *Chem. Ber.*, **94**, 1876 (1961).
14. Ruhlmann, K. and W. Giesecke, *Angew. Chem.*, **73**, 113 (1961).
15. Birkofer, L., Konkol, W., and A. Ritter, *Angew. Chem.*, **71**, 101 (1959).
16. Sawyer, D. T. and J. K. Barr, *Anal. Chem.*, **34**, 1518–1520 (1962).
17. Perrett, R. H. and J. H. Purnell, *J. Chromatogr.*, **7**, 455–466 (1962).
18. Dewar, R. A. and V. E. Maier, *J. Chromatogr.*, **11**, 295–300 (1963).
19. Andrianov, K. A., Astakhin, V. V. and B. P. Nikiforov, *Zh. Obshch. Khim.* (*SSR*), **34**, 914–916 (1964).
20. Birkhofer, L. and A. Ritter, *Chem. Ber.*, **93**, 424–427 (1960).
21. Birkhofer, L., Ritter, A., and P. Neuhausen, *Ann.* **659**, 190–199 (1962).
22. Fessenden, R. and D. Crowe, *J. Org. Chem.*, **25**, 598–603 (1960).
23. Rowland, S. P., Cirino, V. O., and A. L. Bullock, C21, A.C.S. Winter Meeting, Jan. 1966 and C & E News, p. 30, Jan. 31, 1966.
24. Sweeley, C. C. and B. Walker, *Anal. Chem.*, **36**, 1461 (1964).
25. Nair, P. P., Bucana, C., deLeon, S., and D. A. Turner, *Anal. Chem.*, **37**, 631 (1965).
26. Rozanski, A., *Anal. Chem.*, **38**, 36 (1966).
27. Brower, H. E., Jeffrey, J. E., and M. W. Folsom, *Anal. Chem.*, **38**, 362 (1966).
28. Horning, E. C., Horning, M. G., Van denHeuvel, W. J. A., Knox, K. L., Holmstedt, B., and C. J. W. Brooks, *Anal. Chem.*, **36**, 1546 (1964).
29. Capella, P. and E. C. Horning, *Anal. Chem.*, **38**, 316 (1966).
30. Burkhard, C. A. *J. Org. Chem.*, **22**, 592 (1957).
31. Mehrotra, R. C. and B. C. Pant, *J. Indian Chem. Soc.*, **40**, 623 (1963).
32. Friedman, S. and M. L. Kaufmann, *Anal. Chem.*, **38**, 144 (1966).
33. Birkhofer, L. and A. Ritter, "New Methods of Preparative Organic Chemistry", Vol. IV, Academic Press, New York-London.
34. Klebe, J. F., Finkbeiner, H., and D. M. White, *J. Amer. Chem. Soc.*, **88**, 3390–3395 (1966).
35. Thomas, B. S., Eaborn, C., and D. R. M. Walton, *Chem. Commun.*, **13**, 408 (1966).
36. Mason, P. S. and E. D. Smith, *J. Gas Chromatogr.*, **4**, 398 (1966).
37. Smith, E. D. and H. Sheppard, Jr., *Nature*, **208**, 878 (1965).
38. Brittain, G. D. and L. Schewe, Chicago Gas Chromatography Group, Winter Meeting, January 1968.
39. Brobst, K. M. and C. E. Lott, Jr., *Cereal Chem.*, **43**, 35–43 (1966).
40. Horning, M. G., Moss, A. M., and E. C. Horning, *Biochim. Biophys. Acta*, **148**, 597–600 (1967).
41. Donike, M.,*J. Chromatogr.*, **42**, 103–104 (1969).
42. Chambaz, E. M. and E. C. Horning, *Anal. Letters*, **1**, 201–211 (1968).
43. Chambaz, E. M. and E. C. Horning, *Anal. Biochem.*, **30**, 7 (1969).
44. Maume, B., Wilson, W. E., and E. C. Horning, *Anal. Letters*, **1**, 401 (1968).
45. Chambaz, E. M., Maume, G., Maume, B., and E. C. Horning, *Anal. Letters*, **1**, 749–761 (1968).
46. Gardiner, W. L. and E. C. Horning, *Biochim. Biophys. Acta*, **115**, 425 (1966).
47. Horning, M. G., Moss, A. M., and E. C. Horning, *Anal. Biochem.*, **22**, 284–294 (1968).
48. Bacon, G. E. and S. Kokenakes, *J. Lab. Clin. Med.*, **73**, 1030–1035 (1969).
49. Horning, M. G., Moss, A. M., Boucher, E. A., and E. C. Horning, *Anal. Letters*, **1**, 311–321 (1968).
50. Tsuji, K. and J. H. Robertson, *Anal. Chem.*, **41**, 1332–1335 (1969).

58. Procedures for the Esterification and Saponification of Samples for GC Analysis

(a) Boron halide reagents (require well ventilated area!)

1. *Methyl ester reagents*

Reagent: BF_3-methanol (14% w/v) and BCl_3-methanol (10% w/v).

Method: The procedure of Metcalfe and Schmitz is intended chiefly for rapid industrial analysis of fatty acids and has the advantage that the entire procedure can be completed in 10 min. The procedure is as follows:

Place 100 to 200 mg of fatty acid in a 20 × 150 mm test tube; Add 3 to 5 ml of BF_3-MeOH reagent; Boil on a steam bath for 2 min.; (a) If short-chain acids (fewer than 10 carbons) are present, transfer the esters to a separatory funnel containing 20 ml of water and allow the layers to separate. Draw off the ester layer from the aqueous layer and remove the last traces of water by centrifugation. (If esterifying minute amounts of fatty acids, modify the method by adding a few ml of hydrocarbon such as pentane or heptane in order to extract all the esters from the aqueous layer);

(b) If only long-chain acids are present, transfer the boiled mixture to a separatory funnel containing 30 ml of petroleum ether (b.p. 40–60 °C, reagent grade) and add 20 ml of water. Swirl the funnel vigorously, separate the layers, and filter the petroleum ether layer through paper into a 50 ml beaker. Then evaporate the solvent on a 60 °C water bath.

This method does not seem to be quite as quantitative as some others, since the authors claim average recoveries of higher fatty acids amounting to only 90%. In addition to the common fatty acids, Metcalfe and Schmitz successfully esterified 12-hydroxystearic and 12-ketostearic acids.

Morrison and Smith developed a somewhat more elaborate procedure which is adaptable to several groups of compounds. Different heating times and solvent systems are used, depending on the compound to be esterified. Table I, reproduced from Morrison and Smith's paper, gives the types of compounds which they esterified along with the heating times and solvents.

TABLE I

Class of Lipid	Reagent	Heating time at 100 °C
	% by volume	min.
Triglycerides	25% Boron fluoride-methanol, 20% benzene, 55% methanol	30
Triglycerides, Sterol esters	35% Boron fluoride-methanol, 30% benzene, 35% methanol	45
Fatty acids	Boron fluoride-methanol	2
Monoglycerides, Diglycerides, Phosphatidyl ethanolamines, Phosphatidyl serines, Phosphatidyl cholines, Monophosphoinositides, Monogalactosyl glycerides	Boron fluoride-methanol	10
Phosphatidal cholines (choline plasmalogens), Digalactosyl glycerides	Boron fluoride-methanol	30
Sphingomyelins	Boron fluoride-methanol	90

These authors add additional solvents to the BF_3-methanol solution to improve the solubility of compounds to be esterified. For example, even some of the higher fatty acids are insufficiently soluble in methanol at room temperature to be fully esterified, and sterol esters are almost completely insoluble in methanol. When mixtures of widely varying lipid types are to be esterified, the mixture should be treated in the same manner as sphingomyelins (see Table I). After cooling, benzene and methanol can be added and the methanolyzate reheated for 30 min.

The general esterification procedure of Morrison and Smith is as follows:

1. Add boron trifluoride-methanol reagent under nitrogen to the lipid (1 ml reagent per 4–16 mg lipid) which has been placed in a screw-capped centrifuge tube, and close the tube tightly with a Teflon-lined screw cap. 2. Heat the tube in a boiling water bath for the required time, cool the tube, and open it. 3. Extract the esters by adding two volumes of pentane, then one volume of water, shake briefly, then centrifuge until both layers are clear. According to the authors, 97–99% of the esters are extracted by this procedure into the pentane layer.

A minute amount of water in the hydrocarbon layer will not normally affect GC analysis, but for some purposes, notably IR analysis, it will be desirable to remove all water. In this case the hydrocarbon is dried over anhydrous sodium sulfate.

Some losses occur in unsaturated esters prepared by the above method but no more than with other esterification procedures. Active hydroxyl groups like those of cholesterol and related sterols are attacked by the reagent. According to Morrison and Smith, if there are hydroxyl groups adjacent to double bonds in fatty acid methyl esters, these will be dehydrated during gas chromatography to the nonhydroxy ester with one additional double bond conjugated to the original unsaturation. No *cis-trans* isomerization was found to occur with unsaturated esters and no change in conjugated unsaturation.

2. *Saponification-esterification reagent*

Method: Metcalfe, Schmitz, and Pelka have modified their original procedure for the preparation of fatty acid methyl esters to permit methyl esters to be prepared from triglycerides, phospholipids, polyesters, and other lipids, including mixtures found in commercial fats and oils. Their procedure is as follows:

1. Add 4 ml of 0.5N methanolic sodium hydroxide to approximately 150 mg of lipid material in a 50 ml volumetric flask.

2. Heat the mixture on a steam bath until the fatty material goes into solution. This usually requires about 5 min.

3. Add 5 ml of BF_3-methanol and boil for an additional 2 min.

4. Add enough of a saturated solution of sodium chloride to form two layers. The top layer containing the methyl esters may be withdrawn with a pipette. This layer can be used directly for gas chromatographic analysis. If the esters are solid or if completely quantitative recovery is desired, transfer the entire mixture to a separatory funnel and extract it with about 20 ml of a hydrocarbon (petroleum ether, pentane, hexane, heptane, etc.). After shaking the mixture vigorously in a separatory funnel, withdraw the hydrocarbon layer and evaporate on a steam bath or by a stream of air. The methyl esters are now ready for analysis.

An advantage of this method is that quantitative recovery of esters of fatty acids down to C-4 can be obtained. Using this procedure, Metcalfe, Schmitz and Pelka have esterified fatty acids, soaps, triglycerides, polyesters, lipoproteins, phospholipids, and other esters of fatty acids. They also converted fatty acid amides to methyl esters, but not quantitatively. Phenols, rosin acids, and dimer acids cannot be effectively esterified by this procedure.

3. *Butyl ester reagent*

Reagent: BF_3-butanol (14% w/v)

Method: Free fatty acids can be esterified with BF_3-butanol reagent in the following manner. 1. Add 3 ml of the reagent to a test tube or screw-cap vial containing 100–200 mg of fatty acids; 2. Heat for about 10 min. on a steam bath; 3. Add the mixture to a 50%-saturated solution of sodium chloride in a separatory funnel, agitate the funnel, and separate off the butyl ester.

The only limitation of butyl esters is that the higher fatty acid derivatives require higher column temperatures for analysis. For example, Jones and Davison found analysis of butyl esters of dibasic acids containing more than eight carbons to be impractical because of the excessively high temperature required.

(b) Acetylation reagent

The acetylation reagent, as the name implies, is used to prepare acetates of compounds possessing primary or secondary free amino or hydroxyl groups. It fails only in the case of excessive steric hinderance. The reagent contains acetic anhydride and pyridine in a ratio of 1 : 2 and is applicable to many types of compounds. Farquhar, for example, converted long-chain aldehydes to alcohols and esterified them with this reagent. Kuksis described the preparation of mono- and diglyceride derivatives. Galli and Paoletti used the reagent to esterify cholesterol and desmosterol. The procedure for the preparation of acetyl derivatives varies with the stability of the compound to be esterified. Both Kuksis, and Galli and Paoletti dissolved their compounds in the reagent (1–100 mg of sample/10 ml of reagent), then allowed the solution to stand overnight at room temperature under nitrogen in a tightly closed vial. If the compounds are very sensitive the vial should be kept in a dark room. After the reaction was complete, Galli and Paoletti took the derivatives to dryness under vacuum, while Kuksis removed the excess reagent by evaporation under nitrogen. The esters can be suitably diluted with a solvent such as hexane for GC analysis.

A more rapid procedure was used by Farquhar, who was working with comparatively stable alcohols. He dissolved 1–10 mg of fatty alcohols in 10 ml of reagent in a glass stoppered tube and kept the solution at 37 °C, with occasional shaking for 15 min. He then added 5 ml of water and recovered the acetates by three extractions with 5 ml portions of petroleum ether.

[Extracted from Technical Bulletin 17, Applied Science Laboratories, Inc., State College, Pa., by permission of R. F. Kruppa. Ampoules of pre-mixed reagents for these procedures are available from Applied Science Laboratories].

59. Derivative Formation for GC Analysis

(a) Methyl Ester Formation

1. *Diazomethane Method*

(Caution! Diazomethane is very toxic and can explode under certain conditions. Work in hood, do not breathe vapors, do not heat solutions to 100 °C).

Reaction:

$$R{-}COOH + CH_2{<}\begin{matrix}N\\ \|\\ N\end{matrix} \rightarrow R{-}COOCH_3 + N_2$$

The most convenient method is to make up an ether solution of diazomethane. Then add a proper amount of this solution to the methanol solution of the carboxylic acids. Add diazomethane-ether until a yellow color persists. Let the mixture stand for about 10 min. to complete the reaction. With a stream of N_2, evaporate the solution down to a small volume. Inject from this solution into the gas chromatograph.

The diazomethane-ether solution is made by adding 35 ml of 2-(2-ethoxyethoxy)-ethanol and 20 ml of ethyl ether to a solution of 6 g KOH in 10 ml water into a 100-ml long-necked distilling flask equipped with a dropping funnel and a condenser. Heat the flask in a 70 °C water bath. When distilling of the ether starts, add a solution of 21.5 g of

N-methyl-*N*-nitroso-*p*-toluenesulfonamide in 200 ml of ethyl ether through the dropping funnel (approximately 20 min.). Shake the mixture occasionally. When the dropping funnel is empty, add another 40 ml of ether and let it drip into the flask slowly at the same rate as the distillation. Continue distilling until a colorless ether solution is seen, but do not distill all the ether. This ether solution can then be stored at −20 °C for immediate use.

A variation of this method is to use three test tubes in series connected with side arms. N_2 is passed through. Tube 1 contains ether, tube 2 the generated diazomethane, and tube 3 the acids to be esterified dissolved in ether. Tube 2 contains 0.7 ml of 2-(2-ethoxyethoxy)-ethanol, 0.7 ml of ether, and 1 ml of 6 g KOH in 10 ml water. Add 5–30 mg of the fatty acids in ether with 10% methanol in tube 3. Thereafter add 2 moles of *N*-methyl-*N*-nitroso-*p*-toluenesulfonamide per milliequivalent of fatty acids into tube 2. Connect the side arms and let the N_2 carry the diazomethane into tube 3. Disconnect after a yellow color appears in tube 3. Remove excess diazomethane with a stream of N_2. Inject from this solution into the gas chromatograph.

2. *HCl or H_2SO_4-methanol method*

Reaction:

$$\text{R—COOH} + \text{CH}_3\text{OH} \xrightarrow[\text{or } \text{H}_2\text{SO}_4]{\text{HCl}} \text{R—COOCH}_3 + \text{H}_2\text{O}$$

To up to 1 g of the acids add 10 ml of methanol and 0.5 ml of H_2SO_4 and reflux for 2 hr. Transfer the mixture to a separatory funnel, and add water and petroleum ether. Shake vigorously and discard the lower water phase. Evaporate the petroleum ether phase down to convenient volume and inject into the gas chromatograph from this solution.

3. *Tetramethylammonium salt method*

Reaction:

$$\text{R—COOH} + (\text{CH}_3)_4\text{NOH} \xrightarrow{360\text{–}400\ ^\circ\text{C}} \text{R—COOCH}_3 + (\text{CH}_3)_3\text{N} + \text{H}_2\text{O}$$

Titrate the acids in methanol with a 24% methanol solution of tetramethylammonium hydroxide to the phenolphthalein end point. Inject from this solution into the gas chromatograph. Quantitative results can be obtained if the injection port is heated to 360–400 °C and is loosely packed with glass wool to increase surface area and thus pyrolysis.

(b) Oxime Derivatives

A keto group can be converted to the oxime derivative. Methoximes are particularly useful in the analysis of adrenal corticoid steroids. The methoxime group will stabilize the side chain on the corticoids which otherwise is very heat-labile. Other steroids and ketones can also be converted to their methoximes.

Methoxime formation

Reaction:

$$\text{R—}\overset{\overset{\text{O}}{\|}}{\text{C}}\text{—R}_1 + \text{CH}_3\text{—O—NH}_2 \rightarrow \text{R—}\overset{\overset{\text{N—OCH}_3}{\|}}{\text{C}}\text{—R}_1 + \text{H}_2\text{O}$$

Add 10 ml of pyridine and an excess of methoxylamine hydrochloride to the sample (corticoids) in a test tube. Let stand overnight at room temperature. When reaction is completed, evaporate the pyridine with a stream of N_2. Dissolve the residue in 10 ml of ethyl acetate. Add 5 ml of 5% $NaHCO_3$ and 5% NaCl in water. Shake the test tube vigorously and let the two phases separate.

The derivatized sample will be in the upper ethyl acetate phase and can be analyzed from this solution.

(c) Hydrazone Derivatives

Ketones and aldehydes can be converted to their hydrazone derivatives. The *N,N*-dimethylhydrazones have been used for steroid ketones, and the 2,4-dinitrophenylhydrazones for formaldehyde analysis together with other ketones. The gas chromatographic properties of other hydrazone derivatives, such as reaction products with pentafluorophenylhydrazone and aminopiperidine, have been investigated.

N,N-Dimethylhydrazone formation

Reaction:

$$\text{R—}\overset{\overset{\text{O}}{\|}}{\text{C}}\text{—R}_1 + (\text{CH}_3)_2\text{—N—NH}_2 \rightarrow \text{R—}\overset{\overset{\text{N—N(CH}_3)_2}{\|}}{\text{C}}\text{—R}_1 + \text{H}_2\text{O}$$

Add 0.1–1.0 mg of the sample (ketonic steroids) to 0.2–0.5 ml of *N,N*-dimethylhydrazine and about 0.05 ml of acetic acid as a catalyst. Let the reaction mixture stand at room temperature for 1–2 hr. When reaction is completed, remove excess reagent with a stream of N_2. Take up residue in tetrahydrofuran and inject into gas chromatograph.

A solvent such as ethyl acetate can be used with the sample in the reaction mixture to increase solubility for the sample and for other solid hydrazine reagents.

(d) Methyl Ether Derivatives

The hydroxyl group can be converted to a methyl ether by reacting with methyl iodide and silver oxide in dimethylformamide. This derivative method has been used also in the analysis of sugars. Sterols have been converted to their methyl ethers by reacting with methyl iodide in an ether solution in the presence of potassium *tert*-butoxide.

Methyl ether formation

Reaction:

$$2R{-}OH + 2CH_3I \xrightarrow[DMF]{Ag_2O} 2R{-}O{-}CH_3 + 2AgI + H_2O$$

(e) Heptafluorobutyrate Derivatives

These derivatives are useful for picogram detection of steroids, since the fluorine atoms in the derivatives have a high electron affinity which is well suited for the electron capture detector. A method for the analysis of picogram amounts of estrogens in plasma employing these derivatives has been published, as well as a method for the determination of plasma testosterone (*see* Section on Steroids).

Heptafluorobutyrate formation

Reaction:

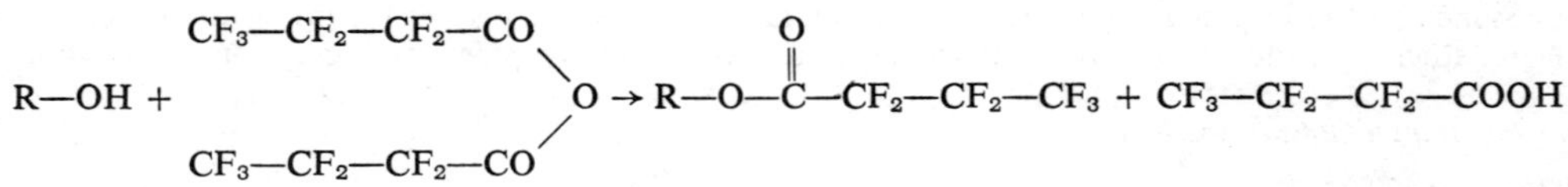

Dissolve the sample (steroids) in tetrahydrofuran and add an excess of heptafluorobutyric anhydride. Heat the solution at 60 °C for 30 min. Evaporate to dryness with a stream of N_2. Take residue up in a small amount of acetone and inject into the gas chromatograph.

(f) *N,O*-Dipivalyl Derivatives

The methylated thyroid hormones can be analyzed employing these derivatives. This procedure converts the amino group to a dipivalyl group.

N,O-Dipivalyl formation

Reaction:

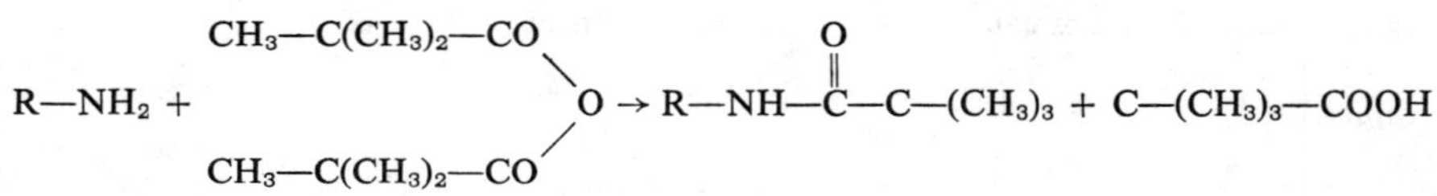

Mix the sample (0.5–1.0 mg) with 0.2 ml pivalic anhydride and 0.05 ml triethylamine in a Teflon-lined screw cap test tube. Heat at 60–70 °C for 30 min. When reaction is completed inject into gas chromatograph.

(g) Metal Chelates (*See* Section on Inorganics)

Many metals can be analyzed by gas chromatography as their chelate derivatives. The trifluoro- and hexafluoroacetyl acetone chelates are the most common, but other chelating agents have also been used. Because of the fluorine atoms in the chelate, picogram amounts can be detected with an electron capture detector.

Hexafluoroacetylacetone formation

Reaction:

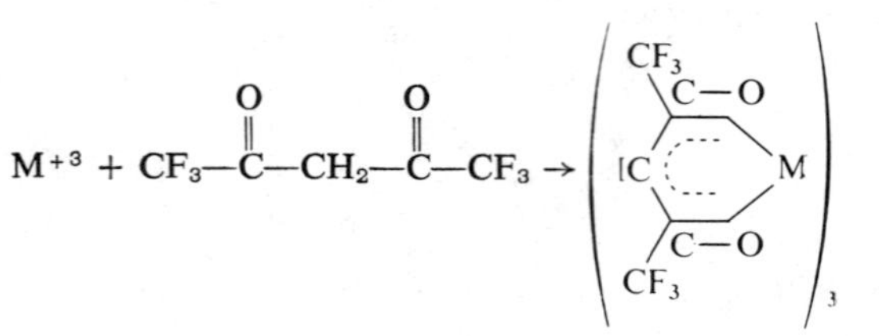

Generally, the metal salts in water are adjusted to a pH of about 5. Add an appropriate amount of the chelating agent in hexane or benzene and shake the mixture vigorously. Discard the water phase and evaporate the solvent phase down to a small volume. Inject from this solution into the gas chromatograph.

Attention should be paid to the fact that some metals require a higher or lower pH than 5 in order to be completely converted to a chelate. A check of pH for best recovery should be made.

[Extracted from "Derivatives" Bulletin 6/68:A-1006, Varian Aerograph Co., Walnut Creek, California, by permission of Dr. K. Hammarstrand.]

HYDROCARBONS

See Number 60

60. Addition of Mercury to Double Bonds of Hydrocarbons

(*a*) The mixture of olefins (gaseous or liquid) is dissolved in pure methanol. The concentration of the individual components should be approximately 0.5 g in 100 ml solvent. Excess solid mercuric acetate is added to the solution, which is then allowed to stand for 30 min at laboratory temperature with frequent stirring. Portions (10–20 μl) of this solution are then spotted. Higher olefins react more slowly and the reaction time must be correspondingly prolonged (about 2 hr). At very low concentrations of olefins, e.g., in a mixture of hydrocarbons, the concentration of methanol should be lowered only slightly, otherwise the conversion will not be quantitative. In this case, the solution after the reaction is concentrated under reduced pressure.

(*b*) Mercuric acetate (9 mg) and absolute methanol (0.5 ml) are added to the sample (containing approximately 6 mg of the dinitrophenylhydrazone of an unsaturated oxo-compound) and the solution is refluxed for 2 hr. After adding benzene (2 ml), excess mercuric acetate is removed by repeated extraction with water. The benzene solution is then applied to paper.

Reference 5, p. 832.

INORGANICS

See Numbers 61 and 62

61. Preparation of Solutions for PC

(*a*) *Biological materials.* A suitable quantity of the sample is oxidized by boiling with nitric and sulfuric acids, successive additions of nitric acid being made until a clear solution is obtained. The sulfuric acid is finally heated to fuming, to expel the last traces of nitric acid.

(*b*) *Crops, fertilizers, etc.* These materials usually have a strongly alkaline ash, and careful dry-ashing at 500 °C may be carried out without loss of the metals to be determined. After ashing, the residue is taken to dryness with aqua regia over a water bath, with suitable precautions to avoid loss from effervescence and splashing. It is then dissolved in the minimum quantity of 50 per cent hydrochloric acid.

(*c*) *Soils* (*trace determination*). Dry ash, as in (*b*) above, a 2.0 g sample ground to pass 50 mesh. Evaporate three times with aqua regia and finally dissolve as in (*b*) above.

(*d*) *Soils* (*geochemical*). 0.5 g of ground soil is mixed with 1 g $KHSO_4$ in a hard-glass tube, and given a moderate fusion for 5 minutes. (*1*) When cool, the melt is brought to the boil with 2.0 ml 50% HCl (+1 % HNO_3) and allowed to cool and settle.

The solutions obtained in (*a*), (*b*) and (*c*) above are washed into a 100 ml separator with about 50 ml of water. 0.2 to 0.5 g of citric acid and a few drops of phenol red indicator are added, and the solution brought to pH 8 with ammonia.

This solution is extracted with successive 10 ml aliquots of 2% oxine in chloroform, until a clear extract is obtained.

The bulked chloroform extracts are evaporated over a water bath, and wet-ashed with perchloric/nitric acids, the last traces of perchloric acid being carefully evaporated without over-heating the residue.

This process serves to concentrate the relevant metals, since the usually preponderant salts of calcium, magnesium, sodium and potassium do not form chloroform soluble oxinates, and are thus removed from the final residue.

The residue is dissolved in the minimum, measured amount of 50% HCl containing 5% HNO_3. This volume will vary according to the size of the residue, but may often be as low as 0.2 ml and seldom exceeds 0.5 ml.

Note. The solution obtained under (*d*) above (geochemical) is not submitted to this final concentration procedure, since the quantities of metals involved are of a much higher order.

Reference 11, Chapter by Duffield, W. D. pp. 815–816.

62. Metal Hexafluoroacetylacetonates and Trifluoroacetylacetonates for GC of Metal Ions

Examples of these chelates have been known for some time (*1, 2*), and the synthesis and spectral properties summarized (*3*) for the Cr, Co, Rh, Al, Ga, In, Mn and Fe complexes.

Solvent extraction studies of Zr and Hf have been reported (*4, 5*), and the extractability of Cu, Fe, Al, Ni, Mn, Cr, Mg and Zn from aqueous solution studied (*6*).

GLC elution of trifluoroacetylacetonates of Be (II), Al (III), Ga (III), In (III), Sc (III), Cr (III), Fe (III), Cu (II), Rh (III), Zr (IV) and Hf (IV), has been reported by Sievers, Moshier and others (*7, 8*), and the efficient resolution of multicomponent mixtures demonstrated. Quantitative aspects of tri- and hexafluoroacetylacetonate gas chromatography have been examined by Hill and Gesser (*9*), and Ross and others (*10, 11*). A thorough study of this promising new method of metal analysis will be found in *Gas Chromatography of Metal Chelates* by Moshier R. W. and R. E. Sievers (*12*).

Recently a method for the GLC determination of toxicological levels of chromium in human serum has been developed by Savory, Mushak and Sunderman (*18*) as the trifluoroacetylacetonate. Other metals are probably amenable to similar procedures and should be valuable in nutritional and toxicological studies and other phases of physiological problems involving trace elements.

The rare-earth chelates are expected to be of interest in laser studies. Gas phase reduction of others shows promise in the vapor deposition of metals at modest temperatures; as an example, copper is plated satisfactorily at only 250 °C (*13*, *14*). The vapor deposition of thin films of cadmium sulfide has been discussed (*15*).

Recent applications of volatile metal chelates include their use in trace analyses in biological systems (*16*), and in the vapor-phase purification of rare earths (*17*).

References:
1. Staniforth, R. A. Doctoral Dissertation, Ohio State University, 1943.
2. Crandall, H. W., Thomas, J. R. and J. C. Reid, U.S. At. Energy Comm., CN 2657 (1945).
3. Fay, R. C. and T. S. Piper, *J. Amer. Chem. Soc.*, **85**, 500 (1963).
4. Larsen, E. M. and G. A. Terry, *J. Amer. Chem. Soc.*, **75**, 1560 (1953).
5. Schultz, B. G. and E. M. Larsen, *J. Amer. Chem. Soc.*, **72**, 3610 (1950).
6. Scribner, W. G. private communication.
7. Moshier, R. W., Schwarberg, J. E., Morris, M. L. and R. E. Sievers, Pittsburgh, Conference, March 1963.
8. Sievers, R. E., Ponder, B. W., Morris, M. L. and R. W. Moshier, *Inorg. Chem.*, **2**, 693 (1963).
9. Hill, R. D. and H. Gesser, *J. Gas Chromatogr.*, **1**, 10 (1963).
10. Ross, W. D. *Anal. Chem.*, **35**, 1596 (1963).
11. Ross, W. D. and G. Wheeler, *Anal. Chem.*, **36**, 266 (1964).
12. Pergamon Press, Oxford, 1965.
13. Sievers, R. E., Moshier, R. W. and L. B. Spendlove, private communication.
14. *J. Electrochem. Soc.*, **112**, 1123 (1965).
15. Sievers, R. E. *J. Inorg. Nucl. Chem.* **28**, 1937 (1966).
16. Ross and Sievers, Proceedings of the Sixth International Symposium on Gas Chromatography, Rome, Italy, Sept. 1966.
17. Sievers, R. E. private communication.
18. Savory, J., Mushak, P. and F. W. Sunderman, Jr., *J. Chromatogr. Sci.*, **7**, 674–679 (1969).

Reprinted from Pierce Handbook GPA-3, 1970, Pierce Chemical Co., Rockford, Ill., by permission.

LIPIDS

See Numbers 58, 63–65

63. Preparation of Aliphatic Lipid Samples for TLC

(a) Preparation of Vegetable Lipids

Vegetable lipids are extracted from seeds and fruits by grinding and pressing and by extracting with solvents.

When working with plant material having a high oil content, it is advisable first to squeeze out the major part of the oil and to grind the residue further to avoid formation of a pulp mush, and then to press it. Appropriate presses and mills are described in handbooks of chemical technology, along with the addresses of their manufacturers. In the laboratory, a simple coffee grinder, or, for soft plant material, a kitchen mixer, will serve one's purpose just as well as an expensive, special apparatus. Processing the material with abrasive sea sand in a mortar is also a very efficient method.

Treating the residue with solvent and extracting it exhaustively in a Soxhlet apparatus, or a similar device, will procure the remainder of the lipids. Extractors and their use are described adequately in several handbooks; commercial suppliers are listed therein also. Pulverized plant particles usually are extracted on a water bath with anhydrous solvents, such as hexane, petroleum ether, B.P. 60 to 70 °C, or benzene, for 4 to 6 hr. Equally suitable are chloroform, carbon tetrachloride, trichloroethylene, and diethyl ether. Ethanol, *n*-propanol, and isopropanol, as well as water-saturated *n*-butanol, sometimes are useful for the isolation of plant lipids. It is advisable to extract, successively, with two or three solvents of different polarities, e.g., diethyl ether, benzene, and petroleum hydrocarbon. It is essential to extract always in an atmosphere of nitrogen, in order to protect unsaturated lipids against autoxidation.

Kates [*Can. J. Biochem. Physiol.*, **35**, 127 (1957)] has shown that aliphatic ethers, ketones, and esters activate the enzyme phosphatidase C. This enzyme hydrolyzes phospholipids rapidly. For this reason, Kates recommends the use of *n*-propanol or isopropanol for the extraction of plant lipids, instead of diethyl ether, acetone, or ethyl acetate.

(b) Extraction of Lipids According to Bloor

One part of tissue homogenate is added to 20 (to 30) parts of a mixture of ethanol-diethyl ether (3 : 1) and left overnight under an atmosphere of nitrogen, at room temperature. The lipid extract is filtered from the residual protein and concentrated at less than 50 °C *in vacuo* under nitrogen, but never evaporated to complete dryness. The lipids are reextracted with three portions of petroleum ether. Material not soluble in petroleum ether is discarded. The petroleum ether solution of lipids is dried over anhydrous sodium sulfate.

Complete extraction of lipids from very fatty tissues requires slight heating of the homogenate with ethanol-diethyl ether. Brain lipids are only partially extracted with the Bloor mixture.

(c) Extraction of Lipids According to Folch, Ascoli, Lees, Meath and LeBaron

This method gives very good yields of complex lipids, such as proteolipids and gangliosides.

The ground tissue is extracted with 20 parts of a mixture of chloroform-methanol (2 : 1) at room temperature. Non-lipids are removed by the diffusion method developed by Folch and co-workers.

A small glass beaker is placed at the bottom of a beaker of tenfold capacity, which is filled with distilled water. The small, submerged beaker is filled two-thirds full with the chloroform-methanol lipid extract by means of a pipette. While standing overnight, the methanol and all water-soluble contaminants of the lipid extract diffuse into the surrounding water. The lipids thus purified remain in the chloroform layer and also in a flocky layer at the interface of the two liquids. The aqueous solution is siphoned off as completely as possible. The small beaker is filled with the same amount of methanol that was present originally. The flakes dissolve again on mixing the methanol with the chloroform layer. Modifications of this method have been worked out for the isolation of proteolipids, phosphatidolipopeptides gangliosides, sulfatides, and triphosphoinositides.

(d) Alkaline Hydrolysis of Lipids

One part, by weight, of potassium hydroxide, is dissolved in one part by weight of distilled water, and after cooling, diluted with 3 to 4 parts of methanol. The lipid material to be saponified is treated with ten times the amount of this potassium hydroxide solution, and left overnight at room temperature. This "cold saponification" is especially recommended for hydrolyzing lipids containing vitamins, conjugated unsaturated fatty acids or conjugated polyenoic acids. Heat usually is applied for saponifying ester lipids. The sample is refluxed under nitrogen for 1–12 hr. The length of boiling depends upon the nature of the lipids to be saponified. The temperature of the saponification mixture may be raised by adding 10–20% of toluene or xylene if lipids are encountered that are hard to hydrolyze.

Reference 3, pp. 142–146.

64. Isolation of Serum Lipids

Nonpolar solvents alone will not extract lipids quantitatively from samples because a large portion of the lipid in serum and in tissue samples is combined with protein. A mixture of a polar and nonpolar organic solvent dissolves the lipid and also overcomes the attraction of the lipid for the protein. Chloroform–methanol (2 : 1) is a popular solvent. Filtration removes the protein. The extract is shaken against saturated NaCl, and the $CHCl_3$ layer is used for chromatography. Other suitable solvents include dimethoxymethane–methanol (4 : 1), ethanol–acetone (1 : 1) and chloroform–methanol (1 : 1).

Reference 6, p. 160.

65. Preparation of Derivatives for GC of Lipids Containing Ether Bonds

(*a*) *Alkyl ethers.* Reaction with acetic anhydride forms diacetates of glyceryl ethers [Blomstrand, R. and J. Gurtler, *Acta Chem. Scand.*, **13**, 1466 (1959)].

(*b*) *Trifluoroacetates.* TFA groups on glyceryl ethers greatly increase volatility and are better suited for GC than acetates. Diol lipids have also been resolved as TFA-derivatives [Wood, R. and F. Snyder, *Lipids*, **1**, 62 (1966); Wood, R. and W. J. Baumann, *J. Lipid Res.*, **10**, 463 (1969)].

(*c*) *Isopropylidenes.* These derivatives, prepared by reaction with acetone, are especially useful for GC analysis of chain lengths and degree of unsaturation [Hanahan, D. J., Ekholm, J., and C. M. Jackson, *Biochemistry*, **2**, 630 (1963); Wood, R. *Lipids*, **1**, 62 (1966)].

(*d*) *Alkoxy acetaldehydes.* These are formed during the reaction of glyceryl ethers with periodate [Mangold, H. K. and W. J. Baumann, in "Lipid Chromatographic Analysis 1," G. V. Marinetti, ed., Marcel Dekker, N.Y., pp. 339–359, 1967].

(*e*) *Alkyl iodides.* Prepared by HI cleavage of the ether bond [Guyer, K. E., Hoffman, W. A., Horrocks, L. A., and D. G. Cornwell, *J. Lipid Res.*, **4**, 385 (1963); Ramachandran, S., Sprecher, H. W., and D. G. Cornwell, *Lipids*, **3**, 511 (1968)].

(*f*) *Dimethoxy derivatives.* Formed by reaction of glyceryl ethers with $BF_3 + CH_2N_2$. These require purification prior to GC [Hallgren, B. and S. Larsson, *J. Lipid Res.*, **3**, 31 (1962)].

(*g*) *Dimethyl acetals of fatty aldehydes.* Reflux the aldehydes or total lipids containing *O*-alk-1-enyl groups with methanolic HCl [Farquhar, J. W. *J. Lipid Res.*, **3**, 21 (1962)].

Reference 10, Vol. 2, chapter a, by F. Snyder, pp. 118–123.

NITROGEN HETEROCYCLICS

See Numbers 66 and 67

66. Preparation of Indolyl-3-acryloylglycine Sample from Urine

This procedure for sample preparation prior to TLC involves use of a Sephadex column; the mechanism is possibly adsorption plus ion exclusion.

Urine is preserved by the addition of 5 ml of a thymol solution in 2-propanol (10% w/v). If urine cannot be analyzed after it is collected, store at −25 °C. Acidify with glacial acetic acid to pH 4, twice (each time for 15 min.) mechanically shake a volume corresponding to 100 mg creatinine with an equal volume of ethyl acetate. Pool and evaporate using a rotary vacuum evaporator. Dissolve the dry residue in three 5 ml portions of a buffer pH 8.3 (71.5 g $Na_2HPO_4 \times 12\ H_2O$, 0.21 g citric acid and 1.3 g NaN_3 per liter) and introduce on a column of Sephadex G-10 (1.8 × 5 cm) previously washed with 30 ml 0.1*N* NaOH and 30 ml 0.1*N* HCl and equilibrated with the buffer. After the sample has entered the column, wash with 150 ml of a buffer pH 7.1 (58.9 g $Na_2HPO_4 \times 12\ H_2O$, 3.7 g citric acid and 1.3 g NaN_3 per liter) at the rate of 1 ml/min. Elute indolylacryloylglycine from the column by 50 ml distilled water, evaporate, dissolve the dry residue in 1 ml water and add 3 ml 96 % ethanol. After 5 min transfer to a siliconized glass dish. Wash the crystals remaining in the flask with three successive 1 ml ethanol aliquots, transfer to the dish and concentrate the pooled sample in a 50–70 °C warm water bath under a current of cold air from a hair-dryer to about 20–30 μl. Transfer this and another 20 μl ethanol (wash quantitatively) to the thin layer of Whatman CC-41 microcrystalline cellulose conveniently prepared in a butanol suspension).

Chromatographic conditions: Two-dimensional TLC in 2-propanol-ammonia (25 %)-water (8 : 1 : 1) and benzene-propionic acid-methanol-water (20 : 14 : 1 : 1), detection 360 nm, elution with 5 ml acidified methanol, read at 323 nm.

Submitted by: Marklová E., and I. M. Hais, Charles University, Hradec Králové, Czechoslovakia.

67. Isolation of Indoles from Plants and Biological Fluids

(a) Plant Materials

The plant sample is frozen to −10 °C with dry ice and macerated at this temperature with small amounts of ethanol. After 24 hr. of storage at −10 °C, the crude extract is centrifuged, the residue is washed several times with ethanol, and the ethanol is evaporated at reduced pressure. The residue is adjusted to pH 3 with H_3PO_4 and extracted for 1½ hr. with ether which is shaken immediately before use with acidic $FeSO_4$. The ether extract is shaken three times with 5 % $NaHCO_3$, the bicarbonate extracts are adjusted to pH 3 with H_3PO_4, reextracted with ether, and washed with a small amount of H_3PO_4 at pH 3. The final extract is evaporated under a stream of nitrogen and redissolved in anhydrous ether.

In an alternate procedure, the sample (e.g., ground sweet corn) is extracted with 50 % acetone under low temperature conditions (cold room). The extract is salted out with NaCl (250 g NaCl per 1.5 liters solution), and the acetone layer is concentrated under reduced pressure to a small volume. The indoles are extracted with ether, concentrated, and the residue is chromatographed.

Note: Indoles isolated from plant sources should be kept under nitrogen during the evaporation steps and stored at low temperatures in dark containers. The compounds are extremely labile and lose their biological activity.

In another procedure for the extraction of tryptamine derivatives, fresh plant leaves are exposed to diethyl ether for 3–5 min. Plant juices are rapidly extracted from a small amount of sample by crushing the sample within a piece of Tygon tubing closed at one end with a Mohr pinch cock clamp; the juice may be withdrawn from the tubing by means of a micropipette. The expressed juice, containing 10–100 μg tryptamine derivatives, is spotted on Whatman No. 1 chromatographic paper. To isolate the tryptamines from dried leaf material, the ground sample (40 mesh) is Soxhlet-extracted for 7 hr. with absolute methanol. The methanol is evaporated and 3–4 volumes of water are added to the liquid residue. The mixture is acidified with 0.1*N* HCl, extracted twice with equal volumes of toluene, then made alkaline with NH_4OH and extracted three times with diethyl ether. The ether is evaporated and the residue is made to volume with methanol; samples are then spotted on the chromatographic paper.

(b) Isolation from Urine, Blood, and Spinal Fluid

Urine. A 5 ml sample of urine in a 25 ml test tube is adjusted to pH 1 (about 5 drops HCl); 10 ml ethyl acetate is added and the tube is stoppered and shaken for 2 min. The ethyl acetate layer (top layer) is removed and placed in a beaker. The ethyl acetate extraction procedure is repeated. The extracts are combined, evaporated, and 0.5 ml 50 % ethanol is added to the residue. A variation of this procedure includes treatment of the sample after the first ethyl acetate extraction with 10 % $NaHCO_3$, then acidified and reextracted with ethyl acetate. Further purification of the extracts is accomplished by passage through a deactivated charcoal column, followed by elution of the indoles with phenol. Indole bases are lost through this procedure. Not all indole acids can be desorbed from charcoal.

The use of sequential solvents of graded polarity under variable pH conditions permits the fractionation of urinary indoles without too much overlapping in the multiple extracts; it also makes possible the analysis of more highly concentrated urine extracts by paper chromatography. In this procedure, urine (200–300 ml) is concentrated 10–20-fold *in vacuo* at 37–40°C. The concentrate is centrifuged and filtered. The filtrate is saturated with crystalline $(NH_4)_2SO_4$, again filtered, and divided into two equal parts. One of the portions is adjusted to pH 10 with 40 % NaOH and then extracted four times with equal volumes of ethyl ether and four times with equal volumes of 2-butanone. The second portion is adjusted to pH 2 with HCl and subjected to the same extraction procedure. The four extracts are evaporated to dryness *in vacuo* and made up to a volume (equivalent to 100 mg creatinine per milliliter of extract) with 95 % ethanol. For chromatography, 0.3 ml of each ethanol extract is applied to Whatman No. 1 chromatographic paper and developed by two-dimensional chromatography.

A modified procedure for group separation and purification of indoleamines has been proposed. The concentrated urine (one fourth of a 24 hr. urine volume) is adjusted to pH 4.5 with NH_4OH. Dowex 50-X2 (100–200 mesh) resin, H^+ form (5 g wet weight) is added, the mixture is stirred for 45 min. and then transferred to a glass column (2 × 30 cm). Prior to use, the resin is prepared as follows. The H^+ form of the resin is successively treated with acetone, 2*N* NaOH, 2*N* HCl, 1*N* NH_4OH in 65 % ethanol, and 2*N* HCl, with water washing of the resin between each treatment. The urine effluent and the combined 30 ml distilled water wash of the column resin is retained for the detection of conjugated amines. The water-washed resin is subsequently eluted with 30 ml 0.1*N* sodium acetate, 30 ml distilled water, and 30 ml 50 % ethanol, respectively, to remove the neutral and aliphatic base substances. Sixty milliliters 0.1*N* sodium acetate followed by 50 ml distilled water are substituted for the 30 ml washes if it is necessary to remove such compounds as tryptophan or 5-hydroxytryptophan from the resin. The indoleamine fraction is eluted with 30 ml of 1*N* NH_4OH in

65% ethanol; the eluate is concentrated *in vacuo* at 36 °C to a volume of 0.5 ml. Absolute ethanol (3 ml) is added to the concentrated extract and again concentrated to 1 ml. After centrifugation, the supernatant liquid is transferred to a conical-bottomed tube and evaporated to dryness *in vacuo* over sulfuric acid. The dried residue should contain any indoleamines, indoleamino acids, and phenolic amines. The above-mentioned fraction which contains any conjugated amines is adjusted to pH 1 with HCl and hydrolyzed for 30 min. on a steam bath. The hydrolyzed solution is cooled, filtered, the pH is adjusted to 4.5, followed by the same procedure as above for the free amines. The samples should be stored *in vacuo* until they are used for chromatographic analysis.

Blood serum. The sample (0.5 ml) is added to 5 ml of a mixture of absolute ethanol acetone (1 : 1) in a 10 ml centrifuge tube. By means of either a magnetic stirrer or wrist action shaker, the contents of the tube are mixed for 10 min. The mixture is centrifuged and the supernatant liquid is decanted into a flask which has a previously calibrated 10 ml mark. The precipitate is washed with 2 ml portions of the solvent mixture, and the washings are added to the liquid until the 10 ml volume is reached; 0.1 ml of this solution is directly chromatographed or concentrated if necessary.

Spinal fluid. The sample (1 ml) is gently heated to boiling, a drop of 10% trichloroacetic acid is added and heated in a water bath for 5 min. at 50 °C, then cooled and centrifuged; 0.1 ml of the supernate is used for chromatography.

The above procedures for blood serum and spinal fluid are applicable to the analysis of tryptophan metabolites.

Reference 1, pp. 283–286.

ORGANOPHOSPHORUS COMPOUNDS

68. Isolation of Phosphoric Esters from Blood

After centrifuging a blood sample, the precipitated erythrocytes are washed at 0 °C with 0.9% NaCl and mixed with an equal volume of distilled water. The hemolyzate is mixed with an equal volume of 20% trichloroacetic acid for 30 min. at 4 °C and centrifuged to separate protein. The clear supernate can be used directly or the high concentration of acid can be removed by double extraction with equal volumes of diethyl ether, which is in turn removed *in vacuo*. The alkaline earths are complexed by adding a small amount of disodium EDTA.

Reference: Bukureshchliev, A. *Vutreshni Bolesti, Uatrechni Bolesti, Nauchno Druzhestvo Internistite*, **3**, 573 (1964).

ORGANIC SULFUR COMPOUNDS

69. Extraction of Sulfonic Acids from Diatoms

The sulfonic acids in fresh water diatoms, labeled with ^{35}S by culturing for 4 days, were extracted from the harvested and washed cells with boiling 80% and 100% ethanol; the extract was evaporated under nitrogen and redissolved in 80% ethanol–$CHCl_3$ to prepare the sample for two-dimensional chromatography on Whatman No. 4 paper in phenol–H_2O (100 : 38 w/w) and *n*-butanol–propionic acid–H_2O (142 : 71 : 100 v/v). Cysteinolic acid and sulfopropanediol were separated and identified.

Reference: Busby, W. F. *Biochim. Biophys. Acta*, **121**, 160 (1966). Permission of Elsevier Publishing Company, Amsterdam, The Netherlands.

70. Preparation of Organic Sulfur Compounds for PC

(a) Preparation of 2,4-Dinitrophenyl Thio-ethers

Pyridine (1 ml) and a slight excess of mercaptan are added to 0.1*M* 1-fluoro-2,4-dinitrobenzene in 95% ethanol (9 ml) and the mixture is heated on a water bath for 10 min. The mixture is then acidified with 20% sulfuric acid until the characteristic smell of pyridine disappears. The precipitated derivatives are dissolved in ethanol and applied to paper.

(b) Stabilization of Thiol Compounds with *N*-Ethylmaleimide

The sample is adjusted to pH 5–8 and 0.05*M* *N*-ethylmaleimide (NEM) solution is added in a quantity of about 2 meq for each meq of the presumed amount of SH-compounds. The solution is then desalted by passing through a sulfonated polystyrene exchanger. In the case of serum, the solution is diluted as soon as possible with 9 volumes of a mixture of acetic acid and oxalate to which, in the case of blood, 1 volume of 0.05*M* NEM is added.

(c) Preparation of Alkyl Isothiuronium Salts

1. *Identification of alkyl halides.* The substance (1–1.5 mg) is heated with thiourea (0.8 mg) and acetone (0.4 ml) in a sealed ampoule on a boiling water bath: Iodides are heated 30 min; *n*-alkyl bromides, 4 hr; bromides with branched alkyls and *n*-alkyl chlorides, 10 hr. (in the presence of a crystal of NaI). After cooling, the ampoule is opened and the acetone solution (5–20 μl) is spotted on the chromatogram.

2. *Identification of O-alkyl groups.* The substance (0.5–1 mg) is boiled with HI. The liberated alkyl iodides are absorbed in an ice-cooled receiver containing thiourea (2 mg) in acetone (1 ml). The absorption solution is then transferred into an ampoule which is sealed and then heated for 30 min. on a boiling water bath. After cooling, the ampoule is opened and its content evaporated to dryness. The residue is dissolved in acetone (0.1 ml) and portions (5–20 μl) are spotted on the chromatogram.

3. *Identification of N-alkyl groups*. The substance (1–2 mg) is processed as in the usual determination of the alkylimide group. The thermal decomposition is performed for 45 min. twice in succession. The alkyl iodides are absorbed and processed as described in 2.

(d) Preparation of Sulfilimines

A solution of sodium *p*-nitrobenzenesulfochloroamide (200 mg) in methanol (5 ml) is applied to the solution containing sulfides (0.5 mmole) in methanol (2 ml). The reaction of sulfides with chloroamine is accompanied by the bleaching of the yellow reaction mixture. After 15 min., the reaction mixture is diluted with water (20 ml), 2*N* NaOH (10 ml) is added and the mixture is extracted twice with chloroform (5 ml). The chloroform solution is applied to the chromatogram. When the chloramine contains alkalies or in the case of slowly reacting sulfides, the reaction mixture should be acidified with one drop of a 1% solution of formic acid in methanol.

(e) Preparation of *N*-Alkylthioureas

Plant material (about 500 g) is first extracted with methanol to isolate glycosides. Isothiocyanates are liberated with myrosinase and separated by steam distillation. The distillate (10 liters) is collected in a cooled receiver containing conc. NH_4OH (4 liters); the solution is allowed to stand overnight and then evaporated to dryness under reduced pressure. The temperature should not exceed 55 °C. The residue is dissolved in chloroform and applied to paper.

(f) Conversion of Sulfonic Acids to Phenols

The sulfonic acid (0.2 g) and KOH (2.5 g) are heated 3–4 min. in a test tube to about 360–370 °C, while stirring with a glass rod. After cooling, water (5 ml) is added and the mixture agitated. After filtration, the solution is extracted with an equal volume of benzene, the aqueous layer acidified with conc. HCl to congo red and then extracted with hexane. The hexane solution is applied to paper.

Reference 5, pp. 865–866.

OXO COMPOUNDS

See Numbers 71–75

71. Preparation of Aldehyde Hydrazones of 2-Hydrazinobenzothiazole

One mmole of the aldehyde is added to 30 ml of ethanol containing 1 mmole of 2-hydrazinobenzothiazole and a drop of glacial acetic acid. The mixture is warmed under reflux on a steam bath for 30 min. to 1 hr. The hydrazone is obtained from the reaction mixture by cooling in an ice bath and if necessary by the addition of water. The hydrazones of citral and isovaleraldehyde are obtained by pouring the reaction mixture into ice water. The derivatives are recrystallized from ethanol–water mixtures. Chloroform or ethyl acetate solutions of the hydrazones are stored under refrigeration.

Reference: Hunt, F. C. *J. Chromatogr.*, **40**, 465 (1969). Permission of Elsevier Publishing Company, Amsterdam, The Netherlands.

72. Preparation of Azines of Aromatic Carbonyls

Fill the extraction thimble of a Soxhlet extractor with 20 g freshly heated calcium oxide, and reflux the ketone and 85% hydrazine hydrate, with 150 ml 95% ethanol for 16–24 hr. Filter the hot alcoholic solution (to remove traces of CaO carried over into the flask), and isolate the hydrazone by concentration of the solution.

To prepare the azines, add conc. H_2SO_4 to a mixture of 0.5 g of the hydrazone and 30 ml 95% ethanol until the mixture is acidic to methyl orange. Two to three drops is usually sufficient. On standing, a white precipitate of hydrazine sulfate precipitates. After 12–15 hr., warm the mixture to dissolve the azine and filter immediately. Isolate the azine from the filtrate and recrystallize from ethyl alcohol or toluene.

Reference: Barber, E. D. *J. Chromatogr.*, **27**, 398 (1967); Szmant H. H., and C. McGinnis, *J. Amer. Chem. Soc.*, **72**, 2890 (1950).

73. Preparation of Carbonyl Oximes

Add 3.13 g hydroxylamine hydrochloride to a solution of 10–100 mg of carbonyl compound in 10 ml. water Add 2.39 g anhydrous sodium carbonate slowly and then extract this solution continuously for one hour with ether which has been distilled from H_2SO_4 and stored over sodium. Dry the extract over Na_2SO_4 and distill ether until only 1 ml solution remains. Transfer the residual solution to a 2 ml volumetric flask using a syringe. Use ether to wash out the distillation flask and bring the volume to 2 ml. Inject this solution for GC.

Reference: Cason, J. and E. R. Harris, *J. Org. Chem.*, **24**, 678 (1959).

74. Preparation of Fatty Aldehyde Dimethyl Acetals

Reflux aldehydes for 2 hr. with 2% anhydrous methanolic HCl (solvent–solute, 20 : 1) for >95% conversion. Cool the solution and neutralize HCl by adding slight excess anhydrous Na_2CO_3. Extract acetals from methanol with petroleum ether (40–60 °C). Shake petroleum ether solution with sodium metabisulfite solution to remove unchanged aldehyde and then with water until neutral. Dry over Na_2SO_4, remove solvent under reduced pressure, and dissolve residue in an appropriate solvent for GC.

Reference: Gray, G. M. *J. Chromatogr.*, **4**, 52 (1960).

75. Preparation of Substituted Hydrazones of Ketones for GC

Eneamines (Schiff bases) of di-*n*-hexyl and di-*n*-heptyl ketones are prepared by treating the ketones with *N*-amino-piperidine, *N*-aminohomopiperidine, pentafluorophenylhydrazine or phenylhydrazine in ethyl acetate solution, with acetic acid as catalyst. Complete condensation occurs in less than one hour in all cases.

Reference: Van denHeuvel, W. J. A., Gardiner, W. L., and E. C. Horning, *J. Chromatogr.*, **18**, 391 (1965).

OXYGEN HETEROCYCLICS

See Numbers 76, 77

76. Concentration of Hydrophilic Plant Constituents for TLC

(*a*) Anthocyanins (anthocyanidin ± sugar) can often be extracted using a cold homogenate of the crushed material with 1% aqueous or methanolic hydrochloric acid. After acid hydrolysis, 15 min. at 100 °C, the anthocyanidins can be extracted with amyl alcohol.

(*b*) Flavonoids and coumarin derivatives, including numerous unwanted impurities, can be obtained by exhaustive extraction using methanol. Glycosides, on the other hand, can be extracted from the plant material with boiling water. In nearly every case, the methanol extracts are carefully and substantially concentrated to a high degree, then diluted with a little water and, quite often, extracted with ethyl acetate-methanol (95 : 5). The di- and triglycosides remain in the aqueous phase, while the monoglycosides and aglycones pass into the ester phase. Further purification can be achieved by precipitation reactions with neutral and/or basic lead acetate. Unwanted substances have been separated out and crystallizing fractions have been obtained using polyamide column chromatography.

Reference 3, p. 373.

77. Preparation of Tannins

Plucked, minced tea shoots are squeezed by hand through cheesecloth. The extract is centrifuged, and the filtrate is rapidly heated to 100 °C and cooled to room temperature. This solution is centrifuged or filtered, if necessary, concentrated *in vacuo*, and aliquots are spotted on filter paper sheets. Tannins may also be extracted from dried tea leaves with three times the weight of water.

For the isolation of chlorogenic acid, potato peelings are extracted with 95% ethanol in a Waring blender. The extracts are taken to dryness *in vacuo*, redissolved in water, and spotted on paper.

Reference 4, p. 374.

PESTICIDES

See Numbers 78–88

78. Universal Extraction System

Schnorbus and Phillips reported that propylene carbonate is an efficient extractant for residues of many classes of pesticides in a wide variety of materials. Three procedures were found applicable for the extraction of chlorine-containing organics and organothiophosphorus compounds from fruits, leafy vegetables, cole crops, root crops, soils, grains, dehydrated products, meats, dairy products, and fats and oils.

1. *Fruits, vegetables, grains, meats and dairy products. Extraction.* Representative samples are finely chopped and mixed prior to subsampling. A subsample is then macerated for 1 min. with 2 ml of propylene carbonate per gram of sample; usually a 50- or 100-g sample is used. The macerate is vacuum-filtered through a fritted-glass Buchner funnel containing glass wool and a ½ in. layer of granular sodium sulfate. The filtered extract is dried over approximately 20 g of sodium sulfate for a minimum of 10 min. This procedure is satisfactory for all the products examined except fresh milk.

Cleanup. Florisil chromatography is generally applicable for separation of organic chlorine and organothiophosphorus compounds from propylene carbonate extracts.

The deactivated Florisil is prepared according to the procedure described by Langlois, Stemp and Liska (1964). Thirty g are added to a chromatographic column (25 mm o.d. × 400 mm) containing 5 g of sodium sulfate. An additional 5 g of sodium sulfate are added on top of the Florisil. The column is prewashed with 50 ml of petroleum ether, and the washings are discarded. Five ml of extract, representing 2.5 g of sample, are transferred to the column and allowed to penetrate the upper portion of the Florisil. The sample is eluted with successive and separate 200 ml portions of 7% diethyl ether in petroleum ether followed by 25% diethyl ether in petroleum ether. The tabulation below lists pesticides eluted by two ether solutions through Florisil deactivated with 5% water. One fraction contains organic chlorine compounds and the other contains organothiophosphorus compounds. This separation is preferred, because it simplifies applications of the multiple detection systems used.

Fraction I, 7% Et_2O in Petroleum Ether	Fraction II, 25% Et_2O in Petroleum Ether
Aldrin	Thimet
DDT, TDE, DDE	Diazinon
Lindane	Methyl parathion
Heptachlor epoxide	Methyl trithion
Dieldrin	Trithion
Endrin	Ethion
Methoxychlor	

(Florisil deactivated with 5% added water.)

Detection. Propylene carbonate extracts following cleanup were analyzed by electron-capture (for organochlorine pesticides), thermionic (for organophosphates), and microcoulometric (for sulfur-containing pesticides) GC.

2. *Soils and dehydrated products. Extraction.* A 100 g sample is weighed in a 500 ml Erlenmeyer flask and mixed with 200 ml of propylene carbonate on a mechanical shaker for 2 hr. The mixture is filtered with the aid of suction and dried over sodium sulfate.

Cleanup. Cleanup for dehydrated products is achieved using the previously described Florisil column. However, soils are first eluted with petroleum ether until a 200 ml fraction is collected in a graduated cylinder. The fraction contains aldrin, chlordane, and the aggregate DDT compounds. Two hundred ml of 7% ethyl ether are then collected to remove the remaining chlorine-containing organic compounds, such as endrin and dieldrin. In the detection systems used, it is advantageous to separate DDT compounds for naphthalenic members of the chlorine class and most organophosphorus compounds.

Detection. The detection techniques described above were also applicable to propylene carbonate extracts of soil and dehydrated products.

3. *Fats and oils. Extraction.* The following procedure is applicable for the extraction of chlorine-containing organic compounds from oils and from fats or red meat, poultry, and butter: Twenty g of melted fat or oil and 20 ml of propylene carbonate are combined and then shaken gently for 30 secs. in a 125 ml separatory funnel, and the layers are allowed to separate. In some instances, centrifugation may be required to separate emulsions. The bottom layer, propylene carbonate, is filtered through a powder funnel containing a small plug of glass wool into a 100 ml bottle. The fat layer is reextracted with another 20 ml portion of propylene carbonate. The extracts are then combined and stored over 5 g of anhydrous sodium sulfate.

Cleanup. Aliquots equivalent to 2 to 5 g of samples are taken through the same cleanup as described for vegetables.

Detection. The detection systems previously described were applicable for this group of foods extracted with propylene carbonate.

4. *Recoveries.* Recoveries are in the range of 80–95% for commodities with both high and low fat content, all extracted in the same way.

5. *Other pesticides.* The urea-type pesticide linuron was extracted as described for vegetables and separated from propylene carbonate when 2 ml of extract (1 g) was chromatographed through Florisil deactivated with 10% water and eluted with 300 ml 25% diethyl ether in petroleum ether. Recovery of free linuron from fortified potato and carrot extracts was approximately 70%. The carbamate pesticide carbaryl was extracted from fortified peaches as described for vegetables, and recovery was about 50%.

Electron capture peak suppression occurs if the injected sample contains more than 0.1% propylene carbonate. The use of Florisil as described separates the pesticides from a maximum of 10 ml of propylene carbonate. If larger aliquots are desired, the amounts of Florisil and eluants must be increased.

Reference: Schnorbus, R. R. and W. F. Phillips, *J. Agr. Food Chem.*, **15**, 661 (1967).

79. Extraction of Pesticides from Water

Pionke *et al.* reported a quantitative method for the unified extraction of organophosphate and organochlorine insecticides contained in waters at the μg per liter level. The sensitivity of the method was later increased by changing the procedure slightly (Konrad *et al.*). The revised method is as follows: A 500 ml sample is extracted with 25 ml of benzene in a single extraction by shaking it in a separating funnel for 2 min. If it is known that organochlorine insecticides alone are present in the water sample, the benzene extract can be concentrated rapidly with a 3-ball Snyder column. If, however, the sample is known to contain organochlorine and organophosphate insecticides, the separated extract is concentrated to 1 ml by blowing a stream of air over the benzene extract. This method preserves the thermally unstable organophosphates in the concentrated extract. The concentrated benzene extract is analyzed directly by gas chromatography with an electron capture detector for organochlorine insecticides, or potassium chloride thermionic detector for organophosphates. If both organochlorine and organophosphates are present in the sample, simultaneous analysis can be accomplished by dividing the column effluent and by using electron capture and potassium chloride thermionic detectors in a parallel arrangement. If emulsification is encountered, anhydrous sodium sulfate is used to remove the water.

Average recoveries ranged from 94 to 99% at concentrations of 0.0620 to 1.16 μg per liter, depending upon detector response. The average recovery of heptachlor was 89%, the loss presumably being due to degradation or volatilization of the pesticides.

Reference: Pionke, H. B., Konrad, J. G., Chesters, G., and D. E. Armstrong, *Analyst*, **93**, 63 (1968); Konrad, J. G., Pionke, H. B., and G. Chesters, *Analyst*, **94**, 490 (1969). Permission of The Analyst, London, England.

80. F.D.A. Method for Nonionic Chlorinated and Phosphate Residues in Fatty Foods

As an example, the analysis of cheese samples will be described:

1. *Extraction.* Twenty-five to 100 g diced cheese, about 2 g sodium oxalate and 100 ml methanol or ethanol are mixed together in a blender for 2–3 mins. Emulsions are broken by centrifuging; if this is not successful, add 1 ml H_2O per 2 g of cheese before blending. The mixture is poured into a 500 ml centrifugate bottle, and 50 ml ethyl ether and 50 ml petroleum ether are added with vigorous shaking for 1 min after each addition. The mixture is centrifuged at 1500 rpm for 5 min. and the solvent layer is then blown off with a wash bottle device into a 1 liter separatory funnel containing 500–600 ml H_2O and 30 ml saturated NaCl solution. Extraction (shake vigorously) with 50 ml portions of mixed ethers (1 : 1) is repeated twice. The combined ethers and water are cautiously mixed, the layers allowed to separate and the water is drained and discarded. The washing of the solvent layer is repeated twice with 100 ml portions of water. The ether layer is passed through a 50 mm x 25 mm o.d. column of anhydrous Na_2SO_4 and the eluate collected in a 400 ml beaker. The column is washed with small portions of petroleum ether and the combined extracts are evaporated at steam bath temperature under an air current to obtain fat.

2. *Acetonitrile partitioning.* Three g of fat as prepared above are put into a 125 ml separatory funnel using small portions of petroleum ether so that the total volume of fat and solvent is 15 ml. Thirty ml acetonitrile saturated with petroleum ether are added and shaken vigorously for 1–2 min. After the layers separate, the acetonitrile is drained into a 1-liter separatory funnel containing 700 ml of 2% NaCl solution and 100 ml of petroleum ether. The petroleum ether layer is reextracted in a 125 ml separatory funnel with three 30 ml portions of acetonitrile saturated with petroleum ether, shaking vigorously for 1 min. each time, and the extracts are added to the 1-liter funnel. The funnel is stoppered, the pressure vented off, and the contents mixed by vigorous tumbling of the funnel. This can be accomplished by holding the funnel horizontally and rotating each end in a circular manner, i.e. a bicycle pedals motion, for 15 sec. After the layers separate, the aqueous layer is drawn into another 1-liter separatory funnel and reextracted with 100 ml petroleum ether. The combined petroleum ether extracts in the original funnel are washed with two 100 ml portions of H_2O. If an emulsion forms, 5 ml of saturated NaCl solution are added to the funnel. The H_2O washings are discarded and the petroleum ether drawn off through a 2 in. column of anhydrous Na_2SO_4 into a 500 ml Kuderna-Danish concentrator. The funnel and the column are washed with three 10 ml portions of petroleum ether, and the total is evaporated to about 10 ml for transfer to the Florisil column.

3. *Florisil column cleanup.* The tube is 22 mm i.d. x 300 mm and contains 4 in. (after settling) of activated Florisil (PR Grade) topped with 0.5 in. of anhydrous Na_2SO_4, prewet with 40–50 ml petroleum ether. The petroleum ether extract from procedure 2 is put on the column at a rate of not more than 5 ml/min. The container is rinsed with two 5 ml portions of petroleum ether which are added to the column, and the sample is washed from the walls of the tube into the bed with a further small portion of petroleum ether. The column is eluted at 5 ml/min. with 200 ml of 6% v/v ethyl ether in petroleum ether, collecting the eluate in a calibrated collection tube. (Elution rates of up to 250 ml/min. have been used without adversely affecting cleanup or recovery of pesticides.) The receiver is changed and elution is continued with 200 ml 15% v/v ethyl ether in petroleum ether. Each eluate is concentrated to a suitable volume in a Kuderna-Danish evaporator.

Table I shows the residues recovered in the 6% eluate. This eluate is generally suitable for gas chromatography without further cleanup. Further cleanup is obtained by evaporating the eluate to 10 ml and repeating the Florisil procedure on a new column or using an acid-Celite column (Section 4) if the pesticide is stable to acid (Table I). If the 15% eluate requires additional cleanup, a MgO-Celite column (Section 5) is used, or alkaline hydrolysis (Section 6) followed by the MgO-Celite treatment. Table I also shows a few pesticides recovered by each of these procedures.

4. *Acid-Celite column.* The eluate from the Florisil column is evaporated to dryness in a beaker, dissolved in 10 ml CCl_4, and transferred to the column. The sample is rinsed from the beaker with three 10 ml portions of CCl_4, which are also added to the column. The solvent is drained just to the top of the bed, and the walls of the tube above the bed are rinsed with two 10 ml portions of CCl_4. The solvent is drained just to the top of the bed and 25 ml CCl_4 is added and drained completely (the column is allowed to go dry). The top of the column is tamped with a flat-end glass rod to expel all free liquid. The eluate is evaporated to dryness and the residue dissolved in a suitable solvent for further cleanup or gas chromatography or TLC.

The column is prepared by grinding and mixing 10 g Celite 545 with 3 ml 15–20% fuming H_2SO_4 in a mortar. Three ml H_2SO_4 is added and ground well. This mixture is transferred at once to a fritted glass funnel (60 ml capacity, 40 mm i.d., coarse porosity) and packed to a firm level surface with a flat-end glass rod. CCl_4 is added to the column to wet the adsorbent and then drained until a 2 mm layer of solvent remains over the bed. For extracts of fatty materials containing maximum of 5 g fat, 30 g Celite plus 9 ml fuming H_2SO_4 and 9 ml H_2SO_4 are used, and elution is with 250 ml CCl_4.

5. *MgO-Celite column.* Ten g MgO-Celite mixture (1 : 1) is packed into a chromatographic tube and prewashed with about 40 ml petroleum ether. Concentrated extract from the Florisil column or the alkaline hydrolysis procedure is transferred to this column, rinsing with small portions of petroleum ether. The column is eluted with 100 ml petroleum ether using slight pressure or vacuum, and the eluate is evaporated to a suitable small volume for gas chromatography.

6. *Alkaline hydrolysis.* The eluate from the Florisil column is evaporated just to dryness in a 125 ml standard taper flask and 20 ml of 2% alcoholic KOH are added and refluxed for 30 min. under an air condenser. The solution is transferred to a 125 ml separatory funnel, the flask rinsed with three 10 ml portions of petroleum ether, and the rinsings

added to the funnel. Twenty ml H_2O are added and shaken vigorously. The water layer is drained into a second separatory funnel containing 20 ml petroleum ether and shaken vigorously. The aqueous layer is discarded and the petroleum ether layer is added to the original funnel. The combined extracts are washed with three 20 ml portions of alcohol-H_2O (1 : 1 v/v). If the first wash causes heavy emulsions, use distilled H_2O only for other washes. Alternatively, all three washes can be with water. The aqueous alcohol is discarded and the petroleum ether layer is passed through a column of anhydrous Na_2SO_4 which is rinsed with petroleum ether. The solvent is concentrated for gas chromatography or further cleanup on the MgO-Celite column.

Reference: *Pesticide Analytical Manual*, Vol. I. Permission of U.S. Food and Drug Administration, Rockville, Md. 20852.

81. F.D.A. Method for Nonionic Chlorinated and Phosphate Residues in Nonfatty Foods

The sample, containing in general not more than 2 g fat per 20–100 g, is extracted with acetonitrile. The pesticides are transferred into petroleum ether and cleaned up on a Florisil column prior to gas chromatography or TLC.

1. *High moisture products (fruits, vegetables)*. One hundred g chopped or blended sample is placed in a blender jar with 200 ml acetonitrile and 10 g Celite filter aid. After blending at high speed for 2 min., the mixture is filtered through a 12 cm Buchner funnel, fitted with sharkskin paper, into a 500 ml suction flask. The filtrate is transferred to a 250 ml graduated cylinder, and the volume of this filtrate is recorded as F. The filtrate is transferred to a 1-liter separatory funnel and exactly 100 ml petroleum ether is added from the same cylinder. The contents are shaken vigorously for 1–2 min., and again for 15 sec. after adding 10 ml saturated NaCl solution and 600 ml H_2O. After the layers separate, the aqueous phase is discarded and the solvent layer is washed gently with two 100 ml portions of water. The washings are discarded and the solvent phase transferred to a glass-stoppered 100 ml graduated cylinder. The volume is recorded as *P*. Fifteen g anhydrous Na_2SO_4 is added and shaken vigorously; the petroleum ether must not be in contact with the Na_2SO_4 for periods greater than 1 hr. or loss of pesticides may result from adsorption. Alternatively, the washed solvent phase can be filtered through a 2-in. column of Na_2SO_4 into a graduate cylinder and the volume recorded as *P*.

The solution is transferred directly to a Florisil column or pre-concentrated to 5–10 ml. The grams of sample (*g*) put on the Florisil column are calculated by the equation

$$g = \frac{SFP}{100T}$$

where S = g sample extracted; T = ml H_2O in sample (assuming 85% water content for most fruits and vegetables) +ml acetonitrile used—correction in ml for volume contraction (5 ml used for 80–95 ml H_2O/200 ml acetonitrile); 100 = ml petroleum ether used for partitioning residues.

2. *Dry products (grains, hays, cereals, feedstuffs, soybeans) and products with intermediate water content (fish, shrimp, silages.* Samples with low (<10%) moisture content are ground to about 20 mesh, and 20-50 g are weighed into a blender jar and blended with 350 ml of 35% v/v water-acetonitrile. If more sample is used, a larger volume of solvent is added to allow blending. The blending is carried out for 5 min. at high speed, and then proceed with filtering as in Section 1 directly above. No more than 260 ml of the filtered extract is taken for analysis; 600 ml of distilled water and 10 ml saturated NaCl solution are used in the acetonitrile dilution step. The grams placed on the Florisil column are given by

$$g = \frac{SFP}{100T_2}$$

where T_2 is the total volume of 35% H_2O-acetonitrile extracting solvent used, ignoring the moisture content of the material if it is 10% or less.

Dry products are hydrated prior to extraction by grinding to 20 mesh, weighing 20–50 g into a blender jar, adding 80 ml H_2O and blending until water is absorbed by the sample. Two hundred ml acetonitrile are added and the procedure outlined in Section 1 is carried out.

3. *Products for which water content is not known*. One hundred g plant material and 150 ml acetonitrile are blended at high speed for 2–3 min. in an Omni-mixer cup. The blades are removed from the cup and washed with a few ml of acetonitrile. The cup containing the extract is centrifuged at 1900 rpm for 10 min., and then all the liquid is decanted into a 2-liter separatory funnel. The plant material in the cup is reextracted using 100 ml acetonitrile and a medium speed. One hundred ml petroleum ether are added to the combined extracts and shaken vigorously for 1 min., venting pressure. Seventy-five ml of 30% Na_2SO_4 solution and 1500 ml H_2O are added and shaken by vigorous tumbling action for 15 sec. After the layers separate, discard the bottom phase and wash the upper with two 100 ml portions of H_2O. If an emulsion forms add 5 ml saturated NaCl solution. Discard the washings, drain the petroleum ether layer into a glass-stoppered container, and add 15 g anhydrous Na_2SO_4 and shake vigorously. A measured portion is added to a Florisil column. The grams sample placed on the column is calculated by

$$g = \frac{SM}{100}$$

4. *Florisil column cleanup*. The procedure above for nonfatty foods is used. The 6% eluate is generally suitable for gas chromatography while the 15% eluate of various products usually requires additional cleanup as described above. Table I in below lists residues known to be recovered by these procedures.

Reference: *Pesticide Analytical Manual*, Volume I. Permission of U.S. Food and Drug Administration, Rockville, Md. 20852.

TABLE I

Behavior of pesticides and related chemicals in methods for organochlorine (nonionic) and organophosphorous compounds in fatty and nonfatty foods

(Data compiled by B. Malone and J. A. Burke and supplied to the authors by J. A. Burke in May 1971)

Pesticide[a]	[b]Method Recovery Fatty Foods[d]	Nonfatty Foods[e]	Florisil Elution[c]
alachlor (Lasso)	ND	ND	NR, 6, 15%
aldrin[g]	C	C	6%
allidochlor (Randox)®	ND	NR	NR, 6, 15%
Aramite®	NR	P	P, 15%
atrazine	ND	P (25)	C, 50%
azinphos-ethyl (Ethyl Guthion)®	ND	P (50)	50%
azinphos-methyl (Guthion)®	ND	NR[h]	NR, 6, 15%
benfluralin (benefin)	ND	C	6%
αBHC[f,g]	C	C	6%
βBHC	C	C	6%
γBHC[f,g] (lindane)	C	C	6%
δBHC	C	C	6, 15% (inconsistent)
binapacryl	ND	P	P, 15%
Bomyl®	ND	NR[h]	
Botran (Dichloran)®	ND	P (35)	P, 15%; C, 15+20%
bromophos-ethyl	ND	C	6%
Bulan®	P (75)	P (60)	15%
butoxy ethanol ester 2,4-D	P	P	15%
butoxy ethanol ester 2,4,5-T	P	P	15%
n-butyl ester 2,4-D	P (10)	C	15%
n-butyl ester 2,4,5-T	P	P (75)	15, 30%
captafol (Difolatan)®	ND	NR	NR, 6, 15%
captan	ND	NR	NR, 6, 15%
captan epoxide	ND	NR	NR, 6, 15%
carbophenothion[g] (Trithion)®	P (60)	C	6%
carbophenothion oxygen analog	ND	NR[h]	
CDEC (Vegadex)®	C	C	6%
chlorbenside	C	C	6%
chlordane (technical)	C	C	6%
chlordane (*cis*)	C	C	6%
chlordane (*trans*)	C	C	6%
chlordecone (Kepone)®	P	P (45)	P, 15, 50% (inconsistent)
chlorfenvinphos	ND	NR[h]	
chlorinated naphthalenes	P (65)	C	6, 15%
Chlorobenzilate®	P (80)	P (80)	15, 30%
chloroneb	ND	P (75)	6%
chloropropylate	ND	C	15%
chlorothalonil (Daconil 2787)	ND	NR	NR, 6, 15%
chloropropham (CIPC)	C	C	15%
Chlorothion®	C	C	15%
coumaphos (Co-ral)®	ND	NR[h]	NR, 6, 15, 30%
crotoxyphos (Ciodrin)®	ND	NR[h]	
crufomate (Ruelene)®	ND	NR[h]	
cypromid	ND	ND	NR, 6, 15%
Dacthal®	P	C	15%
o,p'-DDE	C	C	6%
p,p'-DDE[f,g]	C	C	6%
o,p'-DDT[f]	C	C	6%
p,p'-DDT[f,g]	C	C	6%
Def	ND	C	50%
demeton (Systox)®	ND	NR[h]	
dialifor	ND	C	15%
Diazinon[g]®	C	C	15%
dicaphthon	ND	P (75)	15%
dichlobenil (Casoron)®	ND	P	15%
dichlone	ND	ND	NR, 6, 15%
Dichloran (Botran)	ND	P (35)	P, 15%, C, 15 + 20%
dicofol (Kelthane)®	P	P	6, 15% (inconsistent)
dicrotophos (Bidrin)®	ND	NR[h]	
dieldrin[f]	C	C	15%

TABLE I—continued

Pesticide[a]	Method Recovery[b] Fatty Foods[d]	Nonfatty Foods[e]	Florisil Elution[c]
Dilan®	P (65)	P (65)	15%
dimethoate	ND	NR[h]	
dimethoate oxygen analog	ND	NR[h]	
dinocap (Karathane)®	ND	P	P, 15%
dioxathion (Delnav)®	ND	NR[h]	
disulfoton (Di-Syston)	ND	P (50)	6%
disulfoton oxygen analog	ND	NR[h]	
disulfoton sulfone	ND	NR[h]	
diuron	ND	ND	C, 65%
Dyrens®	P	C	15%
endosulfan I (Thiodan® I)	C	C	15%
endosulfan II (Thiodan® II)	C	C	15, 30%
endosulfan sulfate (Thiodan® sulfate)	C	C	50%
endrin[g]	C	C	15%
endrin alcohol	C	P (50)	C, 15 + 20% or 25% (following 6% only)
endrin aldehyde	C	P (50)	C, 15 + 20% or 25% (following 6% only)
endrin ketone (Delta® Keto 153)	C	C	25% (following 6% only)
EPN	C	C	15%
ethion[g]	C	C	6%
ethyl hexyl ester 2,4-D	C	C	15%
famphur	ND	NR[h]	
fenitrothion	ND	C	15%
fensulfothion	ND	NR[h]	
fensulfothion oxygen analog	ND	NR[h]	
fensulfothion sulfone	ND	NR[h]	
fenthion	ND	P (45)	6, 15%
folpet (Phaltan)®	P	P	C, 15 + 20%
fonofos (Dyfonate)	ND	C	6%
Genite® 923	ND	C	15%
heptachlor[g]	C	C	6%
heptachlor epoxide[f]	C	C	6%
hexachlorobenzene	P (60)	C	6%
hexachlorophene	ND	ND	NR, 6, 15, 50%
isobenzan (Telodrin)®	C	C	6%
isobutyl ester 2,4-D	C	C	15%
Isocrin®	ND	C	6%
iso-octyl ester 2,4,5-T	C	C	15%
iso-octyl ester 2,4-D	P (75)	P	15%
isopropyl ester 2,4,5-T	C	C	15%
isopropyl ester 2,4-D	P (65)	C	15%
korax (Lanstan)	ND	NR	NR, 6, 15%
malathion[g]	ND	C	15, 50% (inconsistent)
malathion oxygen analog	ND	NR[h]	
Merphos	C	C	6, 15, 50% (inconsistent)
methidathion (Supracid)®	ND	P (35)	50%
methoxychlor[f,g]	C	C	6%
methyl parathion[g]	C	C	15%
methyl parathion oxygen analog	ND	NR[h]	
Methyl Trithion®	ND	C	6%
mevinphos (Phosdrin)®	ND	NR	
mirex	P (70)	C	6%
Mocap	ND	P (55)	50%
monocrotophos (Azodrin)	ND	NR[h]	
monuron	ND	ND	C, 65%
naled	ND	NR[h]	
neburon	ND	ND	NR, 6, 15, 30%
Nemacide	ND	C	6%
nitrofen (TOK)	ND	C	15%
octachlor epoxide (oxychlordane)	C	ND	6%
octachloro-dibenzo-*p*-dioxin	ND	ND	NR, 6, 15%
ovex	C	C	15%

TABLE I—continued

Pesticide[a]	Method Recovery[b] Fatty Foods[d]	Nonfatty Foods[e]	Florisil Elution[c]
parathion[g]	C	C	15%
parathion oxygen analog	ND	NR[h]	
Perthane®	C	C	6%
Perthane® olefin	C	C	6%
Phenkaptone	ND	C	6%
phorate (Thimet)®	P (80)	P (75)	6%
phorate oxygen analog sulfone	ND	NR[h]	
phosalone	ND	C	50%
phosmet (Imidan)	ND	NR[h]	
phosphamidon	ND	NR[h]	
Phostex	ND	P (65)	6%
photodieldrin	C	C	15%; final trace, 20%
Planavin	ND	P (60)	P (50), 50%
polychlorinated biphenyls	C	C	6%
Prolan	P (25)	P (40)	15%
Prometryne®	ND	P (50)	P (67), 50%
propachlor (Ramrod)	ND	ND	NR, 6, 15%
propanil (Stam® F-34)	ND	NR	NR, 6, 15%
Propazin®	ND	P (41)	C, 50%
quintozene (PCNB)®	C	C	6%
ronnel[g]	C	C	6%
ronnel oxygen analog	ND	NR[h]	
schradan (OMPA)	ND	NR[h]	
SD 7438	ND	C	15%
simazin	ND	NR	C, 50%
Strobane®	C	C	6%
sulfotepp	ND	C	6%
Sulphenone	ND	ND	20, 25%
o,p'-TDE	C	C	6%
p,p'-TDE[f,g]	C	C	6%
p,p'-TDE olefin	C	C	6%
tecnazene (TCNB)	C	ND	6%
terbacil	ND	ND	NR, 6, 15%
2,3,7,8-tetrachlorodibenzo-*p*-dioxin	P (70)	ND	P, 6, 15% (inconsistent)
tetrachlorvinphos (Gardona)	ND	NR[h]	
tetradifon (Tedion)®	C	C	15%
tetraiodoethylene	P (65)	P (65)	6%
tetrasul	ND	C	6%
thionazin (Zinophos)®	ND	P (59)	15%
toxaphene	C	C	6%
trichlorobenzene	ND	C	6%
trichlorpyrphos (Dursban)®	ND	C	6%
trichlorpyrphos oxygen analog	ND	NR[h]	
trifluralin	C	C	6%
Zytron®	ND	C	6%

[a] Inclusion in list does not necessarily indicate that the compound listed is likely to be the residue.

[b] Code:

C = COMPLETE (>80%) recovery; may apply to the complete method or to only the Florisil column elution by the specific eluant(s) noted.

P = PARTIAL (<80%) recovery; may apply to the complete method or to only the Florisil column elution by the specific eluant(s) noted. Approximate per cent recovery expected is given in parentheses, when known.

NR = NOT RECOVERED: may apply to the complete method or to only the Florisil column elution by the specific eluant(s) noted.

ND = NO DATA: indicates chemical has not been tested through complete method.

[c] Percentages in this column refer to percent ethyl ether in petroleum ether eluants in 200 ml portions. Unless otherwise indicated, percentages above 15% were used successive to the usual 6% and 15% eluants.

Appearance of C, P, or NR plus the appropriate eluant(s) indicates that the information was obtained during testing of Florisil elution only.

Appearance of appropriate eluant *alone* indicates that the information was obtained during testing of the complete method.

[d] Applies to the following methods: extraction with ethyl ether-petroleum ether mixture or petroleum ether; petroleum ether-acetonitrile partitioning; Florisil column chromatography. Does not apply to supplemental cleanups.

[e] Applies to the following methods: extraction with acetonitrile or water-acetonitrile mixtures; aqueous acetonitrile to petroleum ether transfer; Florisil column chromatography. Does not apply to supplemental cleanups.

[f] Pesticides for which fatty-food methods are official AOAC. AOAC status applies to dairy products, vegetable oils, and/or fish.

[g] Pesticides for which nonfatty food methods are official AOAC. AOAC status applies to certain fruits, vegetables, and other nonfatty foods and feeds.

[h] Study of recovery through method included elution of the Florisil column with 6, 15 and 50% ethyl ether-petroleum ether.

82. F.D.A. Method for Ionic Chlorinated Pesticides in Fatty Foods

Chlorophenoxy acids are extracted from refined oils, dairy products or animal tissues, partitioned into a basic solution which is washed with organic solvents, and acidified. The reformed pesticide acids are extracted into $CHCl_3$ and methylated with diazomethane, after which the esters are analyzed by microcoulometric gas chromatography or TLC.

1. *Extraction of acids from animal tissues.* One hundred g of sample is placed in a 500 ml Erlenmeyer flask with a standard-taper top, 25 ml of 10% H_2SO_4 is added, and then enough ethanol to cover the sample by one inch. After refluxing for 3 hr., the mixture is centrifuged for 5–10 min. at 1500 rpm, the liquid poured into a 500 ml Erlenmeyer flask and evaporated to 35 ml on a steam bath with a jet of air. The solution is poured into a 500 ml separatory funnel with 250 ml 50% ethyl ether in petroleum ether, 50 ml 4% $NaHCO_3$ is added and shaken carefully. Extraction is carried out as in Section 4.

2. *Extraction from dairy products.* One hundred g sample is put into a 500 ml centrifuge bottle and 80 ml ethyl ether, 20 ml petroleum ether, 5 ml cencentrated HCl and 10 ml of 20% phosphotungstic acid is added. The mixture is shaken for 1 min. and centrifuged at 1500 rpm for 10 min. Both liquid phases are decanted together through a large glass funnel, plugged with glass wool covered with 5–10 g sea sand, into a 500 ml separatory funnel. The aqueous layer is drained back into the centrifuge bottle, 50 ml ethyl ether-petroleum ether (8 : 2 v/v) is added, and the shaking and centrifuging is repeated. The filtration is repeated, followed by extraction with another 50 ml of solvent. Allow the phases to separate, and discard the aqueous layer; 35 ml ethanol and 50 ml 4% $NaHCO_3$ are added to the ether extract, and extraction is carried out as in Section 4.

3. *Extraction from oils.* The procedure in Section 4 is carried out after adding 50 g oil, 125 ml petroleum ether, 35 ml ethanol and 50 ml 4% $NaHCO_3$ to a 500 ml separatory funnel.

4. *Isolation of acids.* The funnel is shaken vigorously for 1 min., venting pressure. The layers, both of which may be turbid, are allowed to separate, and the lower aqueous phase is drained into another 500 ml separatory funnel. The extraction of the upper layer is repeated twice with 15 ml ethanol and 40 ml 4% $NaHCO_3$ solution each time. The aqueous phases, containing the chlorophenoxy acids, are combined, and the organic phase is discarded. The aqueous solution is extracted twice with 25 ml portions of $CHCl_3$, each of which is discarded. The aqueous solution is then carefully acidified with 25 ml of 10% aqueous H_2SO_4, venting pressure from liberated CO_2 frequently during shaking. The acidified solution is extracted three times with 30 ml of $CHCl_3$. Each $CHCl_3$ extract is drained through a plug of cotton held in a small glass funnel into a Phillips beaker. The cotton is rinsed with $CHCl_3$. The cotton is removed and the funnel is replaced in the Phillips beaker to act as a condenser. Boiling chips are added, and the solution is evaporated just to dryness on a steam bath, removing the last traces of $CHCl_3$ with the aid of ether and an air jet. The entire residue is methylated as in Section 5.

5. *Methylation.* Standards and the sample are methylated using diazomethane prepared from Diazald (Aldrich Chemical Co.). The side walls of the beaker containing the residue are washed with 4 ml ethyl ether and 2 ml diazomethane is added. After standing 10 min. with occasional shaking, the solvent is evaporated with a gentle stream of air. The sample is transferred to a 12 ml stoppered test tube with petroleum ether and evaporated just to dryness with a gentle stream of air. The sample is dissolved in isooctane for injection into the gas chromatograph. Since losses of methylated acids can occur during the evaporation step, standards and samples are carried through the procedures at the same time.

The following residues are recovered by this method: 2,4-D, 2,4-DB, 2,4,5-T, 2,4,5-TP, MCPA, PCP and dicamba. The cleanup procedure is not sufficient for electron capture gas chromatography.

Reference: *Pesticide Analytical Manual*, Volume I, Permission of U.S. Food and Drug Administration, Rockville, Md. 20852.

83. F.D.A. Method for Ionic Chlorinated Pesticides in Nonfatty Foods

Chlorophenoxy acid and ester residues in grains and vegetables are extracted with mixed ethers under acid conditions, extracts are shaken with carbonate solution, and the esters and acids separated by washing the carbonate solution with ether. The esters are analyzed in the ether extracts after further cleanup. The carbonate solution containing isolated acids is acidified and the reformed acids are extracted into chloroform and methylated with diazomethane. Cleanup methods are usually adequate for TLC or microcoulometric gas chromatography.

1. *Extraction of acids and esters from vegetables.* One hundred g of finely chopped sample is blended with 10 ml 10% aqueous H_2SO_4, 25 ml ethanol, 50 ml petroleum ether and 150 ml ethyl ether for 3 min. at high speed with the mixer jar immersed in an ice-water bath. The mixture is then centrifuged for 10 min. at 1500 rpm and the liquid decanted through Na_2SO_4 into a 250 ml graduated cylinder. (To check if the Na_2SO_4 adsorbs chlorophenoxy acids, 20 g of it is placed in a 20 × 150 mm filter tube and 25 ml $CHCl_3$ containing 10 μg 2,4-D acid is added. The column is eluted with two 25 ml portions of $CHCl_3$ and recovery is checked by analyzing the combined filtrates by methylation and gas chromatography). The filtrate is transferred to a 500 ml centrifuge bottle, 75 ml of 4% Na_2CO_3 is added and shaken vigorously for 1 min. After centrifuging for 10 min. at 1500 rpm, the top layer is blown off into a suitable container. The carbonate layer is washed with two 25 ml portions of ethyl ether, shaking and centrifuging as before. The ether layers are added to the container, which is saved for future analysis. The ether solution contains the chlorophenoxy esters as well as most of the pigments and waxes in the extract. The aqueous solution containing the acids is put into a 250 ml separatory funnel and the acids isolated as in Section 3.

2. *Extraction from grains* (*wheat*). The kernels are ground in a mill to 30 mesh, and 100 g is blended with 20 ml 10% alcoholic H_2SO_4, 100 ml petroleum ether and 100 ml ethyl ether, the blender cup being immersed in ice water. After centrifuging, the ethers are filtered through glass wool into a 500 ml separatory funnel. The wheat is reextracted with 100 ml ether-petroleum ether (1 : 1), and the extract combined in the separatory funnel after centrifuging, decanting and filtering. The glass wool is rinsed with 10 ml ethyl ether and 30 ml petroleum ether. One hundred ml 4% Na_2CO_3 or 100 ml 2*N* NaOH and 35 ml ethanol are added to the separatory funnel and shaken vigorously for 1 min. If

the layers do not separate in 10 min. 5 ml portions of ethanol are added with shaking until separation occurs. The aqueous phase is drawn off into a 250 ml separatory funnel, and the ether layer is filtered through Na_2SO_4 into a 500 ml Erlenmeyer flask. The original separatory funnel and the Na_2SO_4 are washed with 5–10 ml petroleum ether, which is added to the flask along with another 250 ml of petroleum ether and saved for analysis of the esters. Fifty ml petroleum ether is added to the 250 ml separatory funnel with shaking. The aqueous phase is drawn off into the original 500 ml separatory funnel and procedure 3 is carried out.

3. *Isolation of acids.* Forty ml $CHCl_3$ is added to the separatory funnel and shaken. The $CHCl_3$ is drawn off and discarded and the washing is repeated with 10 ml $CHCl_3$. The carbonate solution is acidified and the procedure continued as described in Section 4 for nonfatty foods.

4. *Methylation of acids.* The isolated acids are methylated by the procedure given in Section 5 for nonfatty foods prior to determination by microcoulometric gas chromatography. Residues recovered include 2,4-D, 2,4-DB, 2,4,5-T, 2,4,5-TP, MCPA, PCP and dicamba.

5. *Isolation of esters.* The reserved ether extracts are concentrated on a steam bath using a Snyder column. Ten ml hexane is added to the concentrate, and evaporation is continued with a small funnel in place of the Snyder column. The final traces of solvent are removed with the aid of an air jet. All traces of ethers and alcohols must be removed before the next step. The residue is transferred with several portions of petroleum ether to a column containing 7 cm of Florisil topped with 1 in. of Na_2SO_4. The column is eluted with 80 ml 5% ether in petroleum ether. The eluate, collected in a 250 ml Phillips beaker, is concentrated to a small volume on a steam bath using a small glass reflux funnel.

6. *Acetonitrile partitioning.* The esters must be further cleaned up prior to gas chromatography. The concentrated eluate is transferred with 25 ml petroleum ether to a 125 ml separatory funnel and shaken vigorously with 25 ml of 80% acetonitrile in H_2O three times. The acetonitrile layers are combined in a 1-liter separatory funnel and shaken vigorously after adding 750 ml H_2O, 30 g NaCl and 80 ml petroleum ether. The aqueous layer is discarded and the petroleum ether layer reshaken in 100 ml H_2O. The petroleum ether layer is cleaned up further on a 3 in. Florisil column topped with 1 cm of Na_2SO_4. Elution is with a mixture of ether and petroleum ether, the proportions of which are determined by pre-elution of 10 μg of pure isooctyl ester of 2,4-D. The purified esters are finally determined by microcoulometric gas chromatography.

Reference: *Pesticide Analytical Manual*, Volume I. Permission of U.S. Food and Drug Administration, Rockville, Md. 20852.

84. Determination of Triazine Herbicides in Crops

Sample preparation. *s*-Triazine herbicide residues in crop materials (e.g., sugar cane, wheat grain, soybean foliage) are extracted and cleaned up prior to gas chromatography as follows. The crops are chopped in a Hobart food cutter. Two hundred g of the chopped sample are mixed with 500 ml chloroform in a 1-quart jar and shaken for one-half hour on a mechanical shaker. The extract is filtered through filter paper and dried with anhydrous sodium sulfate. An aliquot equivalent to 10 to 20 g is evaporated to dryness using a flash evaporator. The residue is taken up in 2 ml of benzene.

Cleanup. Aluminum oxide of Activity V is used for cleanup. Twelve grams of aluminum oxide, Activity V, are packed into a chromatographic column (20 mm i.d. × 180 mm). The benzene solution is then transferred to the column and the sample is washed into the column with small amounts of *n*-hexane. The column is eluted with a total of 75 ml of *n*-hexane. No triazines are eluted by this eluate. They are quantitatively recovered from the column with 150 ml of a mixture of benzene-hexane (1 : 1 v/v). This solution is evaporated to dryness using a flash evaporator. The residue is transferred quantitatively to a 10 ml centrifuge tube with ethyl ether. The ethyl ether is evaporated to dryness, and the residue is dissolved in a small known volume of benzene (usually 0.5 ml). Aliquots of this solution are used for gas chromatography.

Using these procedures with determination by microcoulometric gas chromatography, 0.25 μg of triazine can be measured quantitatively in the presence of the equivalent of 5 g of crop extract (0.05 ppm). Less than 0.05 ppm can be determined if the crop extracts contain low amounts of impurities.

Reference: Mattson, A. M., Kahrs, R. A., and J. Schneller, *J. Agr. Food Chem.*, **13**, 120 (1965).

85. Determination of Anilide Herbicides in Soil by GC (flame ionization detection)

Extraction from soil. Transfer a 50 g sample to a graduated cylinder and dilute to 250 ml with acetone. Homogenize the suspension for 30 sec. in a Waring Blender and filter. Concentrate aliquots of the clear filtrate 10-fold on a steam bath and use for measurement of propanil, Dicryl, Karsil, TCAB (3,3′,4,4′-tetrachloroazobenzene) and azobenzene. Measure Ramrod, DCA (3,4-dichloroaniline) and aniline in portions of unconcentrated soil extract (injection volume = 1.0 μl).

Reference: Bartha, R. *J. Agr. Food Chem.*, **16**, 602 (1968).

86. Organomercurial Fungicides

Five g of chopped peel of apples or potatoes, or 5 g of the macerated fruit in the case of tomatoes, are macerated with a mixture of 10 ml of 2-propanol and 5 ml of alkaline cysteine hydrochloride solution (1% aqueous solution adjusted to pH 8.0 by the addition of 5*N* ammonia solution). After allowing the liquor to settle, the clear layer is decanted and the extraction repeated twice more with further portions of extractant solutions. The combined extracts are then centrifuged at 2500 rpm. for 5 min. The clear liquor is separated, diluted with 700 ml of 4% sodium sulfate solution and the solution washed with three 50-ml portions of diethyl ether. It was found that, at this stage, potatoes gave a gelatinous precipitate, but this remained in the ether layer and could be discarded without apparently affecting appreciably the recovery of mercury compounds. The organomercurials are then extracted from the aqueous solution using three 25-ml portions of a 0.005% solution of dithizone in diethyl ether. The combined extracts are then dried by passage through a short column of granular anhydrous sodium sulfate and concentrated to a suitable volume, usually 5 ml, in a Kuderna–Danish evaporator. The final solution is used for GC.

Recoveries of 85–95% were reported at the 0.01–5 ppm level. The recommended column is 2% polyethylene glycol succinate on Chromosorb G.

Reference: Tatton, J. O'G. and P. J. Wagstaffe, *J. Chromatogr.*, **44**, 284 (1969). Permission of Elsevier Publishing Company, Amsterdam, The Netherlands.

87. Phenolic Herbicides

An example is the determination of bromoxynil in grain and straw from wheat, barley, oats, and whole flax seed down to 0.05 ppm. The procedure involves hot alkaline hydrolysis to free any bound herbicide and hydrolyzing the octanyl ester to the free phenol form of bromoxynil. The cleanup involves liquid–liquid partition, methylation with diazomethane, chromatography on a Florisil column, and finally microcoulometric GC on a 16% SE-30 column at 180–185°C. For details, *see* Volume 6 of "Analytical Methods for Pesticides, Plant Growth Regulators and Food Additives," G. Zweig, editor, Academic Press, N.Y., 1972.

88. Carbamate Pesticides

The most widely used carbamate insecticide is carbaryl, which is analyzed by GC as follows: A sample of milk is extracted with pentane-ether and cleaned up by acetonitrile partitioning. Subsequently, the residues are hydrolyzed to 1-naphthol, part of which is trichloroacetylated and part brominated and acetylated. Both derivatives are determined by electron capture GC on a column of 7% DC-200 at 190 °C. *See* Butler, L. I. and L. M. McDonough, *J. Ass. Offic. Anal. Chem.*, **53**, 495 (1970), for details.

The official FDA method for carbaryl involves extraction, cleanup, and TLC determination. The method described by Palmer, N. J. and W. R. Benson, *J. Ass. Offic. Anal. Chem.*, **51**, 679 (1968), is applicable to all types of nonfatty products down to the 0.1 ppm level, and serves as an example of the steps involved in the sample preparation of carbamate pesticides for TLC analysis.

Substituted urea and carbamate herbicides in river water are determined by hydrolyzing the compounds to an aromatic amine and preparing 2,4-dinitrophenyl derivatives of the amines, which are amenable to GC with electron-capture detection. The derivatives are formed by reaction on a silica gel thin layer plate. For details *see* Cohen I. C. and B. B. Wheals, *J. Chromatogr.* **43**, 233 (1969).

A method for determining four carbamate insecticides in river waters and vegetables has also been described. The carbamate is hydrolyzed to a phenol followed by formation of the corresponding 2,4-dinitrophenyl ether. Details of this procedure [Cohen, I. C., Norcup, J., Ruzicka, J. H. A. and B. B. Wheals, *J. Chromatogr.* **49**, 215 (1970]) are as follows:

Water

To 1 liter of the sample of water, contained in a 2-liter separating funnel, add freshly prepared ceric sulfate solution (20 mg ceric sulfate in 20 ml $4N$ H_2SO_4). After 15 min dissolve 20 g of anhydrous sodium sulfate in the water and extract with three 50 ml portions of redistilled chloroform, shaking for 1 min for each extraction. Dry the extracts by passage through a column containing 15 g of granular anhydrous sodium sulfate. Combine the dried extracts and evaporate to a small volume in a Kuderna–Danish evaporator fitted with a 10 ml pear-shaped flask, and then reduce the volume still further using a micro-Snyder column. Finally take to dryness in a gentle stream of air, hydrolyze and form the derivative as described below.

Vegetable Material

Macerate 50 g of vegetable tissue for 2 min. with each of three separate 100 ml portions of acetone; centrifuge after each operation. Add the combined supernatant extracts to 1 liter of deionized water containing 20 g of anhydrous sodium sulfate and extract with three 50 ml portions of redistilled chloroform, shaking for 1 min. for each extraction. Pass the extracts down a column containing 15 g of granular anhydrous sodium sulfate into a Kuderna–Danish evaporator. Reduce the volume to 5 ml, wash with chloroform into a 150 ml beaker and evaporate to dryness in a gentle stream of air. Redissolve the extracted vegetable matter in 50 ml of acetone and add 50 ml of coagulating solution (1.25 g NH_4Cl and 2.5 ml conc. H_3PO_4 in 1 liter distilled water). Cover with a watch glass and allow to stand overnight. Filter the coagulated solution, under vacuum, through a tightly packed filter paper pulp pad about 0.5 cm thick contained in a coarse sintered glass filter funnel. Wash the beaker with 30 ml of coagulating solution and pass the washings through the filter pad. Transfer the filtrate, which should be almost colorless, to a 250-ml separating funnel and add 20 ml of freshly prepared ceric sulfate solution. After 15 min., add 10 ml of 2-propanol to minimize emulsion formation. Extract with redistilled chloroform and evaporate to dryness as described above for water samples.

Hydrolysis and Derivative Formation

Pipette 0.5 ml of 1% (w/v) FDNB (1-fluoro-2,4-dinitrobenzene) in acetone into the pear-shaped flask containing the cleaned-up residue and add 10 ml of buffer solution (8.2 ml of $0.1N$ NaOH and 100 ml $0.05M$ Na_2HPO_4 diluted to 200 ml with distilled water). Allow the mixture to react in a water bath at 50 °C for 30 min. Transfer the yellow reaction mixture to a 100 ml separator funnel and shake for 1 min with 10 ml of redistilled hexane. Discard the aqueous layer and dry the hexane phase by passage through a column containing about 5 g of granular anhydrous sodium sulfate. (Any emulsion in the hexane layer may be dispersed by shaking with about 1 g of anhydrous sodium sulfate just prior to passing through the drying column.) Inject 5 μl of the hexane extract for GC analysis. A column of 1.0% XE-60 and 0.1% Epikote 1001 at 211 °C is satisfactory.

PHENOLS

See Numbers 9, 89–92

89. Isolation of Pentachlorophenol from Blood

One to 5 ml blood, 20 ml $0.1N$ H_2SO_4, and 12 ml benzene are placed in a 125 ml glass-stoppered Erlenmeyer flask which contains a Teflon magnetic stirring bar. The flask is stoppered and the contents heated at 50°C with constant stirring on a combination hot plate-magnetic stirrer for 20 min. The flask is removed from the heater and immediately cooled in an ice bath. The contents of the flask are transferred to a 40 ml centrifuge tube and centrifuged for 10 min.; the upper benzene layer is removed by pipette and placed in a test tube. The benzene fraction is concentrated to about 1 ml on a steam bath (40 °C) with the aid of a stream of filtered air or nitrogen. The concentrated extract may be used as is for chromatography or it may be converted to the ether derivative with diazomethane and then chromatographed.

Reference: Bevenue, A., Emerson, M. L., Casarett, L. J., and W. L. Yauger, Jr., *J. Chromatogr.*, **38**, 467 (1968). Permission of Elsevier Publishing Company, Amsterdam, The Netherlands.

90. Isolation of Phenols in Automobile Exhaust

Samples of automobile exhaust are collected in impingers, each containing 250 ml NaOH in a series of three impingers ranging from $0.1N$ to $1.0N$ NaOH at ice-water temperature. The phenols are released by adding HCl to the solutions. Each solution is extracted twice with 100 ml portions of chloroform. About 50 ml of the chloroform extract from each impinger is combined and reacted with 25 ml $0.0105M$ diazotized *o*-nitraniline. The mixture is shaken, allowed to stand 2 min., and made alkaline by the addition of 25 ml Na_2CO_3 (20% by weight). The mixture is then acidified with dilute HCl and the azo dyes are extracted with ether. The solvent phase is dried over anhydrous magnesium sulfate and evaporated to dryness with a stream of cool air. The azo dye extract is dissolved in chloroform, made to a specific volume, and used for chromatography.

Reference: Barber, E. D., Sawicki, E., and S. P. McPherson, *Anal. Chem.*, **36**, 2442 (1964). Permission of American Chemical Society.

91. Colored Phenolic Derivatives Prepared by Coupling

Qualitative separations of many simple phenols by paper chromatography can be made using a mixture of the sodium salts of phenylazo dyes derived by coupling phenols with diazotized sulfanilic acid. The dyes are prepared by the method of Cheronis: A solution is prepared consisting of sulfanilic acid (2.6 g), 20 ml water, and 3 ml $6N$ NaOH. $NaNO_2$ (1 g) is added with stirring, and the mixture is poured slowly into a beaker which contains 30 ml water, 40 g crushed ice, and 2 ml concentrated H_2SO_4. After 30 min. at a temperature of about 5 °C, a slight excess of the phenol is added, and the diazotization is allowed to proceed for 15 minutes. Twelve ml $6N$ NaOH and 50 ml saturated NaCl solution are added, the mixture is cooled for 10 min., and the crystallized dye is filtered by suction.

Reference 1, p. 299–300.

92. Trifluoroacetylation of Phenols for GC

Treat a suspension of 0.1 mole of phenol in 0.11 mole trifluoroacetic anhydride (TFAA) with a trace of 50% NaOH. Reflux until the mixture becomes homogeneous and no longer evolves heat. Remove unreacted TFAA and by-product trifluoroacetic acid by distillation through a short Vigreux column. Then distill the esters at an appropriate temperature. Yields are generally 90% or more, except 70% or less for 2,6-disubstituted phenols.

Reference: Shulgin, A. T. *Anal. Chem.*, **36**, 920 (1964). Permission of American Chemical Society.

O-Methylation of Monohydric Phenols for GC analysis

A four-fold excess of metallic Na is added to the phenol in dioxane solution, the solution is heated under reflux, and a similar excess of dimethyl sulfate is added at 0 °C. Heat under reflux, add methanol to react with unused Na and NaOH solution to decompose unused dimethyl sulfate, and again heat under reflux. The derivative is extracted into ethyl ether and concentrated prior to injection.

Reference: Bhattacharyya, A. C., Bhattacharjee, A., Guha, O. K. and A. N. Basu, *Anal. Chem.*, **40**, 1873 (1968). Permission of American Chemical Society.

PLASTICS

See Number 93

93. Hydrolysis of Polyesters (Plastics)

(*a*) After Arendt and Schenck: The polyester (1 g) is refluxed for 1 hr. in a KOH solution in absolute ethanol and the resulting precipitate of potassium salts of dicarboxylic acids is filtered off after standing overnight. The precipitate is dissolved in water and the acids are liberated on an ion-exchange column (e.g. Permutit RS) from which they are eluted with absolute ethanol. After evaporation of the solvent, a 1% solution in absolute ethanol is prepared and applied to paper.

The filtrate after separation of potassium salts is neutralized with 10% hydrochloric acid in ethanol and dehydrated with Na_2CO_3 (5 g). After filtration, ethanol is evaporated under vacuum and the resulting solution of glycols is applied to paper.

(*b*) After Fijolka and Kayler: The polyester (0.3 g) is dissolved in acetone (25 ml) and hydrolyzed by shaking with $0.5N$ NaOH (an excess of about 20% on the esteric groups). The excess of NaOH is neutralized with $0.5N$ HCl, the dicarboxylic acids are retained on an ion-exchange column (e.g. Wofatit KPS 200) from which they are eluted with absolute ethanol (150 ml). The solution of the acids is concentrated (to 50 ml) and applied in portions (0.01–0.02 ml) to the chromatogram.

Reference 5, p. 871.

PURINES, PYRIMIDINES AND NUCLEIC ACID CONSTITUENTS

See Number 94

94. Procedures for the Isolation and Hydrolysis of Nucleic Acids

(a) Preparation of Sodium Deoxyribonucleate from Calf Thymus According to Signer and Schwander

Nucleoproteins are extracted with fairly concentrated sodium chloride solution. They are then split by saturating the solution with sodium chloride. The sodium deoxyribonucleate is purified by repeated precipitation from its aqueous solution with ethanol.

450 g of fresh calf thymus is cut into small pieces and then further ground in a meat grinder together with pieces of dry ice. Small portions of the brei are homogenized at 0 °C with a total of 4 liters of ice-cold *M* sodium chloride solution containing 0.001 moles of sodium citrate per liter. The gel-like homogenate is slowly stirred at 0 °C for several days until it becomes a reddish, highly viscous liquid. 830 ml portions of this solution are poured into 4.2 liter portions of ice-cold water to precipitate nucleoproteins. The precipitate is stirred in 0.01*M* sodium citrate solution and washed repeatedly with 8 liters of 1% sodium chloride solution containing 0.01*M* sodium citrate. The nucleoproteins are twice dissolved in portions of 4 liters *M* sodium chloride-0.01*M* sodium citrate solution and precipitated by pouring these solutions into water.

The nucleoproteins are redissolved by stirring into 5 liters of a 10% sodium chloride solution containing sodium citrate. This solution is made up to 6 liters with saturated sodium chloride solution, and crystalline sodium chloride is added to saturation. The liquid is stirred for four days at 0 °C and then stored in a refrigerator for two weeks. A suspension of 480 g of Celite 545 in 1.5 liters of saturated sodium chloride solution is added, and the mixture is vigorously stirred for 24 hr. Finally, the suspension is filtered at 40–50 mm through a Celite plate, 5–10 mm thick, which is placed between two filter papers.

The filter cake still contains deoxyribonucleate. It is stirred with 1.5 liters of saturated sodium chloride for about 24 hr and then filtered. The two filtrates are combined and 10 g of Hyflo Super Cel per liter is added. The slurry is stirred for several hours and filtered again through a plate of Celite. One volume of the clear filtrate is poured into 1.5 volumes of ethanol to precipitate the nucleate. The fibrous mass is washed several times with 70% ethanol. The precipitate is squeezed and dissolved in 4.5 liters of ice-cold water by stirring for several days. This aqueous solution is poured into twice its volume of ethanol to precipitate the nucleate. The salt is washed successively with 80%, 96% and absolute ethanol, and finally with diethyl ether and dried *in vacuo* over conc. sulfuric acid. The pure white asbestos-like preparation is stored in a desiccator over sodium chloride solution. It contains less than 0.5% protein.

According to the authors, the yield of sodium deoxyribonucleate is 8 g, i.e., 1.8% of the weight of the starting material.

(b) Isolation of Sodium Ribonucleate from Animal Tissues According to Volkin and Carter

In this method deoxyribonucleic acid is first removed in the form of its protein complex. Thereafter, the ribonucleic acid is precipitated from guanidine hydrochloride solution and further purified by treating with chloroform and repeated precipitation with ethanol.

After cutting frozen animal tissues into small pieces, one part of the tissue is suspended in three parts of ice-cold 0.15 *M* sodium chloride–0.02 *M* phosphate buffer of pH 6.8 and homogenized at 2–5° in a mixer for 6 to 8 minutes. It is recommended that a few drops of octyl alcohol be added to the suspension to avoid excessive foaming. The homogenate is centrifuged at 3000 × g for half an hour at 5 °C. The residue contains practically all the deoxyribonucleic acid in the form of protein complexes, and is discarded.

Crystalline guanidine hydrochloride is added to the supernatant to yield a 2*M* solution. This solution is warmed for half an hour in a water bath at 38 °C and then kept at 0 °C for one hour. A gel-like precipitate of ribonucleic acid containing a small amount of protein is formed.

The crude product is washed twice with an equal volume of ice-cold 2*M* guanidine hydrochloride solution. The suspension of ribonucleic acid in aqueous guanidine hydrochloride solution is shaken at 40 °C with an equal volume of a mixture of octyl alcohol-chloroform (1 : 4) for 30 min. After this time, the suspension is clarified by centrifugation. The upper aqueous phase is twice more extracted with octyl alcohol-chloroform under the conditions stated above. The aqueous guanidine hydrochloride solution is adjusted to pH 4.2–4.5 with glacial acetic acid, and two volumes of ice-cold ethanol are added. The white precipitate is centrifuged off and washed twice with ice-cold 70% ethanol. The ribonucleic acid is dissolved in distilled water, and the solution is carefully adjusted to pH 6.8 by the addition of dilute sodium hydroxide solution. If a precipitate of denatured protein forms, it is removed by centrifugation. The clear aqueous sodium ribonucleate is mixed with sufficient *M* sodium chloride solution to make it 0.05*M*. Two volumes of ice-cold ethanol are added to precipitate the pure ribonucleate. This product is washed twice with 70% ethanol, then isolated as a pure white powder by freeze-drying. A solution of 20 mg of the pure preparation in 1 ml of water does not give the Dische reaction, nor does it give the biuret reaction (heating the sample with 15% sodium hydroxide solution and 0.10% copper sulfate solution). This indicates that it is not contaminated with deoxyribonucleate or with protein. The authors state that the yield amounts to 20–30% of the ribonucleic acid present in the starting material.

Methods for the Hydrolysis of Nucleic Acids

Hydrolytic cleavage of nucleic acids may lead to the formation of oligonucleotides, mononucleotides, purine and pyrimidine bases, sugar phosphates and free carbohydrates. In addition, secondary products may result, e.g., by deamination of amino purines and amino pyrimidines or their nucleosides and nucleotides.

(*a*) *Acid hydrolysis*. The *N*-glycosidic purine-carbohydrate linkage is especially labile to acids, both in ribo- and deoxyribonucleic acids. In contrast, pyrimidine nucleotides and nucleosides resist acid hydrolysis. The phosphoric acid moiety is also more easily removed by the action of mineral acids from purine nucleotides than from pyrimidine nucleotides. If boiled with 0.5*N*, *N* or 2*N* hydrochloric acids or sulfuric acid for one to two hours, ribonucleic acids will yield the purines, adenine and guanine, in addition to the pyrimidine nucleotides, cytidylic and uridylic acids. Deoxyribonucleic acids also yield adenine and guanine if treated with hydrochloric acid at pH 1.6. However, the high-molecular-weight structures of the polynucleotide is, to a great extent, preserved. The purine-free high-molecular products, thymic acids, have molecular weights of around 15,000. They can be further purified by dialysis against hydrochloric acid of pH 1.6 to yield apurinic acids.

Heating of apurinic or deoxyribonucleic acids with methanolic hydrochloric acid at 50 °C for three to five hr. yields cytosine- and thymine deoxyribo-diphosphoric acids.

Pyrimidine deoxynucleotides and nucleosides may be cleaved by heating in a sealed tube at 175 °C with 98–100% formic acid. Hydrolysis with 72% perchloric acid is also useful. Maximum yields of purines and pyrimidines are obtained by heating at 100 °C for 1 hr.

(*b*) *Alkaline hydrolysis.* Dilute aqueous solutions of sodium or potassium hydroxides split ribonucleic acids into mononucleotides. Deoxyribonucleic acids are not hydrolyzed under these conditions. Hence, it is possible to free deoxyribonucleic acids of contaminating ribonucleic acids by treating with *N* sodium hydroxide at room temperature or at 37 °C.

Nucleosides may be obtained from nucleotides by heating them with concentrated aqueous ammonia at 175–180 °C for three to four hr. or by reacting them with boiling pyridine for several days. However, these reactions as well as similar procedures give poor yields and are useless for analytical studies.

(*c*) *Enzymatic hydrolysis*[1]. Degradation of polynucleotides by the action of enzymes serves as a valuable tool for studying the structure of nucleic acids.

The enzyme ribonuclease I from pancreas hydrolyzes ribonucleic acids to mono-, di-, tri- and tetranucleotides. A "core" of the native ribonucleic acids always remains unattacked. Deoxyribonucleic acid is not attacked, but thymic acid is hydrolyzed to some extent.

Deoxyribonuclease I from pancreas splits high-molecular-weight deoxyribonucleic acid into oligonucleotides and small amounts of mononucleotides; large portions of the polynucleotide structure remain unattacked. Ribonucleic acids are not degraded by deoxyribonuclease. Crystalline deoxyribonuclease I is commercially available.

Low-molecular-weight hydrolysis products or ribo- and deoxyribonucleic acids may be separated from high polymer cores by dialysis.

Deoxyribonucleases from snake venoms hydrolyze deoxyribonucleic acids more completely than does deoxyribonuclease I from pancreas. Nucleotidases, i.e. enzymes which dephosphorylate mononucleotides to nucleosides, have also been described. However, little is yet known about these enzymes.

[1] The reader is referred to Gilham, P. T. *Ann. Rev. Biochem.*, **39**, 227–250 (1970) for a discussion of structural specificities in enzymatic hydrolysis and determination of ribonucleic acid sequences.

Reference 3, pp. 443–446.

STEROIDS

See Numbers 95–115

95. Extraction of Aldosterone from Urine

The urine is adjusted to pH 1.0 by adding concentrated HCl. During hydrolysis the urine is kept in the dark at room temperature for 24 hr. Extraction is carried out in a glass-stoppered separatory funnel with 3, 2, and 2 volumes of dichloromethane. The combined dichloromethane extracts are washed successively with a 0.1 volume of 1*N* NaOH, 0.1*N* NaOH, 0.1*N* acetic acid and H_2O, dried over Na_2SO_4 and evaporated under reduced pressure. The residue is dissolved in 8 ml 70% methanol and washed with 2 ml toluene–petroleum ether (1 : 1 v/v). The upper layer is discarded and the methanol is evaporated from the aqueous methanol extract. The aqueous residue is extracted three times with four volumes of dichloromethane and the extract is then evaporated to dryness. The residue is dissolved in a small volume of $CHCl_3$ and applied to the paper.

Reference: Benraad, T. J. and P. W. C. Kloppenborg, *Clin. Chim. Acta*, **12**, 565 (1965). Permission of Elsevier Publishing Company, Amsterdam, The Netherlands.

96. Preparation of Girard T Hydrazones and Estrogen Azo Dyes

(a) Formation of Hydrazones with Girard's Reagent

A convenient sample of the ketosteroid (usually 2.5–5.0 mg), twice this weight of Girard's Reagent T, and 2 ml of an alcoholic acetic acid solution (10% glacial acetic acid in absolute methanol) are refluxed on a steam bath for 30–60 min. under anhydrous conditions. After cooling, the refluxed sample is stored in a refrigerator.

An alternate method is more convenient: The ketosteroid, Girard's Reagent T, and acidic methanol are incubated at 40 °C for 2 hr. (C_3-Ketosteroids do not form a hydrazone with this reagent.)

(b) Formation of Coupling Compounds with Fast Black-Salt K

A saturated aqueous solution of diazotized *p*-nitrobenzeneazodimethoxyaniline (Fast Black-Salt K) is freshly prepared and filtered. One-tenth milliliter of an alcoholic estrogen solution, containing at least 3 μg of the steroids, is placed in a test tube, 0.2 ml of the reagent and 0.1 ml of 20% Na_2CO_3 are added, and the mixture is heated in a boiling water bath for 10 min. The estrogen derivative is extracted by adding 0.2 ml of benzene, shaking the solution, and drawing it up in a medicine dropper. The aqueous phase is expelled and the benzene layer is applied to the paper.

Reference 3, pp. 252–53.

97. Extraction of Bile Acids from Urine

The 24-hr. urine sample is concentrated to 150 ml on a steam bath. Acidic material is precipitated using excess sodium chloride. The precipitate is washed with distilled water, dried, then dissolved in 0.6 ml concentrated HCl and

10 ml methanol. This solution is stored at room temperature 24 hr. to convert the acids to methyl esters. Water is added to precipitate the esters, which are then extracted with 5 × 1 ml $CHCl_3$. The $CHCl_3$ extract is dried (Na_2SO_4) and chromatographed on a Celite 545 column (20 g celite supporting 70% aqueous acetic acid on 1.3 cm diameter column). The eluates (mobile phase: benzene-Skellysolve B) are evaporated on a steam bath and dried in an oven at 80 °C for 6 hr.

Reference: Gregg, J. A. *Nature*, **214**, 29 (1967). Permission of *Nature*, MacMillan (Journals) Limited, London, England.

98. Conversion of Bile Salts to Bile Acids

(*a*) *Basic hydrolysis.* 1.0 g bile salt and 10 ml 2.5*N* NaOH are heated in a sealed metal container at 110–120 °C for 5–6 hr. The product is acidified with HCl, and excess sodium chloride is added. Bile acids precipitate on standing and can be collected by filtration or centrifugation.

(*b*) *Acid hydrolysis.* The sample is added to 0.25 ml 40% trichloroacetic acid in dioxane. After solution, 0.75 ml additional dioxane is added. After several days at room temperature the dioxane is removed at 550 °C under nitrogen. The residue is extracted three times with 3 ml portions of ethyl acetate. The extracts are washed with water and evaporated to dryness.

Reference 6, p. 151.

99. Isolation of Estriol from Urine

A 24-hr. urine sample is collected and 1/200 of the sample is diluted to 10 ml with distilled water.[1] In this fashion differences in urine samples due to variations in volume and concentration of compounds which react with the acid on hydrolysis are minimized. To this 0.6 ml 50% H_2SO_4 is added and the tube is autoclaved at 120° C one hour. The steroids are extracted with ether. This concentration of H_2SO_4 and length of heating was optimal and gave isolations reportedly better than those obtained with HCl. Sulfuric acid has the additional advantage of being less soluble than HCl in the ether used for extraction; however, it did cause the formation of more colored impurities than did HCl.

[1] This procedure is for late pregnancy (high estriol) urines. Early pregnancy urines are scaled up four fold.
Reference: Frandsen, V. A. "The Excretion of Estriol in Normal Human Pregnancy", Copenhagen, Munksgaard, 1965.

100. Enzymic Hydrolysis in Urine-Glucuronides

From a 24-hr. sample 100 ml of urine is adjusted to pH 4.6 with glacial acetic acid. Then 2 ml of 2*M* acetate buffer, pH 4.6, is added. The sample is divided into two portions at this point for duplicate analyses. The samples are warmed 30 min. in a 37 °C water bath[1]. To each is added 5 ml chloroform and 1 ml of a β-glucuronidase solution containing 2500 units of activity. The samples are incubated 24 hr. at 37 °C, then extracted with an organic solvent (chloroform, in this case). This technique is described as satisfactory for clinical needs.

[1] A temperature of incubation of 50 °C for the same time, or 3–4 days at 37 °C, may provide more complete hydrolysis.
Reference 6, p. 108–109.

101. Hydrolysis of Steroid Sulfates in Urine

(*a*) The urine is made 1*M* in H_2SO_4 using 50% aqueous H_2SO_4. One volume of diethyl ether is added and the mixture is shaken five times per day for four days. The ether layer is then removed and processed further as a steroid extract.

(*b*) In another method the urine is adjusted to pH 1.0 and NaCl is added to a 20% concentration. This mixture is incubated with one volume of ethyl acetate at 38 °C for 24 hr. The freed steroids are extracted into the ethyl acetate. Some substitution of chloro groups for hydroxy groups is reported.

Reference 6, p. 109.

102. Direct Isolation of Conjugated Steroids from Urine

A 24-hr. urine specimen is collected for study. The sample taken for study, perhaps 100 ml, is acidified to pH 2. A quantity of ammonium sulfate representing 50 g per 100 ml total sample volume is dissolved by shaking. The high salt concentration reduces the solubility of the conjugates in water—in other words, "salts" them out. The conjugates are now extracted three times into quantities of a 3 to 1 mixture of diethyl ether and anhydrous ethanol. This is attempted initially with volumes half that of the water solution, but if excessive emulsion forms the quantities may be increased to equal that of the water solution. The ether-ethanol extract is filtered, and the solvent is removed under vacuum keeping the temperature under 40 °C. If trouble is experienced removing the trace of water remaining in the sample towards the end of evaporation, the addition of small quantities of anhydrous ethanol facilitates its removal. The residue is dissolved with warming in ethanol. Some water-soluble materials are present at this point, largely ammonium sulfate, which will not dissolve in the alcohol. The extract is cooled to room temperature and the insoluble materials are filtered off. The precipitate is washed with small portions of ethanol to recover all the steroid conjugates and the combined alcohol extracts are stored cold.

Reference 6, p. 109–110.

103. Enzymic Hydrolysis of Extracted Glucuronides

A sample of the alcoholic extract prepared above is evaporated to dryness under vacuum and redissolved in 10 ml of the buffer recommended by the enzyme supplier (often 0.5*M* acetate buffer of pH 4.0–5.0). An immiscible solvent (such as toluene) or penicillin (10,000 units) are added to inhibit bacteria and the mixture is incubated according to the enzyme supplier's recommendations, perhaps 24 hr. at 37 °C. The sample is now ready to be extracted with the appropriate solvent.

Reference 6, p. 110.

104. Hydrolysis of Extracted Sulfates

A sample of alcoholic extract from the conjugate extraction procedure is evaporated to dryness under vacuum. The residue is suspended in an appropriate volume of water containing 20% NaCl. The pH is adjusted to 1.0 using 10% H_2SO_4. The sulfates are hydrolyzed under these conditions, and may be extracted with an appropriate solvent.

Reference 6, pp. 110–111.

105. Removal of Extracted Pigments from Steroid Samples after Hydrolysis

The hydrolysate is dissolved in 10 ml of an appropriate solvent such as benzene or methylene chloride. One gram of activated charcoal is added and the mixture is agitated at room temperature 3–5 min. This should be enough to handle a 24-hr urine extract. The sample is transferred (wash container with solvent for a quantitative transfer) to a 30 ml sintered glass funnel to be filtered under mild suction, stirring to keep the charcoal from packing down. The filtrate is evaporated to dryness at 40 °C under vacuum and the residue extracted with 3–50 ml volumes of absolute ethanol containing 40% benzene.

Reference 6, p. 111.

106. Separation and Purification of Estrone, Estradiol, and Estriol in Urine by TLC prior to GC

The urine is hydrolyzed with acid and the estrogens extracted in the usual fashion. The extract is dissolved in 50–100 μl ethanol, and is streaked onto a silica gel plate (0.25–0.50 mm thick) next to standards. The chromatogram is run with benzene-ethyl acetate (1 : 1), the standards developed, and the three appropriate areas scraped off, eluted with ethanol, and centrifuged. The eluted fractions are acetylated by heating in acetic anhydride-pyridine (5 : 1) at 68 °C for 1 hr. Water (5 ml) is added and the derivatives are extracted into petroleum ether, neutralized (8% $NaHCO_3$ washing, then water washing) and dried. The residues are taken up into acetone and analyzed in the gas chromatograph [4 ft $\frac{1}{8}$ in. column, 3% SE-30 on diatomaceous earth, flame detector].

Reference: Wotiz, H. H. and S. C. Chattoraj, *Anal. Chem.*, **36**, 1466 (1964). Permission of American Chemical Society, Washington, D.C.

107. Hydrolysis of 17-Oxosteroid Conjugates in Urine

Urine is adjusted to pH 4 and 50 g Na_2SO_4/100 ml is added. The urine is extracted once with a three-volume quantity of ethyl acetate. The ethyl acetate is adjusted to 0.01*M* in $HClO_4$ and is allowed to stand 3 hr. at room temperature. The solution is then washed twice with 1/10 volumes 10% KOH, and once with 1/10 volume water. The ethyl acetate is dried with anhydrous Na_2SO_4 filtered, and evaporated to dryness. The residue is dissolved in 3 ml of ethanol 1% in KOH and is allowed to stand at room temperature 1 hr. The solution is then diluted with water and extracted with petroleum ether-benzene (1 : 1).

Reference: De Paoli, J. C., Nishizawa, E. E., and K. B. Eik-Nes, *J. Clin. Endocrinol.*, **23**, 81 (1963). Permission of J. B. Lippincott Company, Philadelphia, Pa.

108. Preparation of 2,4-Dinitrophenylhydrazones of Urine Oxosteroids for Analysis by Thin Layer Densitometry

Urine (5 ml) is acidified to pH 1 with 5*M* HCl, saturated with $(NH_4)_2SO_4$ and extracted with ethyl acetate (2 × 20 ml). The extract is neutralized with aqueous NH_3 (0.5 ml) and evaporated. The residue is shaken with $HClO_4$ (1% in ethyl ether; 40 ml) and kept at 40 °C for 15 hr. The organic layer is washed with 5*M* NaOH (5 ml) followed by H_2O (3 × 5 ml), dried and evaporated, and 2,4-dinitrophenylhydrazine solution (0.2% in ethyl acetate; 0.1 ml) is added. The residue from evaporation is dissolved in trichloroacetic acid (0.03% in benzene; 1 ml) and kept at 40 °C for 40 min. Benzene is added to bring the volume to 5 ml. Aliquots are applied to TLC plates.

Reference: Knapstein, P. and J. C. Touchstone, *J. Chromatogr.*, **37**, 83 (1968). Permission of Elsevier Publishing Company, Amsterdam, The Netherlands.

109. Formation of 17-Ketosteroid Oximes for GC

Oxime, Methoxime, Benzyloxime

Heat a mixture of 4 mg hydroxylamine hydrochloride, 5 mg methoxylamine hydrochloride or 9 mg of *O*-benzylhydroxylamine hydrochloride, 50 μl of pyridine, and 0.1 mg of 5α-androstan-17-one for 30 min. at 60 °C. Use the solutions of MO and BO derivatives directly for GC.

Trimethylsilyloxime and Oxime Acetate

After formation of the oxime, evaporate the pyridine with a stream of nitrogen. 100 μl of trimethylsilylimidazole or 100 μl of acetic anhydride is added to obtain the silyloxime or oxime acetate. The reaction is allowed to proceed 3 hr. at 60 °C, and solutions are used directly.

Reference: Thenot, J. P. and E. C. Horning, *Anal. Letters*, **4**, 683 (1971).

110. Conversion of Ketosteroids to *O*-Methyloxines for GC

Allow the ketone to stand overnight at room temperature with an excess of methoxyamine hydrochloride in pyridine. Evaporate the excess pyridine under a nitrogen stream. Take up the crude adduct in benzene, centrifuge away from excess pyridine hydrochloride, and chromatograph directly. 11-Ketosteroids do not react in the 11 position even after being heated overnight at 100 °C. The 3-, 6-, 16-, 17- and 20-*O*-methyloxines are readily formed.

Reference: Fales, H. M. and T. Luukkainen, *Anal. Chem.*, **37**, 955 (1965).

111. Acetylation of Corticosteroids and Related 20-Oxopregnane Derivatives for GC

The steroid (0.1 to 1 mg) is dissolved in 10–50 μl reagent (10 mg acetic anhydride in 1 ml toluene *p*-sulfonic acid) and the solution is allowed to evaporate to dryness in a vacuum desiccator at room temperature. The residue is extracted with chloroform and a suitable aliquot used for chromatography.

Reference: Brooks, C. J. W. *Anal. Chem.*, **37**, 636 (1965).

112. Preparation of Bismethylenedioxy Derivatives of 17-Hydroxycorticosteroids for GC

10 mg cortisone is suspended in 5.0 ml $CHCl_3$ and 1.3 ml of 12*N* HCl is added, followed by 1.3 ml of 37% formalin solution. Stir the reaction at 5 °C for 48 hr, during which time the steroid dissolves. Wash the reaction mixture with 1*N* NaOH, dry over Na_2SO_4, and filter through glass wool. Inject the solution directly.

Reference: Kirschner, M. A., and H. M. Fales, *Anal. Chem.*, **34**, 1548 (1962).

113. Preparation of a Heptafluorobutyrate Derivative of Plasma Testosterone for Analysis by GC

Blood (15–20 ml) is centrifuged, and the plasma is collected. [4-^{14}C] Testosterone (5 ng) (for samples from male subjects) or [7α-^{3}H] testosterone (0.5 ng) (for those from female subjects) is added as internal standard, the mixture is shaken with an equal volume of 0.33*N* NaOH and extracted with ethyl ether (2 × 100 ml), and the extract is washed with H_2O (2 × 20 ml) and evaporated. The residue is dissolved in methanol-$CHCl_3$ (1 : 1) (3 × 1 ml) and evaporated to dryness under vacuum. A solution of this residue in the same solvent is applied to a plate coated with silica gel G, which is developed with benzene-ethyl acetate (3 : 2), and the testosterone is extracted from the adsorbent with ethanol (3 × 0.05 ml). The ethanol is evaporated, and the residue is heated with heptafluorobutyric anhydride (20 μl), hexane (1 ml) and tetrahydrofuran (40 μl) at 50 °C for 0.5 hr. After evaporation of the solvent *in vacuo*, a solution of the derivative in acetone (3 × 0.5 ml) is subjected to TLC on silica gel with benzene-ethyl acetate (19 : 1) as solvent. The derivative is extracted from the silica with acetone (3 × 0.5 ml), the acetone is evaporated under vacuum, and 20α-dihydroprogesterone heptafluorobutyrate is added as second internal standard (2 ng per 5 μl or 10 μl of male or female plasma extract, respectively). The GC is performed.

Reference: Collins, W. P., Sisterson, J. M., Koullapis, E. N., Mansfield, M. D., and I. F. Sommerville, *J. Chromatogr.*, **37**, 33 (1968). Permission of Elsevier Publishing Company, Amsterdam, The Netherlands.

114. Extraction of Bile Acids from Feces

(*a*) The weighed sample (48 hr. specimen) is treated in a Soxhlet extractor with 1.5 liter $CHCl_3$-methanol (1 : 1) for two days. The extract is concentrated to foaming. Dioxane (10 ml/100 mg) and 4*N* KOH (5 ml/100 mg) are added and the mixture is refluxed 3 hr. A volume equal to the amount of dioxane is removed by distillation. The sample is acidified to pH 3 and is extracted continuously with diethyl ether for 16 hr. This extract is washed with 3 × 0.05 volumes 0.08*M* citrate-phosphate buffer, pH 5.8, and 3 × 1 volumes water. The combined washings are extracted with 3 × 5 volumes diethyl ether to assure no loss of bile acid, and the combined diethyl ether extracts are evaporated to dryness. The sample is redissolved for chromatography.

(*b*) Homogenize 100 g of sample with 100 ml 96% ethanol for 5 min., and dilute to 750 ml with 96% ethanol. Stir and allow the mixture to settle. Transfer 50 ml clear supernate to a Dowex 50 w (H^+) column. Place the effluent on a Dowex 1 (OH^-) column. Wash the column extensively and elute with 0.1*M* $(NH_4)_2CO_3$ in 50% ethanol. Evaporate this to dryness, and drive off the $(NH_4)_2CO_3$ at 100 °C. Redissolve the residue for chromatography.

Reference 6, p. 150.

115. Extraction of Bile Acids from Serum

Add 2.5 ml serum to 25 ml ethanol and heat the mixture 3 min. in a boiling water bath. Filter out precipitated protein. Wash the precipitate with 25 ml and then 10 ml of ethanol. Evaporate the total ethanol extract to dryness and dissolve in a small volume of solvent prior to chromatography.

Reference 6, p. 150.

STEROID GLYCOSIDES

See Number 116

116. Extraction of Cardiac Aglycones

As an illustration, the extraction of cardiac aglycones from *Strophanthus* seeds is described. 1 g of the seed is ground in a coffee mill and then extracted in a Soxhlet apparatus with 150 ml methanol for 2 hr. The extract is then evaporated to 25 ml, diluted with 5 ml water, and extracted three times with 25 ml petroleum ether. The aqueous solution is then diluted with 30 ml 0.1*N* H_2SO_4 and refluxed for 30 min. After cooling, the solution is extracted twice with 50 ml portions of $CHCl_3$ and the extract is evaporated to 5 ml. One drop of this extract is usually sufficient for paper chromatography. Other plant juice material may be extracted with a mixture of chloroform–ethanol (3 : 1), and portions spotted for PC.

Reference 1, pp. 237–238.

VITAMINS

See Numbers 117, 118

117. Isolation of Ascorbic Acid from Urine

A measured volume of urine containing 1–5 μg ascorbic acid is mixed with 1–2 ml 4% oxalic acid and centrifuged for 5 min. Portions of 10–100 μl of supernatant liquid are spotted on paper with drying between applications.

Reference: Zobel, M. and A. Teutloff, *Aerztl. Lab.*, **13**, 293 (1967). Permission of Medicus Verlag GMBH, Berlin, W. Germany.

118. Preparation of Vitamin Samples for PC

(a) Purification of Sample (Vitamin E Panel Method)

(Various steps can be omitted according to the purity of the material, especially the freezing out of sterols). Lipid starting material is obtained by the usual solvent extraction (with acetone in case of animal material). The oil (1 g) and 5% freshly prepared pyrogallol solution in ethanol (4 ml) are heated to boiling under reflux, KOH solution (1 ml; 160 g to 100 ml water) added and refluxed for 3 min. After cooling and addition of water (20 ml), unsaponifiable material is extracted with peroxide-free ether (3 × 25 ml). Ethanol (1–2 ml) may be used to break the emulsion. The extracts are washed with water (4 × 20 ml; until neutral), evaporated under N_2 or *in vacuo*. If necessary, the residue should be dried before re-evaporating with ethanol or benzene. If freeze-drying is considered necessary, the residue is dissolved in boiling methanol (12 ml), cooled to −10 °C and centrifuged; the sterols are redissolved and the process is repeated. The pooled methanol solutions are then evaporated under vacuum and the residue dissolved in benzene (5 ml). Floridin earth (5 g; XS for the determination of vitamin E) and $SnCl_2$ (0.5 g) are mixed with HCl (20 ml), the mixture is boiled and with rapid stirring poured into a chromatographic tube (1.2 × 18 cm) in one operation. The column is washed with ethanol (5 × 5 ml) and benzene (5 × 5 ml). The benzene solution is passed through the column, which is then eluted with benzene (7 × 5 ml) within 45 minutes (under suction or N_2 pressure). The eluate is evaporated under N_2 or under vacuum and redissolved in benzene (0.5–3 ml; 0.5–2 mg tocopherol per ml); total tocopherols (about 100 μg) are applied to the chromatogram.

(b) Preparation, Separation and Determination of Nitroso-Tocopherols (Marcinkiewicz and Green)

Tocopherol mixture (less than 600 μg of $\beta + \gamma$ or $\epsilon + \eta$) is dissolved in ethanol (5 ml) in a small separator, acetic acid (0.2 ml) is added with vigorous swirling, followed rapidly by an addition of 2% $NaNO_2$ solution (3 ml). After exactly 90 sec., KOH (2 ml; 20 g per 100 ml water) is added; the mixture is stirred, and water (12 ml) and petroleum ether (20 ml; b.p. 40–60 °C) are added; the mixture is shaken vigorously for at least 1 min. until all pink color is removed from the aqueous phase. The petroleum ether layer is washed twice with water and evaporated below 30 °C *in vacuo* or in a stream of N_2. The residue is dissolved in petroleum ether (1 ml). Chromatography is carried out on Whatman No. 1 paper impregnated with 3% solution of liquid paraffin, B.P., in petroleum ether to within 1 cm of the starting line (papers may first be impregnated with $ZnCO_3$ + Na fluorescein, to make the traces visible on the chromatogram). At least 5 μg, and optimally 50 μg, of each tocopherol is applied to the starting line. The chromatogram is developed with 93–95% aqueous ethanol for 2–3 hr.; the yellow (UV quenching) bands can be cut out, rolled into cylinders and eluted and estimated.

(c) Extraction of Thiamine from Biological Materials

The sample of the organ, e.g. liver, is ground with sand and deproteinized with 2% trichloroacetic acid (100 ml); the filtrate is diluted with water (25 ml), centrifuged and adjusted to pH 4.5. Thiamine is then adsorbed on fuller's earth. After 5 min., the mixture is centrifuged, the earth is washed with a mixture of ethanol and ether (1 : 1) and eluted with pyridine-water-acetic acid (2 ml; 1 : 4 : 0.1).

(d) Extraction of Riboflavin from Biological Material

The tissue (2.5 g) is thoroughly ground with water (15 ml) and 0.1*N* HCl (about 2 ml) to adjust the solution to pH ≈2. The mixture is allowed to stand for 5 min., and, after neutralization, diluted to 25 ml. $(NH_4)_2SO_4$ (12.5 g) is then added, the precipitate is separated by centrifuging and the filtered liquid is shaken with phenol (10 g). The upper layer is shaken with ether (15 ml) and water (0.3 ml) and the aqueous layer is applied to paper. The denaturation of proteins may also be carried out by heating to 80 °C.

(e) Preparation of Pantoylhydroxamic Acid

A solution (5 ml) containing pantothenic acid (8–15 mg) is heated for 3 hr. on a boiling water bath with conc. HCl (0.3 ml). After cooling, hydroxylamine solution (1 ml; 15 g $NH_2OH \cdot HCl$ in 100 ml 2*N* NaOH) and 5*N* NaOH (1 ml) are added. The solution is allowed to stand for 5 min. adjusted with HCl to pH 2.5–3.2 and diluted with water to 10 ml. The solution of pantoylhydroxamic acid is applied to paper in 20 μl quantities.

(f) Isolation of Pterins from Urine

Urine (100 ml) is acidified with glacial acetic acid to pH 3.5 and the solution is shaken with active charcoal (250 mg). After 10 min., the charcoal is centrifuged and washed in the centrifuge tube with water (3 × 50 ml). After washing, the charcoal is eluted by mixing with 10% ammonia (5 ml). After standing (30 min.), the charcoal is filtered off with a fine filter and the filtrate evaporated to dryness. A concentrated solution of the residue is applied to the chromatogram.

Reference 5, pp. 867–869.

ACKNOWLEDGEMENTS

Acknowledgement is made to the following authors, editors, and publishers whose material has been used in this Section of the Handbook of Chromatography. Permission was received when material was taken directly from the sources.

Reference

1. *Paper Chromatography*, Sherma, J. and G. Zweig, Academic Press, New York, N.Y., (1971).
2. *Thin Layer Chromatography*, J. M. Bobbitt, Reinhold Publishing Corporation, New York, N.Y., (1963).
3. *Thin Layer Chromatography, A Laboratory Handbook*, E. Stahl, ed., Academic Press, New York, N.Y., (1965). Permission received from Springer Verlag, Austria.
4. *Paper Chromatography and Paper Electrophoresis*, Block, R. J., Durrum, E. L., and G. Zweig, Academic Press, New York, N.Y., Second Edition, (1958).
5. *Paper Chromatography*, Hais, I. M. and K. Macek, eds., Academic Press, New York, N.Y., (1963).
6. *Clinical Analysis by TLC*, R. M. Scott, Ann Arbor-Humphrey Science Publishers, Inc., Ann Arbor, Michigan, (1969).
7. *Chromatography*, E. Heftmann, ed., Reinhold Publishing Corporation, New York, N.Y., (1967).
8. *Gas Chromatography*, A. B. Littlewood, Academic Press, New York, N.Y., Second Edition (1970).
9. *The Practice of Gas Chromatography*, Ettre, L. S. and A. Zlatkis, eds., Interscience Publishers, Division of John Wiley & Sons, Inc., New York, N.Y., (1967).
10. *Progress in Thin Layer Chromatography, and Related Methods*, Niederwieser, A. and G. Pataki, eds., Ann Arbor-Humphrey Science Publishers, Inc., Ann Arbor, Michigan, Vol. 1, 1970; Vol. 2, 1971.
11. *Chromatographic and Electrophoretic Technique*, Vol. I, I. Smith, ed., Interscience Publishers, Division of John Wiley & Sons, Inc., New York, N.Y. (1969). Permission received from William Heinemann Medical Books, Ltd., London, England.
12. *Techniques of TLC in Amino Acid and Peptide Chemistry*, Ann Arbor Science Publishers, Inc., Ann Arbor, Michigan, Revised Edition (1968).

VOLUME TWO
SECTION II

II.III Products and Sources of Chromatographic Materials

Section II.III

PRODUCTS AND SOURCES OF CHROMATOGRAPHIC MATERIALS

This Section contains descriptions and sources of widely-used chromatographic materials chosen in order to supplement Section II, Volume One, and Section I, Volume Two, of this Handbook.

Materials not mentioned may serve equally well in many cases as those listed in this section. Other sources may be available for the materials in addition to those given.

The sources described are not necessarily intended as the editor's endorsement.

Readers interested in complete listings of chromatography instruments, accessories, supplies, services, manufacturers and supply dealers are referred to:

1. "1972–1973 International Chromatography Guide", *J. Chromatogr. Sci.*, February 1972, pp G1–G52.
2. "1971–1972 Laboratory Guide", *Anal. Chem.*, July, 1971.
3. "1971–1972 Guide to Scientific Instruments", *Science*, 174A, No. 4010A, Nov. 16, 1971.

Section II.III

PRODUCTS AND SOURCES OF CHROMATOGRAPHIC MATERIALS

TABLE 1
LIQUID PHASES FOR GAS CHROMATOGRAPHY

Phase	Used for:	Max. temp. °C	Solvent[1]	Polarity[2]
Acetonylacetone	Hydrocarbons	25	A	P, I
Acetyl tributyl citrate (Citroflex A-4)		180	A	—
Adiponitrile		50	C	I
Alkaterge T (amine surfactant)		75	C	I
Alkyl aryl sulfonate (Tide washed with n-C7)		225	W	—
Amine 220 [1-ethanol-2-(heptadecyl)2-isoimidazol]		180	W	P
Ansul ether (see tetraethylene glycol dimethyl ether)				
Apiezon H		275	B	N
Apiezon J		300	B	N
Apiezon L	Alcohols Aldehydes and ketones Aromatics and heterocyclics Boron compounds Drugs and alkaloids Essential oils Fatty acids and esters Halogenated compounds Hydrocarbons Inorganic and organo-metallic compounds Nitrogen compounds Pesticides Phosphorus compounds Pyrolysis Sugars Sulfur compounds	300	B	N
Apiezon M	Alcohols Aldehydes and ketones Fatty acids and esters Hydrocarbons Inorganic and organo-metallic compounds Sulfur compounds	275	B	N
Apiezon N	Aromatics and heterocyclics Halogenated compounds Vitamins	325	B	N
Armeen SD	Hydrocarbons Nitrogen compounds	100	A	H, P
Armeen 2S (di-soya amine)		125	A	—
Arneel O.D. (oleyl nitrile distilled)		100	M	—
Arneel S.D. (soya nitrile distilled)		100	M	—
Aroclor (1242) (chlorinated polyphenyl)	Gases	125	A	—
Aroclor (1254)		125	A	I

[1] Solvents for dissolving stationary phase for preparation of column:

A Acetone; B Benzene; C Chloroform; D Dimethyl sulfoxide; E Ethyl acetate; F Formic acid; K Methyl ethyl ketone; L Dichloromethane; M Methanol; T Toluene; W Water; X Xylene

[2] N = Nonpolar; P = Polar; I = Intermediate; H = Hydrogen bonding; S = Specific interaction with solute

TABLE 1—(Continued)
LIQUID PHASES FOR GAS CHROMATOGRAPHY

Phase	Used for:	Max. temp. °C	Solvent	Polarity
Asphalt	Aromatics and heterocyclics Halogenated compounds Hydrocarbons	300	B	N
Atpet 80 (sorbitan partial fatty esters)			C	—
Baymal (colloidal alumina)		300	T	—
Beeswax	Essential oils	200	C	—
Bentone 34	Aromatics and heterocyclics Halogenated compounds	200	B	S
7,8-Benzoquinoline	Aromatics and heterocyclics Hydrocarbons Sulfur compounds	150	C	I
Benzylamine adipate		125	C	—
Benzyl cellosolve [see 2-(benzyloxy) ethanol]				
Benzyl cyanide (phenylacetonitrile)		35	C	I
Benzyl cyanide-silver nitrate (2 : 1)		25	A	S
Benzyldiphenyl	Alcohols Aromatics and heterocyclics Fatty acids and esters Halogenated compounds Hydrocarbons	100	A	—
Benzyl ether	Hydrocarbons	50	A	I
2-(Benzyloxy) ethanol (benzyl cellosolve)		50	A	I
Bis (2-butoxyethyl) phthalate		150	A	—
Bis (2-ethoxyethyl) sebacate		150	A	—
Bis (2-ethoxyethyl) adipate		150	C	I
Bis (2-ethylhexyl) tetrachlorophthalate		150	C	I
1,3-Bis-(2-hydroxyhexafluoro-2-propyl) benzene		—	A	—
4,4-Bis (2-hydroxyhexafluoro-2-propyl) diphenyl ether		—	A	—
Bis (2-methoxyethyl) adipate		150	C	I
Bis (2-(2-methoxyethoxy)ethyl) ether	Hydrocarbons	50	C	P
***m*-Bis (*m*-phenoxy phenoxy) benzene** (see polyphenylether 5 ring)				
***m*-Bis (*m*-phenoxy phenoxy phenyl) ether** (see polyphenylether 6 ring)				
Butanediol adipate (BDA)		225	C	I, P
Butanediol borate		200	M	—
Butanediol succinate (BDS) (Craig polyester)	Alcohols Aromatics and heterocyclics Fatty acids and esters Halogenated compounds Hydrocarbons Nitrogen compounds Sugars	225	C	I, P
Carbitol (glycol-ether MW 134)		60	A	—
Carbowax 200	Aldehydes and ketones	100	A	P
Carbowax 400	Alcohols Aldehydes and ketones Aromatics and heterocyclics Essential oils Fatty acids and esters Halogenated compounds Hydrocarbons Nitrogen compounds	125	A	P
Carbowax 600	Alcohols Amino acids	125	A	P

TABLE 1—(Continued)
LIQUID PHASES FOR GAS CHROMATOGRAPHY

Phase	Used for:	Max. temp. °C	Solvent	Polarity
Carbowax 750		125	C	P
Carbowax 1000	Aldehydes and ketones Halogenated compounds	125	A	P
Carbowax 1000 monostearate		150	C	P
Carbowax 1500	Alcohols Aldehydes and ketones Nitrogen compounds Sulfur compounds	200	A	P
Carbowax 1540	Alcohols Essential oils Hydrocarbons Pyrolysis	200	A	P
Carbowax 1500 monostearate		200	C	P
Carbowax 4000	Alcohols Aldehydes and ketones Aromatics and heterocyclics Essential oils Halogenated compounds Hydrocarbons Sugars	200	A	P
Carbowax 4000 dioleate		220	C	P
Carbowax 4000 monostearate		220	A	P
Carbowax 6000	Sugars	200	C	P
Carbowax 20M	Alcohols Aldehydes and ketones Amino acids Aromatics and heterocyclics Drugs and alkaloids Essential oils Fatty acids and esters Gases Halogenated compounds Hydrocarbons Nitrogen compounds Pesticides Phosphorus compounds Pyrolysis Sulfur compounds	250	C	P
Carbowax 20M terminated with terephthalic acid (20M-TPA)	Pesticides Pyrolysis	250	D or L	P
Castorwax (hydrogenated castor oil)	Essential oils	200	C	P
Celanese ester No. 9	Aldehydes and ketones Fatty acids and esters	200	C	—
Cetyl alcohol (1-Hexadecanol)	Halogenated compounds Hydrocarbons	—	C	—
Chloronaphthalene	Hydrocarbons	75	M	I
Chlorowax 70 (chlorinated paraffin)		140	C	—
Citroflex A-4 (see acetyl tributyl citrate)				
Citroflex 4 (see tributyl citrate)				
Convaclor 20		200	C	—
Convoil 20		200	C	—
Coumarone-indene resin		185	C	—
Cyclodextrin acetate	Fatty acids and esters	250	A	—
Cyanoethyl cyclohexane [see 1,2,3,4,5,6-hexakis(2-cyanoethoxy) cyclohexane]				
Cyanoethyl butane [see 1,2,3,4-tetrakis (2-cyanoethoxy) butane]				

TABLE 1—(Continued)
LIQUID PHASES FOR GAS CHROMATOGRAPHY

Phase	Used for:	Max. temp. °C	Solvent	Polarity
Cyanoethyl propane [see 1,2,3-tris (2-cyanoethoxy) propane]				
Cyanoethyl sucrose		175	A	P
Cyclohexane dimethanol adipate		210	C	I
Cyclohexane dimethanol succinate		210	C	—
***n*-Decane**	Inorganic and organometallic compounds	30	A	N
Dexsil 300GC	Methyl esters Aromatic amines Halogenated alcohols Pesticides Polyphenyl ether Silicone oils	500	C	—
Dibutyl cyanamide	Gases	50	M	—
Dibutyl maleate	Halogenated compounds	50	C	P, I
Dibutyl phthalate	Aldehydes and ketones Halogenated compounds Hydrocarbons Phosphorus compounds	30	A	I
Dibutyl sebacate		50	C	I, P
Dibutyl tetrachlorophthalate		150	C	I, P
Diethylene glycol adipate (DEGA)	Aldehydes and ketones Fatty acids and esters Pesticides	200	A	I, P
Diethylene glycol sebacate	Fatty acids and esters	—	—	I, P
Diethylene glycol sebacate (DEGSB)		200	C	I, P
Diethylene glycol succinate (DEGS)	Alcohols Aldehydes and ketones Amino acids Essential oils Fatty acids and esters Halogenated compounds Phosphorus compounds Steroids Sulfur compounds	200	A	P
Diethylene glycol succinate (stabilized)	Alcohols Aldehydes and ketones Fatty acids and esters Hydrocarbons	250	A	P
Diethylene glycol monoethyl ether		25	M	—
Diethylene glycol stearate		175	C	—
Di (2-ethylhexyl) sebacate	Alcohols Drugs and alkaloids Fatty acids and esters Gases (blood and respiratory) Halogenated compounds	125	A	I, P
Di (2-ethylhexyl) phthalate		150	M	—
Diethyl-*d*-tartrate	Alcohols	75	M	P, S
Di-*n*-decyl phthalate	Alcohols Aromatics and heterocyclics Essential oils Fatty acids and esters Gases Halogenated compounds Hydrocarbons Inorganic and organometallic compounds	160	A	—
Di-*n*-propyl tetrachlorophthalate	Hydrocarbons	75	M	—

TABLE 1—(Continued)
LIQUID PHASES FOR GAS CHROMATOGRAPHY

Phase	Used for:	Max. temp. °C	Solvent	Polarity
Diglycerol	Alcohols Aldehydes and ketones Aromatics and heterocyclics Hydrocarbons	120	M	H
Diisodecyl adipate		150	M	—
Diisodecyl phthalate	Alcohols Aromatics and heterocyclics Essential oils Fatty acids and esters Halogenated compounds Hydrocarbons Sulfur compounds	175	A	I
Diisooctyl adipate		125	A	—
Diisopropyl phthalate		125	M	I
Dimer acid: silicone oil 550 (1 : 1)	Fatty acids	150	A	I
Dimethylformamide (DMF)	Hydrocarbons	50	M	—
Dimethylstearamide (see Hallcomid M18)				
Dimethyl sulfide (DMS)		50	A	—
Dimethyl sulfolane	Hydrocarbons Inorganic and organometallic compounds	50	A	P
Dimethyl sulfone		30	B	—
Dimethyl sulfoxide (DMSO)	Gases	50	A	—
Di-*n*-butyl maleate	Gases	50	A	—
Dinonyl phthalate	Alcohols Aldehydes and ketones Aromatics and heterocyclics Halogenated compounds Hydrocarbons Nitrogen compounds Pyrolysis	50	A	I
Dioctyl phthalate	Aromatics and heterocyclics Halogenated compounds Hydrocarbons	140	A	I
Dioctyl sebacate	Aldehydes and ketones Hydrocarbons	100	C or L	I
Dow Corning high vacuum grease (methyl)	Essential oils Pesticides Phosphorus compounds Sulfur compounds	350	E	N
Dow Corning high vacuum grease (ethyl acetate extract)	Pesticides	350	E	N
Dow Corning silicone 11 (grease)	Fatty acids and esters Inorganic and organometallic compounds Pesticides Phosphorus compounds Sugars	300	E	N
Dow Corning silicone oil 200 (12,500 cs) (methyl) or	Essential oils Fatty acids and esters Pesticides Phosphorus compounds Sulfur compounds	250	T	N
Dow Corning silicone oil 200 (50 cs)		—	T	N
Dow Corning silicone oil 220		—	T	I
Dow Corning silicone oil 200 (500 cs)		—	T	N

TABLE 1—(Continued)
LIQUID PHASES FOR GAS CHROMATOGRAPHY

Phase	Used for:	Max. temp. °C	Solvent	Polarity
Dow Corning silicone gum 410 (methyl)		325	T	—
Dow Corning silicone oil 550 (methyl phenyl)	Amino acids Aromatics and heterocyclics Boron compounds Fatty acids and esters Gases Gases (blood and respiratory) Halogenated compounds Inorganic and organometallic compounds Nitrogen compounds	275	A	I
Dow Corning silicone oil 555 (methyl phenyl)		275	C	—
Dow Corning silicone oil 560 (see silicone fluid F60)				
Dow Corning silicone oil 703 (methyl phenyl)	Halogenated compounds Hydrocarbons	225	C	I
Dow Corning silicone oil 710 (methyl phenyl)	Aromatics and heterocyclics Hydrocarbons Inorganic and organometallic compounds Nitrogen compounds Pesticides	300	A	I
Dowfox 9N15 (nonyl phenol polyethylene glycol ether)		150	C	—
Dowfox 9N9 (nonyl phenol polyethylene glycol ether)		150	A	—
Ducitol		195	W	—
Emulphor ON-870	Aromatics and heterocyclics Essential oils Halogenated compounds Hydrocarbons Phosphorus compounds	175	M	—
Epon 1001	Pesticides Steroids	250	A	P
Estynox (epoxy plasticizer)		200	C	—
Ethofat 60/25 (polyoxyethylene glycol stearate)	Aldehydes and ketones	140	M	I
Ethomeen S/25 (polyoxyethylene soya amine)		75	C	P
Ethyl acetoacetate		15	A	—
Ethyl benzoate	Hydrocarbons	150	M	—
Ethylene glycol adipate	Alcohols Aromatics and heterocyclics Bile and urinary compounds Drugs and alkaloids Essential oils Fatty acids and esters Nitrogen compounds Sulfur compounds	200	A	I, P
Ethylene glycol isophthalate	Nitrogen compounds Steroids	250	C	P
Ethylene glycol phthalate	Aromatics and heterocyclics	250	A	P
Ethylene glycol terephthalate		250	DMSO-DMF (1 : 1)	—
Ethylene glycol sebacate		200	C	I, P

TABLE 1—(Continued)
LIQUID PHASES FOR GAS CHROMATOGRAPHY

Phase	Used for:	Max. temp. °C	Solvent	Polarity
Ethylene glycol succinate	Alcohols Aldehydes and ketones Amino acids Aromatics and heterocyclics Drugs and alkaloids Fatty acids and esters Halogenated compounds Phosphorus compounds	200	C	I, P
Eutectic ($LiNO_3$-$NaNO_3$-KNO_3 27.3% : 18.2% : 54.5%)	Aromatics and heterocyclics Hydrocarbons	400	W	—
Eutectic (KCl-$CdCl_2$ 33% : 67%)		400	W	—
Eutectic ($NaCl$-$AlCl_3$ 41% : 59%)		400	W	—
Eutectic ($BiCl_3$-$PbCl_3$ 89% : 11%)		400	W	—
FFAP	Aldehydes and ketones Pyrolysis	250	C or L	S, P
Flexol plasticizer 8N8 (2,2′-(2-ethyl hexanamido)-diethyl-di-2-ethylhexoate)	Alcohols Nitrogen compounds	180	A	P
Fluorolube HG1200 (polymers of trifluorovinyl chloride)	Halogenated compounds Gases	100	A	—
Fluorolube 530 (polymers of trifluorovinyl chloride)		100	A	—
Fluorolube GR362		100	B	S
Fluoro-ester (pyromellitic acid and trihydrofluoroalcohol)		250	A	I
Fluorosilicone QF-1-0065 (FS1265 10,000 cs)	Alcohols Amino acids Aromatics and heterocyclics Bile and urinary compounds Drugs and alkaloids Essential oils Fatty acids and esters Hydrocarbons Nitrogen compounds Pesticides Phosphorus compounds Steroids Sulfur compounds Vitamins	250	A	I
Glycerol	Alcohols	120	M	H
Hallcomid M18	Alcohols Aldehydes and ketones Fatty acids and esters Hydrocarbons Pyrolysis	150	A	I
Hallcomid M180L (dimethyloleylamide)	Alcohols Aldehydes and ketones Fatty acids and esters Hydrocarbons	150	M	I
Halocarbon oil 13-21		100	A	—
Halocarbon oil 11-14		100	A	—
***n*-Hendecanol**		45	A	—
***n*-Hexadecane**	Hydrocarbons	50	B	N
1,2,3,4,5,6-Hexakis (2-cyano-ethoxy)cyclohexane		200	C	—
2,5-Hexanedione (see acetylacetone)				
Hexamethylphosphoramide (HMPA)	Hydrocarbons	50	A	P
Hyprose SP80 [octakis (2-hydroxypropyl) sucrose]	Alcohols Essential oils Sugars	190	M	P

TABLE 1—(Continued)
LIQUID PHASES FOR GAS CHROMATOGRAPHY

Phase	Used for:	Max. temp. °C	Solvent	Polarity
Igepal CA630 [iso-octyl phenoxy poly (ethyleneoxy) ethanol]		200	M	P
Igepal CO880 [nonyl phenoxy poly (ethyleneoxy) ethanol]	Alcohols	200	A	—
Igepal CO990 [nonyl phenoxy poly (ethyleneoxy) ethanol]		200	M	I
β,β′-Iminodipropionitrile	Halogenated compounds	65	M	—
Isophthalic acid		100	M	—
Isoquinoline	Hydrocarbons	50	M	I, P
Kel-F oil No. 3 (chlorotrifluoro-ethylene polymer)	Inorganic and organometallic compounds	50	A	I
Kel-F No. 10 (chlorotrifluoro-ethylene polymer)	Gases Halogenated compounds Inorganic and organometallic compounds	100	A	I
Kel-F wax (chlorotrifluoro-ethylene polymer)	Halogenated compounds	200	A	—
LAC-1-R-296 (DEGA)	Aromatics and heterocyclics Pesticides	190	A	—
LAC-2-R-446 (cross-linked DEGA)	Alcohols Essential oils Fatty acids and esters Nitrogen compounds Pesticides Sugars	190	A	P
LAC-3-R-728 (DEGS)	Fatty acids and esters	190	A	P
LAC-4-R-886 (EGS)		190	C	I,P
Lanolin	Alcohols Aromatics and heterocyclics Essential oils	200	C	—
Lexan		250	C	P
Lithium chloride	Aromatics and heterocyclics	500	W	—
Lubrol MO		200	T	—
Lustrex HF-77 (polystyrene)		200	T	—
Mannitol	Sugars	200	M	H
Marlex (polyethylene)		240	X	—
Microcrystalline wax bottoms	Aromatics and heterocyclics Hydrocarbons	250	C	—
Montan wax	Halogenated compounds	175	C	—
Naphthylamine	Aromatics and heterocyclics	75	M	—
Neopentyl glycol adipate (NPGA)	Amino acids Drugs and alkaloids Pesticides Steroids	240	A	I
Neopentyl glycol sebacate (NPGSB)	Amino acids Steroids	240	C	I
Neopentyl glycol succinate (NPGS)	Amino acids Bile and urinary compounds Fatty acids and esters Metals and inorganic compounds Steroids	240	A	I
Nitrobenzene	Hydrocarbons Inorganic and organometallic compounds	150	M	—
Nonylphenoxypoly-(ethyleneoxy) ethanol (see Igepal)				
Octylphenoxypoly-(ethyleneoxy) ethanol (see Igepal)				

TABLE 1—(Continued)
LIQUID PHASES FOR GAS CHROMATOGRAPHY

Phase	Used for:	Max. temp. °C	Solvent	Polarity
Nujol (paraffin oil)	Hydrocarbons	200	T	N
Nylon 6		—	F	—
Nylon 66	Aromatics	—	F	—
***n*-Octadecane**	Inorganic and organometallic compounds	55	T	—
Octyl decyl adipate		175	A	—
Oronite polybutene 32		210	T	—
Oronite polybutene 128		210	C	—
Oronite dispersant NI-W		—	A	—
OS 124 (see polyphenyl ether 5 ring)				
OV-1	Hydrocarbons Steroids	350	T, C	N
OV-17	Alcohols	300	T, C	I
OV-25		300	C	I
OV-101		300	C	N
OV-210		275	C	I
OV-225		275	C	I
OV-22		300	C	I
OD-1 (methyl)		375	T	—
β,β′-Oxydipropionitrile	Halogenated compounds	100	A	P
OPN (oxypropionitrile)	Hydrocarbons			
Paraffin wax	Halogenated compounds Inorganic and organometallic compounds Nitrogen compounds	200	C	N
Paraplex U-148 (polyester)		150	A	—
Pluronic P84 (poly[oxypropylene-oxyethylene])		175	A	—
Phenoxathiin		60	A	—
Phenylacetonitrile (see benzyl cyanide)				
Phthalonitrile		150	A	—
Phenyldiethanolamine succinate (PDEAS)	Drugs and alkaloids Hydrocarbons	225	C	P
Phenyldiethanolamine (PDEA)		—	A	—
Phenyl neopentyl phosphite		—	M	—
Polyethylene glycol 600 (Jefferson)		160	M	P
Polyethylene glycol (see Carbowaxes)				
Polyethylene (Alathon 7040)		240	X	P
Polyethyleneimine (PEI 1000)		250	E, M	P
Polyphenyl ether (5 ring)	Aromatics and heterocyclics Essential oils Sulfur compounds	250	C, L	I
Polyphenyl ether (6 ring) (6P5E)	Alcohols Essential oils Fatty acids and esters	350	A, C, L	I
Polypropylene glycol	Alcohols Drugs and alkaloids Fatty acids and esters Nitrogen compounds	150	M	H
Polyvinyl pyrrolidinone (PVP)	Drugs and alkaloids	225	M	P, H
Propylene glycol-silver nitrate (3 : 1)		75	M	S
Propylene carbonate	Gases Hydrocarbons	60	L	P
Quadrol	Alcohols Aldehydes and ketones Amino acids Essential oils Pyrolysis	150	A	H

TABLE 1—(Continued)
LIQUID PHASES FOR GAS CHROMATOGRAPHY

Phase	Used for:	Max. temp. °C	Solvent	Polarity
Reoplex 400 (polypropylene glycol adipate)	Aromatics and heterocyclics Essential oils Fatty acids and esters Pesticides Phosphorus compounds Sulfur compounds Vitamins	190	A	I
Renex 678 (ethylene oxide-nonyl phenol surfactant)	Alcohols	—	M	—
Silastic (LS420) (LS-X-3-0295) (trifluoropropyl and vinyl silicone gum rubber)	Aromatics	275	A	—
Silicone 550 with 10% stearic acid (by weight)	Amino acids	175	A	—
Silicone fluid S.F. 96 (methyl) (1000 cs)	Aromatics and heterocyclics Halogenated compounds Hydrocarbons Pesticides	300	T, C, L	N
Silicone fluid SF96 (methyl) (50cs)		300	T	N
Silicone fluid SF96 (methyl) (100cs)		—	T	N
Silicone fluid 500,000cs (methyl)		300	T	—
Silicone fluid F50 (Versilube) (methyl chlorophenyl)	Steroids	275	A	I
Silicone fluid F60 (DC 560) (chlorophenyl methyl)	Steroids	250	A	I
Silicone fluid GE XF 1150 (5% nitrile)	Aldehydes and ketones Drugs and alkaloids Halogenated compounds	200	A	—
Silicone gum rubber SE-30	Alcohols Aldehydes and ketones Aromatics and heterocyclics Amino acids Bile and urinary compounds Drugs and alkaloids Essential oils Fatty acids and esters Gases Gases (blood and respiratory) Halogenated compounds Hydrocarbons Inorganic and organometallic compounds Nitrogen compounds Pesticides Phosphorus compounds Steroids Sugars Sulfur compounds Vitamins	350	T	N
Silicone rubber OD-1 (methyl)		375	T	—
Silicone rubber SE31 (methyl vinyl)		300	T	—
Silicone rubber SE33 (methyl vinyl)		300	T	—
Silicone rubber SE52 (methyl phenyl)	Alcohols Bile and urinary compounds Fatty acids and esters Halogenated compounds Hydrocarbons Nitrogen compounds Pesticides Steroids Sugars	300	T	I

TABLE 1—(Continued)
LIQUID PHASES FOR GAS CHROMATOGRAPHY

Phase	Used for:	Max. temp. °C	Solvent	Polarity
GE Nitrile silicone gum XE-60 (50% nitrile)	Alcohols Amino acids Aromatics and heterocyclics Bile and urinary compounds Drugs and alkaloids Essential oils Fatty acids and esters Hydrocarbons Nitrogen compounds Phosphorus compounds Pyrolysis Steroids Sulfur compounds	275	A	I
Silicone gum rubber SE54 (methyl phenyl vinyl)		300	T	I
GE Silicone gum rubber XE-61	Alcohols	—	A	—
AN-600		310	K	—
Silicone oil Linde 45 (Linde 46) (methyl)	Fatty acids and esters	250	T	—
Silicone oil W96 (methyl vinyl)		300	T	—
Silicone oil W98 (methyl vinyl)		300	T	—
Silicone oil L525		200	T	—
Silicone oil (May-Baker)	Aldehydes and ketones Amino acids	265	T	—
Siponates DS-10 (sodium dodecyl benzene sulfonate)	Fatty acids and esters	210	A	—
Sorbitan monostearate (see Span)				
Sorbitol	Alcohols Aromatics and heterocyclics	150	M	—
Sorbitol-silicone oil X525 (1 : 1)		150	M	—
Span 60 (sorbitan monostearate)		150	M	P
Span 80 (sorbitan monooleate)		150	M	P
Squalene	Aldehydes and ketones Aromatics and heterocyclics Boron compounds Gases Halogenated compounds Hydrocarbons Inorganic and organometallic compounds Nitrogen compounds Phosphorus compounds Pyrolysis	100–140	B	I, N
Sucrose acetate isobutyrate (SAIB)	Alcohols Essential oils	225	A	I, P
Sucrose diacetate hexaisobutyrate		—	A	—
Sulframin 85		—	W	—
Surfonic N300 (alkyl aryl polyether alcohol)		200	T	—
Tergitol NPX (nonyl phenyl ether of PEG)		200	A	—
Tergitol NP-35 (nonyl phenyl ether of PEG)		200	A	P
Tetracyanoethyl pentaerythritol	Fatty acids and esters	150	M	P
Tetraethylene glycol	Hydrocarbons	70	T	P
Tetraethylene glycol dimethyl ether (Ansul ether)	Hydrocarbons Nitrogen compounds	80	M	P
Tetraethylene pentamine	Nitrogen compounds	150	M	H, P
Tetrahydrofuryl phosphate		125	M	—

TABLE 1—(Continued)
LIQUID PHASES FOR GAS CHROMATOGRAPHY

Phase	Used for:	Max. temp. °C	Solvent	Polarity
Tetrahydroxyethyl ethylenediamine (THEED)	Alcohols Hydrocarbons Nitrogen compounds	135	A	H
1,2,3,4-Tetrakis (2-cyanoethoxy) butane		200	C	—
β,β′-Thiodipropionitrile	Hydrocarbons	100	C	P
Triacetin	Gases	85	C	—
Tributyl citrate (Citroflex 4)		150	M	—
Tributyrin	Gases	100	M	—
Tributyl phosphate		50	A L,	I
Tricresyl phosphate (TCP)	Alcohols Aldehydes and ketones Aromatics and heterocyclics Essential oils Fatty acids and esters Gases Halogenated compounds Hydrocarbons Pyrolysis Sulfur compounds	125	A	I
Triethanolamine	Alcohols Gases	125	A	H
Triethylene glycol	Aldehydes and ketones Hydrocarbons	70	M	—
Triisobutylene	Gases	25	A	—
Trimethylol tripelargonate (see Celanese ester No. 9)				
Trimer acid	Alcohols	200	A	H
2,4,7-Trinitro-9-fluorenone	Aromatics and heterocyclics Hydrocarbons	—	A	—
Triphenyl methane		150	C	—
1,2,3-Tris(2-cyanoethoxy) propane	Alcohols Aldehydes and ketones Halogenated compounds Hydrocarbons Inorganic and organometallic compounds	—	A	P
Tritolyl phosphate (see tricresyl phosphate)				
Trixylol phosphate	Aromatics and heterocyclics	190	A	—
Triton QS-15		190	M	—
Triton X-100 (alkyl aryl polyether alcohol)	Alcohols Aldehydes and ketones Fatty acids and esters Hydrocarbons	190	A	—
Triton X-305 (alkyl aryl polyether)	Alcohols	250	A	P
Tween 80 (polysorbate)	Fatty acids and esters Halogenated compounds Pesticides	150	B	P
Tween 20	Essential oils	—	M	—
Ucon—(water soluble) (polar) (HB or H)	Alcohols Essential oils Nitrogen compounds Pyrolysis	240	M	P

TABLE 1—(Continued)
LIQUID PHASES FOR GAS CHROMATOGRAPHY

Phase	Used for:	Max. temp. °C	Solvent	Poparity
Ucon—(water insoluble) (nonpolar) (LB)	Alcohols Fatty acids and esters	240	M	N
Ucon 50 HB 270X		225	M	P
Ucon 50 HB 280X	Alcohols Aldehydes and ketones Aromatics and heterocyclics Essential oils Hydrocarbons	200	C or L	P
Ucon 50 HB 660		225	A	—
Ucon 50 HB 2000	Alcohols Aldehydes and ketones Aromatics and heterocyclics Essential oils	225	A	P
Ucon 1800 XMP 1018		160	A	—
Ucon 50 HB 5100	Alcohols Aldehydes and ketones Nitrogen compounds	200	C	P
Ucon 50 LB 300X		225	M	—
Ucon 50 LB 550X	Aldehydes and ketones Aromatics and heterocyclics Essential oils Hydrocarbons	225	A	P
Ucon 50 LB 1200X		200	M	—
Ucon 75-H-90,000		250	M	—
Versamid 900 and	Alcohols	450	—	P
Versamid 940 (polyamide resin) (soluble in hot chloroform-butanol) (1 : 1)	Aromatics and heterocyclics Fatty acids and esters Nitrogen compounds Pesticides	200	—	P
Viton (synthetic rubber) (soluble in 2-butanone)	Alcohols Aldehydes and ketones	300	—	—
Zinc stearate		150	M	—
Zonyl E-7 (see fluoro-ester)				
Zytel (Nylon)		—	F	—

Reprinted with permission from "Analabs Guide to Stationary Phases for GC", 1970, pp. 84–106, Analabs Inc., North Haven, Connecticut.
Polarity data reprinted with permission from the 1970 Instruments and Accessories Catalog, pp. 20 and 21, Varian Aerograph, Walnut Creek, California.

TABLE 1—(Continued)
LIQUID PHASES FOR GAS CHROMATOGRAPHY

Listed below are Δ I values between the particular liquid phase and squalane on over 200 liquid phases as determined by W. O. McReynolds [*J. Chromatog. Sci.* **8,** 685 (1970)]. Also shown are the values b, the slope of the curve obtained when the logarithms of the net retention times of decane and dodecane are plotted as a function of the number of carbon atoms, and r, the ratio of the net retention times of adjacent *n*-alkanes calculated from the square root of the ratio of the net retention times of dodecane and decane. All data were obtained at 120°C.

The modified Rohrschneider constants [L. Rohrschneider, *J. Chromatogr.* **22,** 6 (1966)] listed below are useful as an indication of the polarity of the liquid phase, for the comparison of phases and for predicting the retention of various solutes on a particular phase. The average polarity of each liquid phase was determined from the sum of the Δ I values of benzene, butanol, 2-pentanone, nitropropane and pyridine, and the phases are arranged according to increasing polarity. By comparing the values below, it can be seen that the methyl silicones SE-30, E-301, OV-1, L-46, DC-200, OV-101, DC-410, DC 401 and silicone oil (May and Baker) are essentially identical.

Liquid phase	Δ I Benzene	Δ I Butanol	Δ I 2-Pentanone	Δ I Nitropropane	Δ I Pyridine	Δ I 2-Methyl-2-pentanol	Δ I 1-Iodobutane	Δ I 2-Octyne	Δ I 1,4-Dioxane	Δ I *cis*-Hydrindane	b	r
Squalane*	0	0	0	0	0	0	0	0	0	0	0.2891	1.945
Squalane	1	1	1	2	2	1	0	1	1	0	0.2890	1.945
Hexatriacontane	12	2	−3	1	11	0	10	2	5	8	0.2899	1.949
Nujol	9	5	2	6	11	2	9	2	6	6	0.2939	1.967
Mineral oil	10	5	3	7	13	3	11	2	9	7	0.2956	1.975
Liquid paraffin	11	6	2	7	13	2	12	2	9	9	0.2887	1.944
Convoil 20	14	14	8	17	21	10	15	5	14	10	0.2914	1.956
Apiezon M	31	22	15	30	40	12	32	10	28	29	0.2833	1.920
Apiezon L	32	22	15	32	42	13	35	11	31	33	0.2821	1.914
Apiezon L treated	32	24	16	31	43	13	32	10	30	31	0.2836	1.921
Polybutene 32	21	29	24	42	40	18	24	8	40	24	0.2822	1.915
Montan wax	19	58	14	21	47	21	16	5	21	10	0.2871	1.936
Polybutene 128	25	26	25	41	42	14	29	8	43	33	0.2779	1.896
Apiezon L	35	28	19	37	47	16	36	11	33	33	0.2827	1.917
DC 330	13	51	42	61	36	31	0	21	41	−6	0.2494	1.775
SF 96	12	53	42	61	37	31	0	21	41	−6	0.2525	1.788
Apiezon J	38	36	27	49	57	23	42	15	42	35	0.2832	1.919
Apiezon N	38	40	28	52	58	25	41	15	43	35	0.2828	1.918
SE 30	15	53	44	64	41	31	3	22	44	−2	0.2495	1.776
E-301	15	56	44	66	40	32	3	22	45	−1	0.2483	1.771
OV-1	16	55	44	65	42	32	4	23	45	−1	0.2470	1.766
UC L 46	16	56	44	65	41	33	3	22	45	−2	0.2486	1.772
SE 31	16	54	45	65	43	32	3	23	46	−1	0.2485	1.772
W 982	16	55	45	66	42	33	4	23	46	−1	0.2471	1.766
SE 33	17	54	45	67	42	33	4	23	46	−1	0.2478	1.769
M and B silicone oil	14	57	46	67	43	33	2	22	46	−4	0.2507	1.781
DC 200	16	57	45	66	43	33	3	23	46	−3	0.2509	1.782
OV-101	17	57	45	67	43	33	4	23	46	−2	0.2484	1.771
DC 410	18	57	47	68	44	34	5	24	48	0	0.2481	1.770
DC silastic 401	17	58	47	66	46	34	4	23	48	−1	0.2483	1.771
Versilube F-50	19	57	48	69	47	36	7	23	50	−1	0.2579	1.811
DC 11	17	86	48	69	56	36	3	23	51	−2	0.2486	1.772
DC 510	25	65	60	89	57	42	16	32	59	2	0.2557	1.802
SE 52	32	72	65	98	67	44	23	36	67	9	0.2548	1.798
SE 54	33	72	66	99	67	46	24	36	68	10	0.2524	1.788
DC 560	32	72	70	100	68	49	24	35	69	7	0.2600	1.819
DC 556	37	77	80	118	79	53	32	49	77	3	0.2673	1.850
Butyl stearate	41	109	65	112	71	85	37	29	61	−1	0.2917	1.957
OV-3	44	86	81	124	88	55	39	46	84	17	0.2547	1.797

* The absolute values of the retention indices on the Squalane column are as follows: Benzene, 653; Butanol, 590; 2-Pentanone, 627; Nitropropane, 652; Pyridine, 699; 2-Methyl-2-pentanol, 690; 1-Iodobutane, 818; 2-Octyne, 841; 1,2-Dioxane, 654; *cis*-Hydrindane, 1006.

TABLE 1—(Continued)
LIQUID PHASES FOR GAS CHROMATOGRAPHY

Liquid phase	Δ I Benzene	Δ I Butanol	Δ I 2-Pentanone	Δ I Nitropropane	Δ I Pyridine	Δ I 2-Methyl-2-pentanol	Δ I 1-Iodobutane	Δ I 2-Octyne	Δ I 1,4-Dioxane	Δ I *cis*-Hydrindane	b	r
Beeswax	43	110	61	88	122	86	41	24	73	18	0.2844	1.924
Fluorolube HG 1200	51	68	114	144	118	68	12	53	104	3	0.2550	1.799
Kel F Wax	55	67	114	143	116	73	16	57	109	4	0.2594	1.817
Apiezon H	59	86	81	151	129	46	53	23	81	37	0.2836	1.921
Butoxyethyl stearate	56	135	83	136	97	102	49	40	81	5	0.2897	1.948
Halocarbon wax	55	71	116	143	123	70	16	57	110	4	0.2575	1.809
OV-7	69	113	111	171	128	77	68	66	120	35	0.2570	1.807
DC 550	74	116	117	178	135	81	74	72	128	36	0.2608	1.823
Apiezon W	82	135	99	155	154	90	93	42	109	59	0.2789	1.900
Dinonyl sebacate	66	166	107	178	118	130	62	50	106	8	0.2832	1.919
Octoil S	72	167	107	179	123	132	68	49	106	11	0.2836	1.921
Dioctyl sebacate	72	168	108	180	123	132	68	49	106	10	0.2862	1.933
Diethex sebacate	72	168	108	180	125	132	68	49	107	11	0.2829	1.918
DC 703	76	123	126	189	140	89	79	78	134	31	0.2751	1.884
DC 702	77	124	126	189	142	90	79	79	136	31	0.2747	1.882
DC 550	81	124	124	189	145	87	81	77	136	40	0.2610	1.824
Diisodecyl adipate	71	171	113	185	128	134	67	52	114	11	0.2843	1.924
DINA	73	174	116	189	129	137	68	54	116	10	0.2819	1.914
Ditridecyl phthalate	75	156	122	195	140	119	76	51	115	25	0.2811	1.910
Diethex tetraclphth	109	132	113	171	168	104	75	45	137	34	0.2874	1.938
DEG stearate	64	193	106	143	191	147	57	41	121	20	0.2817	1.913
Octyl decyl adipate	79	179	119	193	134	141	72	57	119	10	0.2835	1.921
Dilauryl phthalate	79	158	120	192	158	120	79	52	116	26	0.2811	1.910
Diisooctyl adipate	76	181	121	197	134	144	71	55	119	9	0.2822	1.915
TMP tripelargonate	84	182	122	197	143	143	77	55	127	18	0.2804	1.907
Diisooctyl adipate	78	187	126	204	140	148	72	59	126	8	0.2848	1.926
Diisodecyl phthalate	84	173	137	218	155	133	83	59	130	24	0.2812	1.910
OV-11	102	142	145	219	178	100	103	92	164	59	0.2562	1.803
Dinonyl phthalate	83	183	147	231	159	141	82	65	138	18	0.2804	1.907
Triton X-400	68	334	97	176	131	218	—	36	95	23	0.2810	1.910
Triethex phosphate	71	288	117	215	132	225	71	47	103	7	0.2809	1.909
DC 710	107	149	153	228	190	107	108	98	174	60	0.2595	1.817
Flexol GPE	93	210	140	224	162	166	90	65	146	20	0.2813	1.911
Dioctyl phthalate	92	186	150	236	167	143	92	66	140	25	0.2792	1.902
Diethex phthalate	92	186	150	236	167	143	92	66	140	26	0.2789	1.900
Dioctyl phthalate	96	188	150	236	172	144	92	68	142	27	0.2807	1.908
Hallcomid M-18	79	268	130	222	146	202	82	48	106	16	0.2860	1.932
Diisooctyl phthalate	94	193	154	243	174	149	92	69	147	24	0.2799	1.905
Buoctyl phthalate	97	194	157	246	174	149	96	69	147	27	0.2782	1.897
OV-17	119	158	162	243	202	112	119	105	184	69	0.2551	1.799
Hallcomid M-18 OL	89	280	143	239	165	211	93	58	139	21	0.2844	1.925
Flexol 8N8	96	254	164	260	179	197	98	64	147	23	0.2733	1.876
SP-392	133	169	176	258	219	123	133	114	202	74	0.2666	1.847
Span 60	88	263	158	200	258	201	82	55	180	37	0.2728	1.874
Versamid 930	108	309	137	208	207	222	110	57	148	77	0.2583	1.812
Hercoflex 600	112	234	168	261	194	187	102	77	176	27	0.2704	1.864
Versamid 930	109	313	144	211	209	225	112	57	150	79	0.2590	1.815
Versamid 940	109	314	145	212	209	225	112	57	150	78	0.2592	1.816
Zinc stearate	61	231	59	98	544	98	50	29	78	33	0.2726	1.873
Ucon LB-550-X	118	271	158	243	206	177	96	91	177	40	0.2644	1.838
Span 80	97	266	170	216	268	207	94	66	191	41	0.2719	1.870
UCON 50-HB-1800X	123	275	161	249	212	179	101	95	181	45	0.2616	1.826
Castorwax	108	265	175	229	246	202	105	73	196	49	0.2684	1.855
Flexol B-400	121	284	169	259	217	191	100	95	186	39	0.2640	1.836
OV-22	160	188	191	283	253	133	152	132	228	99	0.2464	1.763

TABLE 1—(Continued)
LIQUID PHASES FOR GAS CHROMATOGRAPHY

Liquid phase	Δ I Benzene	Δ I Butanol	Δ I 2-Pentanone	Δ I Nitropropane	Δ I Pyridine	Δ I 2-Methyl-2-pentanol	Δ I 1-Iodobutane	Δ I 2-Octyne	Δ I 1,4-Dioxane	Δ I *cis*-Hydrindane	b	r
Triton X-200	117	289	172	266	237	180	105	81	192	48	0.2689	1.857
PPG 2000	128	294	173	264	226	196	106	98	194	45	0.2616	1.826
Estynox	136	257	182	285	227	202	130	86	194	52	0.2680	1.853
Trimer acid	94	271	163	182	378	234	94	57	216	60	0.2684	1.855
Pluracol P-2010	129	295	174	266	227	197	106	99	195	46	0.2606	1.822
Atpet 200	108	282	186	235	289	220	106	74	209	48	0.2700	1.862
UCON LB 1715	132	297	180	275	235	201	109	100	199	46	0.2603	1.821
Dibutoxyet adipate	137	278	198	300	235	216	118	104	205	28	0.2704	1.863
Thanol PPG 1000	131	314	185	277	243	214	110	101	205	46	0.2605	1.822
Acetyltribu citrate	135	268	202	314	233	214	112	102	207	26	0.2653	1.842
Diethex phthalate	135	254	213	320	235	200	126	101	202	38	0.2715	1.868
Didecyl phthalate	136	255	213	320	235	201	126	101	202	38	0.2714	1.868
Elastex 50-B	140	255	209	318	239	198	134	103	202	47	0.2734	1.876
Dicyclohexyl phth	146	257	206	316	245	196	144	104	204	58	0.2722	1.871
OV-25	178	204	208	305	280	144	169	147	251	113	0.2428	1.749
Pluronic L81	144	314	187	289	249	211	120	108	212	55	0.2574	1.809
OS 124	176	227	224	306	283	177	169	135	266	103	0.2660	1.845
Tributyl citrate	135	286	213	324	262	226	119	102	229	29	0.2666	1.847
GE SR 119	166	238	221	314	299	175	158	133	257	100	0.2422	1.746
OS 138	182	233	228	313	293	181	176	136	273	112	0.2623	1.829
Diethoxyet sebacate	151	306	211	320	274	238	129	110	224	36	0.2677	1.852
Dibutoxyet phth	151	282	227	338	267	217	138	112	225	48	0.2656	1.843
Dibutoxyet phth	157	292	233	348	272	222	143	117	233	50	0.2636	1.834
Tri(butoxyethyl) PO4	141	373	209	341	274	285	126	104	204	31	0.2658	1.844
Zonyl E-91	130	250	320	377	293	235	81	95	295	10	0.2324	1.707
NPG sebacate	172	327	225	344	326	257	156	109	257	73	0.2550	1.799
Squalene	152	341	238	329	344	248	140	101	265	64	0.2638	1.836
UCON 50-HB-280X	177	362	227	351	302	252	151	130	256	65	0.2540	1.794
Polytergent J-300	168	366	227	350	308	266	149	119	255	61	0.2598	1.819
Tricresyl phosphate	176	321	250	374	299	242	169	131	254	76	0.2630	1.832
SAIB	172	330	251	378	295	264	147	128	276	54	0.2489	1.774
Paraplex G-25	189	328	239	368	312	257	169	124	271	79	0.2504	1.779
Ethomeen 18/25	176	382	230	353	323	275	158	118	265	72	0.2568	1.806
Polytergent J-400	180	375	234	366	317	270	159	127	265	68	0.2556	1.801
Oronite NIW	185	370	242	370	327	267	165	130	275	75	0.2576	1.809
QF-1	144	233	355	463	305	203	136	53	280	59	0.2094	1.619
PPG sebacate	196	345	251	381	328	271	176	129	285	83	0.2482	1.771
UCON 50-HB-660	193	380	241	376	321	265	166	141	274	75	0.2506	1.780
OV-210	146	238	358	468	310	206	139	56	283	60	0.2086	1.616
UCON 50-HB-3520	198	381	241	379	323	264	169	144	278	80	0.2483	1.771
Ethofat 60/25	191	382	244	380	333	277	168	131	279	73	0.2551	1.799
Ethomeen S125	186	395	242	370	339	285	169	127	279	79	0.2551	1.799
Igepal CO-630	192	381	253	382	344	277	172	136	288	78	0.2552	1.800
LSX-3-0295	152	241	366	479	319	208	144	55	291	64	0.2082	1.615
Pluronic P85	201	390	247	388	335	271	172	145	285	82	0.2842	1.771
Pluronic P65	203	394	251	393	340	276	174	146	289	83	0.2477	1.769
Tergitol NPX	197	386	258	389	351	281	176	39	293	81	0.2541	1.795
UCON 50-HB-2000	202	394	253	392	341	277	173	147	289	80	0.2483	1.771
Cresyl diphenyl PO4	199	351	285	413	336	266	190	153	292	88	0.2573	1.808
Emulphor ON-870	202	395	251	395	344	282	179	140	289	80	0.2523	1.787
Emulphor ON-870	202	396	251	395	345	283	179	139	289	80	0.2527	1.789
Polytergent B-350	202	392	260	395	353	284	180	142	297	84	0.2532	1.791
Pluronic L35	206	406	257	398	349	286	177	148	296	85	0.2469	1.765
Polytergent G-300	203	398	267	401	360	290	180	145	303	83	0.2529	1.790
Igepal CO-710	205	397	266	401	361	289	183	144	303	85	0.2517	1.785

TABLE 1—(Continued)
LIQUID PHASES FOR GAS CHROMATOGRAPHY

Liquid phase	Δ I Benzene	Δ I Butanol	Δ I 2-Pentanone	Δ I Nitropropane	Δ I Pyridine	Δ I 2-Methyl-2-pentanol	Δ I 1-Iodobutane	Δ I 2-Octyne	Δ I 1,4-Dioxane	Δ I *cis*-Hydrindane	b	r
Triton X-100	203	399	268	402	362	290	181	145	304	83	0.2521	1.787
Polyglycol 15-200	207	410	262	401	354	289	179	150	301	86	0.2449	1.757
Stephan DS 60	97	550	303	338	402	440	111	60	418	61	0.2524	1.788
Diethoxyet phth	214	375	305	446	364	290	190	159	312	79	0.2504	1.780
UCON 50-HB-5100	214	418	278	421	375	301	185	155	316	86	0.2442	1.754
Siponate DS-10	99	569	320	344	388	466	114	61	437	63	0.2527	1.789
Renex 678	223	417	278	427	381	301	198	156	321	95	0.2471	1.766
Igepal CO-730	224	418	279	428	379	302	198	157	321	95	0.2470	1.766
XE 60	204	381	340	493	367	289	203	120	327	94	0.2237	1.674
OV-225	228	369	338	492	386	282	226	150	342	117	0.2275	1.688
Bis (Ethoethoet) phth	233	408	317	470	389	309	207	170	337	92	0.2460	1.762
NPGA	232	421	311	461	424	335	208	156	357	103	0.2362	1.722
NPGA	234	425	312	462	438	339	210	157	362	103	0.2378	1.729
UCON 75-H-90000	255	452	299	470	406	321	220	180	348	110	0.2369	1.725
Pluronic F88	262	461	306	483	419	327	227	183	359	114	0.2362	1.722
Igepal CO 880	259	461	311	482	426	334	227	180	362	112	0.2414	1.743
Surfonic N 300	261	462	313	484	427	334	228	180	364	114	0.2382	1.730
Pluronic F68	264	465	309	488	423	331	229	184	363	115	0.2356	1.720
Triton X-305	262	467	314	488	430	336	229	183	366	113	0.2404	1.739
HI EFF 8BP	271	444	330	498	463	346	252	175	396	127	0.2317	1.705
CHDMS	269	446	328	493	481	351	248	176	394	124	0.2351	1.718
CW 4000 monostearate	280	486	325	512	449	350	244	191	382	122	0.2345	1.716
Zonyl E-7	223	359	468	549	465	338	146	137	469	62	0.2083	1.615
Paraplex G-40	282	459	355	528	457	364	247	193	414	125	0.2260	1.682
CW 4000 monostearate	282	496	331	517	467	357	247	193	389	45	0.2329	1.709
Quadrol	214	571	357	472	489	431	208	142	379	111	0.2353	1.719
NPGS	272	467	365	539	472	371	243	184	419	124	0.2267	1.685
NPGS	272	469	366	539	474	371	243	184	419	124	0.2261	1.683
NPGS	275	472	367	543	489	374	245	186	423	127	0.2250	1.679
Igepal CO 990	298	508	345	540	475	366	261	205	406	133	0.2303	1.699
EGSP-Z	308	474	399	548	549	373	279	220	469	167	0.2229	1.670
Carbowax 20 M	322	536	368	572	510	387	282	221	434	148	0.2235	1.673
Carbowax 20-M TPA	321	537	367	573	520	387	281	220	435	148	0.2237	1.674
Epon 1001	284	489	406	539	601	378	291	207	502	187	0.2261	1.683
Carbowax 6000	322	540	369	577	512	390	282	222	437	147	0.2239	1.674
MER-21	322	541	370	575	512	392	283	222	438	149	0.2247	1.677
PEG 4000	325	551	375	582	520	399	285	224	443	148	0.2238	1.674
Et Glycol isophth	326	508	425	607	561	400	299	213	498	168	0.2159	1.644
XF-1150	308	520	470	669	528	401	302	174	471	156	0.2053	1.604
Sorbitol hexaacetate	335	553	449	652	543	446	273	247	521	131	0.2094	1.619
FFAP	340	580	397	602	627	423	298	228	473	161	0.2204	1.661
STAP	345	586	400	610	627	428	301	235	484	163	0.2178	1.651
Carbowax 1000	347	607	418	626	589	449	306	240	493	161	0.2174	1.649
Sucrose octaacetate	344	570	461	671	569	457	292	251	546	152	0.2047	1.602
MER 2	381	539	456	646	615	421	337	262	566	197	0.2093	1.619
PEG 600	350	631	428	632	605	472	308	240	503	162	0.2180	1.652
Butanediol succinate	370	571	448	657	611	457	324	242	533	178	0.2106	1.624
EGA	372	576	453	655	617	462	325	250	546	177	0.2091	1.618
EGA	372	577	455	658	619	463	325	250	548	177	0.2094	1.619
Et glycol adipate	371	579	454	655	633	466	323	248	550	175	0.2101	1.622
Butanediol succinate	369	591	457	661	629	476	325	243	544	177	0.2110	1.625
PDEAS	386	555	472	674	654	437	362	242	562	213	0.2100	1.622
Reoplex 400	364	619	449	647	671	482	317	245	540	171	0.2131	1.633
LAC IR-296	377	601	458	663	655	477	328	253	551	177	0.2105	1.623
DEG adipate	378	603	460	665	658	479	329	254	554	176	0.2105	1.623

TABLE 1—(Continued)
LIQUID PHASES FOR GAS CHROMATOGRAPHY

Liquid phase	Δ I Benzene	Δ I Butanol	Δ I 2-Pentanone	Δ I Nitropropane	Δ I Pyridine	Δ I 2-Methyl-2-pentanol	Δ I 1-Iodobutane	Δ I 2-Octyne	Δ I 1,4-Dioxane	Δ I *cis*-Hydrindane	b	r
Resoflex R 296	380	609	463	668	667	483	331	255	557	179	0.2100	1.622
LAC-2-R-446	387	616	471	679	667	489	339	257	567	186	0.2074	1.612
EGSS-Y	391	597	493	693	661	469	335	261	591	190	0.2092	1.619
Hyprose SP-80	336	742	492	639	727	565	310	227	590	196	0.2007	1.587
ECNSS-M	421	690	581	803	732	548	383	259	644	211	0.1935	1.561
Diglycerol	371	826	560	676	854	608	245	141	724	36	0.2568	1.806
DEGS supelco 1045	470	705	558	788	779	556	393	301	677	215	0.1992	1.582
EGSS-X	484	710	585	831	778	566	412	316	713	237	0.1907	1.551
DEGS	492	733	581	833	791	579	418	321	705	237	0.1925	1.558
Et glycol phthalate	453	697	602	816	872	560	419	306	699	260	0.1929	1.564
DEGS supelco 1303	496	746	590	837	835	594	420	325	718	238	0.1906	1.551
DEGS	499	751	593	840	860	595	422	323	725	240	0.1900	1.548
LAC-3-R-728	502	755	597	849	852	599	427	329	726	243	0.1891	1.545
Glycol succinate	536	775	636	897	864	622	450	347	783	259	0.1844	1.529
THEED	463	942	626	801	893	746	427	269	721	254	0.1906	1.550
Tetracyanoethoxy PE	526	782	677	920	837	621	444	333	766	237	0.1887	1.544
EGS	537	787	643	903	889	633	452	348	795	259	0.1807	1.516
TCEP	593	857	752	1028	915	672	503	375	853	267	0.1789	1.509
TCEP	594	857	759	1031	917	680	509	379	854	269	0.1778	1.506
Cyanoethyl sucrose	647	919	797	1043	976	713	544	388	917	299	0.1653	1.463
BCEF	690	991	853	1110	1000	773	557	371	964	279	0.1951	1.593

Permission from *J. Chromatogr. Sci.*, Vol. 8, pp. 685–689 (1970).

TABLE 2
SUPPORT MATERIALS FOR GAS CHROMATOGRAPHY
(including Porasil and Porapak packings)

CHROMOSORB SUPPORTS

There are six basic types of Chromosorb grades—A, G, P, T, W and 100 series. Most are available in both untreated and treated forms, as well as a variety of mesh ranges. A brief outline of properties and mesh sizes is given below.

Chromosorb Mesh Range

	A	G	P	T	W	101	102	103
20/30	×	—	—	—	—	—	—	—
30/60	—	—	×	×	×	—	—	—
45/60	×	×	×	—	×	—	—	—
40/60	—	—	—	×	—	—	—	—
50/60	—	×	—	—	—	×	—	×
60/70	—	×	—	—	—	—	—	—
60/80	×	×	×	—	×	×	×	×
70/80	—	×	—	—	×	—	—	—
80/100	—	×	×	—	×	×	×	×
100/120	—	×	×	—	×	×	×	×
120/140	—	×	—	—	×	—	—	—

"×" denotes availability.

Chromosorb A

Chromosorb A is a diatomite support developed and manufactured specifically as a chromatographic support for use in preparative-scale gas chromatography. It was designed to overcome deficiencies in existing supports for preparative work. It has good capacity to hold liquid phase (25% maximum), a structure that does not readily break down with handling and a surface that is not highly adsorptive. It is available not only in the standard or NAW form, but in a number of mesh ranges. These include coarse fractions such as 10/20, 20/30, etc., which allow the use of long columns with a low-pressure drop.

Chromosorb G

Chromosorb G is a diatomite support developed and manufactured as a chromatographic support for the separation of polar compounds. Its low-surface area, hardness and good handling characteristics make it a good replacement for light, friable supports such as Chromosorb W. Because of its lower surface area and higher density, it is recommended that it be used to replace supports such as Chromosorb W in columns having no more than 12% liquid phase. This corresponds to a top loading of 5% on Chromosorb G.

Chromosorb P

Chromosorb P is prepared from the production of Johns-Manville's Sil-O-Cel C-22 Firebrick. It is a calcined diatomite, pink in color and relatively hard. Its surface is more adsorptive than the other chromosorb grades and is used primarily for hydrocarbon work and also for moderately polar materials on both an analytical and preparative scale.

Chromosorb T

Chromosorb T is a fluorocarbon resin screened from DuPont Teflon 6. It is recommended as a support for use in the separation of highly polar or reactive compounds such as water, hydrazine, sulfur dioxide, halogens, etc. Its surface is inert to these compounds and symmetrical peaks are obtained with it. Because of its relatively poor column efficiency compared to diatomite supports, Chromosorb T is recommended only when its highly inert surface is required.

Chromosorb W

Chromosorb W is a flux-calcined diatomite support prepared from the production of Johns-Manville Celite filter aids such as Celite 545. It is not identical to Celite 545 but is similar to it in performance and properties. Chromosorb W is white in color and friable compared to Chromosorb G. Its surface is relatively nonadsorptive and is used for the separation of polar compounds.

Although Chromosorb W is similar to Celite 545, it has several advantages over supports screened from Celite 545. The density of supports prepared from Celite 545 is heavier and can vary from batch to batch in density. Since the liquid phase is applied to the support on a weight basis, the amount of liquid phase in a column will also vary as the support varies. The special processing of Chromosorb W insures a light, uniform product.

TABLE 2—(Continued)
SUPPORT MATERIALS FOR GAS CHROMATOGRAPHY

Chromosorb 100 Series

CHROMOSORB 101 is a porous polymer resin specifically designed and developed by Johns-Manville for use as a column packing in gas chromatography. It has been synthesized to give fast, efficient separation of free fatty acids, glycols and alcohols.

Chromosorb 101 also separates other organic compounds, such as esters, ketones, aldehydes, ethers, and aliphatic and aromatic hydrocarbons. To a limited extent it can also separate light gases.

CHROMOSORB 102 is a high surface area resin which is size-graded for use as a chromatographic packing. It is prepared from Rohm and Haas Amberlite XAD-2 and is similar to the type of porous resin described by Doctor O. L. Hollis. See *Anal. Chem.* **38**, 309(1966). It is a solid adsorbent of the type used in gas-solid chromatography but because of its organic composition, its chromatographic characteristics are similar to that of a liquid phase in gas-liquid chromatography.

CHROMOSORB 103 is a polyaromatic porous resin, designed and developed by Johns-Manville in an effort to increase the applicability of porous polymers to gas chromatographic problems. Not only will it yield fast, efficient separations of alkyl and aryl amines but also of alcohols, aldehydes, ketones, and some light gases including ammonia.

CHROMOSORB R-6470-1 is a specially produced ultra-fine particle size diatomaceous silica developed for use in gas chromatography to coat the inside walls of capillary columns.

Produced from flux-calcined Celite® diatomaceous silica, Chromasorb R-6470-1 has a surface area of approximately 5–6 sq. meters per gram. It has a predominant particle size of 1–4 microns and retains the typical Celite diatom structure and purity of Chromosorb W.

TREATMENTS

Nonacid Washed (NAW)

All of the Chromosorb supports prepared from diatomite (Chromosorb A, G, P and W) are available in an untreated form referred to as nonacid washed (NAW).

Acid Washed (AW)

Chromosorb G, W and P are available with the acid washed (AW) treatment. Hydrochloric acid is used for the treatment and the support is then washed to near neutral with deionized water. Each production batch is analyzed for residual iron to insure uniformity. The acid-washing operation removes mineral impurities from the support surface and reduces surface activity.

Acid Washed-Dimethyldichlorosilane Treated (AW-DMCS)

Chromosorb G, W and P are available with the combined acid washed and DMCS treatment. The DMCS treatment converts the surface silanol group to silyl ethers. The combined treatment greatly reduces surface activity of the support and reduces tailing to a considerable degree. The AW-DMCS treatment gives the most inert surface for these three types of Chromosorb. Each production batch is performance tested to insure uniformity. The Chromosorb W AW-DMCS is listed as suitable for gas chromatography in the U.S. Pharmacopeia XVII, p. 1038.

AW-DMCS-High Performance or "HP"

The "HP" grade has been developed for use with steroids where the highest possible inertness is required. It is unique in that only a very short conditioning time is needed before the column is put into use. Both the Chromosorb W and G are available in the "HP" grade. Each production batch is performance tested with cholesterol to insure product uniformity.

Hexamethyldisilazane (HMDS)

Chromosorb P and W are available with the HMDS treatment on nonacid-washed supports. The HMDS treatment deactivates the support by conversion of the surface silanol groups to silyl ethers. Tailing is considerably reduced by this method. The HMDS-treated Chromosorb P and W are not so inert as the AW-DMCS-treated forms but are useful where a high degree of deactivation is not required.

Preparative-scale Grades (30/60)

Chromosorb P, W and A (preparative grade 30/60) are low-cost supports developed for use in situations requiring large quantities of support where a precisely sized graded material is not necessary. The preparative grade (30/60) is roughly 30/60 mesh; however, it contains quantities of both oversized and undersized particles as well as some dust. The preparative grade (30/60) is sold in the nonacid-washed form (NAW) in 100-lb bulk units. Because of the nature of the particle size distribution of the product and the bulk quantities involved, the preparative grade (30/60) sells for considerably less than the regular NAW 30/60 mesh fractions.

NEWER SUPPORT MATERIALS

Three new column support materials are Chromosorb 104, W-H.P., and 105. Chromosorb 104 is a polyaromatic type porous polymer bead which shows very short retention times for paraffins but relatively longer retention times for polar compounds. Chromosorb W-H.P. diatomaceous silica support is a highly inert, silane-treated, acid-washed, flux-calcined diatomite support developed for the separation of biochemical compounds. Chromosorb 105 is a polyaromatic porous resin with intermediate polarity. It is stable to 250 °C with proper handling and provides efficient separation of aqueous mixtures containing formaldehyde, acetylene from lower hydrocarbons, and most gases and organic compounds in the boiling range up to 200 °C.

TABLE 2—(Continued)
SUPPORT MATERIALS FOR GAS CHROMATOGRAPHY

		Physical Properties				
Type	Source	Free fall	Packed	Sq m/g	Sq m/cc	pH
Chromosorb T	Fluorocarbon	0.42	0.49	7.8	—	—
Chromosorb G	Diatomite	0.47	0.58	0.5	0.29	8.5
Chromosorb W	Diatomite	0.18	0.24	1.0	0.29	8.5
Chromosorb A	Diatomite	0.40	0.48	2.7	1.3	7.1
Chromosorb P	Diatomite	0.38	0.47	4.0	1.88	6.5
Chromosorb 102	Resin	0.29	—	350.0	105.0	—

[Reprinted with permission from Bulletin FF-101C, Johns-Manville Products Corporation, 22 E. 40th St., New York City.]

GAS-CHROM SUPPORTS

GAS-CHROM S is prepared by carefully screening Celatom, a flux-calcined diatomaceous earth manufactured by Eagle-Picher Industries, Inc. It is a white granular solid with about 0.19 g/cc dry packed bulk density (in the 60/80 mesh size.)

GAS-CHROM A is GAS-CHROM S which has been acid washed and water rinsed to neutrality. All flux-calcined diatomaceous earth is basic in nature (because of the flux) so acid washing is employed to neutralize the Celatom. This treatment also removes iron and other acid-soluble minerals from the support surface.

GAS-CHROM P is made by base washing and water rinsing GAS-CHROM A until it is neutral. Base washing removes any organic contaminants which might be present in the flux-calcined diatomaceous earth.

GAS-CHROM Z is the result of treating GAS-CHROM A with dimethyldichlorosilane (DMCS). Supports prepared from diatomaceous earth contain active surface hydroxyl groups which will cause tailing of polar compounds. These active groups are chemically neutralized by reaction with DMCS.

GAS-CHROM Q is produced by treating GAS-CHROM P with dimethyldichlorosilane. This support is prepared in small batches and rigidly quality controlled by actual test in a gas chromatograph. The finished support is evaluated both as a 10% DC 200 packing and as a 3% QF-1 packing.

GAS-CHROM R is made by crushing Sil-O-Cel C22 Firebrick and screening into the various mesh sizes. Crushing causes the grains of firebrick to be coated with a layer of microfine dust particles. This layer of dust is removed by careful washing with water. Further treatment of GAS-CHROM R produces the remaining supports in the series: GAS-CHROM RA by acid washing GAS-CHROM R and water rinsing to neutrality, GAS-CHROM RP by base washing GAS-CHROM RA and water rinsing to neutrality, and GAS-CHROM RZ by treating GAS-CHROM RA with dimethyldichlorosilane.

[Reprinted with permission from Catalog No. 13, Applied Science Laboratories, State College, Pennsylvania.]

ANALABS SUPPORTS

Anakrom U (untreated)

Anakrom U contains trace amounts of aluminum, iron, magnesium and calcium. It should be used only in those applications where these cations will not interact with either the liquid phase or sample being analyzed.

Anakrom A (acid washed)

Anakrom A is treated with concentrated HCl to remove the trace elements present in Anakrom U, then thoroughly washed with deionized water. Great care is taken to remove all residual water by drying at elevated temperatures for six hours. The material is then classified into close particle sizes, and the drying cycle is repeated. Anakrom A is an excellent general-purpose solid support.

Anakrom AB (acid and alcoholic base washed)

Anakrom AB is prepared in a similar manner to Anakrom A, except that following thorough washing with deionized water, it is treated with alcoholic KOH. The base is then removed by appropriate washing procedures. Like Anakrom A, Anakrom AB is also a superb general-purpose support. Because of the alcoholic base treatment, however, it reduces tailing phenomena which may occur in chromatographic analysis of very polar substances such as amines and hydroxy acids.

Anakrom ABS (acid, alcoholic base washed, and silanized)

Anakrom ABS, a silanized version of Anakrom AB, is today regarded by many expert chromatographers as the finest quality, all-purpose solid support available commercially. After its treatment with DMCS, residual HCl is removed by washing with methanol. The subsequent silanizing process yields a nonreactive, repellent support that greatly diminishes all types of undesirable tailing effects.

Anakrom AS (acid washed and silanized)

Anakrom AS is a silanized version of Anakrom A and is silanized under the same exacting conditions as Anakrom ABS.

TABLE 2—(Continued)
SUPPORT MATERIALS FOR GAS CHROMATOGRAPHY

Anakrom SD (silanized and deactivated)

Anakrom SD is prepared by a special process that is entirely unlike that which is utilized in the manufacture of any other support known. It is made by specially combining different methods of deactivation, including acid washing, chemical deactivation and DMCS treatment.

Anakrom Q

Anakrom Q is a high quality support which has been specially acid washed and treated with DMCS in such a way as to make it suitable for steroid and pesticide work.

Anakrom C22

Prepared from C_{22} firebrick.

Anakrom 545

Prepared from Celite 545.

Anaport KEL-F 300LD

A fluorine-containing polymer.

Anaport TEE SIX

Made from tetrafluoroethylene.

Anaport glass beads

Supplied regular or silicone treated.

Anaprep

A preparative scale diatomaceous earth support.

Cera Beads

A spherical, ceramic support material made from a high alumina sodium-lime-silica glass.

Typical properties of Anakrom U, A, AB, ABS, AS, Q, SD

Typical properties	
Color	white
Type	flux calcined
Free fall density, gms/cc	0.18–0.21
Specific gravity	2.33
Packed column density* vibrated	
gms/cc	0.26–0.35
gms/ft. of ¼ O.D. × .035 wall tubing	2.0–2.2
pH	8–9.5

Typical chemical analysis, weight %	
Moisture and ignition loss	nil
SiO_2	88.79
Al_2O_3	4.58
Fe_2O_3	1.50
CaO	1.16
MgO	0.17
Other oxides	3.8

Typical Properties of Anakrom P and Anakrom PA

Typical properties	
Color	salmon pink
Type	calcined
Free fall density, gms/cc	0.34–0.39
Specific gravity	1.87
Packed column density* vibrated	
gms/cc	0.55–0.65
gms/ft. of ¼ O.D. × .035 wall tubing	3.2–3.4
pH	5.5–6.5

Typical chemical analysis, weight %	
Moisture and ignition loss	0.4
SiO_2	92.0
Al_2O_3	5.0
Fe_2O_3	1.8
CaO	0.2
MgO	0.3
Other oxides	0.3

* Exact density varies inversely with increasing particle size.

Analabs supports are available in a wide variety of 10 mesh cuts.

[Reprinted with permission from the 1969 Analabs Inc. catalog, North Haven, Conn., from which these products are available.]

SUPPORTS FROM WATERS ASSOCIATES

A. Porapak

PORAPAK is used for performing a variety of difficult separations. These porous polymer beads provide sharp symmetrical peaks and low retention volumes for polar materials such as water, alcohols, acids, and glycols. PORAPAK has the partition properties of a highly extended liquid without the problems of support polarity, liquid phase volatility, or freezing point which normally restrict gas liquid chromatography.

TABLE 2—(Continued)
SUPPORT MATERIALS FOR GAS CHROMATOGRAPHY

Eight types of PORAPAK are provided in a broad range of mesh sizes, each with significantly different functionality and retention properties. In order of increasing polarity (water eluting later), the eight PORAPAKS are P, P-S, Q, Q-S, R, S, N, and T. The P-S and Q-S packings are silane-treated PORAPAK P and Q, respectively, and are similar in relative retention characteristics to the parent PORAPAK. Silanization virtually eliminates peak tailing and ghosting with very polar materials.

PORAPAK P—Least polar; separates a wide variety of carbonyl compounds; stable to 250 °C.

PORAPAK P-S—Surface silanized version of "P" eliminates tailing and ghosting; particularly effective for separating aldehydes and glycols; stable to 250 °C.

PORAPAK Q—Most widely used; hydrocarbon structure; particularly effective for separating aliphatic hydrocarbons; stable to 250 °C.

PORAPAK Q-S—Surface silanized version of "Q"; separates organic acids and other polar compounds without tailing; stable to 250 °C.

PORAPAK R—Moderate polarity; long retention and good resolution for ethers; stable to 250 °C.

PORAPAK S—Excellent for separating normal and branched alcohols; stable to 250 °C

PORAPAK N—Separates ammonia in aqueous streams, and acetylene from other C_2 hydrocarbons; exhibits high water retention; stable to 190 °C.

PORAPAK T—Highest polarity and greatest water retention of the PORAPAK series for determining formaldehyde in aqueous samples; stable to 190 °C.

PORAPAK is used for all gases and most compounds in the moderate boiling range (up to 250 °C) with some applications for compounds boiling as high as 350 °C. Using temperature programming, wide boiling range mixtures can be analyzed with a single column. Relative retention data of the eight types of PORAPAKS at 30 °C and 175 °C are listed in the following tables.

Relative Retention of Porapak Column Packings

1 meter × 2.3mm I.D. Temp = 30 °C Flow rate = 25 ml/min Detector = TC at 150 ma

Sample	P	P-S	Q	Q-S	R	S	N	T
Oxygen	0.426	0.484	0.153	0.176	0.204	0.180	0.162	0.154
Nitrogen	0.426	0.484	0.153	0.176	0.204	0.180	0.162	0.154
Argon	0.426	0.484	0.153	0.176	0.204	0.180	0.162	0.154
Carbon monoxide	0.426	0.484	0.153	0.176	0.231	0.180	0.162	0.154
Nitric oxide	0.500	0.500	0.187	0.213	0.238	0.192	0.189	0.180
Methane	0.486	0.500	0.231	0.273	0.279	0.279	0.236	0.256
Nitrogen dioxide	0.647	0.532	0.374	0.432	0.361	0.192	0.189	0.190
Carbon dioxide	0.662	0.694	0.409	0.420	0.517	0.483	0.602	0.820
Nitrous oxide	0.780	0.806	0.478	0.534	0.565	0.593	0.623	0.790
Acetylene	0.986	1.02	0.596	0.705	1.00	0.884	1.33	1.92
Ethylene	0.838	0.887	0.720	0.739	0.776	0.744	0.812	0.857
Ammonia	1.22	1.36	0.950	0.636	1.62	1.30	1.26	1.76
Ethane	1.00 (0.535 min)	1.00 (0.488 min)	1.00 (1.60 min)	1.00 (1.39 min)	1.00 (1.16 min)	1.00 (1.36 min)	1.00 (1.50 min)	1.00 (1.54 min)
Water	2.44	2.85	1.33	1.17	6.75	5.44	9.14	15.6
Carbonyl sulfide	2.13	2.21	2.08	2.31	2.44	2.55	2.70	3.06
Difluoroethane	2.15	2.47	2.44	2.77	3.42	3.40	5.99	7.75
Chlorodifluoromethane	2.27	2.50	2.70	2.40	4.83	4.12	7.31	9.00
Sulfur dioxide	4.66	4.52	3.67	3.65	9.35	17.5	11.0	14.6
Methyl chloride	3.90	4.57	3.85	3.99	4.94	5.14	6.51	7.74
Propylene	2.59	2.06	4.02	3.84	3.82	3.96	4.76	4.72
Propane	2.59	2.06	4.52	4.51	4.31	4.39	4.76	4.72
Dichlorodifluoroethane	2.65	3.10	4.64	5.03	4.93	5.24	6.52	6.67
Ethylene oxide	8.24	9.67	7.94	8.46	10.8	10.9	16.5	22.1
Chlorodifluoroethane	3.78	5.12	9.65	8.08	10.1	10.1	—	—
Dichlorotetrafluoroethane	19.5	—	16.1	16.8	16.5	17.1	—	—

TABLE 2—(Continued)
SUPPORT MATERIALS FOR GAS CHROMATOGRAPHY

Relative Retention of Porapak Column Packings

1 meter × 2.2 mm I.D. column Temp = 175 °C Flow rate = 25 ml/min Detector = FID (except TC for water)

Sample	P	P-S	Q	Q-S	R	S	N	T
Water	0.467	0.408	0.056	0.082	0.131	0.109	0.135	0.188
Methanol	0.542	0.475	0.127	0.134	0.180	0.168	1.193	0.244
Formaldehyde	0.517	0.475	0.134	0.127	0.190	0.172	0.195	0.172
Acetaldehyde	0.542	0.475	0.169	0.170	0.190	0.187	0.222	0.259
Ethanol	0.666	0.592	0.218	0.230	0.307	0.291	0.367	0.462
Formic acid	0.717	0.717	0.225	0.189	0.368	0.386	0.819	0.187
Acetonitrile	0.934	0.792	0.287	0.286	0.358	0.348	0.497	0.670
Propylene oxide	0.784	0.666	0.314	0.327	0.336	0.329	0.406	0.444
Propionaldehyde	0.808	0.750	0.338	0.343	0.376	0.383	0.476	0.543
Acetone	0.850	0.758	0.343	0.349	0.390	0.391	0.544	0.666
Isopropanol	—	—	0.351	—	—	—	—	—
Methylene chloride	0.950	0.960	0.373	0.403	0.407	0.438	0.510	0.545
Acrylonitrile	1.00	0.892	0.388	0.404	0.474	0.475	0.660	0.853
Acetic acid	1.03	0.926	0.419	0.379	1.31	1.91	1.34	1.90
Methyl acetate	0.883	0.800	0.419	0.434	0.445	0.438	0.598	0.735
Propanol	0.984	0.883	0.479	0.478	0.660	0.641	0.862	1.06
Pentane	0.684	0.666	0.501	0.536	0.481	0.469	0.490	0.467
Isobutyraldehyde	1.05	0.934	0.598	0.623	0.670	0.676	0.905	1.04
Butyraldehyde	1.22	1.10	0.711	0.710	0.776	0.802	1.09	1.28
2-Butanone	1.26	1.18	0.734	0.730	0.820	0.846	1.20	1.41
Chloroform	1.35	1.28	0.753	0.718	0.854	0.791	0.966	1.24
Ethyl acetate	1.22	1.13	0.812	0.852	0.864	0.862	1.20	1.44
Isobutanol	1.36	1.26	0.902	0.900	1.24	1.21	1.76	2.07
Propionic acid	1.67	1.53	0.909	0.843	—	—	—	4.27
Hexane	1.00 (0.945 min)	1.00 (0.944 min)	1.00 (4.93 min)	1.00 (5.50 min)	1.00 (4.67 min)	1.00 (4.97 min)	1.00 (6.94 min)	1.00 (4.84 min)
Butanol	1.58	1.48	1.07	1.07	1.47	1.46	2.08	2.50
Benzene	1.86	1.69	1.16	1.16	1.24	1.25	1.42	1.67
Carbon tetrachloride	1.53	1.53	1.16	1.14	1.07	1.07	1.17	1.34
Isopropyl acetate	1.46	1.47	1.33	1.43	3.48	1.44	2.04	2.38
Propyl acetate	1.83	1.85	1.72	1.83	4.20	1.83	2.64	3.19
Isopentanol	2.27	2.29	2.10	2.09	2.91	2.85	4.25	5.10
Heptane	1.58	1.64	2.28	2.28	2.18	2.05	2.18	2.20
Pentanol	2.63	2.61	2.46	2.46	3.38	3.35	4.93	5.86
Toluene	3.18	2.92	2.71	2.69	2.43	2.85	3.24	3.65

B. Durapak

A Series of Chromatographic Packings with Chemically-Bonded Liquid Phases

Permanently Bonded Functional Group

DURAPAK's functional activity is chemically bonded to the core material, its vapor pressure is zero and it does not bleed. The chemical bond eliminates base line drift up to the decomposition temperature of the functional group.

Speeds of Analysis up to 50 Plates/Second

DURAPAK permits analysis speeds otherwise attainable only with capillary columns.

High Efficiency Separations

Columns of 1000 plates per foot and over are possible using DURAPAK.

Better Reproducibility Due to Permanent Functional Group

The thickness and density of the bonded functional groups is controlled in the manufacturing process. Reproduction of analysis is excellent.

Greater Loadability

The orientation and density of the bonded functional groups permit high sample loads without peak distortion. This permits preparative analytical work with mass, infrared, or ultraviolet spectrometry.

TABLE 2—(Continued)
SUPPORT MATERIALS FOR GAS CHROMATOGRAPHY

High Relative Retensions

DURAPAK provides higher relative retention values than conventional liquid-coated materials. Uniform coating and absence of pooling yield high k' (up to 50) peaks that do not tail or skew.

Sharp Symmetrical Peaks With Nonpolar and Polar Materials

Unlike conventional liquid-coated packings, DURAPAK gives symmetrical peaks for polar as well as nonpolar compounds. The uniformity of the bonded coating and the absence of "pooling" on the surface of the support material provide the mechanism necessary for achieving sharp, symmetrical peaks.

Separation Efficiencies Independent of Temperature, Retention Time, Sample Functionality and Sample Size

The geometry of the functional group bonded to the core material is responsible for DURAPAK's unique qualities of being independent of temperature, sample size, retention time, and sample functionality—historical limiting factors of the liquid-coated packing for GC. Temperatures can be programmed with no bleed of bonded phase below the critical bonding temperature. Paraffins, aromatics, oxygenated and chlorinated compounds are separated on DURAPAK without difficulty.

Useful Temperature Range

DURAPAK should not be exposed to temperatures in excess of those listed in the table. Thermal degradation of the functional group bonded to the core materials may occur if the temperature levels are excceded.

Column Packing

DURAPAK is a free-flowing, rigid solid which may be packed into gas chromatographic columns using the same column packing techniques used for conventional GC packings.

Type	Particle size (mesh)	Polarity	Temperature limits (°C)	
			Single column temperature programming	Isothermal or dual column operation
OPN/Porasil C	80–100	Medium	135	150
Carbowax 400/Porasil C[a]	100–120	Nonpolar	150	175
***n*-octane/Porasil C**	120–150	Polar	160	175
Carbowax 400/Porasil S	80–100	Nonpolar	200	230
Phenyl isocyanate/Porasil C	80–100	Polar	60	60
Carbowax 4000/Porasil S	80–100	Polar	200	230

[a] Low k' Durapak of this type is also available.

C. Porasil[1]

PORASIL is a unique siliceous material with applications throughout the field of chromatography. It offers the advantages of controlled pore size, controlled surface area, and chemical inertness.

Porasil Uncoated

PORASIL can be used as a gas-solid packing to separate many chemical mixtures. Increasing pore size (decreasing surface area) decreases the retention of volatile materials. Type A is the most active with the longest retention and Type F the least active with the shortest retention. Selection of the proper type of PORASIL depends upon the selectivity desired and on the boiling point of the materials to be separated. Gases are usually separated on Types A and B, moderate boiling materials on Types C and D, and very high boiling materials on Types E and F.

Porasil With Liquid Coatings

PORASIL can be used as support in gas-liquid chromatography. Loadings from 1% to 40% with conventional liquids such as SE-30, dinonyl phthalate, DEGS, etc., can be made on PORASIL. Polar liquid coatings reduce tailing. The amount of modifier required to reduce tailing depends on the type of liquid coating, the type of PORASIL, and the material being separated. The lower the surface area of PORASIL the less modifier needed. PORASIL has less surface activity than other gas-solid packings and, therefore, requires less surface modification.

Column Packing Techniques

The spherical porous silica beads may be packed into gas chromatography columns using the same techniques as used with conventional packing materials. The particles do not crush or fracture.

Strength: PORASIL beads are dry-free-flowing rigid solids. They are easily handled and packed into columns.

Stability: PORASIL is inert and is not subject to deterioration at high temperatures.

Porosity and surface area: The pore size and surface area of each grade of PORASIL is controlled. Chromatographic separations can be optimized by proper choice of pore size and surface area.

Spherical shape and particle size: The spherical shape of Porasil combined with narrow particle size ranges give reproducible efficient columns with minimum pressure drop.

[1] Porasil is manufactured by Pechiney-St-Gobain.

TABLE 2—(Continued)
SUPPORT MATERIALS FOR GAS CHROMATOGRAPHY

SELECTED BIBLIOGRAPHY

Devries, A. J. and M. LePage. Sur la Determination de la Repartition Moleculaire des Polymers au Moyen de la Chromatographie sur Gel, Proceedings, Third International Symposium GPC, Geneva, May 1966.

Guillemin, C. L., LePage, M., deVries, A. J., and R. Beau. A New Support for Gas-Solid Chromatography: The Porous Silica Bead, Sixth International Symposium on Gas Chromatography, Rome, September 1966.

Guillemin, C. L., LePage, M., Beau, R., and A. J. deVries. Packing Material for Chromatographic Columns, *Anal. Chem.*, Vol. **32** (8), 940–945 (1967).

Cadogan, D. F. and D. T. Sawyer. Gas–Solid Chromatography Using Various Thermally Activated and Chemically Modified Silicas. *Anal. Chem.*, **42**, (2), 19 (1970).

Gas Grades of Porasil

Porasil type	Surface area (m^2/g)	Pore diameter (Angstroms)	Particle size (mesh)
A	350–500	<100	80–100
A			100–150
B	125–250	100–200	80–100
B			100–150
C	50–100	200–400	80–100
C			100–150
D	25–45	400–800	80–100
D			100–150
E	10–20	800–1500	80–100
E			100–150
F	2–6	>1500	80–100
F			100–150

D. Alumina

Two Woelm Aluminas for gas chromatography (GSC-120 and GSC-121) are particularly well suited for the separation of hydrocarbons. GSC-120 is used to separate hydrocarbons from C_1 to C_5. GSC-121 has been deactivated by an alkali treatment and is optimized for the separation of longer chain hydrocarbons such as gasoline fractions.

E. Corning Etched Surface Glass Beads

Corning etched beads are solid glass beads with a textured surface which permits liquid loadings up to 0.5% without "pooling". This packing is optimized for high temperature separations where low liquid loaded packings are necessary for the elution of high molecular weight materials in a minimum time.

Corning Textured Glass Bead Supports (GLC 100 and 110)

Type	Mesh	Type	Mesh
Regular	60/80	Regular	100/120
DMCS*	60/80	DMCS*	100/120
Regular	80/100	Regular	120/140
DMCS*	80/100	DMCS*	120/140

* DMCS = dimethyldichlorosilane treated.

SELECTED BIBLIOGRAPHY

1. Filbert, A. M. and M. L. Hair, Glass Beads as a Chromatographic Support Material, *J. Gas Chromatogr.*, **6**, 150 (1968).
2. Filbert, A. M. and M. L. Hair, Glass Beads as a Chromatographic Support Material (Part II), Etched Glass Beads, *J. Gas Chromatogr.*, **6**, 218 (1968).
3. MacDonnell, H. L. and D. L. Eaton, Thermal Decomposition of Endrin as a Measure of Surface Activity of Gas Chromatographic Support Media, *Anal. Chem.*, **40**, 1453 (1968).

[Material above reprinted from 1970 Waters Associates Chromatography Catalog.]

TABLE 2—(Continued)
SUPPORT MATERIALS FOR GAS CHROMATOGRAPHY

SUPELCOPORT

A high quality support from Supelco, Inc., recommended for steroids, pesticides, bile acids, or any application requiring a high degree of inertness.

SUPELCOPORT is an acid washed, silane treated diatomite support prepared from the Johns-Manville Chromosorb W. A special procedure is used to rid the support of fine cutting dust down to a minimum. Little or no conditioning of the support is required once it is coated. When using the high temperature phases, such as PPE-20, OV-1, etc, the column can be used within an hour after it is put into the chromatograph.

Supelcoport is available in 60–80, 80–100 and 100–120 mesh.

Czechoslovak Supports

Chromaton N—a white diatomaceous earth support, also available in acid-washed and DMCS- or HMDS-treated versions.

Chezasorb—a pink diatomaceous earth support of the firebrick type, also available in AW- and AW-HMDS versions.

TABLE 3
SELECTED COMMERCIAL SOURCES OF ADSORBENTS FOR LIQUID COLUMN CHROMATOGRAPHY

1. Bio-Rad Laboratories, Richmond, California

Bio-Gel HT (hydroxyapatite in $0.001M$ Na_2PO_4 buffer).
Bio-Gel HTP (hydroxyapatite powder).
Calcium phosphate gel (in $0.001M$ Na_2PO_4 buffer).
Bio-Sil A (silicic acid, 100–200 mesh, 200–325 mesh, or 20–44 μ).
Bio-Sil CW (chloroform washed).
Bio-Sil HA (for lipid chromatography).
Alumina (all activity I; neutral (AG 7), basic (AG 10), and acidic (AG 4) are available; 100–200 or minus 200 mesh).
Alumina Cγ gel (for batch purification of proteins, enzymes, viruses).

2. H. Reeve Angel and Co., Clifton, New Jersey

Silica gel SG 31: a general purpose silica gel (100–200 mesh).
SG 32: a highly purified, low iron product (100–200 mesh).
SG 33: similar to SG 31 with a wider particle size range (28–200 mesh).

Cellulose Powder CF 1: Coarse fibrous powder, high purity, for rapid separations.
CF 2: Same as CF 1, but with a higher ash content.
CF 11: Similar to CF 1, but with finer fibrous particles, ashless.
CF 12: Finer particle form of CF 2.
CC 31: Very pure microgranular powder (100–200 mesh), for high resolution separations.

3. Schleicher and Schuell Co., Keene, New Hampshire

Cellulose powder S and S No. 286: for general column chromatography.
No. 389: for closely packed columns (100–200 mesh).
No. 2200: same as No. 389 but highly purified.
No. 124/6ac: acetylated linters powder containing ca. 6% CH_3COO.
No. 124/21ac: contains 21% CH_3COO.
No. 124/45ac: contains 45% CH_3COO.

4. Brinkmann Instruments, Westbury, New York

A. *E. Merck sorbents*
Aluminum oxide, acidic, Class I/II.
Aluminum oxide, basic, Class I/II.
Aluminum oxide, neutral, Class I/II.
Aluminum oxide, Brockmann, Class II/III.
Aluminum oxide, basic, type-E, Class I (recommended for chlorinated pesticides).
Silica gel, less than 0.08 mm.
Silica gel, 0.2 to 0.5 mm.
Silica gel, 0.05 to 0.2 mm.
Silica gel, 0.05 to 0.2 mm, specially purified.
Silica gel, coarse, for FIA (recommended for hydrocarbons).
Silica gel, fine, for FIA.
Kieselguhr (celite).
PEI-Cellulose.

B. *Cellulose powders (from Machery-Nagel and Co., Duren)*
MN 100: normal powder.
MN 2100: acid washed powder.
MN 2100 ff: acid washed and fat free.
MN 2100 WA: acid washed and impregnated with silicone oil.
MN 2200: acid washed linters.
MN 2200 ff: acid washed and fat free.
MN 2200 APATIT-50: calcium hydroxyapatite-cellulose.
MN 2100 AC: acid washed and acetylated (10%, 20%, 30% or 40% available).
MN 2100 CdS: impregnated with CdS (3%, 4% or 8%).

C. *MN-Polyamide powders*
CC 66: –0.07 mm, composed of Nylon 66.
CC 6: –0.07 mm, composed of Perlon.
CC 6: –0.16 mm, composed of Perlon.
CC 6-AC: –0.16 mm, composed of acetylated Perlon.

TABLE 3—(Continued)

SELECTED COMMERCIAL SOURCES OF ADSORBENTS FOR LIQUID COLUMN CHROMATOGRAPHY

5. Waters Associates, Framingham, Mass.

A. *Corasil*

With CORASIL liquid chromatography packing, efficiencies as high as 5,000 plates per meter and 40 plates per second are obtainable. CORASIL consists of a solid glass core with a porous silica surface and may be used as an adsorbent in liquid-solid chromatography, or as the support in liquid partition chromatography. The unique combination of solid core and thin porous surface results in the lowest mass transfer coefficient of all packing materials available. With CORASIL, liquid chromatography separations are often faster than with gas chromatography.

Two grades of CORASIL are available—single layer CORASIL I, and CORASIL II with double thickness layer. The double layer gives added capacity needed in tougher separations. Both are 37–50 microns particle size.

For Liquid–Solid Separations

CORASIL is used as an adsorbent for liquid–solid separations and is handled similar to any other adsorbent packing material. CORASIL is used with all types of solvents and solvent combinations, as well as with gradient systems.

The surface of the CORASIL bead must be activated to achieve maximum separation effectiveness. Highest surface activity is obtained by heating the CORASIL overnight at 110 °C. Where required, temporary reduction in surface activity may be achieved by adding small amounts of water (up to 2% by weight) to the packing. Irreversible reduction in surface activity may be achieved by heating CORASIL overnight at 300–400 °C.

For Liquid–Liquid Separations

Liquid coatings are applied to CORASIL in the conventional manner—i.e., the liquid phase to be coated is dissolved in a volatile solvent, slurried with the CORASIL beads and excess solvent removed by evaporation. For maximum effectiveness, the liquid load level on CORASIL I should be approximately 1%. The maximum liquid load level on CORASIL II should be approximately 2%. Exceeding these recommended liquid load limits may cause pooling of the stationary phase with a consequent loss in column efficiency. To ensure equilibrium in the chromatographic system, solvents must be saturated with the same liquid phase as is coated on the CORASIL beads. Pre-saturator columns are also required to prevent stripping of the liquid phase from the column packing. Pre-saturator columns should be positioned before the injection port.

Instrumentation Requirements

To optimize the effectiveness of the CORASIL packings, it is essential to employ low dead volume chromatographs (i.e., low dead volume and low peak width spreading in the total system which includes injection port, transport, tubing, columns, and detectors). Highest column efficiencies may be obtained by using 1.0 to 4.0 mm I.D. columns. With columns and chromatographs so selected, CORASIL can give up to 5000 plates/meter and efficiencies of 40 plates/second for early eluting peaks with low k'.

Column Packing Techniques

CORASIL is a dry, free-flowing, rigid solid which may be packed in chromatographic columns employing the same basic packing techniques as used with conventional LC column packings. CORASIL will not crush or fracture, and columns may be packed by vibration or tapping to cause the particles to settle tightly. The bulk density of CORASIL is approximately 1 gram/ml.

B. *LC Durapak*

Provides high speed separations where the functional group separating power of liquid-liquid chromatography is combined with the non-bleed properties of liquid-solid chromatography. DURAPAK's functional activity is chemically bonded to the core material. This bonding eliminates the problems of liquid-liquid chromatography which require a pre-saturator column and elaborate precautions to reduce. column bleed. Due to the nature of the bond, DURAPAK is not recommended for use in water, acids, bases and low boiling alcohols. Columns of 1,000 plates per foot and over are possible using DURAPAK.

Available grades:	OPN/Porasil C	37–75μ
	Carbowax 400/Porasil C	37–75μ
	n-Octane/Porasil C	75–125μ
	Carbowax 400/Corasil	37–50μ

TABLE 3—(Continued)
SELECTED COMMERCIAL SOURCES OF ADSORBENTS FOR LIQUID COLUMN CHROMATOGRAPHY

C. *Woelm Adsorbents*

Column Adsorbent Properties

Woelm Grade	Brockmann activity	Approx. pH	Methylene blue exchange	Orange GG exchange	Water soluble matter	Bulk density g/ml	Fluorescent indicator content	Particle size	BET surface m^2/g		
100	I	10	+	0	<0.2	0.9	0	70–290 mesh 50–200μ (100–102)	—	basic	Alumina
101	I	7.5	0	0	<0.2	0.9	0		—	neutral	
102	I	4	0	+	<0.4	0.9	0		—	acid	
103	II to III	7.5	0	0	<0.2	0.9	0.5	70–150 mesh 100–200μ	—	neutral	
104	Super II	10	+	0	<0.2	0.9	0	70–290 mesh 50–210μ (104–107)	200	basic	
105	Super I	7.5	0	0	<0.2	0.9	0		200	neutral	
106	Super I	4	0	+	<0.4	0.9	0		200	acid	
107	II to III	10	+	0	<0.2	0.9	0		—	basic	
120	NA	Basic	NA	NA	NA	1.0	0	70–110 mesh 140–210μ (120–121)	—	basic	
121	NA	Basic	NA	NA	NA	1.0	0		—	basic	
200	I	1.0	+	0	<0.2	0.7	0	60–150 mesh 100–250μ	—	adsorption	Silica gel
201	NA	7.0	+	0	<0.2	0.7	0	120–290 mesh 50–125μ	—	partition	
202	II to III	7.0	+	0	<0.2	0.7	0.5	60–150 mesh 100–250μ	—	dry column	
203	—	7.0	+	0	<0.2	0.7	0	190 mesh Less than 80μ	—	partition	
204	—	7.0	+	0	<0.2	0.7	0	70–290 mesh 50–200μ	—	adsorption	
300	I	9.0	NA	NA	<0.2	0.3	0	50–150 mesh 100–300μ (300–400)	—	magnesium silicate	
400	NA	7.0	NA	NA	<0.3	0.25	0		—	polyamide	
500	NA	NA	NA	NA	NA	0.4	0	—	—	acetyl cellulose	

[The above material is reprinted from Waters Associates 1970 Chromatography Catalog.]

D. *Aquapak, Poragel, Porasil*—see Table 4

6. **Scientific Glass Apparatus Co., Bloomfield, New Jersey**
SilicAR (Mallinckrodt) chromatographic grades of silicic acid.
CC-4, 100–200 mesh, approx. pH = 4.
CC-4, 200–325 mesh.
CC-7, 100–200 mesh, approx. pH = 7.
CC-7, 200–325 mesh.

7. **Applied Science Laboratories, Inc., State College, Pennsylvania**
Adsorbosil-CAB: Silica gel adsorbent useful for the purification of lipids.
Adsorbosil-CABN: Adsorbosil-CAB impregnated with 25% $AgNO_3$; for separations based on varying degrees of carbon-chain saturation and on *cis-trans* isomerism.
(Available in mesh size ranges of 30–60 to 200–250).
Reversil-1 (30–60 mesh), -2 (60–100 mesh), and -4 (100–140 mesh):
Hydrophobic support prepared by treating Adsorbosil with dimethyldichlorosilane for reversed-phase separations.

8. **Rohm and Haas Co., Philadelphia, Pennsylvania**
Amberlite XAD-1, -2 and -4: Stable nonionic macroreticular resins composed of polystyrene crosslinked with polystyrene. They have uniform pore size distribution and high surface area, and are designed to adsorb water-soluble organic compounds.

TABLE 4
COLUMN PACKINGS FOR GEL PERMEATION AND FILTRATION CHROMATOGRAPHY

From Waters Associates

1. Corning CPG-10 controlled porosity glass.
   Corning Controlled Porosity Glass (CPG) packings are porous granules that have closely controlled pore size. Each particle consists of a network of interconnecting pores of approximately the same size. CPG packing density averages between .3 and .5 grams per ml depending upon the specific pore size in percent pore volume. Pore volume is .7 ml per gram or greater.
   CPG is a rigid, insoluble packing not affected by changes in the solvent system. CPG can be easily cleaned, sterilized and reused. Pore size and column depth dimensions are stable, independent of solvent, and unaffected by pressure. Particles are attacked by strong bases and HF, but are not affected by hot nitric acid.

Pore size Angstroms	Particle size range (microns)	Approximate exclusion limits and operating range[a]
75	37–75	
75	75–125	200–28,000
125	37–75	
125	75–125	520–47,000
175	37–75	
175	75–125	1,300–70,000
240	37–75	
240	75–125	2,300–97,000
370	37–75	
370	75–125	4,800–170,000
700	37–75	
700	75–125	17,000–360,000
1250	37–75	
1250	75–125	41,000–600,000
2000	37–75	
2000	75–125	120,000–1,200,000

[a] For dextran polymers in water, molecular weight.

2. Aquapak A-440—lightly sulfonated crosslinked polystyrene with molecular weight exclusion of 100,000. Available in a 37–75 μ particle-size range.

3. Poragel crosslinked polystyrene packings for small molecule size separations in organic solvents.

MW range for polystyrene in THF	
Poragel 60 Å	100–2400
Poragel 100 Å	100–4000
Poragel 200 Å	100–8000
Poragel 500 Å	100–20,000

   The following are Poragels with different functional groups permanently attached to polystyrene for use in liquid adsorption chromatography.
   Poragel PS—contains an aryl nitrogen molecule
   Poragel PR—aryl oxygen and nitrogen
   Poragel PN—intermediate number of hydroxyl groups and keto groups
   Poragel PT—more hydroxyl and keto groups than the PN.

   All Poragel P packings have an exclusion limit of 150,000 mw.
   Poragel packings are available in the following particle-size ranges: < 37 μ; 37–75 μ; 75–125 μ.
   Poragel is also available in pre-packed columns; Styragel polystyrene beads are now available only in packed columns.

4. Porasil porous silica beads.

TABLE 4—(Continued)
COLUMN PACKINGS FOR GEL PERMEATION AND FILTRATION CHROMATOGRAPHY

Liquid Grades of Porasil

Type*	Average pore diameter (Angstroms)	Surface area (m^2/g)	Particle size range (microns)
A (60)	< 100	350–500	37–75
A (60)			75–125
B (250)	100–200	125–250	37–75
B (250)			75–125
C (400)	200–400	50–100	37–75
C (400)			75–125
D (1000)	400–800	25–45	37–75
D (1000)			75–125
E (1500)	800–1500	10–20	37–75
E (1500)			75–125
F (2000+)	> 1500	2–6	37–75
F (2000+)			75–175
Porasil T	150	300	15–25
Porasil T	150	300	25–37
Porasil T	150	300	37–50

Deactivated Porasil

Type*	Average pore diameter (Angstroms)	Particle size range (microns)
AX (60X)	< 100	75–125
BX (250X)	100–200	75–125
CX (400X)	200–400	75–125
DX (1000X)	400–800	75–125
EX (1500X)	800–1500	75–125

* Parentheses refer to old designation.

5. EM Gel-Type SI.

EM Gel Type SI is used as:

1. A liquid-solid packing,
2. A liquid-liquid support packing,
3. An organic GPC packing,
4. An aqueous GPC packing.

EM Gel Type SI is available in three different pore size grades:

1. 150– 50,000 mw exclusion limit,
2. 500– 400,000 mw exclusion limit,
3. 1000–1,000,000 mw exclusion limit.

EM gels have been used for steroid separations and as a GPC column packing. The surface area of the EM gels, Type SI, are in reverse order of their pore sizes. EM Gel Type SI is a crushed porous silica bead and is available from Waters Associates in the United States and Canada. It is manufactured by E. Merck, Darmstadt, West Germany.

TABLE 4—(Continued)
COLUMN PACKINGS FOR GEL PERMEATION AND FILTRATION CHROMATOGRAPHY

BIBLIOGRAPHY ON EM GEL TYPE OR

1. Halpapp, H. and K., *J. Chromatogr.*, **33**, 80 (1968).

Type	Molecular weight exclusion limit (polystyrene in THF)	Mean pore diameter (Angstroms)	Particle size range (microns)
SI 150	50,000	150	37–75
SI 150	50,000	150	75–125
SI 500	400,000	500	37–75
SI 500	400,000	500	75–125
SI 1000	1,000,000	1000	37–75
SI 1000	1,000,000	1000	75–125

6. EM Gel-Type OR.
The EM Gel Type OR materials are semi-rigid "organic" packings for GPC. They are manufactured by E. Merck, Darmstadt, West Germany. The materials are a cross-linked polyvinyl acetate for molecular-size separations in organic solvents. The EM Gel Type OR materials give excellent separations of polystyrene, oligophenylenes, polyethylene glycols, and phenolic polymers. The materials are thermally stable to 100 °C and are extremely useful in alcohol solvents.

BIBLIOGRAPHY ON EM GEL TYPE SI

1. Heitz, W., *Makromolekulare Chemie*, **127**, 113 (1969).

Type	Molecular weight exclusion limit (polystyrene in THF)	Particle size (microns)	Swell factor (in THF)
OR 750	750*	20–55	1 : 2
OR 1,500	1,500	20–55	1 : 3
OR 5,000	5,000	20–55	1 : 4.5
OR 20,000	20,000	20–55	1 : 4

* The E. Merck materials are packaged on the basis of weight alone and will swell to slightly different volumes in different solvents (e.g. TYPE OR-750 25g (dry) = 50 cc (dry volume) = 100 cc (swollen in THF).

[The above information is reprinted from Waters Associates 1970 Chromatography Catalog.]

TABLE 4—(Continued)
COLUMN PACKINGS FOR GEL PERMEATION AND FILTRATION CHROMATOGRAPHY

From Bio-Rad Laboratories
1. **Bio-Gel polyacrylamide gels.**

	Exclusion limit	Operating range	Hydrated* bed vol. ml/g	Water* regain g/g	Flow† rates
Bio-Gel P-2, 50–100 Mesh					250
Bio-Gel P-2, 100–200 Mesh			3.8	1.5	150
Bio-Gel P-2, 200–400 Mesh	1,800	200–1,800			40
Bio-Gel P-2, –400 Mesh					
Bio-Gel P-4, 50–100 Mesh					225
Bio-Gel P-4, 100–200 Mesh			5.8	2.4	125
Bio-Gel P-4, 200–400 Mesh	4,000	800–4,000			40
Bio-Gel P-4, –400 Mesh					
Bio-Gel P-6, 50–100 Mesh					200
Bio-Gel P-6, 100–200 Mesh			8.8	3.7	110
Bio-Gel P-6, 200–400 Mesh	6,000	1,000–6,000			40
Bio-Gel P-6, –400 Mesh					
Bio-Gel P-10, 50–100 Mesh					200
Bio-Gel P-10, 100–200 Mesh			12.4	4.5	100
Bio-Gel P-10, 200–400 Mesh	20,000	1,500–20,000			35
Bio-Gel P-10, –400 Mesh		For thin layer chromatography			
Bio-Gel P-30, 50–100 Mesh					150
Bio-Gel P-30, 100–200 Mesh	40,000	2,500–40,000	14.8	5.7	90
Bio-Gel P-30, –400 Mesh		For thin layer chromatography			
Bio-Gel P-60, 50–100 Mesh					125
Bio-Gel P-60, 100–200 Mesh	60,000	3,000–60,000	19.0	7.2	40
Bio-Gel P-60, –400 Mesh		For thin layer chromatography			
Bio-Gel P-100, 50–100 Mesh					90
Bio-Gel P-100, 100–200 Mesh	100,000	5,000–100,000	19.0	7.5	40
Bio-Gel P-100, –400 Mesh		For thin layer chromatography			
Bio-Gel P-150, 50–100 Mesh					60
Bio-Gel P-150, 100–200 Mesh	150,000	15,000–150,000	24.0	9.2	35
Bio-Gel P-150, –400 Mesh		For thin layer chromatography			
Bio-Gel P-200, 50–100 Mesh					30
Bio-Gel P-200, 100–200 Mesh	200,000	30,000–200,000	34.0	14.7	15
Bio-Gel P-200, –400 Mesh		For thin layer chromatography			
Bio-Gel P-300, 50–100 Mesh					20
Bio-Gel P-300, 100–200 Mesh	400,000	60,000–400,000	40.0	18.0	8
Bio-Gel P-300, –400 Mesh		For thin layer chromatography			

* Values ± 10%.
† 1.3 × 13 cm column.

TABLE 4—(Continued)
COLUMN PACKINGS FOR GEL PERMEATION AND FILTRATION CHROMATOGRAPHY

2. **Bio-Gel agarose gel.**

	Minimum[a] flow rates ml/hr/cm²	Molecular[b] weight exclusion limit	Molecular weight operating range	Approximate % agarose in gel
Bio-Gel A-0.5 m, 50–100 mesh	110			
Bio-Gel A-0.5 m, 100–200 mesh	35	0.5×10^6	< 10,000 to 500,000	10
Bio-Gel A-0.5 m, 200–400 mesh	15			
Bio-Gel A-1.5 m, 50–100 mesh	90			
Bio-Gel A-1.5 m, 100–200 mesh	30	1.5×10^6	< 10,000 to 1,500,000	8
Bio-Gel A-1.5 m, 200–400 mesh	10			
Bio-Gel A-5 m, 50–100 mesh	70			
Bio-Gel A-5 m, 100–200 mesh	20	5×10^6	10,000 to 5,000,000	6
Bio-Gel A-5 m, 200–400 mesh	9			
Bio-Gel A-15 m, 50–100 mesh	50			
Bio-Gel A-15 m, 100–200 mesh	15	15×10^6	40,000 to 15,000,000	4
Bio-Gel A-15 m, 200–400 mesh	6			
Bio-Gel A-50 m, 50–100 mesh	30	50×10^6	100,000 to 50,000,000	2
Bio-Gel A-50 m, 100–200 mesh	10			
Bio-Gel A-150 m, 50–100 mesh	15	150×10^6	1,000,000 to > 150,000,000	1
Bio-Gel A-150 m, 100–200 mesh	4			

[a] With water on a 2 × 95 cm column with a 50 cm water head.
[b] For globular materials.

Recommended gel filtration operation with Bio-Gel P and Bio-Gel A.

Bio-Gel P and Bio-Gel A are handled and operated in the same manner as most chromatographic materials. Attention to careful packing and flow control, as well as selection of proper column design and sample application technique contribute to superior gel filtration.

Bio-Gel P is supplied as a dry spherical powder. To hydrate, pour the dry beads slowly into a constantly stirred container of buffer or distilled water. (For this purpose, a magnetic stirrer is excellent.) The water regain values given in the properties table show the minimum quantity of liquid necessary to hydrate each gram of dry gel; approximately three times this amount should be used when preparing the gels for column use.

The following hydration times are recommended:

P-2 through P-10	2 to 4 hours
P-30 and P-60	10 to 12 hours
P-100 and P-150	24 hours
P-200 and P-300	48 hours

Bio-Gel A is supplied ready for use. It is only necessary to wash the preservative, sodium azide, from the column with 2 bed volumes of buffer.

Packing the Column

All gels and buffers should be deaerated prior to use. This can be done by putting the fully hydrated gel, together with the excess of buffer or distilled water, in a vacuum flask and aspirating until bubbling ceases. This will remove any entrapped air bubbles.

For actually packing the column use the following procedure:

1. Attach a wide stem funnel to the top of the chromatographic column, using either a rubber stopper or standard laboratory tubing. Make certain that the funnel is large enough to hold *all* the hydrated gel so only one pouring will be necessary.
2. Fill the column completely with buffer.
3. Add all of the gel suspension, fully hydrated, to the funnel in one pour. Stir constantly to prevent blockage as the suspension settles through the stem of the funnel into the column.
4. Let the bed settle for a few centimeters with the outlet at the bottom of the column closed, then gradually open the outlet to pack the column more tightly.

TABLE 4—(Continued)
COLUMN PACKINGS FOR GEL PERMEATION AND FILTRATION CHROMATOGRAPHY

Applying the Sample

There are many methods for applying the sample, but the following method works well with columns of Bio-Gel P:

1. Rinse the column (last step above), then elute the buffer to the top of the bed level.
2. Carefully add the sample to the top of the bed, using a curved tip pipette.
3. Drain the sample down to the bed level, then wash it carefully into the top of the bed with a small amount of buffer.
4. Add buffer to the desired level and attach the column to the buffer reservoir.

3. **Bio-Beads S polystyrene beads**

	Mesh size (dry)	Mol. wt. exclusion limit	Operating range	Swollen bed vol.—ml/g in benzene
Bio-Beads S-X1	200–400	14,000 MW	600–14,000	9.8
Bio-Beads S-X2	200–400	2,700 MW	100– 2,700	6.2
Bio-Beads S-X3	200–400	2,000 MW	Up to 2,000	5.1
Bio-Beads S-X4	200–400	1,400 MW	Up to 1,400	4.2
Bio-Beads S-X8	200–400	1,000 MW	Up to 1,000	3.9
Bio-Beads SM-1*	20– 50	14,000 MW	600–14,000	3.1
Bio-Beads SM-2*	20– 50	14,000 MW	600–14,000	2.9

* Macroporous polystyrene gels.

4. **Bio-Glas granular porous glass.**

	Mesh size*	Mol. wt. exclusion limit	Mol. wt. operating range	Average pore diameter
Bio-Glas 200	50–100 80–100 100–120 100–200 200–325 minus 325	30,000	3,000–30,000	200 Å
Bio-Glas 500	50–100 80–100 100–120 100–200 200–325 minus 325	100,000	10,000–100,000	500 Å
Bio-Glas 1000	50–100 80–100 100–120 100–200 200–325 minus 325	500,000	50,000–500,000	1000 Å
Bio-Glas 1500	50–100 80–100 100–120 100–200 200–325 minus 325	2,000,000	400,000–2,000,000	1500 Å
Bio-Glas 2500	50–100 80–100 100–120 100–200 200–325 minus 325	9,000,000	800,000–9,000,000	2500 Å

* Available with or without binder.

TABLE 4—(Continued)
COLUMN PACKINGS FOR GEL PERMEATION AND FILTRATION CHROMATOGRAPHY

From Pharmacia Fine Chemicals

1. **Sephadex G cross-linked dextran.**

Sephadex type		Dry particle diameter, microns	Water regain	Expected bed volume, ml/g of dry Sephadex	Molecular-weight fractionation ranges	
					Globular proteins	Dextrans
G-10		40–120	1.0 ± 0.1	2– 3	700	700
G-15		40–120	1.5 ± 0.2	2.5– 3.5	1,500	1,500
G-25	Coarse	100–300	2.5 ± 0.2	4– 6	1,000– 5,000	100– 5,000
G-25	Medium	50–150				
G-25	Fine	20– 80				
G-25	Superfine	10– 40				
G-50	Coarse	100–300	5.0 ± 0.3	9–11	1,500– 30,000	500– 10,000
G-50	Medium	50–150				
G-50	Fine	20– 80				
G-50	Superfine	10– 40				
G-75		40–120	7.5 ± 0.5	12–15	3,000– 70,000	1,000– 50,000
G-75	Superfine	10– 40				
G-100		40–120	10.0 ± 1.0	15–20	4,000–150,000	1,000–100,000
G-100	Superfine	10– 40				
G-150		40–120	15.0 ± 1.5	20–30	5,000–400,000	1,000–150,000
G-150	Superfine	10– 40				
G-200		40–120	20.0 ± 2.0	30–40	5,000–800,000	1,000–200,000
G-200	Superfine	10– 40				

(Superfine grades are for thin-layer gel filtration)

2. **Sephadex LH-20 (alkylated Sephadex G-25).**
   Swelling characteristics:

Solvent	Appr. solvent regain ml solvent/g dry gel	Appr. bed volume ml/g dry gel
Dimethylformamide	2.2	4
Water	2.1	4
Methanol	1.9	3.5–4.0
Ethanol	1.8	3.0–3.5
Chloroform*	1.8	3.0–3.5
***n*-Butanol**	1.6	3
Dioxane	1.4	2.5–3.0
Tetrahydrofuran	1.4	2.5–3.0
Acetone	0.8	1.5
Ethyl acetate	0.4	0.5–1.0
Toluene	0.2	0.5

* Containing 1% ethanol. Particle size 25–100μ

3. **Sepharose agarose gel.**

	Approx. exclusion limits MW Polysaccharides	Proteins
Sepharose 6B	1×10^6	4×10^6
Sepharose 4B	5×10^6	20×10^6
Sepharose 2B	20×10^6	40×10^6

TABLE 4—(Continued)
COLUMN PACKINGS FOR GEL PERMEATION AND FILTRATION CHROMATOGRAPHY

4. **Sephadex ion exchangers.**

Types	Description	Ionic form	Capacity meq/g	Approx. hemoglobin cap. g/g	Particle size (microns)
DEAE—	Weakly basic anion exchanger				
Sephadex A-25	Functional groups:	Cl^-	3.5 ± 0.5	0.5 at pH 8.0	40–120
A-50	diethylaminoethyl			0.5	
QAE—	Strongly basic anion exchanger				
Sephadex A-25	Functional groups:	Cl^-	3.0 ± 0.4	0.3 at pH 8.0	40–120
A-50	diethyl-(2-hydroxypropyl) aminoethyl			0.6	
CM—	Weakly acidic cation exchanger				
Sephadex C-25	Functional groups:	Na^+	4.5 ± 0.5	0.4 at pH 5.0	40–120
C-50	carboxymethyl			0.9	
SE—	Strongly acidic cation exchanger				
Sephadex C-25	Functional groups:	Na^+	2.3 ± 0.3	0.2 at pH 5.0	40–120
C-50	sulphoethyl			0.7	

Technical information taken from literature supplied by Waters Associates Inc., Framingham, Massachusetts; Bio-Rad Laboratories, Richmond, California; and Pharmacia Fine Chemicals, Inc., Piscataway, New Jersey, from which the products and further information are available.

TABLE 5
COMMERCIAL ION-EXCHANGE RESINS

Trade Name	Classification	Matrix	Active Group(s)
Allassion CS	Strong acid	polystyrene	$—SO_3^{\ominus}$
Allassion CC	Weak acid	acrylic	—COOH
Allassion AQ217	Strong base	polystyrene	$—N(CH_3)_3^{\oplus}$
Allassion AQ227	Strong base	polystyrene	$—N(CH_3)_2(C_2H_4OH)^{\oplus}$
Allassion A33-03	Weak base	polystyrene	$—NR_2$
Allassion AWB-3	Weak base	epoxy-amine	$—NR_2$, $—NR_3^{\oplus}$
Amberlite IR-116, -118, -120, -120PD, -122, Stratabed-122, -124, and XE-100	Strong acid	polystyrene	$—SO_3^{\ominus}$
Amberlite IRC-50, -72	Weak acid	methacrylic[a]	—COOH
Amberlite IRC-84, Stratabed 84	Weak acid	acrylic	—COOH
Amberlite IRA-400, -402, -400C, -401, -401S, Stratabed 402, and -425	Strong base	polystyrene	$—N(CH_3)_3^{\oplus}$
Amberlite IRA-410	Strong base	polystyrene	$—N(CH_3)_2(C_2H_4OH)^{\oplus}$
Amberlite IRA-45	Weak base	polystyrene	$—NR_2$, —NHR, $—NH_2$
Amberlite IRA-68	Weak base	acrylic	$—NR_2$
Amberlite MB-1	Mixed	polystyrene	$—SO_3^{\ominus}$, $—N(CH_3)_3^{\oplus}$
Amberlite MB-3	Mixed	polystyrene	$—SO_3^{\ominus}$, $—N(CH_3)_2(C_2H_4OH)^{\oplus}$
Amberlite 200, 200C, 252	Strong acid	polystyrene[a]	$—SO_3^{\ominus}$
Amberlite IRA-900, 900C, -904, -938	Strong base	polystyrene[a]	$—N(CH_3)_3^{\oplus}$
Amberlite IRA-458	Strong base	acrylic	$—N(CH_3)_3^{\oplus}$
Amberlite IRA-47	Weak base	condensate	$—NR_2$
Amberlite IRA-910, -911	Strong base	polystyrene[a]	$—N(CH_3)_2(C_2H_4OH)^{\oplus}$
Amberlite IRA-93, Stratabed 93	Weak base	polystyrene[a]	$—NR_2$
Amberlyst 15	Strong acid	polystyrene[a]	$—SO_3^{\ominus}$
Amberlyst A-21	Weak base	polystyrene[a]	$—N(CH_3)_2$
Amberlyst A-26	Strong base	polystyrene[a]	$—N(CH_3)_3^{\oplus}$
Amberlyst A-29	Strong base	polystyrene[a]	$—N(CH_3)_2(C_2H_4OH)^{\oplus}$
[Amberlite IRP and IRN resins are special products for pharmaceutical and nuclear applications, respectively; PD grades are partially dried and free flowing; Stratabed resins have narrow particle-size distributions; analytical grade, chromatographic grade (CG, with closely controlled mesh cuts) and liquid exchangers are also available].			
De-Acidite MIP	Weak base	polystyrene	$—NH_2$, —NHR
De-Acidite HIP	Mixed base	polystyrene	$—NR_2$, $—N(CH_3)_3^{\oplus}$
De-Acidite PIP, FFIP, FX	Strong base	polystyrene	$—N(CH_3)_3^{\oplus}$
De-Acidite NIP, NX	Strong base	polystyrene	$—N(CH_3)_2(C_2H_4OH)^{\oplus}$
De-Acidite KMP	Strong base	polystyrene[a]	$—N(CH_3)_3^{\oplus}$
Zeo-Karb 216	Weak acid	phenol-formaldehyde[b]	—OH, $—SO_3^{\ominus}$
Zeo-Karb 226	Weak acid	acrylic	—COOH
Zeo-Karb 227	Strong acid	acrylic	$—SO_3^{\ominus}$, —COOH
Zeo-Karb 225, 325, 425	Strong acid	polystyrene	$—SO_3^{\ominus}$
Diaion SK-1B	Strong acid	polystyrene	$—SO_3^{\ominus}$
Diaion SA-10A	Strong base	polystyrene	$—N(CH_3)_3^{\oplus}$
Diaion SA-20A	Strong base	polystyrene	$—N(CH_3)_2(C_2H_4OH)^{\oplus}$
Dowex A1	Chelating	polystyrene	imminodiacetate
Dowex 1, 21K, 11	Strong base	polystyrene	$—N(CH_3)_3^{\oplus}$
Dowex 2	Strong base	polystyrene	$—N(CH_3)_2(C_2H_4OH)^{\oplus}$
Dowex 44	Weak base	epoxy-amine[b]	$—NR_2$, —NHR, $—NH_2$
Dowex 50, 50W	Strong acid	polystyrene	$—SO_3^{\ominus}$
Dowex 3	Weak base	polystyrene	$—NR_2$, —NHR, $—NH_2$
Dowex CCR-1	Weak acid	phenolic[b]	$—CH_2(OH)COOH$
Dowex MPC-1	Strong acid	polystyrene[a]	$—SO_3^{\ominus}$
Dowex AG-11A8	Ion retardation	polystyrene-acrylic	$—COO^{\ominus} \ldots {}^{\oplus}R_3N—$

[X numbers of Dowex resins indicate the degree of crosslinking (% divinylbenzene) in the polymer; e.g., Dowex 50-X8 is Dowex 50 crosslinked with 8% DVB].

TABLE 5—(Continued)
COMMERCIAL ION-EXCHANGE RESINS

Trade Name	Classification	Matrix	Active Group(s)
Duolite A-101D, ES-109, -104, -111	Strong base	polystyrene	$—N(CH_3)_3^{\oplus}$
Duolite A-102D	Strong base	polystyrene	$—N(CH_3)_2(C_2H_4OH)^{\oplus}$
Duolite A-30, -30B, -57	Intermediate base	epoxy-amine	$—NR_2$, $—N(CH_3)_3^{\oplus}$
Duolite A-6	Weak base	phenolic[b]	$—NR_2$
Duolite A-7	Weak base	phenolic[b]	—NHR
Duolite C-3	Strong acid	phenolic[b]	$—CH_2SO_3^{\ominus}$
Duolite C-20, -25, -25D	Strong acid	polystyrene	$—SO_3^{\ominus}$
Duolite ES-26	Strong acid	polystyrene[a]	$—SO_3^{\ominus}$
Duolite ES-63	Intermediate acid	polystyrene	$—OP(O)(OH)_2$
Duolite CC-3	Weak acid	acrylic	—COOH
Imac C-12	Strong acid	polystyrene	$—SO_3^{\ominus}$
Imac C-16P	Strong acid	polystyrene[a]	$—SO_3^{\ominus}$
Imac Z-5	Weak acid	acrylic	—COOH
Imac S 5-40	Strong base	polystyrene[a]	$—N(CH_3)_3^{\oplus}$
Imac S 5-50	Strong base	polystyrene	$—N(CH_3)_3^{\oplus}$
Imac S 5-52	Strong base	polystyrene[a]	$—N(CH_3)_2(C_2H_4OH)^{\oplus}$
Imac A-20	Weak base	polystyrene[a]	$—NR_2$, —NHR, $—NH_2$
Imac A-21	Weak base	polystyrene[a]	$—NR_2$
Ionac C-240	Strong acid	polystyrene	$—SO_3^{\ominus}$
Ionac C-270	Weak acid	na	—COOH
Ionac A-540	Strong base	polystyrene	$—N(CH_3)_3^{\oplus}$
Ionac A-550	Strong base	polystyrene	$—N(CH_3)_2(C_2H_4OH)^{\oplus}$
Ionac A-315	Weak base	polystyrene[a]	$—NR_2$, —NHR, $—NH_2$
Ionac A-300	Weak base	epoxy-amine[b]	$—NR_2$, $NR_3^{\oplus}$
Ionac A-310	Weak base	epoxy-amine	$—NR_2$, $—NR_3^{\oplus}$
Kastel C-300	Strong acid	polystyrene	$—SO_3^{\ominus}$
Kastel C-100	Weak acid	acrylic	—COOH
Kastel A-500	Strong base	polystyrene	$—N(CH_3)_3^{\oplus}$
Kastel A-300	Strong base	polystyrene	$—N(CH_3)_2(C_2H_4OH)^{\oplus}$
Kationite KU-2	Strong acid	polystyrene	$—SO_3^{\ominus}$
Kationite KU-1	Strong acid	phenolic	$—(OH)SO_3^{\ominus}$
Anionite AV-17	Strong base	polystyrene	$—N(CH_3)_3^{\oplus}$
Anionite EDE-10P	Weak base	epoxy-amine	$—NR_2$, —NHR, $—NH_3^{\oplus}$
Anionite AV-16	Weak base	epoxy-amine	—NHR, $—NR_2$, $—NC_6H_5R$
Lewatit S-100, -115	Strong acid	polystyrene	$—SO_3^{\ominus}$
Lewatit SP-100, -120	Strong acid	polystyrene[a]	$—SO_3^{\ominus}$
Lewatit CNP	Weak acid	na[a]	—COOH
Lewatit MP-60, -62	Weak base	polystyrene[a]	$—NR_2$
Lewatit M-500	Strong base	polystyrene	$—N(CH_3)_3^{\oplus}$
Lewatit MP-500	Strong base	polystyrene[a]	$—N(CH_3)_3^{\oplus}$
Lewatit MN	Strong base	polystyrene[b]	$—N(CH_3)_3^{\oplus}$
Lewatit MIH-59	Weak base	condensate[b]	—NHR, $—NR_2$
Lewatit CNO	Weak acid	phenolic[b]	$—OCH_2COOH$
Lewatit KSN	Strong acid	phenolic[b]	$—SO_3^{\ominus}$ (OH)
Lewatit CNS	Mixed acid	na[b]	$—SO_3^{\ominus}$, —COOH
Lewatit M-600	Strong base	polystyrene	$—N(CH_3)_2(C_2H_4OH)^{\oplus}$
Lewatit MP-600	Strong base	polystyrene[a]	$—N(CH_3)_2(C_2H_4OH)^{\oplus}$
Wofatit KPS	Strong acid	polystyrene	$—SO_3^{\ominus}$
Wofatit F	Strong acid	phenolic[b]	$—CH_2SO_3^{\ominus}$
Wofatit CP	Weak acid	methacrylic[a]	—COOH
Wofatit CN	Weak acid	phenolic[b]	$—(OH)CH_2COOH$
Wofatit SBW, SBT, ES	Strong base	polystyrene	$—N(CH_3)_3^{\oplus}$
Wofatit L-150	Weak base	epoxy-amine[b]	$—NR_2$, $—NR_3^{\oplus}$
Wofatit CV	Weak acid	condensate	—COOH
Wofatit SBK	Strong base	polystyrene	$—N(CH_3)_2(C_2H_4OH)^{\oplus}$
Wofatit SBU	Strong base	polystyrene	quaternary heterocyclically combined N
Wofatit EZ	Weak base	na[b]	aromatic amines
Wofatit EA-60	Strong base	polystyrene[a]	$—N(CH_3)_3^{\oplus}$
Wofatit MBW	Mixed	polystyrene	$—N(CH_3)_3^{\oplus}$, $—SO_3^{\ominus}$
Wofatit AK-40	Weak base	polystyrene[a]	$—NH_2$, —NHR
Wofatit MD	Weak base	condensate[b]	$—C_6H_4NH_2$, —NHR

TABLE 5—(Continued)
COMMERCIAL ION-EXCHANGE RESINS

A. *Manufacturers of Resins:*

1. Allassion—Dia-Prosim, Vitry-sur-Seine, France.
2. Amberlite—Rohm & Haas Co., Philadelphia, Pennsylvania. (Amberlite analytical grade (AR) and chromatographic grade (CG) resins are distributed by the Mallinckrodt Chemical Works, St. Louis, Mo.)
3. De-Acidite and Zeo-Karb are Permutit resins—Zerolit Ltd. (London), Pemberton House, 632–652, London Road, Isleworth, Middlesex.
4. Diaion—Mitsubishi Chemical Ind., Ltd., Tokyo, Japan.
5. Dowex—Dow Chemical Co., Midland, Michigan (Dowex resins are subjected to further sizing and purification and are sold as analytical and reactor grade resins (AG and Bio-Rex) by Bio-Rad Laboratories, Richmond, California).
6. Duolite—Diamond Shamrock Chemical Co., Resinous Products Div., Cleveland, Ohio.
7. Imac—Industrieele Maatschappij Activit, Amsterdam.
8. Ionac—Ionac Chemical Co., Birmingham, New Jersey.
9. Kastel—Montecatini, Milan, Italy.
10. Kationite and Anionite—Russian.
11. Lewatit—Naftone, Inc., 425 Park Ave., New York City.
12. Wofatit—VEB Farbenfabrik Wolfen, 444 Wolfen Kr. Bitterfeld, East Germany.

B. *Notes*

1. Resins with a macroporous rather than a gel or semiporous structure are designated [(a)].
2. Resins with granular rather than spherical beaded particles are designated [(b)].
3. na = Information not available.
4. Waters Associates supplies an ion exchange material designated WBAX consisting of a weak base amine anion exchanger on a silica support.

INDEX OF RESIN TYPES

1. Strong acid—polystyrene (R = Macroreticular).
   Allassion CS.
   Amberlite IR-116, -118, -120, -122, -124, XE-100, -200(R), -200C(R), -252(R).
   Amberlyst 15(R).
   Zeo-Karb 225, 325, 425.
   Diaion SK-1B.
   Dowex 50, 50W, MPC-1(R).
   Duolite C-20, -25, -25D, ES-26(R).
   Imac C-12, C-16P(R).
   Ionac C-240.
   Kastel C-300.
   Kationite KU-2.
   Lewatit S-100, -115, SP-100(R), -120(R).
   Wofatit KPS.
2. Strong acid—acrylic
   Zeo-Karb 227.
3. Strong acid—phenol-formaldehyde
   Duolite C-3.
   Kationite KU-1.
   Lewatit KSN.
   Wofatit F.
4. Weak acid—polystyrene (R = Macroreticular)
   Lewatit CNP.
5. Weak acid—acrylic (M = Methacrylic) (R = Macroreticular)
   Allassion CC.
   Amberlite IRC-50(M), -72, -84.
   Zeo-Karb 226.
   Duolite CC-3.
   Imac Z-5.
   Kastel C-100.
   Wofatit CP (M) (R).
6. Weak acid—phenol-formaldehyde
   Zeo-Karb 216.
   Dowex CCR-1.
   Lewatit CNO.
   Wofatit CN, CV.
   Kationite KU-1.
7. Intermediate acid—polystyrene
   Duolite ES-63.

TABLE 5—(Continued)
COMMERCIAL ION-EXCHANGE RESINS

8. Mixed acid—phenol-formaldehyde
   Lewatit CNS.
9. Strong base—polystyrene (—$N(CH_3)_3^{\oplus}$) (R = Macroreticular)
   Allassion AQ217.
   Amberlite IRA-400, -402, -400C, -401, -401S, -425, -900 (R), -900C, -904(R), -938(R).
   Amberlyst A-26(R).
   De-Acidite PIP, FFIP, FX, KMP(R).
   Diaion SA-10A.
   Dowex 1, 21K, 11.
   Duolite A-101D, ES-109, -104, -111.
   Imac S 5-40(R), S 5-50.
   Ionac A-540.
   Kastel A-500.
   Anionite AV-17.
   Lewatit M-500, MP-500(R), MN.
   Wofatit SBW, SBT, ES, SBU, EA-60(R).
10. Strong base—polystyrene (—$N(CH_3)_2(C_2H_4OH)^{\oplus}$) (R = Macroreticular)
   Allassion AQ 227.
   Amberlite IRA-410, -910(R), -911(R).
   Amberlyst A-29(R).
   De-Acidite NIP, NX.
   Diaion SA-20A.
   Dowex 2.
   Duolite A-102D.
   Imac S 5-52(R).
   Ionac A-550.
   Kastel A-300.
   Lewatit M-600, MP-600(R).
   Wofatit SBK.

10a. Strong base—acrylic
   Amberlite IRA-458.

11. Weak base-polystyrene (R = Macroreticular)
   Allassion A33-03.
   Amberlite IRA-45, -93(R).
   Amberlyst A-21(R).
   De-Acidite MIP.
   Dowex 3.
   Imac A-20(R), A-21(R).
   Ionac A-315(R).
   Lewatit MP-60(R), -62(R).
   Wofatit EZ, AK-40(R).
12. Weak base—epoxy-amine
   Allassion AWB-3.
   Dowex 44.
   Ionac A-300, A-310.
   Anionite EDE-10P, AV-16.
   Wofatit L-150.
13. Weak base—acrylic
   Amberlite IRA-68.
14. Weak base—phenol-formaldehyde
   Duolite A-6, A-7.
   Lewatit MIH-59.
   Wofatit MD.
   Amberlite IRA-47.
15. Mixed base—polystyrene
   De-Acidite HIP.
16. Mixed base—epoxy-amine
   Duolite A-30, A-30B, -57.
17. Mixed anion and cation—polystyrene
   Amberlite MB-1, MB-3.
   Wofatit MBW.
18. Chelating
   Dowex A1.
19. Ion retardation
   Dowex AG-11A8.

TABLE 6
ION-EXCHANGE CELLULOSES FOR COLUMN CHROMATOGRAPHY

A. Whatman

Whatman cellulose ion exchangers are available in three series. Series I are the original fibrous materials available as a powder for column work ("11" grades) and in some cases as a coarse fibrous floc ("1" grades) for the removal of ions by batch procedures. Series II ("22" and "23" grades) are advanced fibrous exchangers which provide greater resolution than the "11" grades. The "22" and "23" grade materials have about the same average fiber length as the "11" grade, but have a more uniform charge distribution throughout the molecular structure plus an increased effective macromolecular capacity. The "22" grades contain some "fines" (short fibers) which may reduce the flow rate or give nonuniform column packing and, therefore, decreased resolution. Series III ("32" and "52" grades) are microgranular materials having an open, crosslinked structure with a high degree of molecular orientation. The particulate nature of these exchangers leads to greater resolution than is possible with fibrous materials.

Series	Grade	Type	Ionic form	Capacity (meq/g)	Active group	Comments
I	P 11	Cellulose phosphate	Monoammonium	7.4**	$-O-P(=O)(O^-)-O^-$	A cation exchanger which is not ionized below pH 2; a monofunctional exchanger in weakly acid solution; bifunctional in slightly basic solution
	CM 11	Carboxymethyl cellulose	Na^+	0.7	$-O-CH_2-C(=O)-O^-$	Functions as a cation exchanger above pH 4–5
	DE 11	Diethylaminoethyl cellulose	Free base	1.0	$-O-CH_2-CH_2-NH^+(Et)_2$	Anion exchanger below pH 7
	ET 11	Ecteola (epichlorohydrin triethanolamine) cellulose	Free base	0.5	tertiary amino	Structurally complex weak base anion exchanger which has special applications in biochemistry

Series	Grade	Type	Ionic form	Nominal Capacity meq/g	Protein Capacity mg/g	pH	Water regain g/g dry exchanger
II	DE 22	Fibrous cellulose anion exchanger. DEAE—diethylaminoethyl functional group.	Free base	1.0 ± 0.1	750 insulin	8.5	1.7–2.2
	DE 23	Fibrous cellulose anion exchanger (fines reduced). DEAE—diethylaminoethyl functional group.	Free base	1.0 ± 0.1	750 insulin	8.5	1.7–2.2
	CM 22	Fibrous cellulose cation exchanger. CM—carboxymethyl functional group.	*Na^+	0.6 ± 0.06	600 lysozyme	5.0	2.0–2.8

TABLE 6—(Continued)
ION-EXCHANGE CELLULOSES FOR COLUMN CHROMATOGRAPHY

Series	Grade	Type	Ionic form	Nominal Capacity meq/g	Protein Capacity mg/g	pH	Water regain g/g dry exchanger
	CM 23	Fibrous cellulose cation exchanger (fines reduced). CM—carboxymethyl cation exchanger.	*Na⁺	0.6 ± 0.06	600 lysozyme	5.0	2.0–2.8
III	DE 32	Microgranular cellulose anion exchanger. DEAE—diethylaminoethyl functional group.	Free base	1.0 ± 0.1	850 insulin	8.5	2.3–2.8
	DE 52	Microgranular cellulose anion exchanger (pre-swollen). DEAE—diethylaminoethyl functional group.	Free base	1.0 ± 0.1	850 insulin	8.5	2.3–2.8
	CM 32	Microgranular cellulose cation exchanger. CM—carboxymethyl functional group.	*Na⁺	1.0 ± 0.1	1260 lysozyme	5.0	2.3–2.7
	CM 52	Microgranular cellulose cation exchanger (pre-swollen). CM—carboxymethyl functional group.	*Na⁺	1.0 ± 0.1	1260 lysozyme	5.0	2.3–2.7

* Small proportion in the H^+ form due to water washing.
** Maximum theoretical capacity, bifunctional exchanger.
[Data and comments from Technical Bulletins 1032, 2000 and 15M, H. Reeve Angel and Co., Clifton, New Jersey, from which these products are available.]

B. Schleicher and Schuell, Inc.

Anion Exchangers

No.	Type	Capacity (meq/g)	Fiber length (μ)	Comments
70	Diethylaminoethyl cellulose	0.9 ± 0.1	100–300	For separation and purification of proteins, peptides, enzymes, hormones, etc.
	(No. 71 and No. 72 are also DEAE cellulose with 20% and 40% shorter fibers, respectively)			
73	Ecteola	0.3 ± 0.1	100–300	Particularly useful for the separation and purification of viruses
	(No. 74 and No. 75 are also Ecteola celluloses with 20% and 40% shorter fibers, respectively)			
	Cation Exchangers			
76	Carboxymethyl cellulose	0.7 ± 1	100–300	Weak acid cation exchanger, most effective above pH 4.
	(No. 77 and No. 78 are also CM celluloses with 20% and 40% shorter fibers, respectively)			
79	Cellulose phosphate	0.9 ± 1	100–300	Bifunctional exchanger which can adsorb certain cations from very acidic solutions.

[Data and comments from Quick Reference Catalog No. 4, Schleicher and Schuell Co., Keene, N.H., from whom these products are available.]

TABLE 6—(Continued)
ION-EXCHANGE CELLULOSES FOR COLUMN CHROMATOGRAPHY

C. Machery-Nagel & Co.

	Grade	Description	Capacity meq/g
Cation exchangers	MN 2100 P	Phosphorylated cellulose	0.7
	MN 2100 CM	Carboxymethyl cellulose	0.7
	MN 2100 Poly-P	Polyphosphate-impregnated cellulose	0.7
Anion exchangers	MN 2100 DEAE	Diethylaminoethyl cellulose	0.7
	MN 2100 ECTEOLA	ECTEOLA cellulose	0.35
	MN 2100 PEI	Polyethyleneimine impregnated cellulose	1.0

[Data from Machery-Nagel & Co. literature PSDC el/02/0/3.69.]

D. Applied Science Laboratories, Inc.

Name	Type	Exchange capacity
TEAE	Anion	0.9 ± 0.1 meq/g
DEAE	Anion	0.9 ± 0.1 meq/g
ECTEOLA	Anion	0.3 ± 0.1 meq/g
CM	Cation	0.7 ± 0.1 meq/g
P	Cation	0.9 ± 0.1 meq/g

(Ultrapure DEAE cellulose with a similar exchange capacity is also available.)

APPENDIX

LABORATORY METHODS FOR WHATMAN ION-EXCHANGE CELLULOSES

I. General Handling

A. Storage
1. Store exchangers at room temperature.
2. Always keep bottles firmly closed when not in use.
3. Before removing dry exchangers ("22", "23" and "32" series) from the bottles, insure even distribution of particles by carefully turning the bottles over a few times.
4. Do not leave exchangers in contact with buffers or solutes for more than one week without the addition of a preservative, e.g., 0.03% toluene.

B. Usage
1. Cellulose ion-exchangers should never be dried at any stage of use.
2. All stages of pretreatment: precycling, (degassing—DEAE exchangers only), equilibration, removal of fines, must be carried out on the dry ion-exchange celluloses ("22", "23" and "32" series) in order to obtain best possible performance.
3. Precycling is not necessary for pre-swollen microgranular ("52") series, but they must be equilibrated and their fines must be removed. DEAE exchangers must be degassed before equilibration.
4. Never subject exchangers to strong acids, alkalis or oxidizing agents. (Limits: 0.5 *N* acid or alkali—2 hours.)
5. Always use distilled or deionized water. When working with enzymes or other materials sensitive to trace amounts of metal impurities, use glass distilled water.

II. Exchanger Preparation

A. Precycling*
1. In order to avoid the generation of fines, mechanical or manual stirring should not be too vigorous or too prolonged.
2. Gently stir while pouring the exchanger into a beaker containing 15 volumes (volume liquor/dry weight exchanger) of 0.5 *N* HCl for DEAE or 0.5 *N* NaOH for CM and leave for a minimum of 30 minutes, but not more than 2 hours.
3. Decant off supernatant liquor and wash the exchanger until the effluent is at pH 4 for DEAE or pH 8 for CM.

* Not necessary for pre-swollen microgranular "52" series; precycling releases the full capacity of the exchanger and optimizes its interaction with large molecules while also serving as a procedure for washing and converting the exchanger to a particular form.

TABLE 6—(Continued)
ION-EXCHANGE CELLULOSES FOR COLUMN CHROMATOGRAPHY

4. Gently stir while pouring the exchanger into a beaker containing 15 volumes of 0.5 *N* NaOH for DEAE or 0.5 *N* HCl for CM and leave for a minimum of 30 minutes, but not more than 2 hours. Decant supernatant.
5. Repeat step no. 4 and then wash the exchanger in a funnel until the effluent is near neutral.

B. Degassing

DEAE cellulose ion-exchangers are bases which will, under certain conditions, react with CO_2 in the air to form DEAE carbonate and bicarbonate. The carbonate and bicarbonate anions show high affinity for DEAE and unless removed, may interfere with ion-exchange chromatography. Degassing removes these carbonate and bicarbonate ions.

1. Place the fully swollen exchanger in the acid component of the buffer.*
2. Apply a good vacuum down to below 10 cm Hg pressure with stirring until no more bubbles are noticed, but before boiling occurs. This can be carried out by stirring the slurry with a magnetic stirrer in a stoppered Buchner flask connected to a water pump.
3. Add the basic component of the buffer. Then complete the equilibration.

Note: This method is applicable to all buffers with the obvious exception of carbonate buffers, and is carried out before equilibration.

C. Equilibration

Equilibration is the single most important step in the preparation of an ion-exchange cellulose. Inadequate or incomplete equilibration will cause poor, irreproducible results.

The two most commonly used methods of equilibration are:

Method 1

1. Stir the exchanger into a volume of the chosen buffer (15–30 ml/dry gram exchanger).**
2. Leave for 10 minutes.
3. Filter off the supernatant liquor. Check pH and conductivity of filtrate.
4. Repeat steps 1, 2, and 3 at least 6 times.
5. Make certain that the filtrate of the supernatant has exactly the same pH and conductivity as the equilibration buffer. If not, repeat steps 1-3 until no drift occurs.

Method 2

1. Stir the exchanger into a volume of the chosen buffer (15–30 ml/dry gram exchanger).**
2. Titrate slowly, with stirring, to the correct pH with either the acid or the base portion of the buffer, as needed.
3. Remove supernatant liquor and replace it with two changes of the chosen buffer at the correct pH and concentration.
4. After step 3, make certain that the pH and conductivity of the filtrate remain constant at the correct values. If they do not, repeat buffer change.

For column separations starting with very low buffer concentrations:

1. First equilibrate the exchanger with a more concentrated (3–10 times) buffer of the same pH as the starting buffer, using either Method 1 or Method 2 described above.
2. Equilibrate the exchanger with the low concentration starting buffer, using either Method 1 or Method 2.

D. Removal of Fines

1. Stir the equilibrated exchanger into 20 volumes of starting buffer and allow it to settle for 15 to 30 minutes in a measuring cylinder. Note the wet settled volume. The shorter settling time gives a faster column flow rate.
2. Pour off the supernatant liquor which contains the fines.
3. Repeat steps 1 and 2 at least two times.

III. Column Techniques

A. Column Packing

1. Pumped Flow Method.

   This technique can be used with columns up to 90 cm in length, for both the advanced fibrous and microgranular exchangers.

   a. Add buffer so that the final slurry volume is 150% of the wet settled volume.
   b. Use a peristaltic pump having a positive or semi-positive pumping action which can deliver a minimum of 5 to 80 $ml/hr/cm^2$ of column area.
   c. Use a column with a volume 1.5 times the wet settled volume. Attach an extension tube at least 0.5 times the final bed length required.
   d. Stir the slurry gently and pour into a column through a wide neck funnel. Allow eluant to drain and discard.

* Make certain the pH is below 4.5. If the concentration of the acid component of the buffer gives a pH of 4.5 or above, use a higher concentration of the acid.

** Pre-swollen "52" series wt (g) × 0.30 = equivalent of dry exchanger (g).

TABLE 6—(Continued)
ION-EXCHANGE CELLULOSES FOR COLUMN CHROMATOGRAPHY

e. Immediately after all the slurry is added, attach and tighten column end unit to the extension tube. Pump buffer through the column at a minimum flow rate of 45 ml/hr/cm² cross-sectional area.
f. Pack column under these conditions until the bed height is stable. Usually, this point will be reached within 60 minutes for a 30 cm bed.
g. After the bed is packed, disconnect pump. Shut off column flow when buffer level is below extension tube. Remove extension tube.
h. Fill column with buffer to its maximum capacity, and insert end unit so as to exclude all air.
i. Carefully depress end unit until it firmly touches the top of the bed and tighten. Displaced buffer should be allowed to escape via the top feed tube.
j. Reconnect the top end unit to the pump and open the bottom tap. Pump one bed volume of buffer through the column at the desired rate. Make sure there is no dead space between the end unit and column bed before loading the sample.

For further details on fines removal and column packing, as well as alternative packing methods, see "Laboratory Methods of Column Packing" Data Sheet from H. Reeve Angel.

B. Column Checking

1. For DEAE exchangers, use trace amounts of cytosine or *pure* cetylpyridinium chloride (CPC); for CM exchangers, use trace amounts of sodium benzene disulphonate, which is slightly retarded, but acceptable.
2. Peak shape after elution should be sharp and symmetrical.
3. For those who prefer a visual check of packing and loading efficiency, use trace amounts of malachite green for DEAE cellulose, and orange II for CM cellulose. A properly packed column will result in the dye being eluted as a narrow band with a uniform front.

C. Sample Preparation

Samples must be fully equilibrated with the starting buffer to eliminate unexpected salt gradients which can result in non-reproducible elution patterns.
There are two methods for sample preparation:
Method 1—For Salt-free Materials
Dissolve salt-free solids in the starting buffer and adjust the pH to the correct value.
Method 2—For Materials Containing Salts
Dissolve solids containing salt in the starting buffer and dialyze against starting buffer. After dialysis, titrate sample to starting pH.
or:
Dissolve solids containing salt and apply to a column of small pore gel previously equilibrated with buffer. The gel must exclude all polyelectrolytes to be chromatographed. The polyelectrolytes will then emerge as a peak in the desired buffer.

D. Sample Loading

1. Load the sample onto the column so that it is spread evenly over the surface of the column bed.
2. The length of time for sample addition should be kept to a minimum. The rate of addition, however, should not be so fast as to exceed the kinetics of adsorption and desorption of the sample.
3. The sample volume should be kept to a minimum, but the sample should not be excessively concentrated as this may result in "double peaking."

E. Elution Methods

The selection of an elution method in an ion-exchange cellulose separation is so closely linked with the particular application that only general comments can be made. It is always helpful to consult previous publications describing the chromatography of the substances you are working with. Careful attention must be given to the relationship between the column volume and the total volume of the eluting buffer for best separation and reproducible results.
In the selection of a suitable elution method, it is good practice to start by running a simple gradient, e.g. a straight line, which passes through the likely elution conditions. On the basis of the results obtained, it will then be possible to either alter the gradient shape to achieve improved resolution or to select a possible pH and concentration for starting buffer or stepwise elution.

IV. Re-Use

In most instances the exchanger need only be washed with concentrated buffer to remove any material remaining on the column and then be re-equilibrated before a second adsorption cycle is attempted. It is essential to give the exchanger the full treatment, including acid-alkali precycling if:
1. Any interfering component, such as unidentified pigment or denatured protein, of the first adsorption cycle was left on the column. (The contaminated portion of the column should be discarded.)
2. The exchanger was not used for a long time before re-use. Exchanger should be stored in 0.03% toluene.

When working on a laboratory scale, re-equilibration can be done in the column but recycling is best done in a beaker.

[Appendix reprinted with permission of H. Reeve Angel & Co.]

TABLE 7
COMMERCIAL SOURCES FOR CHROMATOGRAPHY PAPERS

CARL SCHLEICHER & SCHUELL CO., KEENE, NEW HAMPSHIRE

1. **Ashless Papers**

   589 Green Ribbon-C
   For chromatography of mixtures having a wide variety of R_F values. A moderately thick and open-textured paper. 0.013[a]; 145[b].

   589 Orange Ribbon-C
   For a wide variety of chromatographic work and electrophoresis as well as circular chromatography. 0.009; 115.

   589 Black Ribbon-C
   Suitable for chromatography of mixtures having a wide variety of R_F values and for easily resolvable systems. 0.008; 155.

   589 White Ribbon-C
   Suitable for most chromatographic and electrophoretic work as well as for circular chromatography. 0.007; 98.

   589 Red Ribbon-C
   For circular chromatograms and ascending chromatograms. This is a dense paper, possessing no water mark. This grade sometimes permits a better resolution of compounds with similar R_F values than does No. 589 Blue Ribbon-C. 0.0065; 70.

   589 Blue Ribbon-C.
   For circular chromatograms and ascending chromatograms. This dense paper often permits the resolution of compounds with similar R_F values. 0.007; 75.

   507-C. For circular chromatograms and ascending chromatograms. This is a thin, ultra-dense, hard paper with a smooth surface. No. 507-C sheets absorb relatively little liquid, and are suitable for the separation of small quantities of materials with similar R_F values. 0.004; 55.

2. **Standard Papers**

   2040a—Fast flow rate. Recommended for amino acids and sugars. 0.006[a]; 115[b].

   2043a—A standard paper for chromatography and electrophoresis. The S. & S. grade used most for chromatography and electrophoresis and photometric evaluation of results. This grade has a special smooth, uniform surface. 0.006; 100.

   2045a—For circular and ascending chromatography. 0.006; 65.

   2040b—A medium texture paper, especially useful in the descending method in chromatography. 0.0075; 105.

   2043b—For most chromatographic work, circular chromatograms and evaluation by the elution method. 0.0075; 100.

   2045b—For circular filter paper chromatograms and descending chromatography. 0.0075; 65.

   2041—Similar to No. 2043a, but slightly thinner.

   2316—For chromatography and electrophoresis of larger quantities of materials. This grade has been found to be especially effective for this type of work. 0.01; 105.

   470-C—A soft, thick open-texture paper. For chromatography and electrophoresis of larger quantities of material. It is used for the chromatographic isolation of individual components, for example isolation of amino acids from complex mixtures. 0.035; 270.

   470A-C—Similar to No. 470-C, but with special smooth surface. For chromatography and electrophoresis of larger quantities. 0.022; 270.

   598-C—Suitable for preparative chromatography and separations in which columns composed of circles are used. Also for chromatography of mixtures having a wide variety of R_F values. A moderately thick and open textured paper. 0.012; 145.

   598YD-C—Similar to No. 598-C but without the water mark. It is used with the elution method, and for the chromatographic analysis of larger quantities of materials. 0.0085; 110.

---

[a] = Thickness in inches.
[b] = Average absorption rate of demineralized water in mm per 30 min.

TABLE 7—(Continued)
COMMERCIAL SOURCES FOR CHROMATOGRAPHY PAPERS

903-C—A soft paper of medium thickness for chromatographic and electrophoretic analysis of larger quantities of materials. 0.017; 210.

576-C—A thin paper suitable for photometric analysis and work with small samples. For circular chromatograms and ascending chromatography. The paper possesses a smooth, regular surface. 0.004; 55.

3. Impregnated Paper

287—Paper impregnated with infusorial earth for the separation of hydrophobic substances, such as carotenoids.

288 (35–40% Aluminium oxide)
For chromatography of chloroplast pigments, plant growth factors, and lipophilic dyes.

966 (25–40% Silica gel)
For chromatography of phosphatides, phospholipids and many related materials, as well as dyes such as sudan black.

2493 (Anion 5% Dowex 2 × 8)
Anion-exchange paper. Impregnated with 5% Dowex 2 × 8. Medium absorption. Fraction identification and estimation may be made quickly and efficiently on the paper. 0.009.

2494 (Cation 5% Dowex 50)
Cation-exchange paper. Impregnated with 5% Dowex 50. Especially useful for chromatography of amino acids and various inorganic mixtures. 0.009.

2492 (5% Acetylated CH_3COO)
Effective for the chromatography of aliphatic alcohols, aromatic hydrocarbons and related compounds. This is a hydrophobic paper for reverse phase paper chromatography. Medium absorption. 0.0075.

2495 (21% Acetylated CH_3COO)
A medium absorption paper similar to No. 2492, but with a greater extent of acetylation. 0.0075.

2496 (21% Acetylated CH_3COO)
Useful for the chromatography of aliphatic alcohols, aromatic hydrocarbons and related compounds. This is a hydrophobic paper for reverse-phase chromatography. Slow absorption 0.0075.

2497 (45% Acetylated CH_3COO)
This grade is thinner than No. 2496 and is used for similar separations. 0.006.

2498 (5% Dowex 1107)
Impregnated with Dowex 1107. This is a hydrophobic paper useful for reverse phase work and chromatography of fatty acids. 0.006.

2499 (5% Dowex 1107)
Impregnated with Dowex 1107. This paper is similar to No. 2498, but is about 25% thicker. 0.0075.

Glass Fiber
26—This hand-made paper is used in chromatography and electrophoresis. Rapid separation is possible (a major advantage of glass fiber paper is that reagents can be used which are too corrosive for use with cellulose papers). 0.008.

27-A—A machine-made paper which contains no binder. For chromatography and electrophoresis of substantial quantities.

(The number after the description indicates thickness in inches.)

[From Schleicher and Schuell Bulletin "Chromatography and Electrophoresis Products".]

TABLE 7—(Continued)
COMMERCIAL SOURCES FOR CHROMATOGRAPHY PAPERS

EATON-DIKEMAN CO., MOUNT HOLLY SPRINGS, PENNSYLVANIA

Unmodified Cellulose Papers

Grade	ml/min rapidity	Klemm mm/30 min	Weight 20 × 20″–500	Weight g/sq. m	Min. wt. strength H_2O	Thickness (in.)
4	105	98.0	22	77.6	4.5	0.0065
5	58	104.0	24	84.4	5.0	0.0065
7	170	123.0	20	70.3	4	0.0065
048	29	84.5	25	88.0	5	0.0065
248	15	70.0	25	88.0	5	0.0065
301–85	70	157.0	85	299.8	7.5	0.030
320	220	162.0	200	700.0	7.0	0.100
611	58	90.0	16	56.2	3.25	0.0050
613	58	86.0	20	70.3	5.0	0.0057
629	114	128.0	35	123.0	7.0	0.0120
641	170	147.0	41	144.0	7.0	0.015
652	19	137.0	150	532.0	16.5	0.050

[Courtesy of T. F. Patchel, Manager, Scientific Sales, Eaton-Dikeman Co.]

MACHERY-NAGEL & CO., DÜREN, GERMANY

1. Standard Chromatography Papers
These papers have received no special pre-treatment. They are suitable for all routine investigations.

Grade	Weight g/m²	Thickness mm	Flow rate mm/30 min	Surface
MN 212	120	0.21	80– 90	Smooth
MN 214	140	0.28	90–100	Smooth
MN 218	180	0.36	90–100	Smooth
MN 260	90	0.20	130–150	Smooth
MN 261	90	0.18	90–100	Smooth
MN 263	90	0.15	60– 70	Smooth
MN 827	270	0.70	130–140*	Soft, smooth
MN 866	650	1.70	150–160*	Soft, smooth

* mm/10 minutes. Stock size: sheets of 58 × 60 cm.

TABLE 7—(Continued)
COMMERCIAL SOURCES FOR CHROMATOGRAPHY PAPERS

2. Special Papers

The chromatography papers listed below are standard papers which have been specially pre-treated or chemically modified. The data presented in the preceding table apply approximately, with regard to height of wetting, weight and thickness.

Code No.	Description	Parent paper
MN 214 ff	De-fatted papers	MN 214
MN 261 ff	De-fatted papers	MN 261
MN 2214	Acid-washed papers	MN 214
MN 2261	Acid-washed papers	MN 261
MN 2214 ff	Acid-washed and de-fatted papers	MN 214
MN 2261 ff	Acid-washed and de-fatted papers	MN 261
MN 214 WA	Silicone-impregnated paper	MN 214
MN 214 AC/ca. 10%	Acetylated papers	MN 214
MN 214 AC/ca. 20%	Acetylated papers	MN 214
MN 261 AC/ca. 10%	Acetylated papers	MN 261

MN Ion-exchange papers with strong-acid and base groups are also available.

[From Bulletin PSDC el/02/0/3.69, Machery-Nagel & Co.]

H. REEVE ANGEL & CO., CLIFTON, NEW JERSEY

1. Unmodified Cellulose Papers Specifically Manufactured for Chromatography

Whatman 1—Standard paper for chromatography.
2—Slightly slower than Whatman 1.
3MM—Thick, smooth-surface paper with flow rate similar to Whatman 1.
3MC—Low carboxyl version of No. 3MM.
3—Similar to 3MM but with a rough surface.
4—Fast flow rate.
17—Extremely thick with fast flow rate for preparative chromatography.
20—Very slow flow rate; for high resolution.
31ET—Very rapid flow rate and low ash, useful for electrophoresis.

2. Papers Selected for Chromatography (sfc) but Not Specially Manufactured

40 sfc—Medium flow rate, similar to No. 2, but ashless.
41 sfc—Rapid flow rate, similar to No. 4, but ashless.
42 sfc—Very slow flow rate, similar to No. 20, but ashless.
54 sfc—Similar to No. 4, but wet-strengthened.
540 sfc—Similar to No. 40, but wet-strengthened.
541 sfc—Similar to No. 41, but wet-strengthened.
542 sfc—Similar to No. 42, but wet-strengthened.

3. Silicone Treated Papers

Type	Basis weight g/m^2	Thickness mm	Silicone content as SiO_2%	Flow rate*–min Methanol	Flow rate*–min Benzene	
ST 81	90	0.17	5	100	50	(medium flow rate)
ST 82	98	0.17	5	170	90	(slow flow rate)
ST 84	98	0.19	5	40	30	(fast flow rate)

* Descending—15 cm.

TABLE 7—(Continued)
COMMERCIAL SOURCES FOR CHROMATOGRAPHY PAPERS

4. Adsorbent-Loaded Papers

Grade	Basis Weight g/m² (*a*)	Thickness mm (*b*)	Diffusion rate min (*c*)	(*d*)	Loading (*e*)	pH (*f*)
SG 81	100	0.25	15	100	22% SiO_2	7
AH 81	100	0.20	22	100	7.5% Al_2O_3	9

(*a*) Mean total basis weight, cellulose + loading.
(*b*) By deadweight micrometer.
(*c*) Time taken for water to ascend 7.5 cm up a vertical strip of paper.
(*d*) Time taken for benzene to descend 15 cm down a vertical strip of paper.
(*e*) Estimated as ignited oxides by weight.
(*f*) pH of aqueous suspension.

5. Glass Fiber Papers

Grade	Basis weight g/m² (*a*)	Thickness mm (*b*)	Diffusion rate min (*c*)	Water absorption μl/sq. cm (*d*)
GF 81	52.5	0.25	2.5	25
GF 82	150	0.64	4.5	82
GF 83*	55	0.26	2.5	25

(*a*) Mean basis weight.
(*b*) By deadweight micrometer.
(*c*) Time taken for water to ascend 7.5 cm up a vertical strip of paper.
(*d*) Weight of water absorbed at equilibrium.
* Fiber diameter less than one half that of GF 81 and 82.

6. Ion-Exchange Cellulose Papers

Type	Basis weight g/m²	Thickness mm	Capacity μequiv/cm²	Flow rate* min	Ionic form as supplied	
P 81	85	0.17	18.0	10	Mono-ammonium	(cellulose phosphate paper)
CM 82	85	0.17	2.5	15	Hydrogen	(carboxymethyl cellulose paper)
AE 81	85	0.17	5.0	15	Free base	(aminoethyl cellulose paper)
DE 81	85	0.17	3.5	20	Free base	(diethylaminoethyl cellulose paper)
ET 81	85	0.17	2.0	10	Free base	(Ecteola cellulose paper)

* Time taken for water to ascend 7.5 cm up a vertical strip of paper.

TABLE 7—(Continued)
COMMERCIAL SOURCES FOR CHROMATOGRAPHY PAPERS

7. Ion-Exchange Resin Loaded Papers

Physical Properties

Property	SA-2	WA-2	SB-2	WB-2
Resin	Amberlite* IR-120	Amberlite* IRC-50	Amberlite* IRA-400	Amberlite* IR-4B
Resin type	Strong acid	Weak acid	Strong base	Weak base
% Resin in paper	45–50%	45–50%	45–50%	45–50%
Resin form supplied	Na^+	H^+	Cl^-	OH^-
Paper color	Tan	White	Cream	Yellow
Basis weight (20 × 20/500)	37 lb	37 lb	37 lb	37 lb
Thickness (mils)	14	14	14	14
Wet strength	Good	Good	Good	Good
Flow rate	Fast	Fast	Fast	Fast
Approximate exchange capacity meq/g dry resin	4	10	3.3	10

* Amberlite® is the registered trademark of Rohm & Haas Co., Philadelphia, Pa.
[Data from Bulletins C-1, C-4 and "Ion-Exchange Resin-Loaded Papers Technical Bulletin", H. Reeve Angel & Co., Clifton, New Jersey.]

VEB SPEZIALPAPIERFABRIK NIEDERSCHLAG, NIEDERSCHLAG/ERZGEBIRGE

(Filtrak-Niederschlag Papers)

Grade	Weight per surface area g/sq. m	Thickness mm	Absorption height mm/30 min	Moving periods in: n-BuOH-AcOH-H_2O hr/35 cm	Moving periods in: formamide/benzene-cyclohexane hr/35 cm	Surface	Moving velocity	Comparison with: Whatman	Comparison with: Schleicher & Schuell
FN 1	85– 90	0.18–0.2	140–160	9	2.5	mat	quick	4	2040a
FN 2	120–125	0.20–0.23	140–160	15	3	smooth	quick	–	2040b
FN 3	85– 90	0.18–0.2	90–100	16	3.5	mat	medium	1	2043a
FN 4	120–125	0.20–0.23	90–100	19	4	smooth	medium	–	2043b
FN 5	85– 90	0.17–0.19	60– 70	24	4	mat	slow	20	2045a
FN 6	120–125	0.20–0.23	60– 70	21	4.5	smooth	slow	–	2045b
FN 7	145–150	0.28–0.3	140–160	9	2	mat	quick	3	598L
FN 8	270–280	0.51–0.55	170–190	9	2	mat	quick	–	2247

FN 11–18 are acid-washed papers, analogous to FN 1–8. These are supplied with mat surface only, have a higher absorption velocity, and may give a different shade with a few detection reagents (e.g., ninhydrin).

TABLE 8
ADSORBENTS, ION-EXCHANGERS AND PREFORMED LAYERS FOR THIN-LAYER CHROMATOGRAPHY

SCHLEICHER & SCHUELL INC., KEENE, NEW HAMPSHIRE

1. Powders

Number	Sorption medium
Cellulose powders	
142dg	Cellulose powder double-acid-washed
144	Very fine and pure crystalline cellulose powder
144 LS 254	Cellulose powder containing 3% inorganic luminescent material (254 nm)
144/6ac	6% acetylated cellulose powder (254 nm)
144/21ac	21% acetylated cellulose powder (254 nm)
144/45ac	45% acetylated cellulose powder (254 nm)
Silica gel	
150	Silica gel, normal
150 G	Silica gel, bonded with 15% gypsum
150 S	Silica gel, bonded with 15% starch
150 LS 254	Silica gel, normal, inorganic luminescent materials added (254 nm)
150 G/LS 254	Silica gel bonded with gypsum, luminescent materials added (254 nm)
150 S/LS 254	Silica gel bonded with starch, luminescent materials added (254 nm)

2. Selectacel powders

Anion exchangers

TLC/DEAE (No. 66). Contains diethylaminoethyl residues as functional groups. Useful for the separation and purification of many proteins, enzymes, hormones and related materials.

TLC/ECTEOLA (No. 67). Prepared by the reaction of epichlorohydrin and triethanolamine with cellulose. Particularly valuable in work with nucleic acids and related materials.

Cation exchangers

TLC/CM (No. 68). Based on carboxymethyl cellulose. Most effective at pH's slightly above 4.

TLC/P (No. 69). Prepared by phosphoric acid esterification of cellulose. This is a bifunctional type material containing strongly acidic as well as weakly acidic groups. Selectacel P is characterized by a relatively high exchange capacity and is capable of some unusual separations, e.g., the sorption of certain cations from very acidic media.

Pure cellulose powder (No. 65). A pure cellulose powder especially developed for thin-layer chromatography. It is used when the ion-exchange properties of the other Selectacel TLC powders are not needed. Especially suitable for separation of amino acids, sugars and related compounds.

3. Selecta Pre-coated Sheets

F 1440—cellulose
F 1500—Silica gel
F 1600—Polyamide
F 1700—Polyamide, coated on both sides

Available with or without 254 nm fluorescent indicator.

4. Ready-Plates (preformed layers on glass plates)

Number	Sorption medium
1440	Cellulose powder Nr. 144
1440 Z	Cellulose powder Nr. 144 in ten. 7 mm wide strips for single chromatograms
1440 LS 254	Cellulose powder Nr. 144 with inorganic fluorescent material
1440/21 ac	Cellulose powder Nr. 144/21 ac
1440/45 ac	Cellulose powder Nr. 144/45 ac
1440/A5	Cellulose powder Nr. 144 with 5% Dowex 2-X8 (Anion Exchanger)
1440/A10	10% Dowex 2-X8 (Anion Exchanger)
1440/K5	5% Dowex 50W-X8 (Cation Exchanger)
1440/K10	10% Dowex 50W-X8 (Cation Exchanger)
1440 PEI	PEI-Cellulose
1500	Silica gel-acid fast
1500 LS 254	Silica gel with fluorescent material added (254 mm)
1500 S	Silica gel, binder: starch
1500 S/LS 254	Silica gel with inorganic fluorescent material added (254 mm), binder: starch
1600	Polyamide, binder: starch

TABLE 8—(Continued)
ADSORBENTS, ION-EXCHANGERS AND PREFORMED LAYERS FOR THIN-LAYER CHROMATOGRAPHY

Methods for Impregnation of Thin-Layer Plates

Impregnation with paraffin oil

Cellulose plates which have been quick dried for several hours at 110 °C are impregnated with a 5–10% solution of paraffin in low-boiling petroleum ether. This is accomplished by allowing the solution in the closed chamber to rise to the opposite edge, chromatographically.

Impregnation with formamide

The cellulose plate is immersed for several minutes in a 20% acetone solution of formamide, and then dried at normal temperature until the odor of acetone has disappeared.

Impregnation with silicone

The plate is placed for about 30 minutes under reduced pressure in a vacuum desiccator which has been saturated with 3–5 ml of dichlorodimethylsilane. It should then be left exposed to air for another 30 minutes.

Impregnation with fatty substances

Example: A 7% solution of palm oil in petroleum ether. This solution is allowed to rise under chromatographic conditions, within the plate, to the opposite edge. Subsequently the plate is dried in air.

Impregnation with undecane

The plates (cellulose or silica gel) are placed in a 15% solution of undecane (190–220 °C) in petroleum ether, left in this solution for a little while, and then dried in air.

[The above material is from Schleicher & Schuell Bulletins 55.68, 42-5M-4-65, and 51A.]

H. REEVE ANGEL, CLIFTON, NEW JERSEY

CC 41—Ultrapure microgranular cellulose powder.
P 41—Cellulose phosphate.
CM 41—Carboxymethyl cellulose.
AE 41—Aminoethyl cellulose.
DE 41—Diethylaminoethyl cellulose.
ET 41—Ecteola cellulose.

J. T. BAKER CHEMICAL CO., PHILLIPSBURG, NEW JERSEY

Baker-Flex Preformed Layers on Flexible Plastic Sheets

No.	Type
4448	Silica gel IB2
4449	Silica gel IB2-F
4462	Silica gel IB
4463	Silica gel IB-F
4464	Silica gel S
4465	Silica gel S-F
4466	Aluminum oxide IB
4467	Aluminum oxide IB-F
4468	Cellulose
4469	Cellulose-F
4470	Polyamide 11, coated with polyamide 11 powder
4471	Polyamide 11-F
4472	Cellulose AC-10, coated with 10% acetylated cellulose powder
4473	Cellulose PEI, coated with polyethyleneimine cellulose powder; fluoresces strongly at 3660Å and weakly at 2540Å
4474	Cellulose PEI-F, enhanced fluorescence at 2540Å
4475	Polyamide 6, coated with polyamide 6 powder
4476	Polyamide 6-F
4477	Cellulose DEAE, coated with diethylaminoethyl cellulose powder
4478	Cellulose Ecteola, coated with Ecteola cellulose
4479	Cellulose CM, coated with carboxymethyl cellulose powder
4480	Microcrystalline cellulose
4481	Microcrystalline cellulose-F

(Products designated F contain a zinc silicate fluorescent indicator activated at 2540 Å; IB designation indicates an inert binder and a layer 200 μ thick; S layers have a starch binder: these and the other unbound layers are 100 μ thick; IB2 layers have an inert binder with characteristics more like silica gel G.)

TABLE 8—(Continued)
ADSORBENTS, ION-EXCHANGERS AND PREFORMED LAYERS FOR THIN-LAYER CHROMATOGRAPHY

Baker TLC Reagents
- Silica Gel 7—Neutral silica gel containing no binder.
- Silica Gel 7G—Neutral silica gel with $CaSO_4 \cdot 1/2H_2O$ binder.
- Silica Gel 7GF—Neutral silica gel with binder and fluorescent indicator.
- Aluminum oxide 9F—basic aluminum oxide with fluorescent indicator.
- Microcrystalline cellulose.
- Cellulose AC-10—10% acetylated cellulose.
- Cellulose CM—carboxymethyl cellulose.
- Cellulose DEAE—Diethylaminoethyl cellulose.
- Cellulose Ecteola.
- Cellulose PEI—Polyethyleneimine cellulose.
- Polyamide 6—Polycaprolactam.
- Polyamide 11—Polyaminoundecanoic acid.
- Kieselguhr.

DISTILLATION PRODUCTS INDUSTRIES, ROCHESTER, NEW YORK

Eastman Chromagram Preformed Layers on Flexible Plastic Sheets

No. 6060—Silica gel-F.
6061—Silica gel.
6062—Alumina.
6063—Alumina-F.
6064—Cellulose.
6065—Cellulose-F.
6066—Polyamide.
6067—Polycarbonate (for partition chromatography with all solvents except chlorinated ones).

(All layers are 100 μ thickness; the first four listed contain a binder which does not allow the use of charring reagents; F indicates the presence of a fluorescent indicator.)

SCIENTIFIC GLASS APPARATUS CO., BLOOMFIELD, NEW JERSEY

SilicAR (Mallinckrodt) TLC silicic acid sorbents; SilicAR TLC-7GF contains a gypsum binder and fluorescent indicator.

ChromAR (Mallinckrodt) Sheet 500—a 500 μ sheet of 70% silicic acid and 30% glass fiber containing a short-wave UV phosphor.

GELMAN INSTRUMENTS CO., ANN ARBOR, MICHIGAN

Instant Thin Layer (ITLC) Media

Glass microfiber sheets impregnated with silica gel (Type SG) or silicic acid (Type SA).

WATERS ASSOCIATES, FRAMINGHAM, MASS.

1. **Woelm Powders**

Alumina, acid	Silica Gel F
Alumina, basic	Silica Gel G
Alumina, neutral	Silica Gel GF
Alumina G	Magnesium Silicate
Silica Gel	Polyamide

(Products designated G have a gypsum binder, F have a fluorescent indicator.)

2. **Woelm Precoated Plates**
   Silica Gel.
   Silica Gel F (254/366 nm).

3. **Woelm Precoated Aluminum Sheets**
   Silica Gel.
   Silica Gel F (254/366 nm).

BIO RAD LABORATORIES, RICHMOND, CALIFORNIA

1. **Silicic Acid for TLC**
   Bio-Sil A for TLC, 2–10 microns, without binder.
   Bio-Sil A for TLC, 2–10 microns, with 5% binder.
   Bio-Sil A is also available with fluorescent zinc silicate.

TABLE 8—(Continued)
ADSORBENTS, ION-EXCHANGERS AND PREFORMED LAYERS FOR THIN-LAYER CHROMATOGRAPHY

2. Ion-Exchange Celluloses for TLC
Cellex D for TLC (DEAE cellulose).
Cellex E for TLC (ECTEOLA cellulose).
Cellex PEI for TLC (polyethyleneimine cellulose).
Cellex CM for TLC (carboxymethyl cellulose).
Cellex P for TLC (phosphonic acid cellulose).
Cellex N-1 for TLC (cellulose powder).
Cellex MX for TLC (microcrystalline cellulose).

KENSINGTON SCIENTIFIC CORP., OAKLAND, CALIFORNIA

Precoated TLC plates are custom-prepared with any adsorbent (including hydroxyapatite, Sephadex, etc.) of more than ten manufacturers in a wide range of layer thicknesses.

CAMAG, INC., MILWAUKEE, WISCONSIN

1. Adsorbents

+ Denotes "present" — Denotes "absent"				
Adsorbents with fluorescent indicator	−	+	−	+
Adsorbents with 5% $CaSO_4$ binder	−	+	+	−
Aluminum oxide DS for all adsorption-chromatographic separations, DS-0 and DSF-0 grades for preparative layers of 2 mm and over, in some cases also for thin-layer electrophoresis.	DS-0	DSF-5	DS-5	DSF-0
Silica gel DS for all adsorption-chromatographic separations, DS-0 and DSF-0 grades for preparative layers of 2 mm and over, and for TLE.	DS-0	DSF-5	DS-5	DSF-0
Silica gel D for analytical separations, particularly for partition chromatography, for preparative layers up to 1 mm.	D-0	DF-5	D-5	DF-0
Cellulose powder D for analytical partition chromatographic separations (layer thickness 0.5 recommended), layer thickness of 1.5 mm should not be exceeded.	D-0			DF-0
Cellulose powder DS microcrystalline cellulose for all kinds of partition chromatography and thin-layer electrophoresis.	DS-0			DSF-0

2. Precoated Plates

	A	F-A	S-A	SF-A	S-O	SF-O
Silica gel	30-079	30-179	31-079	31-179	—	—
Aluminum oxide	—	—	33-079	33-179	—	—
Cellulose, microcrystalline	—	—	—	—	35-089	35-189

Grade designations: A—starch bound; O—no binder; F—fluorescent indicator; S—quick-running (larger particle size).
Note: starch-bound plates cannot be used when detecting with iodine or sulfuric acid. Cellulose plates are binder free.

ANALTECH, INC., WILMINGTON, DELAWARE

Precoated plates with layer thickness up to 2000 μ made from the following sorbents:

Merck. Silica gel H, HF, HR and GF, aluminum oxide H, HF and GF, polyamide powder 7435, and kieselguhr GF.
Mallinckrodt. SilicAR 7G and 7GF.
Machery Nagel. Silica gel G-HR and G-HR/UV, 10 and 20% acetylated cellulose MN300 and cellulose MN300F.
Woelm. Silica gel G; basic, acidic and neutral alumina.
S & S. Cellulose DEAE, Ecteola, CM and phosphate.
FMC. PEI Avicel.
Floridin. Florisil.

TABLE 8—(Continued)
ADSORBENTS, ION-EXCHANGERS AND PREFORMED LAYERS FOR THIN-LAYER CHROMATOGRAPHY

APPLIED SCIENCE LABORATORIES, INC., STATE COLLEGE, PENNSYLVANIA

1. Adsorbents

Adsorbosil-1—Silica gel with 10% $CaSO_4$ binder.
Adsorbosil-2—Same as 1 without binder.
Adsorbosil-3—Silica gel with 10% magnesium silicate added.
Adsorbosil-4—Extra high purity Adsorbosil-3.
Adsorbosil-5—Silica gel with no binder but the toughest binding characteristics of any Adsorbosil.
Adsorbosil-ADN—Silica gel impregnated with silver nitrate. Adsorbosils-1, -2, or -5 are available with 5% or 25% impregnation.
Adsorbosil-G-1—Porous glass with 13% $CaSO_4$ binder.
Adsorbosil-G-2—Porous glass without binder.
Reversil-3—Silica gel treated with dimethyldichlorosilane.
Aluminum oxide GA—with 10% $CaSO_4$ binder.
Aluminum oxide HA—without binder.
Silica gel GA—Less pure grade of silica gel than Adsorbosil, with 10% $CaSO_4$ binder.
Silica gel HA—without binder.
Cellulose—microcrystalline.
Adsorbosil-M-1—Magnesium silicate with binder.
Adsorbosil-M-2—Magnesium silicate without binder.
(Adsorbosils-1-P, -2-P, and -5-P contain an inorganic phosphorescent indicator.)

2. "Prekotes" Precoated TLC Plates

Adsorbosil-5 precoated on glass plates in a 250 μ layer.

MACHERY-NAGEL & CO., DÜREN, GERMANY

1. Normal and Acetylated MN-Cellulose Powders

Type	Comments
MN 300	Native, fibrous cellulose
MN 300 UV_{254}	MN 300 with fluorescent additive
MN 300 HR	Highly purified MN 300
MN 300 AC/ca. 10%	
MN 300 AC/ca. 20%	
MN 300 AC/ca. 30%	Acetylated cellulose
MN 300 AC/ca. 40%	
Avicel	Microcrystalline cellulose

(All types except MN 300 HR and Avicel can be supplied with gypsum binder, in which case the designation "G" will follow the code number.)

Analytical data for the most important MN-Cellulose powders.

		MN 300	MN 300 HR
Ignition residue at 850 °C, in ppm	max.	800	100
Iron as Fe, in ppm	max.	15	2
Copper as Cu, in ppm	max.	6	1
Phosphate as P, in ppm	max.	7	—
Methylene chloride extract, in %	max.	0.12	0.01
Average degree of polymerization		400–500	400–500
Fiber length, in μ (> 95%)		2–20	2–20
Specific surface according to Blaine cm^2/g	approx.	15,000	15,000

TABLE 8—(Continued)

ADSORBENTS, ION-EXCHANGERS AND PREFORMED LAYERS FOR THIN-LAYER CHROMATOGRAPHY

2. Ion-Exchange Celluloses

	Variety[a]	Binder[b]	Type	Capacity meq/g
Cation-exchanger	MN 300 P	None	Phosphorylated cellulose	Approx. 0.7
	MN 300 CM	None	Carboxymethyl cellulose	Approx. 0.7
	MN Poly-P	None	Polyphosphate impregnated cellulose	Approx. 0.7
Anion-exchanger	MN 300 DEAE	None	Diethylaminoethyl cellulose	Approx. 0.7
	MN 300 ECTEOLA	None	Cellulose derivative	Approx. 0.35
	MN 300 PEI	None	Polyethyleneimine impregnated cellulose	Approx. 1.0

[a] Fibrous material with a fiber length in the range 5–25 μ.
[b] Upon request all types may be supplied with gypsum binder (suffix "G").

3. MN-Silica gels

Silica gels for TLC are supplied in two grades of purity, namely

1. Standard quality.
2. Highly pure ("HR") quality.

These basic types of silica gel are mixed with various additives and yield the range of media given below.

Standard grades	Standard grades with fluorescent additive[a]	Highly pure grades[b]	Highly pure grades with fluorescent additive[a]
Silica gel G	Silica gel G/UV_{254}	Silica gel G-HR	Silica gel G-HR/UV_{254}
Silica gel N	Silica gel N/UV_{254}	Silica gel N-HR	Silica gel N-HR/UV_{254}
Silica gel S	Silica gel S/UV_{254}	Silica gel S-HR	Silica gel S-HR/UV_{254}

G = With gypsum added. N = Normal (without binder). S = With starch added.
UV_{254} = Fluorescent additive with an absorption maximum in short-wavelength UV light at 254 mm.

[a] The inorganic fluorescent additive emits a strong green fluorescence when under short-wavelength UV light of 254 nm. The range of solvents which may be used in conjunction with silica gels containing this additive is restricted since certain solvents quench the fluorescence. Silica gels containing the additive are favored in preparative TLC where they facilitate detection without damage to substances sought after.

[b] Highly pure silica gel ("HR") varieties are manufactured from silica gels of standard quality by removing inorganic impurities with acids and fully deionized water. The residual inorganic impurities (particularly iron compounds) are reduced to such minimal levels that they no longer interfere with chromatographic separations and quantitative determinations. Organic impurities which may still be present, must be removed by the selected developing solvent which should be at least of analytical grade purity. This may be accomplished by allowing the solvent to ascend the layer before the mixtures are applied to the plate. The purity of the layer then depends largely on that of the developing solvent.

Analytical data for the silica gels listed above.

	Standard grades	Highly pure (HR) grades
Particle size	2–40 μ	5–40 μ
Iron	Max. 0.01 %	Max. 0.001 %
Chloride	Max. 0.01 %	Max. 0.003 %
pH of 10% aqueous suspension	Approx. 6.8	Approx. 6.8

4. MN-Kieselguhr

MN-Kieselguhr G (with gypsum).
MN-Kieselguhr N (without binder).

5. MN-Aluminum Oxide

MN-Aluminum oxide G (with gypsum).
MN-Aluminum oxide G/UV_{254} (with gypsum and fluorescent additive).
MN-Aluminum oxide N (without binder).
MN-Aluminum oxide N/UV_{254} (without binder, but with a fluorescent additive).

6. MN-Polyamide Powders

Grade	Nylon 66 Polyhexamethylene diaminoadipate	Nylon 6 (Perlon) Polycaprolactam	Nylon 11 Polyaminoundecanoic acid
Standard grade	Polyamide-TLC 66	Polyamide-TLC 6	Polyamide-TLC 11
With fluorescent additive	Polyamide-TLC 66 UV_{254}	Polyamide-TLC 6 UV_{254}	Polyamide-TLC 11 UV_{254}
Acetylated polyamide	Polyamide-TLC 66 AC	Polyamide-TLC 6 AC	Polyamide-TLC 11 AC

TABLE 8—(Continued)
ADSORBENTS, ION-EXCHANGERS AND PREFORMED LAYERS FOR THIN-LAYER CHROMATOGRAPHY

7. Precoated Polygram Plastic Foils

Polygram®-foil	Coated with MN-sorbent	Thickness of layer mm	Binder
ALOX N	Aluminum oxide N	0.2	Inert, resists H_2SO_4[b]
ALOX N/UV_{254}	Aluminum oxide N/UV_{254}[a]	0.2	Inert, resists H_2SO_4[b]
CEL 300	Cellulose MN 300	0.1	—
CEL 300 UV_{254}	Cellulose MN 300 UV_{254}[a]	0.1	—
CEL 400	Microcrystalline cellulose	0.1	—
CEL 400 UV_{254}	Microcrystalline cellulose UV_{254}[a]	0.1	—
CEL 300 AC-10	Acetylated (10%) cellulose MN 300	0.1	—
CEL 300 AC-30	Acetylated (30%) cellulose MN 300	0.1	—
CEL 300 PEI	MN 300 cellulose PEI-impregnated	0.1	—
CEL 300 PEI/UV_{254}	MN 300 cellulose PEI-impregnated[a]	0.1	—
CEL 300 DEAE	Cellulose MN 300 DEAE	0.1	—
CEL 300 ECTEOLA	Cellulose MN 300 ECTEOLA	0.1	—
CEL 300 CM	Cellulose MN 300 CM	0.1	—
POLYAMIDE-11	MN-Polyamide-TLC 11	0.1	—
POLYAMIDE-11 UV_{254}	MN-Polyamide-TLC 11 UV_{254}[a]	0.1	—
POLYAMIDE-6	MN-Polyamide-TLC 6	0.1	—
POLYAMIDE-6 UV_{254}	MN-Polyamide-TLC 6 UV_{254}[a]	0.1	—
SIL N-HR	Silica gel N-HR	0.2	Inert, resists H_2SO_4[b]
SIL N-HR/UV_{254}	Silica gel N-HR/UV_{254}[a]	0.2	Inert, resists H_2SO_4[b]
SIL S-HR	Silica gel S-HR	0.1	Starch
SIL S-HR/UV_{254}	Silica gel S-HR/UV_{254}[a]	0.1	Starch

[a] Sorbent with fluorescent additive.

[b] The binder resists corrosive detecting reagents and charring technique, i.e. spraying with concentrated sulfuric acid and heating to 110 to 120 °C for 10 min. A large excess of H_2SO_4 should be avoided.

[Information from Machery Nagel Bulletin PSDC el/02/0/3.69.]

BRINKMANN INSTRUMENTS INC., WESTBURY, NEW YORK
E. MERCK SORBENTS

1. Analytical Sorbents

- Aluminum oxide G, type-E[a] (1090)
- Aluminum oxide GF-254, type-E[a] (1092)
- Aluminum oxide H, type-E[a] (1085)
- Aluminum oxide HF-254, type-E[a] (1094)
- Aluminum oxide, acidic, type-T[a] (1106)
- Aluminum oxide, basic, type-T[a] (1105)
- Aluminum oxide, neutral, type-T[a] (1101)
- Kieselguhr G (8129)
- Polyamide powder (7435)
- Silica gel G (7731)
- Silica gel GF-254 (7730)
- Silica gel H (7736)
- Silica gel HR (7744)
- Silica gel HF-254 (7739)
- Silica gel HF-254, silanized (7750)
- Silica gel HF-254 + 366 (7741)
- Fluorescent indicator (luminous pigment) F-254
- Avicel micro crystalline cellulose
- PEI—Cellulose (2336)
- Powder for TLC

2. Preparative Sorbents

- Aluminum oxide PF-254, type-E[a] (1103)
- Aluminum oxide PF-254, type-T[a] (1064)
- Aluminum oxide PF-254 + 366, type-T[a] (1065)
- Aluminum oxide PF-254 + 366, type E[a] (1104)
- Silica gel PF-254 (7747)
- Silica gel PF-254, silanized (7751)
- Silica gel PF-254 + 366 (7748)
- Silica gel PF-254 with calcium sulfate (7749)

[a] Type-E materials are especially recommended for pesticides. Type-T materials are especially recommended for steroids and higher peptides.

Suffix: G—indicates $CaSO_4$ binder.
H—without binder.
S—starch binder.
HR—exceptionally pure.
F—2% inclusion of UV indicator.
P—sorbents for making preparative layers.

TABLE 8—(Continued)
ABSORBENTS, ION-EXCHANGERS AND PREFORMED LAYERS FOR THIN-LAYER CHROMATOGRAPHY

3. Precoated Glass Plates

Carrier	Layer thickness	UV indicator
Analytical Layers		
Aluminum oxide F-254, type-T([b]), *with* fluorescent indicator, pH 9.0	250 microns	Inorganic 2540 Å
Aluminum oxide F-254, type-E([a]), *with* fluorescent indicator, pH 9.0	250 microns	Inorganic 2540 Å
Silica gel, *without* fluorescent indicator	250 microns	—
Silica gel F-254, *with* fluorescent indicator	250 microns	Inorganic 2540 Å
Cellulose micro crystalline avicel, *without* fluorescent indicator	100 microns	—
Cellulose micro crystalline avicel, *with* fluorescent indicator	100 microns	Inorganic 2540 Å
Preparative Layers		
Silica gel F-254, *with* fluorescent indicator	0.5 mm	Inorganic 2540 Å
Silica gel F-254, *with* fluorescent indicator	2 mm	Inorganic 2540 Å
Aluminum oxide F-254, type-T([b]), *with* fluorescent indicator	1.5 mm	Inorganic 2540 Å

[a] Aluminum oxide type-E has the same properties as aluminum oxide H. Its special binder permits spraying with silver nitrate solutions making it especially good for the visualization of pesticides.

[b] Aluminum oxide type-T has a lower specific surface area and a larger pore size. It is especially suited for the separation of steroids and higher peptides (i.e. testosterone and epi-testosterone).

4. Precoated Aluminum Sheets

Sorbent	Layer thickness	UV indicator
Aluminum oxide F-254, type-T([a])	0.2 mm	Inorganic 2540 Å
Aluminum oxide F-254, type-E([a])	0.2 mm	Inorganic 2540 Å
Cellulose, micro crystalline avicel	0.1 mm	No
Kieselguhr F-254	0.2 mm	Inorganic 2540 Å
Magnesium silicate F-254	0.2 mm	Inorganic 2540 Å
Polyamide F-254, type II	0.15 mm	Inorganic 2540 Å
Silica gel F-254	0.25 mm	Inorganic 2540 Å
Silica gel	0.25 mm	No

[a] Aluminum oxide type-T sheets have the same binder as silica gel sheets, and are especially recommended for the separation of steroids and higher peptides. Aluminum oxide type-E sheets have a special binder which permits spraying with silver nitrate, and are especially recommended for pesticides.

[Brinkmann also supplies Machery-Nagel TLC powders and Polygram plastic sheets.]
(See also Table 4 for Sephadex Gels for TLC.)

VOLUME TWO
SECTION II

II.IV International Chromatography Book Directory

Section II.IV

International Chromatography Book Directory

Reproduced with permission of the Editor and Publisher of *Journal of Chromatographic Science*, Preston Technical Abstracts, 2101 Dempster St., Evanston, Illinois, 60601; from *J. Chromatogr. Sci.* **8**, D1–D23 (1970). Numbers at the end of each citation refers to Author's Index at the end of this section.

	Electrophoresis	Gas	Gel Permeation	Ion Exchange	Liquid (Column)	Paper	Thin Layer	Other Chrom. Tech.	General
ACADEMIC PRESS INC., 111 5th Avenue, New York, New York 10003 212 677-6713									
BIER, M. *Electrophoresis: Theory, Methods and Applications*, Volume 1 (1959), 563 pp, $16.50. 20	×	—	—	—	—	—	—	—	—
BIER, M. *Electrophoresis: Theory, Methods and Applications*, Volume 2 (1967), 553 pp, $21.00. 25	×	—	—	—	—	—	—	—	—
BLOCK, R. J. *A Manual of Paper Chromatography and Paper Electrophoresis* (1958), 710 pp, $16.50. 30	×	—	—	—	—	×	—	—	—
BRENNER, N., CALLEN, J. E., and WEISS, M. D. *Third International Gas Chromatography Symposium* (see Instrument Society) (1962), 719 pp, $22.00. 35	—	×	—	—	—	—	—	—	—
BURCHFIELD, H. P. and STORRS, E. H. *Biochemical Applications of Gas Chromatography* (1962), 680 pp, $25.00. 40	—	×	—	—	—	—	—	—	—
CANTOW, M. J. R. *Polymer Fractionation* (1967), 527 pp, $22.50. 45	—	—	×	—	×	—	—	—	—
FOWLER, L. *Gas Chromatography* (1963), 226 pp, $10.50. 50	—	×	—	—	—	—	—	—	—
HAIS, I. M. and MACEK, K. *Bibliography of Paper Chromatography 1944–1956* (1960), 766 pp, $24.00. 55	—	—	—	—	—	×	—	—	—
HAIS, I. M. and MACEK, K. *Bibliography of Paper Chromatography 1957–1960* (1962), 706 pp, $24.00. 60	—	—	—	—	—	×	—	—	—
HAIS, I. M. and MACEK, K. *Paper Chromatography: A Comprehensive Treatise* (1963), 955 pp, $26.50. 65	—	—	—	—	—	×	—	—	—
LITTLEWOOD, A. B., *Gas Chromatography*, Second Edition (1970), 521 pp, $22.50. 70	—	×	—	—	—	—	—	—	—
MACKENZIE, R. C. *Differential Thermal Analysis*, Volume 1 (1970), $33.00. 72	—	×	—	—	—	—	—	—	—
POLVANI, F., SURACE, and LUISI, M. *Gas Chromatographic Determination of Hormonal Steroids* (1968), 324 pp, $15.00. 75	—	×	—	—	—	—	—	—	—
RANDERATH, K. *Thin-Layer Chromatography*, Second Edition (see Verlag Chemie) (1966), 285 pp, $9.50. 80	—	—	—	—	—	—	×	—	—
SHAW. *Electrophoresis* (1969), 144 pp, $4.95. 85	×	—	—	—	—	—	—	—	—
SHELLARD, E. J. *Quantitative Paper and Thin-Layer Chromatography* (1968), 140 pp, $6.50. 90	—	—	—	—	—	×	×	—	—
WOLF, F. *Separation Methods in Organic Chemistry and Biochemistry* (1969), 199 pp, $11.50. 95	—	—	×	×	×	×	×	×	—
WHITAKER, J. R. *Electrophoresis*, Volume 1 (1967), 420 pp, $16.50. 100	×	—	—	—	—	—	—	—	—
ZWEIG, G. and SHERMA, J. *Paper Chromatography*, Volume 2 (1971), app 614 pp. $21.00. 105	—	—	—	—	—	×	—	—	—
ZWEIG, G. and SHERMA, J. *Analytical Methods for Pesticides and Plant Growth Regulation*, Volume 6. *Gas Chromatographic Analysis* (1972), 765 pp, $35.00.									
AKADEMISCHE VERLAGSGESELLSCHAFT, Cronstettenstrasse 6a, 6000 Frankfurt/Main, West Germany 59 06 47									
HESSE, G. *Chromatographisches Praktikum* (1968), 236 pp, DM39. 125	—	—	—	—	—	—	—	—	×
JENTZSCH, D. and OTTE, E. *Detektoven in der Gas-Chromatographie* (1970), 400 pp, DM50. 130	—	×	—	—	—	—	—	—	—

INTERNATIONAL CHROMATOGRAPHY BOOK DIRECTORY—(Continued)

	Electrophoresis	Gas	Gel Permeation	Ion Exchange	Liquid (Column)	Paper	Thin Layer	Other Chrom. Tech.	General
AKADEMIE-VERLAG GmbH, Leipziger Strasse 3-4, 108 Berlin, West Germany 22 04 41									
STRUPPE, H. G. *Gas-Chromatographie 1965* (1966), 583 pp, DM48. 150	—	×	—	—	—	—	—	—	—
VÁMOS. *Papierelektrophorese* (1970), 288 pp, DM36. 155	×	—	—	—	—	—	—	—	—
AMERICAN ELSEVIER PUBLISHING CO., INC. (See Elsevier Publishing Company)									
AMERICAN SOCIETY FOR TESTING AND MATERIALS, 1916 Race Street, Philadelphia, Pennsylvania 19103 215 569-4200									
SCHUPP, O. E., III, and LEWIS, J. S. *Compilation of Gas Chromatographic Data* (1967), 732 pp, $40.00. 175	—	×	—	—	—	—	—	—	—
ANALABS, INC., 80 Republic Drive, North Haven, Connecticut 06473 203 288-8463									
LYNN, T. R., HOFFMAN, C. L., and AUSTIN, M. M. *Guide to Stationary Phases for Gas Chromatography* (1970), 116 pp, $0.55. 195	—	×	—	—	—	—	—	—	—
ANALYTICAL BIOCHEMISTRY LABORATORIES, INC., P.O. Box 1097, Columbia, Missouri 65201 314 474-6050									
GEHRKE, C., ROACH, D., ZUMWALT, R., STALLING, D., and WALL, L. L. *Quantitative Gas-Liquid Chromatography of Amino Acids in Proteins and Biological Substances* (1968), 168 pp, $8.50 U.S.A., $9.00 Foreign. 215	—	×	—	—	—	—	—	—	—
ANN ARBOR-HUMPHREY SCIENCE PUBLISHERS, INC., Drawer No. 1425, 2155 Jackson Avenue, Ann Arbor, Michigan 48106 313 761-5010									
ARQUEMBOURG, P. C., SALVAGGIO, J. E., and BICKERS, J. N. *Primer of Immunoelectrophoresis* (see S. Karger) (1970), 83 pp, $8.25. 235	×	—	—	—	—	—	—	—	—
CHIN, H. P. *Cellulose Acetate Electrophoresis*, Techniques and Applications (1970), 140 pp, $15.75. 240	×	—	—	—	—	—	—	—	—
HAER, F. C. *An Introduction to Chromatography on Impregnated Glass Fiber* (1969), 174 pp, $15.00. 245	—	—	—	—	—	—	—	×	—
HAYWOOD, B. J. *Electrophoresis Technical Applications*, A Bibliography of Abstracts (1969), 440 pp, $18.75. 250	×	—	—	—	—	—	—	—	—
HAYWOOD, B. J. *Thin-Layer Chromatography*, An Annotated Bibliography (1968), 284 pp, $15.00. 255	—	—	—	—	—	—	×	—	—
LA GRANGE, G. and RENOZ, L. *Fifth International Symposium of Chromatography and Electrophoresis* (see Presses Academiques) (1969), 594 pp, $21.50. 260	×	—	—	—	—	—	—	—	×
MAURER, H. R. *Disc Electrophoresis* (see Walter De Gruyter) (1970), $18.75. 265	×	—	—	—	—	—	—	—	—
NIEDERWIESER, A. and PATAKI, G., Editors. *New Techniques in Amino Acid, Peptide and Protein Analysis* (1970), 400 pp, $22.50. 270	—	×	—	—	—	—	×	—	—
NIEDERWIESER, A. and PATAKI, G., Editors. *Progress in Thin-Layer Chromatography and Related Methods*, Volume 1 (1970), 240 pp, $15.00. 275	—	—	—	—	—	—	×	—	—
NIEDERWIESER, A. and PATAKI, G., Editors. *Progress in Thin-Layer Chromatography and Related Methods*, Volume 2 (1970), 400 pp, $18.75. 280	—	—	—	—	—	—	×	—	—
NIEDERWIESER, A. and PATAKI, G., Editors. *Progress in Thin-Layer Chromatography and Related Methods*, Volume 3 (1970), 400 pp, $18.75. 285	—	—	—	—	—	—	×	—	—

INTERNATIONAL CHROMATOGRAPHY BOOK DIRECTORY—(Continued)

	Electrophoresis	Gas	Gel Permeation	Ion Exchange	Liquid (Column)	Paper	Thin Layer	Other Chrom. Tech.	General
OUCHTERLONY, O. *Handbook of Immunodiffusion and Immunoelectrophoresis* (1968), 215 pp, $12.75. 290	×	—	—	—	—	—	—	—	—
PATAKI, G. *Techniques of Thin-Layer Chromatography in Amino Acid and Peptide Chemistry* (1969), 252 pp, $18.75. 295	—	—	—	—	—	—	×	—	—
SCOTT, R. M. *Clinical Analysis by Thin-Layer Chromatography Techniques* (1969), 228 pp, $18.75. 300	—	—	—	—	—	—	×	—	—
ASSOCIATION OF GREEK CHEMISTS, 27 Kaningos Street, Athens 147, Greece 621-524									
PARISSAKIS, G., Editor. *Chromatographie et Méthodes de Separation Immédiate*, Tome 1 (1966), 426 pp, $11.00. 320	—	—	—	—	—	—	—	—	×
PARISSAKIS, G., Editor. *Chromatographie et Méthodes de Séparation Immédiate*, Tome 2 (1966), 317 pp, $11.00. 325	—	—	—	—	—	—	—	—	×
AVI PUBLISHING CO., INC., P.O. Box 388, Westport, Connecticut 06881 203 227-0534									
SCHULTZ, H. W., DAY, E. A., and LIBBEY, L. M., Editors. *Symposium on Foods: The Chemistry and Physiology of Flavor* (1967), 552 pp, $3.00. 345	—	×	—	—	—	—	—	—	—
BDH CHEMICALS LTD., Poole, Dorset, England Parkstone 5520									
SARGENT, J. R. *Methods in Zone Electrophoresis* (1969), 118 pp, 25 s 365	×	—	—	—	—	—	—	—	—
BARNES & NOBLE, INC., 105 Fifth Avenue, New York, New York 10003 212 255-8100									
GREGG, S. J. *The Surface Chemistry of Solids*, Second Edition (1961), 393 pp, $9.50. 385	—	—	—	×	—	—	—	—	×
KNOX, J. H. *Gas Chromatography* (1962), 126 pp, $2.50. 390	—	×	—	—	×	—	—	×	—
LAWRIE, J. *Natural Gas and Methane Sources* (1961), 204 pp, $5.50. 395	—	—	—	—	—	—	—	—	×
PASS, G. and SUTCLIFFE, H. *Practical Inorganic Chemistry: Preparation, Reactions and Instrumental Methods* (1968), 225 pp, $6.50. 400	—	×	—	—	—	—	—	—	—
STOCK, R. and RICE, C. B. F. *Chromatographic Methods*, Second Edition (see Chapman & Hall and Reinhold) (1967), 256 pp, $3.50 Paper. 405	×	×	—	×	×	×	×	×	—
BIBLIOGRAPHISCHES INSTITUT AG, Friedrich-Karl-Strasse 12, 68 Mannheim-1, West Germany 0621 47 07 7									
KAISER, R. *Chromatographie in der Gasphase*, Band 1 (in German), (see Butterworth) (1965), 206 pp, DM7.90. 425	—	×	—	—	—	—	—	—	—
KAISER, R. *Chromatographie in der Gasphase*, Band 2, Kapillar-Chromatographie (in German), (see Butterworth) (1966), 339 pp, DM8.90. 430	—	×	—	—	—	—	—	—	—
KAISER, R. *Chromatographie in der Gasphase*, Band 3, Tabellen, 1 Teil (in German), (see Butterworth) (1969), 184 pp, DM7.90. 435	—	×	—	—	—	—	—	—	—
KAISER, R. *Chromatographie in der Gasphase*, Band 3, Tabellen, 2 Teil (in German), (see Butterworth) (1961), 165 pp, DM7.90. 440	—	×	—	—	—	—	—	—	—
KAISER, R. *Chromatographie in der Gasphase*, Band 4, Quantitative Auswertung, 1 Teil (in German), (see Butterworth) (1969), 185 pp, DM7.90. 445	—	×	—	—	—	—	—	—	—
KAISER, R. *Chromatographie in der Gasphase*, Band 4, Quantitative Auswertung, 2 Teil (in German), (see Butterworth) (1961), 118 pp, DM7.90. 450	—	×	—	—	—	—	—	—	—

INTERNATIONAL CHROMATOGRAPHY BOOK DIRECTORY—(Continued)

	Electrophoresis	Gas	Gel Permeation	Ion Exchange	Liquid (Column)	Paper	Thin Layer	Other Chrom. Tech.	General
BUTTERWORTH & CO (PUBLISHERS) LTD , 88 Kingsway, London W.C.2, England									
KAISER, R. *Gas Phase Chromatography*, Volume 1; *Gas Chromatography* (in English), (see Bibliographisches . . .) (1963), 199 pp, $7.95. 470	—	×	—	—	—	—	—	—	—
KAISER, R. *Gas Phase Chromatography*, Volume 2; *Capillary Chromatography* (in English), (see Bibliographisches . . .) (1963), 120 pp, $6.95. 475	—	×	—	—	—	—	—	—	—
KAISER, R. *Gas Phase Chromatography*, Volume 3; Tables for Gas Chromatography (in English), (see Bibliographisches . . .) (1963) 162 pp, $7.75. 480	—	×	—	—	—	—	—	—	—
CAMAG, INC., 11830 West Ripley Avenue, Milwaukee, Wisconsin 53226 414 476-7655 Foreign Headquarters: CAMAG Switzerland, Homburgerstrasse 24 4132 Muttenz, Switzerland									
JÄNCHEN, D. *Thin-Layer Chromatography Cumulative Bibliography 1965–1967*, Volume 1 (1967), 164 pp, $4.75. 500	—	—	—	—	—	—	×	—	—
JÄNCHEN, D. *Thin-Layer Chromatography Cumulative Bibliography 1967–1969*, Volume 2 (1970), 220 pp, $7.50. 505	—	—	—	—	—	—	×	—	—
CAMBRIDGE UNIVERSITY PRESS, 32 East 57th Street, New York, New York 10022 212 688-8885									
GRANT, J. K., Editor. *The Gas Liquid Chromatography of Steroids* (1967), 294 pp, $13.50. 525	—	×	—	—	—	—	—	—	—
CENTREX PUBLISHING COMPANY, Eindhoven, The Netherlands									
KRUGERS, J., Editor. *Instrumentation in Gas Chromatography* (1968), 245 pp, $12.00. 545	—	×	—	—	—	—	—	—	—
CHAPMAN & HALL, LTD., 11 New Fetter Lane, London E.C.4, England									
STOCK, R. and RICE, C. B. F. *Chromatographic Methods* (see Barnes & Noble and Reinhold) (1967), 256 pp, $4.00. 565	×	×	—	×	×	×	×	×	—
CHROMATOGRAPHY SYMPOSIUM, Chemistry Department, University of Houston, Houston, Texas 77004 713 748-6600									
ZLATKIS, A., Editor. *Advances in Chromatography 1970* (1970), 440 pp, $19.50, paper $12.95. 585	—	×	×	—	×	—	×	×	—
J. & A. CHURCHILL LTD., 104 Gloucester Place, London W.1, England									
PORTER, RUTH, Editor. *Gas Chromatography in Biology and Medicine* (1969), 213 pp. 665	—	×	—	—	—	—	—	—	—
CLEARINGHOUSE FOR FEDERAL SCIENTIFIC & TECHNICAL INFORMATION, 5285 Port Royal Road, Springfield, Virginia 22151 703 321-8500									
BRIGHT, R. N. and MATULA, R. A. *Gas Chromatographic Separation of Low Molecular Weight Fluorocarbons* (AD 670 834) (1968), 16 pp, $3.00. 605	—	×	—	—	—	—	—	—	—
CHANIN, L. M. *Research Directed Toward Experimental Investigation of Electrophoresis in Plasmas* (AD 691 007) (1969), 51 pp, $3.00. 610	×	—	—	—	—	—	—	—	—
ESPOSITO, G. G. and JAMISON, R. G. *Gas Chromatographic Determination of Ethylene Glycol in Used Oils* (AD 694 360) (1969), 14 pp, $3.00. 615	—	×	—	—	—	—	—	—	—

INTERNATIONAL CHROMATOGRAPHY BOOK DIRECTORY—(Continued)

	Electrophoresis	Gas	Gel Permeation	Ion Exchange	Liquid (Column)	Paper	Thin Layer	Other Chrom. Tech.	General
ESPOSITO, G. G. and JAMISON, R. G. *Rapid Analysis of Antifreeze Using Gas-Liquid Chromatography* (AD 686 289) (1969), 18 pp, \$3.00. 620	—	×	—	—	—	—	—	—	—
HEUNISCH, G. W. *Analysis of the Thermal Decomposition of Tetraethoxysilane by Gas Chromatography* (AD 675 398) (1968), 15 pp, \$3.00. 625	—	×	—	—	—	—	—	—	—
HEUBNER, V. R. *Rapid Identification of Microorganisms by Continuous Particle Electrophoresis* (AD 677 189) (1968), 24 pp, \$3.00. 630	×	—	—	—	—	—	—	—	—
ROSS, W. D. *Investigation of High-Temperature Gas Chromatography Substrates* (AD 684 558) (1968), 54 pp, \$3.00. 635	—	×	—	—	—	—	—	—	—
STUDIER, M. H., HAYATSU, R., and FUSE, K. *Analyses of Pyrimidine and Purine Bases by a Combination of Paper Chromatography and Time of Flight Mass Spectrometry* (1967), 11 pp, \$3.00. 640	—	—	—	—	—	×	—	—	—
ZYRIN, N. G., OVCHINNIKOVA, M. F., and ORLOV, D. S. *Amino Acids of Fulvic and Humic Acids in Certain Types of Soils* (N 68 15166) (1968), 15 pp, \$3.00. 645	—		—	—	—	×	—	—	—
CONSOLIDATED PRINTERS, 2630 8th Street, Berkeley, California 94710 415 853-8524									
MCNAIR, H. M. and BONNELLI, E. J. *Basic Gas Chromatography*, Fifth Edition (see Gow-Mac) (1969), 306 pp, 685	—	×	—	—	—	—	—	—	—
DEBTON COMPANY P.V.B.A., Langeleemstraat 259, Antwerp, Belgium (03) 30-86-01									
PRESTON, S. T. *A Guide to Selected Liquid Phases and Adsorbents Used in Gas Chromatography* (1970), 193 pp, \$10.00. 705	—	×	—	—	—	—	—	—	—
MARCEL DEKKER, INC., 95 Madison Avenue, New York, New York 10016 212 679-3991									
GIDDINGS, J. C. *Dynamics of Chromatography: Principles and Theory*, Part 1 (1965), 336 pp, \$17.75. 725	—	—	—	—	—	—	—	—	×
GIDDINGS, J. C. and KELLER, R. A. *Advances in Chromatography*, Volume 1 (1966), 336 pp, \$17.75. 730	—	—	—	—	—	—	—	—	×
GIDDINGS, J. C. and KELLER, R. A. *Advances in Chromatography*, Volume 2 (1966), 392 pp, \$17.75. 735	—	—	—	—	—	—	—	—	×
GIDDINGS, J. C. and KELLER, R. A. *Advances in Chromatography*, Volume 3 (1966), 286 pp, \$14.75. 740	—	—	—	—	—	—	—	—	×
GIDDINGS, J. C. and KELLER, R. A. *Advances in Chromatography*, Volume 4 (1967), 400 pp, \$18.75. 745	—	—	—	—	—	—	—	—	×
GIDDINGS, J. C. and KELLER, R. A. *Advances in Chromatography*, Volume 5 (1968), 336 pp, \$16.75. 750	—	—	—	—	—	—	—	—	×
GIDDINGS, J. C. and KELLER, R. A. *Advances in Chromatography*, Volume 6 (1968), 344 pp, \$17.75. 755	—	—	—	—	—	—	—	—	×
GIDDINGS, J. C. and KELLER, R. A. *Advances in Chromatography*, Volume 7 (1968), 336 pp, \$16.75. 760	—	—	—	—	—	—	—	—	×
GIDDINGS, J. C. and KELLER, R. A. *Advances in Chromatography*, Volume 8 (1969), 400 pp, \$18.75. 765	—	—	—	—	—	—	—	—	×
GUDZINOWICZ, B. J. *Gas Chromatographic Analysis of Drugs and Pesticides* (1967), 616 pp, \$31.75. 770	—	×	—	—	—	—	—	—	—
HELFERICH, F. and KLEIN, G. *Multicomponent Chromatography: Theory of Interfaces* (1970), 432 pp, \$24.50. 775	—	—	—	—	—	—	—	—	×
KELLER, R. A., Editor. *Separation Techniques in Chemistry and Biochemistry* (1967), 415 pp. 780	—	×	—	—	—	—	—	—	—
LODDING, W., Editor. *Gas Effluent Analysis* (1967), 209 pp, \$13.50. 781	—	×	—	—	—	—	—	—	—

INTERNATIONAL CHROMATOGRAPHY BOOK DIRECTORY—(Continued)

	Electrophoresis	Gas	Gel Permeation	Ion Exchange	Liquid (Column)	Paper	Thin Layer	Other Chrom. Tech.	General
MARINETTI, G. V., Editor. *Lipid Chromatographic Analysis* (1969), 596 pp, $28.50. 782	—	×	—	—	—	—	—	—	—
MARINSKY, J. A., Editor. *Ion Exchange* (1969), 250 pp, $13.75. 783	—	×	—	—	—	—	—	—	—
SNYDER, L. R. *Principles of Adsorption Chromatography: The Separation of Nonionic Organic Compounds* (1968), 413 pp, $17.50. 785	—	×	—	—	—	—	—	—	—
STEVENS, M. P. *Characterization and Analysis of Polymers by Gas Chromatography* (1969), 216 pp, $12.75. 790	—	×	—	—	—	—	—	—	—
ELSEVIER PUBLISHING COMPANY, Jan van Galenstraat 335, P.O. Box 211, Amsterdam, Netherlands **Foreign Headquarters: American Elsevier Publishing Co., Inc., 52 Vanderbilt Avenue, New York, New York 10017** **212 686-5277** **Elsevier Publishing Company, Limited, 22 Rippleside Commercial Estate, Ripple Road, Barking, Essex, England**									
ANONYMOUS. *Tswett Memorial Symposium* (J. Chromatogr., Volume 49, No. 1) (1970), 150 pp. 810	—	—	—	—	—	—	—	—	×
BAYER, E. *Gas Chromatography* (1961), 252 pp, $8.00. 815	—	×	—	—	—	—	—	—	—
BLOEMENDAL, H. *Zone Electrophoresis in Blocks and Columns* (1963), 219 pp, fl. 30.00. 820	×	—	—	—	—	—	—	—	—
BUTLIN, A. G., D'OYLY-WATKINS, C., and KNAPMAN, C. E. H., Editors. *Gas Chromatography Abstracts Cumulative Indexes 1958–1963* (see Institute of Petroleum) (1967), 311 pp, fl. 37.50. 825	—	×	—	—	—	—	—	—	—
FLETT, M. ST. C. *Physical Aids to the Organic Chemist* (1962), 400 pp, $11.00. 830	—	×	—	—	×	—	—	—	×
GOLDUP, A., Editor. *Gas Chromatography 1964: Proceedings of the Fifth International Symposium, 1964* (1965), 386 pp, $17.50. 835	—	×	—	—	—	—	—	—	—
HAIS, I. M., LEDERER, M., and MACEK, K. *Identification of Substances by Paper and Thin-Layer Chromatography* (J. Chromatogr., Volume 48, Nos. 1 and 2) (1970), 300 pp. 840	—	—	—	—	—	×	×	—	—
HARBOURN, C. L. A. *Gas Chromatography 1968* (see Institute of Petroleum) (1969), 499 pp, fl. 73.50. 845	—	×	—	—	—	—	—	—	—
KNAPMAN, C. E. H., Editor. *Gas Chromatography Abstracts 1963* (1964), 195 pp, $8.50. 850	—	×	—	—	—	—	—	—	—
KNAPMAN, C. E. H., Editor. *Gas Chromatography Abstracts 1964* (1965), 392 pp, $12.00. 855	—	×	—	—	—	—	—	—	—
KNAPMAN, C. E. H., Editor. *Gas Chromatography Abstracts 1965* (1966), 304 pp, fl. 38.00. 860	—	×	—	—	—	—	—	—	—
KNAPMAN, C. E. H., Editor. *Gas Chromatography Abstracts 1966* (1967), 320 pp, $11.00. 865	—	×	—	—	—	—	—	—	—
KNAPMAN, C. E. H., Editor. *Gas Chromatography Abstracts 1967* (1968), 282 pp, fl. 40.00. 870	—	×	—	—	—	—	—	—	—
KNAPMAN, C. E. H. *Gas Chromatography Abstracts 1968* (1969), 285 pp, fl. 45.00. 875	—	×	—	—	—	—	—	—	—
KRUGERS, J. and KEULEMANS, A. I. M., Editors. *Practical Instrumental Analysis* (1965), 273 pp, $12.50. 880	×	×	—	—	×	—	×	—	—
LEDERER, E. and LEDERER, M. *Chromatography* (1957), 711pp, fl. 45.00. 885	—	—	—	×	—	—	—	—	×
LEDERER, M. *Chromatographic Reviews*, Volume 3 (1961), 187 pp, fl. 54.00. 890	—	—	—	—	—	×	—	—	×
LEDERER, M. *Chromatographic Reviews*, Volume 4 (1962), 184 pp, fl. 54.00. 895	—	×	—	—	—	×	—	—	×
LEDERER, M. *Chromatographic Reviews*, Volume 5 (1963), 244 pp, fl. 54.00. 900	—	×	—	—	—	×	×	—	×
LEDERER, M. *Chromatographic Reviews*, Volume 6 (1964), 220 pp, fl. 54.00. 905	—	—	—	—	×	×	—	—	×

INTERNATIONAL CHROMATOGRAPHY BOOK DIRECTORY—(Continued)

	Electrophoresis	Gas	Gel Permeation	Ion Exchange	Liquid (Column)	Paper	Thin Layer	Other Chrom. Tech.	General
LEDERER, M. *Chromatographic Reviews*, Volume 7 (1965), 202 pp, fl. 54.00. 910	×	—	—	—	—	×	×	—	×
LEDERER, M. *Chromatographic Reviews*, Volume 8 (1966), 298 pp, fl. 54.00. 915	—	×	—	—	×	×	—	—	×
LEDERER, M. *Introduction to Paper Electrophoresis and Related Methods* (1955), 213 pp, fl. 27.50. 920	×	—	—	—	—	—	—	—	—
LEDERER, M. *Symposium on the Gas Chromatography of Amine Drugs* (1968), 224 pp, fl. 30.00. 925	—	×	—	—	—	—	—	—	—
LEDERER, M., MACEK, K., and HAIS, I. M. *Reproducibility in Paper and Thin-Layer Chromatography* (J. Chromatogr., Volume 33, Nos. 1 and 2) (1968), 412 pp, fl. 57.00. 930	—	—	—	—	—	×	×	—	—
LITTLEWOOD, A. B., Editor. *Gas Chromatography 1966: Proceedings of the Sixth International Symposium, 1966* (1967), 464 pp, fl. 60.00. 935	—	×	—	—	—	—	—	—	—
LOWENTHAL. *Agar Gel Electrophoresis in Neurology* (1964), 204 pp, fl. 32.50. 940	×	—	—	—	—	—	—	—	—
MACEK, K. *Bibliography of Paper and Thin-Layer Chromatography 1961–1965* (1968), 1041 pp, fl. 99.00. 945	—	—	—	—	—	×	×	—	—
MACEK, K. and HAIS, I. M. *Stationary Phase in Paper and Thin-Layer Chromatography* (1965), 358 pp, fl. 47.50. 950	—	—	—	—	—	×	×	—	—
MARINI-BETTÓLO, G. B. *Thin-Layer Chromatography* (1964), 232 pp, fl. 37.50. 955	×	—	—	—	—	—	×	—	—
NAKAMURA, S. *Cross Electrophoresis* (1967), 203 pp, $17.00. 960	×	—	—	—	—	—	—	—	—
NEHER, R. *Steroid Chromatography* (1964), 389 pp, fl. 37.50. 965	—	×	—	—	×	×	×	—	—
RIBEIRO, MITIDIERI, and ALFONSO. *Paper Electrophoresis* (1961), 463 pp, fl. 52.50. 970	×	—	—	—	—	—	—	—	—
RITCHIE, A. S. *Chromatography in Geology*, Volume 1 (1964), 185 pp, fl. 27.50. 975	—	—	—	—	—	—	—	—	×
TRANCHANT, J., Editor. *Practical Manual of Gas Chromatography* (1969), 387 pp, fl. 85.00. 980	—	×	—	—	—	—	—	—	—
TRANCHANT, J., Editor. *Practical Manual of Gas Chromatography* (1970), 407 pp, $30.00. 985	—	×	—	—	—	—	—	—	—
WIEME, R. J. *Agar Gel Electrophoresis* (1965), 425 pp, fl. 57.50. 990	×	—	—	—	—	—	—	—	—
WILSON, C. L. and WILSON, D. W. *Comprehensive Analytical Chemistry*, Volume 2B (1968), 460 pp, $25.00. 995	—	×	—	×	×	—	—	—	—
WILSON, C. L. and WILSON, D. W. *Comprehensive Analytical Chemistry*, Volume 2C (1970), 350 pp. 1000	—	—	—	—	—	×	×	—	—
WUNDERLY, C. *Principles and Applications of Paper Electrophoresis* (1961), 255 pp, fl. 22.50. 1005	×	—	—	—	—	—	—	—	—
GORDON AND BREACH, SCIENCE PUBLISHERS, INC., 150 Fifth Avenue, New York, New York 10011 212 989-1120									
SCHOLLER, R. and JAYLE, M. F. *Gas Chromatography of Hormonal Steroids* (1968), 574 pp, $33.00. 1025	—	×	—	—	—	—	—	—	—
GOW-MAC INSTRUMENT COMPANY, 100 Kings Road, Madison, New Jersey 07940 201 377-3450									
MCNAIR, H. M. and BONELLI, E. J. *Basic Gas Chromatography*, 5th Edition (see Consolidated) (1968), 306 pp, $5.00. 1045	—	×	—	—	—	—	—	—	—
MILLER, J. M. *Experimental Gas Chromatography* (1965), 99 pp, Paperback. 1050	—	×	—	—	—	—	—	—	—
GRUNE & STRATTON, INC., 757 Third Avenue, New York, New York 10017 212 572-5000									
KROMAN, H. S. and BENDER, S. R., Editors. *Theory and Application of Gas Chromatography in Industry and Medicine* (1970), 320 pp, $19.50. 1070	—	×	—	—	—	—	—	—	—

INTERNATIONAL CHROMATOGRAPHY BOOK DIRECTORY—(Continued)

	Electrophoresis	Gas	Gel Permeation	Ion Exchange	Liquid (Column)	Paper	Thin Layer	Other Chrom. Tech.	General
WALTER DE GRUYTER & CO., Gentheiner Street 13, Berlin, W.30, West Germany									
MAURER, H. R. *Disc Electrophoresis* (see Ann Arbor-Humphrey) (1970), $18.75. 1080	×	—	—	—	—	—	—	—	—
W. A. HAMMOND DRIERITE COMPANY, 138 Dayton Avenue, Xenia, Ohio 45385 513 372-6101									
HAMMOND, W. A. *Drierite and Its Applications* (1958), 84 pp, no charge. 1090	—	—	—	—	—	—	—	—	×
HEYDON AND SON, LTD., Spectrum House, Alderton Crescent, London, NW4, England 01-202-5333									
PATTISON, J. B. *A Programmed Introduction to Gas-Liquid Chromatography* (1969), 303 pp, $4.95. 1110	—	×	—	—	×	—	—	—	×
WELTI, D. *Infrared Vapour Spectra:* Group Frequency Correlations. Sample Handling and the Examination of Gas Chromatographic Fractions (1970), 150 pp, $21.00. 1115	—	—	—	—	—	—	—	×	—
HOUGHTON MIFFLIN COMPANY, Educational, 110 Tremont Street, Boston, Massachusetts 02107 617 423-5725									
ABBOTT, D. and ANDREWS, R. S. *An Introduction to Chromatography* (Concepts in Chemistry Series) (1965), 70 pp, $1.75 Paper. 1135	—	×	—	×	×	×	×	—	×
HUTHIG & WEPF VERLAG, Postfach 727, 6900 Heidelberg, 1, West Germany									
KAGLER, S. H. *New Mineral Analysis: Spectroscopy and Chromatography; Background, Apparatus and Applications* (1969), 714 pp. 1155	—	×	—	—	—	—	—	—	—
ILIFFE BOOKS, LTD., Dorset House, Stamford Street, London SE 1, England									
SAVIDAN, L. *Chromatography* (1965), 112 pp, £1.75. 1175	—	×	—	—	×	—	—	—	×
INDIAN INSTITUTE OF PETROLEUM, Library, P.O. 11P, Mohkampur, Dehra Dun, U.P., India									
GUPTA, P. L. and MALLIK, K. L. *Gas Chromatography Manual* (1968), 114 pp, Rs 5.00. 1195	—	×	—	—	—	—	—	—	—
INSTITUTE OF PETROLEUM, Gas Chromatography Discussion Group, 61 New Cavendish Street, London, W1, England									
BUTLIN, A. G., D'OYLY-WATKINS, C., and KNAPMAN, C. E. H., Editors. *Gas Chromatography Abstracts Cumulative Indexes 1958–1963* (see Elsevier) (1968), 311 pp, £3.15. 1215	—	×	—	—	—	—	—	—	—
HARBOURN, C. L. A., Editor. *Gas Chromatography 1968* (see Elsevier) (1969), 499 pp, £5.25. 1220	—	×	—	—	—	—	—	—	—
HARBOURN, C. L. A., Editor. *Gas Chromatography Abstracts 1969* (1970), 300 pp, £3.50. 1225	—	×	—	—	—	—	—	—	—
INSTRUMENT SOCIETY OF AMERICA, 400 Stanwix Street, Pittsburgh, Pennsylvania 15222 412 281-3171									
BRENNER, N., CALLEN, J. E., and WEISS, M. D., Editors. *Proceedings of the Third International ISA Gas Chromatography Symposium* (see Academic Press) (1962), 719 pp, $22.00. 1245	—	×	—	—	—	—	—	—	—

INTERNATIONAL CHROMATOGRAPHY BOOK DIRECTORY—(Continued)

	Electrophoresis	Gas	Gel Permeation	Ion Exchange	Liquid (Column)	Paper	Thin Layer	Other Chrom. Tech.	General
COATES, V. J., NOEBELS, H. J., and FAGERSON, I. S., Editors. *Proceedings of the First International ISA Gas Chromatography Symposium* (1958), 323 pp, $12.00. 1250	—	×	—	—	—	—	—	—	—
CONNELLY, B., FOWLER, L., and KRUEGER, R., Editors. *Analysis Instrumentation*, Volume 7 (1969), 330 pp, $15.00. 1255	—	—	—	—	—	—	—	—	×
FOWLER, L., Editor. *Proceedings of the Fourth International ISA Gas Chromatography Symposium* (1963), 270 pp, $10.50. 1260	—	×	—	—	—	—	—	—	—
FOWLER, L., CONNELLY, B., and KRUEGER, R., Editors. *Analysis Instrumentation*, Volume 6 (1969), 380 pp, $18.50. 1265	—	—	—	—	—	—	—	—	×
NOEBELS, H. J., WALL, R. F., and BRENNER, N., Editors. *Proceedings of the Second International ISA Gas Chromatography Symposium* (1961), 461 pp, $16.00. 1270	—	×	—	—	—	—	—	—	—
S. KARGER, Basel, Switzerland									
ARQUEMBOURG, P. C., SALVAGGIO, J. E., and BICKERS, J. N. *Primer of Immunoelectrophoresis* (see Ann Arbor-Humphrey) (1970), 83 pp, $8.25. 1290	×	—	—	—	—	—	—	—	—
LITTLE, BROWN AND COMPANY, Medical Division, 34 Beacon Street, Boston, Massachusetts 02106 617 277-0730									
CAWLEY, LEO P. *Electrophoresis and Immunoelectrophoresis* (1969), 360 pp, $15.00. 1310	×	×	—	—	×	×	—	×	—
MASSON & CIE, 120 Boulevard Saint Germain, Paris, 6 éme, France 326 56-11									
DETERMANN, H. *Chromatographie sur gel* (traduit de l'allemand) (1969), 194 pp, 54 F. 1315	—	—	×	—	—	—	—	—	—
KISELEV, A. V. and YASHIN, Y. I. *La chromatographie gaz-solide* (traduit du russe) (see Plenum Press) (1969), 290 pp, 88 F. 1320	—	—	—	—	—	—	—	×	—
LEDERER, M. *Chromatographie en chimie organique et builogique*, Volume 2 (1960), 876 pp, Br. 141 F. Cart. 157 F. 1325	—	—	—	—	—	—	—	—	×
MEUNIER and VINET. *Chromatographie et mésomérie* (1957), 126 pp, 16 F. 1330	—	—	—	—	—	—	—	—	×
TRANCHANT, J. *Manuel practique de chromatographie en phase gazeuse* (2éme édition) (1968), 362 pp, 78 F. 1335	—	×	—	—	—	—	—	—	—
NESTER FAUST MANUFACTURING CORP., 2401 Ogletown Road, Newark, Delaware 19711 302 737-6330									
ANONYMOUS. *Gas Chromatographic Infrared Spectra Book* (1965), 23 pp, $15.00 Paperback. 1355	—	×	—	—	—	—	—	—	—
NORTH-HOLLAND PUBLISHING COMPANY, 305–311 Keizersgracht, Amsterdam, The Netherlands 020/223522									
CLAUSEN, J. *Immunochemical Techniques for the Identification and Estimation of Macromolecules* (1969), 176 pp, fl. 15.00 Paperback. 1375	×	—	—	—	—	—	—	—	—
FISCHER, L. *An Introduction to Gel Chromatography* (1969), 246 pp, fl. 25.00 Paperback. 1380	—	—	×	—	—	—	—	—	—
GORDAN, A. H. *Electrophoresis of Proteins in Polyacrylamide and Starch Cells* (1969), 150 pp, fl. 15.00 Paperback. 1385	×	—	—	—	—	—	—	—	—
LEHMAN, H. and HUNTSMAN, R. G. *Man's Hemoglobins* (1966), 343 pp, fl. 42.00. 1390	×	—	×	—	—	—	—	—	—
WORK, T. S. and WORK, E., Editors. *Laboratory Techniques in Biochemistry and Molecular Biology*, Volume 1 (1969), 572 pp, fl. 90.00. 1395	×	—	×	—	—	—	—	—	—

INTERNATIONAL CHROMATOGRAPHY BOOK DIRECTORY—(Continued)

	Electrophoresis	Gas	Gel Permeation	Ion Exchange	Liquid (Column)	Paper	Thin Layer	Other Chrom. Tech.	General
GEORGE NEWNES LTD., Tower House, Southampton Street, London W.C.2, England									
GORDON, A. H. and EASTOE, J. E. *Practical Chromatographic Techniques* (1964), 200 pp. 1415	—	×	—	—	—	—	—	—	—
PERGAMON PRESS, INC., Maxwell House, Fairview Park, Elmsford, New York 10523 914 592-7700									
ALIMARIN, I. P. and PETRIKOVA, M. N. *Inorganic Ultramicroanalysis* (1964), 168 pp, $6.00. 1435	—	—	—	—	—	—	—	—	×
ANONYMOUS. *Proceedings of the International Symposium on Microchemistry* (1960), 583 pp, $15.00. 1440	—	—	—	—	—	—	—	—	×
BUSH, I. E. *The Chromatography of Steroids* (1961), 388 pp, £4.00. 1442	—	×	—	—	—	—	—	—	—
HARTLAND, S. *Counter-Current Extraction* (1970), 252 pp, $9.00. 1445	—	—	—	—	×	—	—	—	—
HENGLEIN, F. A. *Chemical Technology*, Eleventh Edition (1969), 874 pp, $40.00. 1450	—	—	—	—	—	—	—	—	×
HOLMAN, R. T., Editor. *Progress in the Chemistry of Fats and Other Lipids*, Volume 7, Pt. 2: Gas Chromatography of Lipids (1963), 132 pp, $5.00. 1455	—	×	—	—	—	—	—	—	—
HOLMAN, R. T., Editor. *Progress in the Chemistry of Fats and Other Lipids*, Volume 8, Pt. 3: Chromatography (1965), 132 pp, $6.50. 1460	—	—	—	—	—	×	×	—	—
HOLMAN, R. T., Editor. *Progress in the Chemistry of Fats and Other Lipids*, Volume 10, Pt. 3: Biochemistry of Lipids Containing Ether Bonds. (AND) Diol Lipids (1969), 98 pp, $5.00. 1465	—	—	—	—	—	—	—	—	×
INCZEDY, J. *Analytical Applications of Ion Exchangers* (1966), 420 pp, $19.00. 1470	—	—	—	×	—	—	—	—	—
JEFFERY, P. G. and KIPPING, P. J. *Gas Analysis by Gas Chromatography* (1964), 228 pp, $10.00. 1475	—	×	—	—	—	—	—	—	—
JOHNSON, R. M. and SIDDIGI, I. W. *The Determination of Organic Peroxides* (1970), 132 pp, $6.75. 1480	—	—	—	—	—	—	—	—	×
KORKISCH, J. *Modern Methods for Separation of Rarer Metal Ions* (1969), 586 pp, $20.00. 1485	—	—	—	—	—	—	—	—	×
LOWRIE, R. S. *Selected Readings in Chromatography*. 1490	—	×	—	—	—	—	×	—	×
MALINA, F. J., Editor. *Research in Chemistry and Physics* (1969), 154 pp, $13.50. 1495	—	×	—	—	—	—	—	—	—
MOSHIER, R. W. and SIEVERS, R. E. *Gas Chromatography of Metal Chelates* (1965), 172 pp, $7.50. 1500	—	×	—	—	—	—	—	—	—
STEVENSON, C. E., Editor. *Progress in Nuclear Energy*, Series III, Volume 4; Process Chemistry (1970), $27.00. 1505	—	—	—	—	—	—	—	—	×
STEWART, D. C. and ELION, H. A., Editors. *Progress in Nuclear Energy*, Series IX, Volume 10, Pts. 1 and 2 (1970), 480 pp, $27.00. 1510	—	—	—	×	—	—	—	—	—
WILSON, H. N. *An Approach to Chemical Analysis* (1966), 384 pp, $6.00. 1515	—	—	—	—	—	—	—	—	×
PIERCE CHEMICAL COMPANY, P.O. Box 117, Rockford, Illinois 61105 815 968-0747									
BRITTAIN, G. D. *A Bibliography of Silylation: Synthetic Methods and Analytical Uses* (1967), 11 pp, Free. 1535	—	×	—	—	—	—	—	—	—
BRITTAIN, G. D. *Handbook of Silylation with Other Special Techniques for Gas Phase Analysis: Methods, Reagents and Accessories* (1970), 60 pp, Free. 1540	—	×	—	—	—	—	—	—	—
OLIVER, R. E. *The "AMAC" Handbook: Methods and Reagents for Amino Acid and Protein Chemistry* (1969), 64 pp, Free. 1545	—	—	—	×	—	—	—	—	—

INTERNATIONAL CHROMATOGRAPHY BOOK DIRECTORY—(Continued)

	Electrophoresis	Gas	Gel Permeation	Ion Exchange	Liquid (Column)	Paper	Thin Layer	Other Chrom. Tech.	General
PIERCE, A. *Silylation of Organic Compounds: A Technique for Gas Analysis* (1968), 487 pp, $19.50. 1550	—	×	—	—	×	—	×	—	—
PLENUM PUBLISHING CORPORATION, 114 Fifth Avenue, New York, New York 10011 212 255-0713									
ANONYMOUS									
ACADEMY OF SCIENCES OF USSR. *Research in Ion Exchange Chromatography*, Transactions of the Sessions on Applications of Ion Exchange Chromatography in Medicine and the Food Industries (SBN 306-10546-2) (1958), 179 pp, $35.00. 1570	—	—	—	×	—	—	—	—	—
BEREZKIN, V. G. *Analytical Reaction Gas Chromatography* (SBN 306-30338-8) (1968), 193 pp, $12.50. 1575	—	×	—	—	—	—	—	—	—
ETTRE, L. S. *Open Tubular Columns in Gas Chromatography* (SBN 306-30188-1) (1965), 163 pp, $12.50. 1580	—	×	—	—	—	—	—	—	—
KISELEV, A. V. and YASHIN, Y. I. *Gas-Adsorption Chromatography* (SBN 306-30370-1) (see Masson & Cie) (1969), 250 pp, $20.00. 1600	—	×	—	—	—	—	—	—	—
LIPSETT, M. B. *Gas Chromatography of Steroids in Biological Fluids* (SBN 306-30204-7) (1965), 315 pp, $17.50. 1605	—	×	—	—	—	—	—	—	—
MATTICK, L. R. and SZYMANSKI, H. A., Editors. *Lectures on Gas Chromatography*, Volume 3 (SBN 306-30289-6) (1967), 277 pp, $15.00. 1610	—	×	—	—	—	—	—	—	—
RACHINSKII, V. V. *The General Theory of Sorption Dynamics and Chromatography* (SBN 306-10711-2) (1965), 90 pp, $15.00. 1615	—	—	—	—	—	—	—	—	×
SIGNEUR, A. V. *Guide to Gas Chromatography Literature*, Volume 1 (SBN 306-68201-x) (1964), 351 pp, $25.00. 1620	—	×	—	—	—	—	—	—	—
SIGNEUR, A. V. *Guide to Gas Chromatography Literature*, Volume 2 (SBN 306-68202-8) (1967), 379 pp, $25.00. 1625	—	×	—	—	—	—	—	—	—
SZYMANSKI, H. A., Editor. *Biomedical Applications of Gas Chromatography*, Volume 1 (SBN 306-37581-8) (1964), 324 pp, $17.50. 1630	—	×	—	—	—	—	—	—	—
SZYMANSKI, H. A., Editor. *Biomedical Applications of Gas Chromatography*, Volume 2 (SBN 306-37582-6) (1968), 198 pp, $12.50. 1635	—	×	—	—	—	—	—	—	—
SZYMANSKI, H. A., Editor. *Lectures on Gas Chromatography*, Volume 1 (SBN 306-30161-x) (1963), 282 pp, $15.00. 1640	—	×	—	—	—	—	—	—	—
SZYMANSKI, H. A. and MATTICK, L. R., Editors. *Lectures on Gas Chromatography*, Volume 2 (SBN 306-30196-2) (1965), 256 pp, $15.00. 1645	—	×	—	—	—	—	—	—	—
SZYMANSKI, H. A., Editor. *Progress in Industrial Gas Chromatography*, Proceedings of the Advanced Sessions of the Third Annual Gas Chromatography Institute (SBN 306-30147-4) (1961), 235 pp, $15.00. 1650	—	×	—	—	—	—	—	—	—
WOTIZ, H. H. and CLARK, S. J. *Gas Chromatography in the Analysis of Steroid Hormones* (SBN 306-30227-6) (1966), 288 pp, $17.50. 1655	—	×	—	—	—	—	—	—	—
POLYSCIENCE CORPORATION, P.O. Box 791, Evanston, Illinois 60204 312 475-2909									
PRESTON, S. T. *A Guide to the Analysis of Alcohols by Gas Chromatography* (1966), 87 pp, $5.00. 1675	—	×	—	—	—	—	—	—	—
PRESTON, S. T. *A Guide to the Analysis of Amines by Gas Chromatography* (1965), 52 pp, $5.00. 1680	—	×	—	—	—	—	—	—	—
PRESTON, S. T. *A Guide to the Analysis of Fatty Acids and Esters by Gas Chromatography* (1970), 130 pp, $15.00. 1685	—	×	—	—	—	—	—	—	—
PRESTON, S. T. *A Guide to the Analysis of Hydrocarbons by Gas Chromatography*, Second Edition (1969), 577 pp, $20.00. 1690	—	×	—	—	—	—	—	—	—
PRESTON, S. T. *A Guide to the Analysis of Ketones by Gas Chromatography* (1965), 36 pp, $5.00. 1695	—	×	—	—	—	—	—	—	—

INTERNATIONAL CHROMATOGRAPHY BOOK DIRECTORY—(Continued)

	Electrophoresis	Gas	Gel Permeation	Ion Exchange	Liquid (Column)	Paper	Thin Layer	Other Chrom. Tech.	General
PRESTON, S. T. *A Guide to the Analysis of Pesticides by Gas Chromatography*, Second Edition (1968), 249 pp, $10.00. 1700	—	×	—	—	—	—	—	—	—
PRESTON, S. T. *A Guide to the Analysis of Phenols by Gas Chromatography* (1966), 114 pp, $10.00. 1705	—	×	—	—	—	—	—	—	—
PRESTON, S. T. *A Guide to the Analysis of Sulfur Compounds by Gas Chromatography* (1966), 75 pp, $10.00. 1710	—	×	—	—	—	—	—	—	—
PRESSES ACADEMIQUES EUROPEENNES S.C., International Booksellers and Publishers, 98, chaussee de Charlerol, Brussels 6, Belgium **38-32-43 38-36-97**									
LAGRANGE, G. and RENOZ, L. *Chromatographie Symposium II 1962* (1962), 310 pp, B.F. 350.00. 1730	×	×	×	×	×	×	×	×	×
LAGRANGE, G. and RENOZ, L. *Chromatographie Symposium III 1964* (1964), 391 pp. B.F. 600.00. 1735	×	×	×	×	×	×	×	×	×
LAGRANGE, G. and RENOZ, L. *Chromatographie Symposium IV 1966* (1968), 625 pp, B.F. 780.00. 1740	×	×	×	×	×	×	×	×	×
LAGRANGE, G. and RENOZ, L. *Chromatographie Symposium V 1968* (see Ann Arbor-Humphrey) (1969), 594 pp, B.F. 780.00. 1745	×	×	×	×	×	×	×	×	×
PRESTON TECHNICAL ABSTRACTS COMPANY, 2101 Dempster Street, Evanston, Illinois 60201 **312 475-4397**									
MCKINNEY, R. W. *Computer-Based Retrieval System of the Gas Chromatography Literature*, updated through 1969, $800.00 tape and program. 1765	—	×	—	—	—	—	—	—	—
MCREYNOLDS, W. O. *Gas Chromatographic Retention Data* (1966), 335 pp, $25.00. 1770	—	×	—	—	—	—	—	—	—
PRESTON, S. T. *Gas Chromatography Abstracts Service*, monthly, 2,000+ pp yr, $240.00/yr. 1775	—	×	—	—	—	—	—	—	—
ZLATKIS, A. and ETTRE, L. S. *Advances in Gas Chromatography 1965* (1966), 182 pp, $12.00. 1780	—	×	—	—	—	—	—	—	—
ZLATKIS, A. *Advances in Gas Chromatography 1967* (1967), 213 pp, $12.50. 1785	—	×	—	—	—	—	—	—	—
ZLATKIS, A. *Advances in Chromatography 1969* (1969), 381 pp, $25.00. 1790	—	×	—	—	×	—	—	—	—
REINHOLD BOOK COMPANY, 430 West 33rd Street, New York, New York 10001 **212 594-8660**									
BOBBITT, J. M., SCHWARTING, A. E., and GRITTER, R. J. *Introduction to Chromatography* (1968), 192 pp, $3.95. 1810	—	—	—	—	—	—	—	—	×
HEFTMAN, E., Editor. *Chromatography*, Second Edition (1967), 851 pp, $27.50. 1815	—	—	—	—	—	—	—	—	×
STOCK, R. and RICE, C. B. F. *Chromatographic Methods* (see Chapman & Hall and Barnes & Noble) (1967), 256 pp, $4.00. 1820	×	×	—	×	×	×	×	×	—
SADTLER RESEARCH LABORATORIES, INC., 3316 Spring Garden Street, Philadelphia, Pennsylvania 19104 **215 382-7800**									
PATERSON, R. *An Introduction to Ion Exchange* (1970), 118 pp, $6.00. 1840	—	—	—	×	—	—	—	—	—
SHANDON SCIENTIFIC COMPANY, INC., 515 Broad Street, Sewickley, Pennsylvania 15143 **412 741-8400**									
SMITH, I. and FEINBERG, J. G. *Paper and Thin-Layer Chromatography and Electrophoresis*, A Teaching Level Manual (1965), 241 pp, $7.50. 1875	×	—	—	—	—	×	×	—	—

INTERNATIONAL CHROMATOGRAPHY BOOK DIRECTORY—(Continued)

	Electrophoresis	Gas	Gel Permeation	Ion Exchange	Liquid (Column)	Paper	Thin Layer	Other Chrom. Tech.	General
SPRINGER-VERLAG NEW YORK, INC., 175 Fifth Avenue, New York, New York 10010 **212 673-2660**									
DETERMANN, H. *Gel Chromatography*, Gel Filtration, Gel Permeation, Molecular Sieves: A Laboratory Handbook, Second Edition (1969), 202 pp, $8.80. 1895	—	—	×	—	—	—	—	—	—
EIK-NES, K. B. and HORNING, E. C. *Gas Phase Chromatography of Steroids:* Monographs on Endocrinology, Volume 2 (1968), 382 pp, $9.50. 1900	—	×	—	—	—	—	—	—	—
MABRY, T. J., MARKHAM, K. R., and THOMAS, M. B. *The Systematic Identification of Flavonoids* (1970), 354 pp, $27.00. 1905	—	×	—	—	—	×	×	—	—
NEEDLEMAN, S. B. *Protein Sequence Determination:* Molecular Biochemistry, Biology and Biophysics, Volume 8 (1970), 450 pp, $23.10. 1910	—	×	—	—	—	—	—	×	—
NOWOTNY, A. *Basic Exercises in Immunochemistry: A Laboratory Manual* (1969), 197 pp, $9.50. 1915	×	×	—	—	—	×	—	×	—
STAHL, E., Editor. *Thin-Layer Chromatography:* A Laboratory Handbook, Second Edition (1969), 1,041 pp, $32.50. 1920	×	×	—	—	—	—	×	×	—
TECHNISCHE HOGESCHOOL, Eindhoven, The Netherlands									
KUPPENS, P. S. H. *High Resolution Gas Chromatography in Steroid Analysis:* An Introduction to the Use for Clinical Purposes (1968), 106 pp, Paperback. 1940	—	×	—	—	—	—	—	—	—
UNITED STATES GOVERNMENT PRINTING OFFICE, Superintendent of Documents, Washington, D.C. 20402 **202 541-3000**									
BURCHFIELD, H. P., JOHNSON, D. E., and STORRS, E. H. *Guide to the Analysis of Pesticide Residues*, Volumes 1 and 2 (1965), 8 Sections, $12.75/set. 1960	—	×	—	—	—	—	—	—	—
UNITED TRADE PRESS LIMITED, 9 Gough Square, Fleet Street, London, E.C.4, England **01-353 3172**									
KAHN, M. A. *The Fundamental Aspects of Gas Chromatography* (1967), 28 pp, 27½p. 1980	—	×	—	—	—	—	—	—	—
STAHL, E. *Thin-Layer Chromatography*, A series of articles reprinted from "Laboratory Practice" (1967), 83 pp, £1.00. 1985	—	—	—	—	—	—	×	—	—
D. VAN NOSTRAND CO., LTD., Windsor House, 46 Victoria Street, London, S.W.1, England **Foreign Headquarters:** **D. Van Nostrand Co., Inc., 126 Alexander Street, Princeton, New Jersey 08540** **609 921-6000**									
AMBROSE, D. and AMBROSE, B. A. *Gas Chromatography* (1962), 220 pp, $6.75. 2005	—	×	—	—	—	—	—	—	—
BOBBITT, J. *Thin-Layer Chromatography* (1963), 220 pp, $9.95. 2010	—	—	—	—	—	—	×	—	—
MIKES, O., Editor. *Laboratory Handbook of Chromatographic Methods* (1967), 434 pp. 2015	—	—	—	—	—	—	—	—	×
VERLAG CHEMIE GmbH, Pappelallee 3, Weinheim, Bergstrasse, West Germany **3635**									
CRAMER, F. *Papierchromatographie* (1962), 218 pp, DM21.00. 2035	—	—	—	—	—	×	—	—	—
KEULEMANS, A. I. M. *Gas-Chromatographie* (1959), 208 pp, DM24.00. 2040	—	×	—	—	—	—	—	—	—

INTERNATIONAL CHROMATOGRAPHY BOOK DIRECTORY—(Continued)

	Electrophoresis	Gas	Gel Permeation	Ion Exchange	Liquid (Column)	Paper	Thin Layer	Other Chrom. Tech.	General
RANDERATH, KURT. *Dünnschicht-Chromatographie* (1965), 291 pp, DM28.00. 2045	—	—	—	—	—	—	×	—	—
RANDERATH, KURT. *Thin-Layer Chromatography* (see Academic Press) (1966), 285 pp, DM38.00. 2050	—	—	—	—	—	—	×	—	—
WATERS ASSOCIATES INC., 61 Fountain Street, Framingham, Massachusetts 01701 617 879-2000									
ANONYMOUS. *Fifth International Seminar, London: Gel Permeation Chromatography* (1968), 224 pp, $7.50. 2070	—	—	×	—	—	—	—	—	—
ANONYMOUS. *Sixth International Seminar, Miami Beach: Gel Permeation Chromatography* (1968), 478 pp, $10.00. 2075	—	—	×	—	—	—	—	—	—
ANONYMOUS. *Seventh International Seminar, Monaco: Gel Permeation Chromatography* (1970) $12.50. 2080	—	—	×	—	—	—	—	—	—
JOHN WILEY & SONS, Wiley-Interscience, 605 Third Avenue, New York, New York 10017 212 867-9800									
CASSIDY, H. G. *Fundamentals of Chromatography* (1957), 465 pp, $15.95. 2100	—	—	—	—	—	—	—	—	×
DAL NOGARE, S. and JUVET, R. S. *Gas-Liquid Chromatography* (1962), 450 pp, $14.95. 2105	—	×	—	—	—	—	—	—	—
ETTRE, L. S. and MCFADDEN, W. H. *Ancillary Techniques for Gas Chromatography* (1969), 395 pp, $17.50. 2110	—	×	—	—	—	—	—	—	—
ETTRE, L. S. and ZLATKIS, A. *Practice of Gas Chromatography* (1967), 591 pp, $16.50. 2115	—	×	—	—	—	—	—	—	—
HARRIS, W. E. and HABGOOD, H. W. *Programmed Temperature Gas Chromatography* (1968), 305 pp, $14.95. 2120	—	×	—	—	—	—	—	—	—
JOHNSON, J. and PORTER, R. S. *Analytical Gel Permeation* (1968), 344 pp, $16.50. 2125	—	—	×	—	—	—	—	—	—
KIRCHNER, J. G. *Thin-Layer Chromatography* (1967), 788 pp, $24.50. 2130	—	—	—	—	—	—	×	—	—
MARCUS, Y. and KERTES, A. S. *Ion Exchange and Solvent Extraction of Metal Complexes* (1969), 1018 pp, $44.95. 2135	—	—	—	×	—	—	—	—	—
MARCUS, Y. and KERTES, A. S. *Solvent Extraction Research* (1969), 472 pp, $29.50. 2140	—	—	—	×	—	—	—	—	—
PURNELL, H. *Gas Chromatography* (1962), 441 pp, $15.95. 2145	—	×	—	—	—	—	—	—	—
PURNELL, H. *Progress in Gas Chromatography*, Advances in Analytical Chemistry, Volume 6 (1968), 392 pp, $14.95. 2150	—	×	—	—	—	—	—	—	—
SCHUPP, O. E. *Gas Chromatography* (1968), 437 pp, $19.95. 2155	—	×	—	—	—	—	—	—	—
SMITH, I. *Chromatographic and Electrophoretic Techniques:* Chromatography, Volume 1, Third Edition (1969), 1,080 pp, $24.00. 2160	—	—	—	—	—	—	—	—	×
SMITH, I. *Chromatographic and Electrophoretic Techniques:* Zone Electrophoresis, Volume 2, Second Edition (1968), 524 pp, $10.00. 2165	×	—	—	—	—	—	—	—	—
TRUTTER, E. V. *Thin Film Chromatography* (1963), 205 pp. 2170	—	—	—	—	—	—	×	—	—
WILLIAMS & WILKINS COMPANY, 428 East Preston Street, Baltimore, Maryland 21202 301 727-2870									
ANONYMOUS. *Gas Chromatography*, CIBA Foundation Symposium (1970), 213 pp, $11.50. 2190	—	×	—	—	—	—	—	—	—

SECTION II.IV
AUTHOR'S INDEX

JOURNALS

Papers on chromatography appear regularly in journals devoted to analytical chemistry (e.g., *Analytical Chemistry*, *Analytica Chimica Acta*, *Talanta*, *Journal of the Association of Official Analytical Chemists*) as well as the following specialized Journals:

Journal of Chromatography — Elsevier Publishing Co.
Journal of Chromatographic Science — Preston Technical Abstract Co.
Separation Science — Marcel Dekker, Inc.
Chromatographia — Pergamon Press

Volume Two

SECTION II.V

SUBJECT INDEX

SUBJECT INDEX

D

S